Algebraic Combinatorics Via Finite Group Actions

Algebraic Combinatorics Via Finite Group Actions

Prof. Dr. Adalbert Kerber
Universität Bayreuth

Wissenschaftsverlag
Mannheim/Wien/Zürich

CIP-Titelaufnahme der Deutschen Bibliothek

Kerber, Adalbert:
Algebraic combinatorics via finite group actions / Adalbert
Kerber. – Mannheim; Wien; Zürich: BI-Wiss.-Verl., 1991
    ISBN 3-411-14521-8

Printed on acid-free paper

Contents

Preface

This book is an introduction to the theory of classification, enumeration, construction and generation of certain discrete structures in mathematics and sciences. The structures in question are those which can be defined as equivalence classes on finite sets and in particular on finite sets of mappings. Prominent examples are graphs, switching functions, physical states and chemical isomers. Since powerful computers are now available for a cheap price, this theory has gained a rapidly increasing interest. The method used is to replace the equivalence relation by a finite group action and to apply algebraic tools like the Cauchy–Frobenius Lemma and its refinements. This will be worked out in full detail, starting with mere enumeration, refining it to enumeration by weight, counting by stabilizer class, by weight and stabilizer class etc. Finally we shall reach the point where we can describe several algorithmic methods which allow to construct the structures in question or to generate them uniformly at random.

In order to describe all this I assume on the side of the reader that he knows the basic concepts of algebra, but not more than the usual undergraduate level.

I have tried to give a survey of the present situation of this theory, but in view of the enormous flood of publications, many results had to be excluded, for example asymptotic methods. Other parts – like the theory of q-analogues, the theory of species or the theory of Schubert polynomials – are hardly touched, they deserve separate monographs. On the other hand the so–called Pólya theory of enumeration is described in full detail, and most of the examples are taken from there. This theory is easy to subsume and it provides many beautiful examples, in particular in graph theory, but also in physics and chemistry. It was in fact the problem of chemical isomerism which led to its early development.

6

For a deeper insight I shall refine the basically permutation theoretical arguments to considerations of the corresponding linear representations of the groups in question and in particular of symmetric groups. Therefore, I did not hesitate to include linear representation theory giving a selfcontained and problem oriented introduction based mainly on finite group actions and set theoretic arguments.

The manuscript is the result of various lectures and seminars at Aachen and Bayreuth, of theses of my students, of research projects on the algebraic and combinatorial description of molecules, of helpful discussions, of many talks I heard or gave at the various meetings of the Lotharingian Seminar of Combinatorics and in particular of joint efforts of K.-J. Thürlings and myself which led to an earlier German version already published in the *Bayreuther Mathematische Schriften* (vols. **12** (1983), **15** (1983) and **21** (1986)). Hence I would like to express my sincerest thanks in particular to K.-J. Thürlings and also to M. Clausen, A. Dress, N. Esper, D. Foata, A. Golembiowski, J. Grabmeier, W. Hässelbarth, D. Jungnickel, A. Kohnert, A. Lascoux, R. Laue, A. O. Morris, J. Neubüser, W. Oberschelp, P. Paule, E. Ruch, F. Sänger, Th. Scharf, D. Stockhofe, F. Stötzer, V. Strehl, J. Tappe, B. Wagner, W. Lehmann and all the other people I had and have the pleasure to work with.

Moreover thanks are due to the Stiftung Volkswagenwerk and the Deutsche Forschungsgemeinschaft, which have supported research on molecular structure elucidation. It produced several results on combinatorial enumeration and a satisfactory solution of the basic problem of this theory, namely the program system MOLGRAPH that provides the molecular graphs corresponding to a chemical formula, the so-called connectivity isomers. This program system was implemented by D. Moser, and it was supported by many students among which I would like to mention in particular F. Bauer, W. Decker, R. Grund, R. Hager, B. Schmalz and W. Weber.

Furthermore I am indebted to H. Engesser for friendly, patient and efficient cooperation with the publishing company.

Last not least thanks are due to D.E. Knuth for providing both his generalization of the Robinson–Schensted construction and TEX, to L. Lamport for the development of LATEX, and to Stürtz, the printing company, for making the best of it.

Bayreuth, December 5, 1990   Adalbert Kerber

Chapter 1

Actions

This introductory chapter contains the basic notions: actions of groups, orbits, stabilizers, fixed points, and so on. Various examples are given. The Cauchy-Frobenius Lemma is derived, which yields the number of orbits in the case when both the group and the set on which it acts are finite.

In order to prepare the applications of this lemma and its refinements which follow in the next chapters, a detailed description of the conjugacy classes of symmetric and of monomial groups is added. The paradigmatic actions which we discuss and apply in full detail here and later on are several natural actions on the set Y^X, consisting of all the mappings from X into Y. These actions on Y^X are induced in a natural way by actions of groups on X or on Y. The corresponding orbits are called symmetry classes of mappings and there are many structures in mathematics and sciences which can be defined as symmetry classes of this kind.

The enumeration of symmetry classes of mappings is described in full detail, in order to prepare refinements which are given in the following chapters.

A very simple case of a group action leads to another important enumerative concept, the so-called involution principle. Finally we discuss the enumeration of symmetry classes which consist of injective or surjective mappings only.

1.1   Actions of groups

Let G denote a multiplicative group and X a nonempty set. An *action* of G on X is described by a mapping

$$G \times X \to X : (g,x) \mapsto gx, \text{ such that } g(g'x) = (gg')x, \text{ and } 1x = x.$$

We abbreviate this by saying that G *acts* on X or simply by calling X a *G–set* or by writing

$$_GX,$$

in short, since G acts from the left on X. Before we provide examples, we mention a second but equivalent formulation. A homomorphism δ from G into the symmetric group S_X on X is called a *permutation representation of G on X*. It is easy to check (exercise 1.1.1) that the definition of action given above is equivalent to

$$\delta : g \mapsto \bar{g}, \text{ where } \bar{g} : x \mapsto gx, \text{ is a permutation representation.}$$

The *kernel* of δ will be denoted by $\widehat{G}$, and so we have, if $\bar{G} := \delta[G]$, the isomorphism

1.1.1 $$\bar{G} \simeq G/\widehat{G}.$$

In the case when $\widehat{G} = \{1\}$, the action is said to be *faithful*. A very trivial example is the *natural action* of S_X on X itself, where the corresponding permutation representation $\delta : \pi \mapsto \bar{\pi}$ is the identity mapping. A number of less trivial examples will follow in a moment. An action of G on X has first of all the following property which is immediate from the two conditions mentioned in its definition:

1.1.2 $$gm = m' \iff m = g^{-1}m'.$$

This is the reason for the fact that $_GX$ induces several structures on X and G, and it is the close arithmetic and algebraic connection between these structures which makes the concept of group action so efficient. First of all the action induces the following equivalence relation on X (exercise 1.1.2):

$$x \sim_G x' \; :\iff \; \exists \, g \in G : x' = gx.$$

The equivalence classes are called *orbits*, and the orbit of $x \in X$ will be indicated as follows:

$$G(x) := \{gx \mid g \in G\}.$$

As $\sim_G$ is an equivalence relation on X, a *transversal* $\mathscr{T}$ of the orbits yields a *set partition* of X, i.e. a complete dissection of X into the pairwise disjoint and nonempty subsets $G(t), t \in \mathscr{T}$:

1.1.3
$$X = \dot{\bigcup}_{t \in \mathscr{T}} G(t).$$

The *set* of orbits will be denoted by

$$G \backslash\backslash X := \{G(t) \mid t \in \mathscr{T}\}.$$

In the case when both G and X are finite, we call the action a *finite action*. We notice that, according to 1.1.1, for each finite G–set X, we may also assume without loss of generality that G is finite. If G has exactly one orbit on X, i.e. if and only if $G \backslash\backslash X = \{X\}$, then we say that the action is *transitive*, or that G acts *transitively* on X.

According to 1.1.3 an action of G on X yields a partition of X. It is trivial but very important to notice that also the converse is true: Each set partition of X gives rise to an action of a certain group G on X as follows. Let, for an index set I, X_i, $i \in I$, denote the blocks of the set partition in question, i.e. the X_i are nonempty, pairwise disjoint, and their union is equal to X. Then the following subgroup of the symmetric group S_X acts in a natural way on X and has the X_i as its orbits:

1.1.4
$$\bigoplus_i S_{X_i} := \{\pi \in S_X \mid \forall\, i \in I \colon \pi X_i = X_i\}.$$

Summarizing our considerations in two sentences, we have obtained:

1.1.5 Lemma *An action of a group G on a set X is equivalent to a permutation representation of G on X and it yields a set partition of X into orbits. Conversely, each set partition of X corresponds in a natural way to an action of a certain subgroup of the symmetric group S_X which has the blocks of the partition as its orbits.*

To the orbits $G(x)$, which are *subsets* of X, there correspond certain *subgroups* of G. For each $x \in X$ we introduce its *stabilizer*:

$$G_x := \{g \mid gx = x\}.$$

The last one of the fundamental concepts induced by an action of G on X is that of *fixed points*. A *point* $x \in X$ is said to be *fixed* under

$g \in G$ if and only if $gx = x$, and the set of all the fixed points of g is indicated by

$$X_g := \{x \mid gx = x\}.$$

More generally, for any subset $S \subseteq G$, we put

$$X_S := \{x \mid \forall g \in S: gx = x\}.$$

The particular case X_G is called the set of *invariants*.

The first bunch of examples which illustrate these concepts will show that various important group theoretical structures can be considered as orbits or stabilizers:

1.1.6 Examples If G denotes a group, then

- G acts on itself by *left multiplication*: $G \times G \to G : (g, x) \mapsto g \cdot x$. This action is called the *(left) regular representation* of G, it is obviously transitive, and all the stabilizers are equal to the identity subgroup $\{1\}$.

- G acts on itself by *conjugation*: $G \times G \to G : (g, x) \mapsto g \cdot x \cdot g^{-1}$. The orbits of this action are the *conjugacy classes* of elements, and the stabilizers are the *centralizers* of elements:

$$G(x) = C^G(x) := \{gxg^{-1} \mid g \in G\},$$

and

$$G_x = C_G(x) := \{g \mid gxg^{-1} = x\}.$$

- If U denotes a subgroup of G (in short: $U \leq G$), then G acts on the set $G/U := \{xU \mid x \in G\}$ of its *left cosets* as follows:

$$G \times G/U \to G/U : (g, xU) \mapsto gxU.$$

This action is transitive, and the stabilizer of xU is the subgroup xUx^{-1} which is conjugate to U.

- G acts on the set $L(G) := \{U \mid U \leq G\}$ of all its subgroups by *conjugation*: $G \times L(G) \to L(G) : (g, U) \mapsto gUg^{-1}$. The orbits of this action are the *conjugacy classes of subgroups*, and the stabilizers are the *normalizers*:

$$G(U) = \tilde{U} := \{ gUg^{-1} \mid g \in G\},$$

and

$$G_U = N_G(U) := \{g \mid gU = Ug\}.$$

$\diamond$

Returning to the general case we first state the main (and obvious) properties of the stabilizers of elements belonging to the same orbit:

1.1.7 $\quad G_{gx} = gG_xg^{-1}, \widetilde{G_x} = \{gG_xg^{-1} \mid g \in G\} = \{G_{x'} \mid x' \in G(x)\}.$

But the crucial point is the following natural bijection between the orbit of x and the set of left cosets of its stabilizer:

1.1.8 Lemma *The mapping* $G(x) \to G/G_x : gx \mapsto gG_x$ *is a bijection.*

Proof: It is clear from 1.1.2 that, for a given $x \in X$, the following chain of equivalences holds:

$$gx = g'x \iff g^{-1}g' \in G_x \iff g'G_x = gG_x.$$

Reading it from left to right we see that $gx \mapsto gG_x$ defines a mapping, reading it from right to left we obtain that it is injective. Furthermore it is obvious that this mapping is also surjective.

$\square$

This result shows in particular that *the length of the orbit is the index of the stabilizer*, so that we obtain

1.1.9 Corollary *If G is a finite group acting on the set X, then for each $x \in X$ we have*
$$|G(x)| = |G|/|G_x|.$$

$\square$

An application to the examples given above yields:

1.1.10 Corollary *If G is finite, $g \in G$, and $U \leq G$, then the orders of the conjugacy classes of elements and of subgroups satisfy the following equations:*
$$|C^G(g)| = |G|/|C_G(g)| \, , \; and \; |\widetilde{U}| = |G|/|N_G(U)|.$$

$\square$

The result in 1.1.9 is very important, it is essential in the proof of the following counting lemma which, together with later refinements, forms *the basic tool of the theory of enumeration under finite group action*:

1.1.11 The Lemma of Cauchy-Frobenius *The number of orbits of a finite group G acting on a finite set X is equal to the average number of fixed points:*
$$|G \backslash\backslash X| = \frac{1}{|G|} \sum_{g \in G} |X_g|.$$

Proof:

$$\sum_{g \in G} |X_g| = \sum_g \sum_{x \in X_g} 1 = \sum_x \sum_{g \in G_x} 1 = \sum_x |G_x|,$$

which is, by 1.1.9, equal to $|G| \sum_x |G(x)|^{-1} = |G| \cdot |G \backslash\!\backslash X|$.

□

The next remark helps considerably to shorten the calculations necessary for applications of this lemma. It shows that we can replace the summation over all $g \in G$ by a summation over a *transversal* of the conjugacy classes, as the number of fixed points turns out to be constant on each such class:

1.1.12 Lemma *The mapping*

$$X_{g'} \to X_{gg'g^{-1}} : x \mapsto gx$$

is a bijection, and hence

$$\chi : G \to \mathbb{N} : g \mapsto |X_g|$$

is a class function, *i.e. it is constant on the conjugacy classes of G. More formally, for any $g, g' \in G$, we have that $|X_{g'}| = |X_{gg'g^{-1}}|$.*

Proof: That $x \mapsto gx$ establishes a bijection between $X_{g'}$ and $X_{gg'g^{-1}}$ is clear from the following equivalence:

$$g'x = x \iff gg'g^{-1}(gx) = gx.$$

□

The mapping χ is called the *character* of the action of G on X, or of $_G X$, in short.

1.1.13 Corollary *Let $_G X$ be a finite action and let $\mathscr{C}$ denote a transversal of the conjugacy classes of G. Then*

$$|G \backslash\!\backslash X| = \frac{1}{|G|} \sum_{g \in \mathscr{C}} |C^G(g)||X_g| = \sum_{g \in \mathscr{C}} |C_G(g)|^{-1} |X_g|.$$

Another formulation of the Cauchy-Frobenius Lemma makes use of the permutation representation $g \mapsto \bar{g}$ defined by the action in question. The permutation group $\bar{G}$ which is the image of G under this representation, yields the action $_{\bar{G}} X$ of $\bar{G}$ on X, which has the same orbits, and so we also have:

1.1.14 Corollary *If X denotes a finite G–set, then (for any group G) the following identity holds:*

$$|G\backslash X| = \frac{1}{|\bar{G}|} \sum_{\bar{g} \in \bar{G}} |X_{\bar{g}}| = \frac{1}{|\bar{G}|} \sum_{\bar{g} \in \bar{\mathscr{C}}} |C^{\bar{G}}(\bar{g})| |X_{\bar{g}}|,$$

where $\bar{\mathscr{C}}$ denotes a transversal of the conjugacy classes of $\bar{G}$.

Under enumerative aspects $_G X$ is essentially the same as $_{\bar{G}} X$. This leads to the question of a suitable concept of morphism between actions of groups. To begin with, two actions will be called *isomorphic* iff they differ only by an isomorphism $\eta : G \simeq H$ of the groups and a bijection $\theta : X \to Y$ between the sets which satisfy $\eta(g)\theta(x) = \theta(gx)$. In this case we shall write

$$_G X \simeq {}_H Y,$$

in order to indicate the existence of such a pair of mappings. If $G = H$ we call $_G X$ and $_G Y$ *similar* actions, if and only if they are isomorphic by (η, θ), where moreover $\eta = \mathrm{id}_G$, the identity mapping (cf. exercise 1.1.4). We indicate this by

$$_G X \approx {}_G Y.$$

An important special case follows directly from the proof of 1.1.8:

1.1.15 Lemma *If $_G X$ is transitive then, for any $x \in X$, we have that*

$$_G X \approx {}_G(G/G_x).$$

Exercises

E 1.1.1 Assume X to be a G–set and check carefully that $g \mapsto \bar{g}$ is in fact a permutation representation, i.e. that $\bar{g} \in S_X$ and that $\overline{g_1 \cdot g_2} = \bar{g}_1 \cdot \bar{g}_2$.

E 1.1.2 Prove that $\sim_G$ is in fact an equivalence relation.

E 1.1.3 Let $_G X$ be finite and transitive. Consider an arbitrary $x \in X$ and prove that

$$|G_x \backslash X| = \frac{1}{|G|} \sum_{g \in G} |X_g|^2.$$

E 1.1.4 Consider the following definition: We call actions $_GX$ and $_GY$ *inner isomorphic* if and only if there exists a pair (η, θ) such that $_GX \simeq {}_GY$ and where η is an *inner* automorphism , which means that

$$\eta: G \to G: g \mapsto g'gg'^{-1},$$

for a suitable $g' \in G$. Show that this equivalence relation has the same classes as $\approx$.

1.2   Symmetry classes of mappings

From a given action we can derive various other actions in a natural way, e.g. $_GX$ yields $_{\bar{G}}X$, $\bar{G}$ being the homomorphic image of G in S_X, which was already mentioned. We also obtain the *subactions* $_GM$ on subsets $M \subseteq X$ which are nonempty unions of orbits. Furthermore there are the *restrictions* $_UX$ to the subgroups U of G. As the orbits of $_GX$ are unions of orbits of $_UX$, the comparison of actions and restrictions is a suitable way of generalizing or specializing structures if they can be defined as orbits. The following example will show what is meant by this.

1.2.1 Example Let U denote a subgroup of the direct product $G \times G$. Then U acts on G as follows:

$$U \times G \to G : ((a,b), g) \mapsto agb^{-1}.$$

The orbits $U(g) = \{agb^{-1} \mid (a,b) \in U\}$ of this action are called the *bilateral classes* of G with respect to U. By specializing U we obtain various interesting group theoretical structures some of which have been mentioned already:

- If A is a subgroup of G, then both $A \times \{1\}$ and $\{1\} \times A$ are subgroups of $G \times G$. Their orbits are the subsets

$$(A \times \{1\})(g) = Ag,$$

 the *right cosets* of A in G, and

$$(\{1\} \times A)(g) = gA,$$

 the *left cosets* of A in G.

- If B denotes a second subgroup of G, then we can put U equal to the subgroup $A \times B$, obtaining as orbits the (A, B)–*double cosets* of G:

$$(A \times B)(g) = AgB.$$

- Another subgroup of $G \times G$ is its *diagonal* subgroup

$$\Delta(G \times G) := \{(g, g) \mid g \in G\}.$$

Its orbits are the conjugacy classes:

$$\Delta(G \times G)(g) = \{g' g g'^{-1} \mid g' \in G\}.$$

$\diamond$

Hence left and right cosets, double cosets and conjugacy classes turn out to be special cases of bilateral classes. The set of (A, B)–double cosets will be denoted as follows:

$$A \backslash G / B := \{AgB \mid g \in G\} = (A \times B) \backslash\backslash G.$$

The Cauchy-Frobenius Lemma yields the order of this set. The number $|G_{(a,b)}|$ of fixed points of $(a, b) \in A \times B$ is

$$|\{g \mid a = gbg^{-1}\}| = \begin{cases} |C_G(a)| = |C_G(b)| & \text{if } a, b \text{ are conjugates,} \\ 0 & \text{otherwise.} \end{cases}$$

Thus, by the Cauchy-Frobenius Lemma, we obtain

$$|A \backslash G / B| = \frac{1}{|A||B|} \sum_{a \in A} |C^G(a) \cap B||C_G(a)|$$

$$= \frac{1}{|A||B|} \sum_{g \in \mathscr{C}} |C^G(g) \cap A||C^G(g) \cap B||C_G(g)|,$$

where $\mathscr{C}$ denotes a transversal of the conjugacy classes of G. This proves

1.2.2 Lemma *For each finite group G with subgroups A and B, we have for the order of the set of (A, B)–double cosets:*

$$|A \backslash G / B| = \frac{|G|}{|A||B|} \sum_{g \in C} |C^G(g) \cap A||C^G(g) \cap B| / |C^G(g)|.$$

 $\diamond$

Further actions of G which can be derived from $_GX$ are the actions of G on the sets

$$\binom{X}{k} := \{M \subseteq X \mid |M| = k\},$$

of *k–subsets* of X, $1 \leq k \leq |X|$, which are defined as follows:

1.2.3 $G \times \binom{X}{k} \to \binom{X}{k} : (g, M) \mapsto \bar{g}M = \{gm \mid m \in M\},$

The action $_GX$ is called *k–homogeneous* if and only if the corresponding action of G on $\binom{X}{k}$ is transitive. An obvious example is the natural action of S_X on X, it is k–homogeneous for $k \leq |X|$. The following is a very important application of actions on k–subsets:

1.2.4 Example The regular representation of G yields, in accordance with 1.2.3, the G-sets $\binom{G}{k}$, for $1 \leq k \leq |G|$. If G is finite and p a prime dividing $|G|$, say $|G| = p^r \cdot q, r \geq 1, q = p^s t$, where p does not divide t, then we can put $k := p^r$ and consider the particular G–set $\binom{G}{p^r}$, as H. Wielandt did in his famous proof of *Sylow's Theorem* in order to show that G possesses subgroups of order p^r. His argument runs as follows: p^s is the exact power of p dividing the order of $\binom{G}{p^r}$. This is clear from

$$\binom{|G|}{p^r} = \frac{p^r q}{p^r} \cdot \frac{p^r q - 1}{1} \cdots \frac{p^r q - (p^r - 1)}{p^r - 1},$$

as each power of p contained in the denominator cancels. Thus p^r–subsets M exist, the orbit length of which is not divisible by p^{s+1}. We consider such an M and show that its stabilizer G_M is of order p^r by proving that p^r is both an upper and lower bound: For each $m \in M$ and $g \in G_M$ we have that $gm \in M$, hence

$$|G_M| \leq |M| = p^r.$$

On the other hand, the fact that p^{s+1} does not divide the orbit length $|G(M)| = |G|/|G_M|$ yields

$$|G_M| \geq p^r.$$

This proves

1.2.5 Sylow's Theorem *A finite group G contains subgroups of order p^r, for each prime power p^r dividing its order $|G|$.*

This example shows clearly that the consideration of suitable group actions can be very helpful, at least in group theory. Applications to other fields of mathematics will follow soon.

Now we take *two* actions into account, $_GX$ and $_HY$, say, and derive further actions from these. Without loss of generality we can assume $X \cap Y = \emptyset$ since otherwise we can rename the elements of X, in order to replace $_GX$ by a similar action $_GX'$, for which $X' \cap Y = \emptyset$. Now we form the (disjoint) union $X \dot\cup Y$ and let $G \times H$ act on this set as follows:

1.2.6 $\quad (G \times H) \times (X \dot\cup Y) \to X \dot\cup Y : ((g,h), z) \mapsto \begin{cases} gz & \text{if } z \in X, \\ hz & \text{if } z \in Y. \end{cases}$

The corresponding permutation group will be denoted by $\bar{G} \oplus \bar{H}$ (cf. 1.1.4) and called the *direct sum* of $\bar{G}$ and $\bar{H}$. Another canonical action of $G \times H$ is that on the cartesian product:

1.2.7 $\quad (G \times H) \times (X \times Y) \to X \times Y : ((g,h), (x,y)) \mapsto (gx, hy).$

The corresponding permutation group will be denoted by $\bar{G} \otimes \bar{H}$ and called the *cartesian product* of $\bar{G}$ and $\bar{H}$. An important particular case is

1.2.8 Example Assume two finite and transitive actions of G on X and Y. They yield, as was just described, a canonical action of $G \times G$ on $X \times Y$ which has as one of its restrictions the action of $\Delta(G \times G)$, the diagonal, which is isomorphic to G, on $X \times Y$. We notice that, for fixed $x \in X$, $y \in Y$, the following is true (exercise 1.2.4):

- Each orbit of G on $X \times Y$ contains an element of the form (x, gy).
- The stabilizer of (x, gy) is $G_x \cap gG_yg^{-1}$, hence the action of G on the orbit of (x, gy) is similar to the action of G on $G/(G_x \cap gG_yg^{-1})$ (recall 1.1.15).
- (x, gy) lies in the orbit of $(x, g'y)$ if and only if
$$G_xgG_y = G_xg'G_y.$$

Hence the following is true:

1.2.9 Corollary *If G acts transitively on both X and Y, then, for fixed $x \in X, y \in Y$, the mapping*

$$G\backslash\backslash(X \times Y) \to G_x\backslash G/G_y : G(x, gy) \mapsto G_xgG_y$$

*is a bijection (note that $G\backslash\backslash(X \times Y)$ stands for $\Delta(G \times G)\backslash\backslash(X \times Y)$).
Moreover, the action of G on the orbit $G(x, gy)$ and on the set of left
cosets*

$$G/(G_x \cap gG_yg^{-1})$$

*are similar. Hence, if $\mathcal{T}$ denotes a transversal of the (G_x, G_y)–double
cosets, for $x \in X, y \in Y$, then we have the following similarity:*

$$_G(X \times Y) \approx {}_G\left(\dot{\bigcup}_{t \in \mathcal{T}} G/(G_x \cap tG_yt^{-1})\right).$$

$\Diamond$

Finally we introduce the actions derived from $_GX$ and $_HY$ which form
our *paradigmatic examples*, and which will be discussed in full detail
in later sections. In order to prepare this we form the set of all the
mappings from X into Y:

$$Y^X := \{f \mid f : X \to Y\},$$

and notice:

1.2.10 Examples If G acts on X and H acts on Y, then G, H and
$H \times G$ act on Y^X as follows:

- $G \times Y^X \to Y^X : (g, f) \mapsto f \circ g^{-1}$, i.e. (g, f) is mapped onto $\tilde{f}$,
  where $\tilde{f}(x) := f(g^{-1}x)$. The corresponding permutation group
  on Y^X will be denoted by $E^{\bar{G}}$.

- $H \times Y^X \to Y^X : (h, f) \mapsto h \circ f$, i.e. (h, f) is mapped onto $\tilde{f}$, where
  $\tilde{f}(x) := hf(x)$. The corresponding permutation group will be
  denoted by $\bar{H}^E$.

- $(H \times G) \times Y^X \to Y^X : ((h, g), f) \mapsto h \circ f \circ g^{-1}$, i.e. $((h, g), f)$ is
  mapped onto $\tilde{f}$, where $\tilde{f}(x) := hf(g^{-1}x)$. The corresponding
  permutation group on Y^X will be denoted by $\bar{H}^{\bar{G}}$, and it will be
  called the *power group* of $\bar{H}$ by $\bar{G}$.

There is a fourth action which contains these three actions as subactions, but in order to describe it we first need to introduce the *wreath
product* $H \wr_x G$: Its underlying set is

$$H \wr_x G := H^X \times G = \{(\psi, g) \mid \psi : X \to H, g \in G\},$$

and the multiplication is defined by

$$(\psi, g)(\psi', g') := (\psi\psi'_g, gg'), \quad \psi\psi'_g(x) := \psi(x)\psi'_g(x) := \psi(x)\psi'(g^{-1}x).$$

The actions $_GX$ and $_HY$ yield the following natural action of $H \wr_x G$ on Y^X:

1.2.11 $\quad H \wr_x G \times Y^X \to Y^X : ((\psi, g), f) \mapsto \tilde{f}, \tilde{f}(x) := \psi(x)f(g^{-1}x).$

The corresponding permutation group on Y^X will be denoted by $[\bar{H}]^{\bar{G}}$, and it will be called the *exponentiation group* of $\bar{H}$ by $\bar{G}$. The orbits of $G, H, H \times G$ and $H \wr_x G$ on Y^X will be called *symmetry classes of mappings* .

A few remarks concerning the wreath product $H \wr_x G$ are in order, they will in particular show that the actions of G, H, and $H \times G$ on Y^X are restrictions of the action of $H \wr_x G$ on Y^X defined above. The reader is kindly asked carefully to check the following statements on wreath products $H \wr_x G$:

1.2.12 Lemma *The wreath product $H \wr_x G$ has the following properties:*

- *The identity element of $H \wr_x G$ is $(\iota, 1)$, where $\iota : x \mapsto 1_H$.*

- *If we define $\psi^{-1} \in H^X$ by $\psi^{-1}(x) := \psi(x)^{-1}$, we get*

$$(\psi, g)^{-1} = (\psi_{g^{-1}}^{-1}, g^{-1}), \quad \text{where } \psi_{g^{-1}}^{-1} := (\psi^{-1})_{g^{-1}} = (\psi_{g^{-1}})^{-1}.$$

- *The normal subgroup*

$$H^* := \{(\psi, 1) \mid \psi \in H^X\} \trianglelefteq H \wr_x G,$$

  is called the base group, *and it is the direct product of $|X|$ copies H^x of H:*

$$H^x := \{(\psi, 1) \mid \forall \, x' \neq x : \psi(x') = 1_H\} \simeq H, \text{ for each } x \in X.$$

- *The subgroup $G' := \{(\iota, g) \mid g \in G\} \simeq G$ is a complement of H^*, so that we have*

$$H \wr_x G = H^* \cdot G', \quad H^* \trianglelefteq H \wr_x G, \quad H^* \cap G' = \{(\iota, 1)\}.$$

- *The diagonal*

$$\Delta(H^*) := \{(\psi, 1) \mid \psi \text{ constant}\} \simeq H,$$

  satisfies

$$\Delta(H^*) \cdot G' = \{(\psi, g) \mid \psi \text{ constant}, \, g \in G\} \simeq H \times G.$$

This shows that the subgroups G', $\Delta(H^*)$ and $\Delta(H^*) \cdot G'$ are natural embeddings of G, H and $H \times G$ into $H \wr_x G$, in short:

1.2.13 $\qquad G \hookrightarrow H \wr_x G, \ H \hookrightarrow H \wr_x G, \ H \times G \hookrightarrow H \wr_x G,$

so that in fact the actions of G, H, and $H \times G$ on Y^X introduced above are restrictions of the action of $H \wr_x G$ on Y^X.

Exercises

E 1.2.1 Consider a G-set X, a normal subgroup $U \trianglelefteq G$, and the corresponding restriction $_U X$. Check the following facts:

- For each orbit $U(x)$ and any $g \in G$, the set $gU(x)$ is also an orbit of U on X.

- The orbits of U on X form a G/U-set, in a natural way.

- The orbits of G/U on $U \backslash\backslash X$ are just the orbits of G on X.

- The U-orbits which belong to the same G-orbit are of the same order.

E 1.2.2 Evaluate the number of bilateral classes.

E 1.2.3 Let G denote a finite group, p a prime number, and p^r its maximal power in $|G|$. The subgroups $U \leq G$ of order p^r are called the *Sylow p–subgroups* of G. Show, by considering suitable actions of groups, that they are all conjugate and that their number is congruent to 1 modulo p.

E 1.2.4 Prove the statements of 1.2.8.

E 1.2.5 Let $_G X$ be transitive, $x \in X$ and $U \leq G$. Prove that $U \backslash\backslash X$ and $U \backslash G / G_x$ are bijective and show that, if $\mathscr{T}$ is a transversal of $U \backslash G / G_x$, then

$$U \backslash\backslash X = \{U(tx) \mid t \in \mathscr{T}\}.$$

E 1.2.6 Show that $E^{\bar{G}}$ is normal in $\bar{H}^{\bar{G}}$ and in $[\bar{H}]^{\bar{G}}$, and that $\bar{H}^{\bar{G}}$ is not in general normal in $[\bar{H}]^{\bar{G}}$. Check that the factor group $\bar{H}^{\bar{G}}/E^{\bar{G}}$ is isomorphic to $\bar{H}$, while $[\bar{H}]^{\bar{G}}/[\bar{H}]^{\bar{E}}$ is isomorphic to $\bar{G}$. What does this mean, in the light of exercise 1.2.1, for the enumeration of the orbits of $\bar{H}^{\bar{G}}$ and $[\bar{H}]^{\bar{G}}$?

1.3 Finite symmetric groups

In the first section we mentioned the symmetric group S_X on the set X. In order to prepare further examples and detailed descriptions of actions we need to consider this group in some detail, in particular for finite X. A first remark shows that it is only the order of X which really matters:

1.3.1 Lemma *For any two finite and nonempty sets X and Y, the natural actions of S_X on X and S_Y on Y are isomorphic if and only if $|X| = |Y|$.*

This is very easy to check and therefore left as exercise 1.3.1. We call $|X|$ the *degree* of S_X, of any subgroup $P \leq S_X$ and of any $\pi \in S_X$. In order to examine permutations of degree n it therefore suffices to consider a particular set of order n and its symmetric group. For technical reasons we introduce two such sets of order n:

$$ n := \{0, \ldots, n-1\} \quad \text{and} \quad \underline{n} := \{1, \ldots, n\}, $$

hoping that it will be always clear from the context if this *set n* is meant or its *cardinality n*. It is an old tradition to prefer the set $\underline{n}$ and its symmetric group which we should denote by $S_{\underline{n}}$ in order to be consistent. Hence let us fix the notation for the elements of $S_{\underline{n}}$, the corresponding notation for the elements of S_n is then obvious. A permutation $\pi \in S_{\underline{n}}$ is written down in full detail by putting the images πi in a row under the points $i \in \underline{n}$, say

$$ \pi = \left(\begin{array}{ccc} 1 & \ldots & n \\ \pi 1 & \ldots & \pi n \end{array} \right). $$

This will be abbreviated by

$$ \pi = \left(\begin{array}{c} i \\ \pi i \end{array} \right). $$

Hence, for example, $S_{\underline{3}}$ consists of the following elements:

$$ \left(\begin{array}{c} 123 \\ 123 \end{array} \right), \left(\begin{array}{c} 123 \\ 213 \end{array} \right), \left(\begin{array}{c} 123 \\ 321 \end{array} \right), \left(\begin{array}{c} 123 \\ 132 \end{array} \right), \left(\begin{array}{c} 123 \\ 231 \end{array} \right), \left(\begin{array}{c} 123 \\ 312 \end{array} \right). $$

The points which form the first row need not be written in their natural order, e.g.

$$ \left(\begin{array}{c} 123 \\ 231 \end{array} \right) = \left(\begin{array}{c} 213 \\ 321 \end{array} \right). $$

Keeping this in mind, we call a permutation $\pi \in S_n$ a *cyclic* permutation or a *cycle* if and only if it can be written in the form

$$\begin{pmatrix} i_1 & i_2 & \cdots & i_{r-1} & i_r & i_{r+1} & \cdots & i_n \\ i_2 & i_3 & \cdots & i_r & i_1 & i_{r+1} & \cdots & i_n \end{pmatrix},$$

where $r \geq 1$. In order to emphasize r we also call it an *r-cycle*. We note that in this case the orbits of the subgroup generated by this permutation are the following subsets of $\underline{n}$: $\{i_1, \ldots, i_r\}, \{i_{r+1}\}, \ldots, \{i_n\}$. We therefore abbreviate this cycle by $(i_1, \ldots, i_r)(i_{r+1}) \ldots (i_n)$, where the points which are *cyclically permuted* are put together in round brackets. For example $\begin{pmatrix} 1 & 2 & 3 \\ 1 & 3 & 2 \end{pmatrix} = (2,3)(1)$. Commas which seperate the points may be omitted if no confusion can arise (e.g if $n \leq 10$), and 1-cycles can be left out if it is clear which n is meant. Hence we can write $\pi = (i_1 \ldots i_r)$ for the r–cycle introduced above. This cycle π can also be expressed in terms of i_1 alone: $\pi = (i_1 \, \pi i_1 \ldots \pi^{r-1} i_1)$. Using all these abbreviations and denoting by $1 := (1) \ldots (n)$ the identity element, we obtain for example

$$S_{\underline{3}} = \{1, (12), (13), (23), (123), (132)\}.$$

The notation for a cyclic permutation is not uniquely determined, since

1.3.2 $(i_1 \ldots i_r) = (i_2 \ldots i_r i_1) = \ldots = (i_r i_1 \ldots i_{r-1}).$

2-cycles are called *transpositions*. The *order* of a cycle $(i_1 \ldots i_r)$, i.e. the order of the cyclic group $\langle (i_1 \ldots i_r) \rangle$ generated by this cycle, is equal to its *length*:

1.3.3 $|\langle (i_1 \ldots i_r) \rangle| = r.$

Two cycles π and ρ are called *disjoint*, if the two sets of points which are not fixed by π and ρ are disjoint sets. Notice that, for example, $1 = (1)(2)(3)$ *and* (123) are disjoint cycles. Disjoint cycles π and ρ commute, i.e. $\pi\rho = \rho\pi$. (We read compositions of mappings from right to left, so that $(\pi\rho)x = \pi(\rho x)$.) *Each permutation of a finite set can be written as a product of pairwise different disjoint cycles*, e.g.

$$\begin{pmatrix} 12345678 \\ 75263418 \end{pmatrix} = (17)(253)(64)(8).$$

The disjoint cyclic factors $\neq 1$ of $\pi \in S_n$ are uniquely determined by π and therefore we call these factors together with the fixed point cycles of π *the cyclic factors* of π. Let $c(\pi)$ denote the number of these cyclic factors of π (including 1-cycles), let l_v be their lengths, $v \in c(\pi)$ (recall that $\underline{c(\pi)} = \{1, \ldots, c(\pi)\}$), choose, for each v an element j_v of the v-th cyclic factor. Then

1.3.4
$$\pi = \prod_{v \in \underline{c(\pi)}} (j_v \, \pi j_v \ldots \pi^{l_v - 1} j_v).$$

This notation becomes uniquely determined if we choose the j_v so that

1.3.5
$$\forall \, m \in \mathbb{N}: \, j_v \leq \pi^m j_v, \text{ and } \forall \, v < c(\pi): \, j_v < j_{v+1}.$$

If this holds, then 1.3.4 is called the *(standard) cycle notation* for π. We note in passing that the sets $\{j_v, \pi j_v, \ldots, \pi^{l_v - 1} j_v\}$ of points which are cyclically permuted by π are just the orbits of the cyclic group $\langle \pi \rangle$ generated by π.

Having described the elements of S_n, we show which of them are in the same conjugacy class, i.e. in the same orbit of the group S_n on the set S_n under the conjugation action (cf. 1.1.6). In order to do this, we first note how $\rho \pi \rho^{-1}$ is obtained from the permutation π:

$$\rho \pi \rho^{-1} = \begin{pmatrix} i \\ \rho i \end{pmatrix} \begin{pmatrix} i \\ \pi i \end{pmatrix} \begin{pmatrix} \rho i \\ i \end{pmatrix} = \begin{pmatrix} \rho i \\ \rho(\pi i) \end{pmatrix}.$$

Thus, in terms of cyclic factors of π, $\rho \pi \rho^{-1}$ arises from

$$\pi = (\ldots i \pi i \ldots) \ldots$$

by simply applying ρ to the points in the cycles of π:

1.3.6
$$\rho \pi \rho^{-1} = \ldots (\ldots \rho i \, \rho(\pi i) \ldots) \ldots .$$

(For any mapping $\varphi: S \to T$ we mean by that s has to be replaced by t and *not* "replace t by s" as it is sometimes understood.) This equation shows that the lengths of the cyclic factors of π are the same as those of $\rho \pi \rho^{-1}$. It is easy to see that, conversely, for any two elements $\pi, \sigma \in S_n$ with the same lengths l_v of cyclic factors there exists a $\rho \in S_n$ such that $\rho \pi \rho^{-1} = \sigma$. Hence the lengths of the cyclic factors of π characterize its conjugacy class. To make this more explicit, we introduce the notion of *(proper) partition* of $n \in \mathbb{N}$, by which we mean any sequence $\alpha = (\alpha_1, \alpha_2, \ldots)$ of natural numbers α_i which satisfy

$$\forall \, i: \, \alpha_i \geq \alpha_{i+1}, \text{ and } \sum_i \alpha_i = n.$$

The α_i are called the *parts* of α. The fact that α is a partition of n is abbreviated by

$$\alpha \vdash n.$$

If $\alpha \vdash n$ then there exists an h such that $\alpha_i = 0$ for all $i > h$. We may therefore write

$$\alpha = (\alpha_1, \ldots, \alpha_h),$$

for any such h. The minimal h with this property will be denoted by $l(\alpha)$ and called the *length* of α. The following abbreviation is useful in the case when several nonzero parts of α are equal, say a_i parts are equal to $i, i \in \underline{n}$:

$$\alpha = (n^{a_n}, (n-1)^{a_{n-1}}, \ldots, 1^{a_1}).$$

If $a_i = 0$, then i^{a_i} is usually omitted, e.g. $(3, 1^2) = (3, 1, 1, 0, \ldots)$. For $\pi \in S_n$ the ordered lengths $\alpha_i(\pi), i \in \underline{c(\pi)}$, of the cyclic factors of π in cycle notation form a uniquely determined proper partition

$$\alpha(\pi) = (\alpha_1(\pi), \alpha_2(\pi), \ldots, \alpha_{c(\pi)}(\pi)) \vdash n,$$

which we call the *cycle partition* of π. The corresponding n-tuple

$$a(\pi) := (a_1(\pi), \ldots, a_n(\pi))$$

consisting of the multiplicities $a_i(\pi)$ of the parts of length i in $\alpha(\pi)$ is called the *cycle type* of π. Correspondingly we call an n-tuple $a := (a_1, \ldots, a_n)$ a cycle type of n if and only if each $a_i \in \mathbb{N}$, and $\sum i \cdot a_i = n$. This will be abbreviated by

$$a \vDash n.$$

The conjugacy class of $\pi \in S_n$ will be denoted by $C^S(\pi)$, the centralizer by $C_S(\pi)$, so that we obtain the following descriptions and properties of conjugacy classes and centralizers of elements of S_n:

1.3.7 Corollary *Let π and σ denote elements of S_n. Then*

- $C^S(\pi) = C^S(\sigma) \iff \alpha(\pi) = \alpha(\sigma) \iff a(\pi) = a(\sigma)$.

- $C^S(\pi) = C^S(\pi^{-1})$, *i.e. S_n is ambivalent , which means that each element is a conjugate of its inverse.*

- $|C_S(\pi)| = \prod_i i^{a_i(\pi)} a_i(\pi)!$, *and* $|C^S(\pi)| = n! / \prod_i i^{a_i(\pi)} a_i(\pi)!$.

- $|\langle\pi\rangle| = \mathrm{lcm}\{\alpha_i(\pi) \mid i \in \underline{c(\pi)}\} = \mathrm{lcm}\{i \mid a_i(\pi) > 0\}$.

- Each proper partition $\alpha \vdash n$ occurs as the cycle partition of some $\pi \in S_n$.

For the sake of simplicity we can therefore parametrize the conjugacy classes of elements in S_n (and correspondingly in S_n) by partitions or cycle types putting

$$C^\alpha := C^a := C^S(\pi), \text{ when } \alpha(\pi) = \alpha, \text{ and } a(\pi) = a.$$

Since
1.3.8 $$(i_1 \ldots i_r) = (i_1 i_2)(i_2 i_3) \ldots (i_{r-1} i_r)$$

each cycle, and hence every element of S_n, can be written as a product of transpositions. Thus S_n is generated by its subset of transpositions (if this is empty, then $n \leq 1$, and both $S_1 = S_0 = \{1\}$ are generated by the empty set $\emptyset$). But, except for the case when $n = 2$, we do not need every transposition in order to generate the symmetric group, since, for $1 \leq j < k < n$, we derive from 1.3.6 that

$$(j, k+1) = (k, k+1)(j, k)(k, k+1).$$

Thus the transposition $(j, k+1)$ can be obtained from (j, k) by conjugation with the transposition $(k, k+1)$ of adjacent points. Therefore the subset

$$\Sigma_n := \{\sigma_i := (i, i+1) \mid 1 \leq i < n\} = \{(12), (23), \ldots, (n-1, n)\},$$

consisting of the *elementary transpositions* σ_i, generates S_n. A further system of generators of S_n is obtained from

1.3.9 $$(1 \ldots n)^i (12)(1 \ldots n)^{-i} = (i+1, i+2), 1 \leq i \leq n-2,$$

so that we have proved

1.3.10 Corollary

$$S_n = \langle (12), (23), \ldots, (n-1, n) \rangle = \langle (12), (1 \ldots n) \rangle.$$

Another useful result describes the cycle structure of a power of a cycle:

1.3.11 Lemma *For each natural number m the power $(i_1 \ldots i_r)^m$ consists of exactly $\gcd(r, m)$ disjoint cyclic factors, they all are of length $r / \gcd(r, m)$.*

Proof: Let l denote the length of the cyclic factor of $(i_1 \ldots i_r)^m$ containing i_1. This cycle is

$$(i_1 \, i_{\overline{m+1}} \, i_{\overline{2m+1}} \cdots i_{\overline{(l-1)m+1}}),$$

where $\overline{k}$ denotes the residue class of k modulo r. Correspondingly the cyclic factor containing i_2 (if $r > 1$) must be $(i_2 \ldots i_{\overline{(l-1)m+2}})$, so that all the cyclic factors of $(i_1 \ldots i_r)^m$ have the same length l. Thus l is the order of $(i_1 \ldots i_r)^m$, an element of the group $\langle (i_1 \ldots i_r) \rangle$ which is of order r. Hence r divides $l \cdot m$ and $r/\gcd(r,m)$ divides $l \cdot (m/\gcd(r,m))$ and therefore also l. But

$$(i_1 \ldots i_r)^{m \cdot (r/\gcd(r,m))} = (i_1 \ldots i_r)^{r \cdot (m/\gcd(r,m))} = 1,$$

so that also l must divide $r/\gcd(r,m)$, which proves that in fact $l = r/\gcd(r,m)$.

$\square$

Let us now consider an application of the preceding result to the paradigmatic G–set Y^X corresponding to given Y and $_GX$ (cf. 1.2.10). This yields a nice proof of a famous number theoretic result.

1.3.12 Example Let $C_{\underline{p}}$ denote the following cyclic subgroup of $S_{\underline{p}}$:

$$C_{\underline{p}} := \langle (1 \ldots p) \rangle \leq S_{\underline{p}}.$$

It acts on the set $X := \underline{p} = \{1, \ldots, p\}$ and hence, see 1.2.10, also on the set $Y^X := \underline{m}^{\underline{p}}$, which can be considered as the set of all the colourings of the regular p–gon in m colours. For example, in the case when $p := 5$ and $m = 2$, $C_{\underline{5}}$ acts on the set $\underline{2}^{\underline{5}}$, consisting of all the 32 colourings of the regular pentagon with two colours (black and white), some of which are shown in figure 1.1. We now assume

Figure 1.1: Three colourings of the regular 5–gon.

that p is a prime. Lemma 1.3.11 shows that $C_{\underline{p}}$ contains, besides the identity element, p–cycles only. The identity element of $C_{\underline{p}}$ keeps each $f \in \underline{m}^{\underline{p}}$ fixed, while each p–cycle fixes the m monochromatic colourings only (notice that $(1 \ldots p)$ acts as a clockwise rotation of the p–gon after having numbered the vertices of the p-gon from 1 to p, counterclockwise). Hence we obtain from the Cauchy-Frobenius Lemma that

$$|C_{\underline{p}} \backslash\backslash \underline{m}^{\underline{p}}| = \frac{1}{p}(m^p + (p-1)m),$$

provided that p is a prime number. This implies that $m^p + (p-1)m$, and hence also $m^p - m$, is congruent zero modulo p, for each positive integer m. It is clear that this is then also true for any integer z, so that we get

1.3.13 Fermat's Theorem $\forall z \in \mathbb{Z}$, p *prime*: $z^p \equiv z$ (p).

$$\diamond$$

This shows that group actions can also be useful in elementary number theory, and it seems appropriate to emphasize the following immediate implication of the Cauchy-Frobenius Lemma:

1.3.14 Corollary *For any action of a finite group G on a finite set X we have the congruence*

$$\sum_{g \in G} |X_g| \equiv 0 \ (|G|).$$

Later on we shall return to this result and we shall refine it considerably. It is a very helpful tool for number theoretic purposes and shows again the efficiency of finite group actions.

Another important fact exhibits a normal subgroup $A_{\underline{n}}$ of $S_{\underline{n}}$. In order to show this we introduce the *sign* $\epsilon(\pi)$ as follows:

$$\epsilon(\pi) := \prod_{1 \le i < j \le n} \frac{\pi j - \pi i}{j - i} \in \mathbb{Z}, \text{ if } n \ge 2, \text{ while } \epsilon(1_{S_{\underline{0}}}) := \epsilon(1_{S_{\underline{1}}}) := 1_{\mathbb{z}}.$$

As $S_{\underline{n}}$, $n \ge 2$, acts transitively on $\binom{n}{2}$, we have $\epsilon(\pi) = \pm 1_{\mathbb{z}}$. Furthermore ϵ is a homomorphism of $S_{\underline{n}}$ into $\{1, -1\}$:

$$\epsilon(\pi\rho) = \prod_{i<j} \frac{\pi\rho j - \pi\rho i}{j - i} = \prod_{i<j} \frac{\pi\rho j - \pi\rho i}{\rho j - \rho i} \prod_{i<j} \frac{\rho j - \rho i}{j - i} = \epsilon(\pi)\epsilon(\rho),$$

again since $S_{\underline{n}}$, $n \ge 2$, acts transitively on $\binom{n}{2}$. This proves

1.3.15 Corollary *The sign map*

$$\epsilon : S_{\underline{n}} \to \{1, -1\} : \pi \mapsto \epsilon(\pi)$$

is a homomorphism which is surjective for each $n \geq 2$. Hence its kernel

$$A_{\underline{n}} := \ker \epsilon = \{\pi \in S_{\underline{n}} \mid \epsilon(\pi) = 1\}$$

is a normal subgroup of $S_{\underline{n}}$:

$$A_{\underline{n}} \trianglelefteq S_{\underline{n}}, \ |A_{\underline{n}}| = |S_{\underline{n}}|/2 = n!/2, \ \text{if } n \geq 2.$$

The elements of $A_{\underline{n}}$ are called *even* permutations, while the elements of $S_{\underline{n}} \setminus A_{\underline{n}}$ are called *odd* permutations. Correspondingly, an r–cycle is even if and only if r is odd. In the case when $_G X$ is a finite action, we can apply the sign map ϵ to $\bar{G}$, the permutation group induced by G on X. Its kernel

$$\bar{G}^+ := \{\bar{g} \in \bar{G} \mid \epsilon(\bar{g}) = 1\}$$

is either $\bar{G}$ itself or a subgroup of index 2, as is easy to see. Denoting its inverse image by

$$G^+ := \{g \in G \mid \epsilon(\bar{g}) = 1\},$$

we obtain a useful interpretation of the *alternating sum* of fixed point numbers:

1.3.16 Lemma *For any finite action $_G X$ such that $G \neq G^+$, the number of orbits of G on X which split over G^+ (i.e. which decompose into more than one — and hence into two — G^+–orbits) is equal to*

$$\frac{1}{|G|} \sum_{g \in G} \epsilon(\bar{g}) |X_g| = \frac{1}{|\bar{G}|} \sum_{\bar{g} \in \bar{G}} \epsilon(\bar{g}) |X_{\bar{g}}|.$$

Proof: As $G \neq G^+$, and hence $|G^+| = |G|/2$, we have

$$\frac{1}{|G|} \sum_{g \in G} \epsilon(\bar{g}) |X_g| = \frac{2}{|G|} \sum_{g \in G^+} |X_g| - \frac{1}{|G|} \sum_{g \in G} |X_g|$$

$$= \frac{1}{|G^+|} \sum_{g \in G^+} |X_g| - \frac{1}{|G|} \sum_{g \in G} |X_g| = |G^+ \backslash\backslash X| - |G \backslash\backslash X|.$$

Each orbit of G on X is either a G^+–orbit or it splits into two orbits of G^+, since $|G^+| = |G|/2$. Hence $|G^+ \backslash\backslash X| - |G \backslash\backslash X|$ is the number of orbits which split over G^+. Finally the stated identity is obtained by an application of the homomorphism theorem.

$\square$

1.3.17 Corollary *In the case when $G \neq G^+$, the number of G–orbits on X which do not split over G^+ is equal to*

$$\frac{1}{|G|} \sum_{g \in G} (1 - \epsilon(\bar{g})) |X_g|.$$

Note what this means. If G acts on a finite set X in such a way that $G \neq G^+$, then we can group the orbits of G on X into a set of orbits which are also G^+–orbits. In figure 1.2 we denote these orbits by the symbol $\otimes$. The other G–orbits split into two G^+–orbits, we indicate one of them by $\oplus$, the other one by $\ominus$, and call the pair $\{\oplus, \ominus\}$ an *enantiomeric pair* of G–orbits. Hence 1.3.16 gives us the number of enantiomeric pairs of orbits, while 1.3.17 yields the number of *selfenantiomeric* orbits of G on X. The elements $x \in X$ belonging to selfenantiomeric orbits are called *achiral* objects, while the others are called *chiral*. These notions of *enantiomerism* and *chirality* are taken from chemistry, where G is usually the symmetry group of the molecule while G^+ is its subgroup consisting of the proper rotations. We call $_G X$ a *chiral* action if and only if $G \neq G^+$. Using this notation

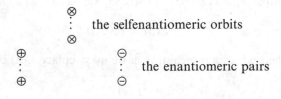

Figure 1.2: Enantiomeric pairs and selfenantiomeric orbits

we can now rephrase 1.3.16 and 1.3.17 in the following way:

1.3.18 Corollary *If $_G X$ is a finite chiral action, then the number of selfenantiomeric orbits of G on X is equal to*

$$\frac{1}{|G|} \sum_{g \in G} (1 - \epsilon(\bar{g})) |X_g| = 2|G \backslash\backslash X| - |G^+ \backslash\backslash X|,$$

while the number of enantiomeric pairs of orbits is

$$\frac{1}{|G|} \sum_{g \in G} \epsilon(\bar{g}) |X_g| = |G^+ \backslash\backslash X| - |G \backslash\backslash X|.$$

The sign of a cyclic permutation is easy to obtain from the equation 1.3.8 and the homomorphism property of the sign, described in 1.3.15:

1.3.19 $(i_1 \ldots i_r) \in A_{\underline{n}} \iff r$ is odd.

But in fact we need not check the lengths of the cyclic factors of π since an easy calculation shows (exercise 1.3.5) that, in terms of the number $c(\pi)$ of cyclic factors of π, we have

1.3.20 $\epsilon(\pi) = (-1)^{n-c(\pi)}$, if $\pi \in S_{\underline{n}}$.

There exists a useful code for permutations that is closely related to this sign map. It is based on the fact that another way of describing permutations $\pi \in S_{\underline{n}}$ is, to put down the *list* of their values:

$$\pi = [\pi 1, \ldots, \pi n], \text{ or } \pi = [\pi 1 \ldots \pi n], \text{ if possible.}$$

It gives rise to the *Lehmer code*

$$L(\pi) := \overline{l_1(\pi) \ldots l_n(\pi)}, \text{ where } l_i(\pi) := |\{j > i \mid \pi j < \pi i\}|.$$

For example $\pi := (124653) = [241635]$ yields

$$L(\pi) = \overline{120200}.$$

If it is clear which n is meant, then we may replace $L(\pi)$ by the shorter sequence
$$L(\pi)^+$$
arising from $L(\pi)$ by canceling the zeros at the end of $L(\pi)$, for example $L((124635))^+ = \overline{1202}$. It is not difficult to see how π can be reconstructed from $L(\pi)$. Clearly $\pi 1$ is the $(l_1(\pi) + 1)$-th element of $\underline{n}$, with respect to the natural order of $\underline{n}$. Correspondingly, $\pi 2$ is the $(l_2(\pi) + 1)$-th element of $\underline{n} \setminus \{\pi 1\}$, and so on. For example

$$L(\pi) := \overline{23100} \text{ yields } \pi = [35214].$$

Furthermore, each $L(\pi)$, $\pi \in S_{\underline{n}}$, is $\leq \overline{n-1, n-2, \ldots, 1, 0}$, with respect to the lexicographic order. Since there are $n!$ such sequences in $\mathbb{N}^{\underline{n}}$, we have obtained:

1.3.21 Corollary *The Lehmer code establishes a bijection between $S_{\underline{n}}$ and the set of sequences $\overline{l_1(\pi) \ldots l_n(\pi)}$ in $\mathbb{N}^{\underline{n}}$, $l_i(\pi) \leq n - i$, for each i.*

Applying the equivalences

$$l_i(\pi) \leq l_{i+1}(\pi) \;\Leftrightarrow\; \pi i < \pi(i+1), \; l_i(\pi) > l_{i+1}(\pi) \;\Leftrightarrow\; \pi i > \pi(i+1),$$

we can easily derive that right multiplication of π by the elementary transposition $\sigma_i = (i, i+1)$ has the following effect on $L(\pi)$:

1.3.22 Lemma *For each $\pi \in S_{\underline{n}}$ and each $\sigma_i \in \Sigma_{\underline{n}}$ we have*

$$L(\pi\sigma_i) = \overline{l_1(\pi), \ldots, l_{i-1}(\pi), l_{i+1}(\pi), l_i(\pi) - 1, l_{i+2}(\pi), \ldots},$$

if $l_i(\pi) > l_{i+1}(\pi)$, while

$$L(\pi\sigma_i) = \overline{l_1(\pi), \ldots, l_{i-1}(\pi), l_{i+1}(\pi) + 1, l_i(\pi), l_{i+2}(\pi), \ldots},$$

$l_i(\pi) \leq l_{i+1}(\pi).$

The main point is that the shift from π to $\pi\sigma_i$ amounts (cf. 1.3.22) to an increase or a decrease in

$$l(\pi) := \sum_i l_i(\pi)$$

by 1. Hence the following holds:

1.3.23 Lemma *The sum $l(\pi)$ of the entries of the Lehmer code $L(\pi)$ of $\pi \in S_{\underline{n}}$ is equal to the minimal number of elementary transpositions σ_i which are needed in order to express π as a product of elementary transpositions.*

We therefore call $l(\pi)$ the *reduced length* of π and notice that

1.3.24 $$\epsilon(\pi) = (-1)^{l(\pi)}.$$

(The symmetric group $S_{\underline{n}}$ is in fact a *Coxeter group* with respect to the generating system $\Sigma_{\underline{n}}$, and $l(\pi)$ is the corresponding reduced length.) Furthermore this leads us to introduce the *weak Bruhat order* $\preceq$ on $S_{\underline{n}}$, which is the transitive closure of

$$\pi \prec\!\cdot\, \rho \;:\Longleftrightarrow\; l(\rho) = l(\pi) + 1, \text{ and } \exists\sigma_i: \rho = \pi\sigma_i.$$

It is often helpful to consider besides $L(\pi)$, which is a sequence of *numbers* of inversions, also the *set* $I(\pi)$ of inversions of π:

$$I(\pi) := \{(i, j) \in \underline{n}^2 \mid i < j \wedge \pi i > \pi j\}.$$

In order to describe how $I(\pi\sigma_i), \sigma_i \in \Sigma_n$, arises from $I(\pi)$, we use that S_n acts on $\underline{n}^2$ in a canonic way: $\rho(i,j) = (\rho i, \rho j)$. Keeping this in mind, we easily obtain:

$$1.3.25 \qquad I(\pi\sigma_i) = \begin{cases} \sigma_i I(\pi) \cup \{(i, i+1)\} & \text{if } \pi i < \pi(i+1) \\ \sigma_i I(\pi) \setminus \{(i, i+1)\} & \text{if } \pi i > \pi(i+1). \end{cases}$$

This yields for the corresponding reduced lengths:

$$1.3.26 \qquad l(\pi\sigma_i) = \begin{cases} l(\pi) + 1 & \text{if } \pi i < \pi(i+1) \\ l(\pi) - 1 & \text{if } \pi i > \pi(i+1). \end{cases}$$

If ω_n denotes the permutation $[n, \ldots, 1]$ of maximal length, then

$$1.3.27 \qquad l(\omega_n) = \binom{n}{2}, \ l(\omega_n\rho) = \binom{n}{2} - l(\rho) = l(\rho\omega_n).$$

Proof: Clearly $I(\omega_n) = \{(i,j) \in \underline{n}^2 \mid i < j\}$, and hence $l(\omega_n) = \binom{n}{2}$. Moreover

$$\rho\omega_n = [\rho n, \ldots, \rho 1],$$

so $I(\rho\omega_n) = \underline{n}^2 \setminus I(\rho)$, and $l(\rho\omega_n) = \binom{n}{2} - l(\rho)$. Finally we note that

$$l(\omega_n\rho) = l((\omega_n\rho)^{-1}) = l(\rho^{-1}\omega_n) = \binom{n}{2} - l(\rho^{-1}) = \binom{n}{2} - l(\rho),$$

which completes the proof.

$\square$

An expression

$$\pi = \sigma_{i_1} \ldots \sigma_{i_l}, \sigma_i \in \Sigma_n,$$

of π in terms of elementary transpositions and *minimal* $l = l(\pi)$ is called a *reduced decomposition* of π. The set of corresponding sequences of indices is indicated as follows:

$$R(\pi) := \{(i_1, \ldots, i_l) \mid \pi = \sigma_{i_1} \ldots \sigma_{i_l}, \sigma_i \in \Sigma_n, l \text{ minimal}\}.$$

These sequences are called *reduced sequences* of π.

1.3.28 Lemma *If* $(i_1, \ldots, i_l) \in R(\pi)$, *then*

$$I(\pi) = \{\sigma_{i_l} \ldots \sigma_{i_{r+1}} (i_r, i_r + 1) \mid 1 \le r \le l = l(\pi)\}.$$

Proof: By induction on $l = l(\pi)$. The case $l = 0$ yields the empty set which is in fact the set of inversions of $\pi = 1$. If $l \geq 1$, then we can consider $\pi' := \pi\sigma_{i_l} = \sigma_{i_1} \ldots \sigma_{i_{l-1}}$, which is of reduced length $l(\pi) - 1$. The induction hypothesis gives

$$I(\pi') = \{\sigma_{i_{l-1}} \ldots \sigma_{i_{r+1}}(i_r, i_r + 1) \mid 1 \leq r \leq l - 1\},$$

and from 1.3.25 we know how $I(\pi)$ can be obtained from $I(\pi')$, since $l(\pi) = l(\pi') + 1$ shows which of the two cases holds:

$$I(\pi = \pi'\sigma_{i_l}) = \sigma_{i_l}I(\pi') \cup \{(i_l, i_l + 1)\}$$

$$= \{\sigma_{i_l} \ldots \sigma_{i_{r+1}}(i_r, i_r + 1) \mid 1 \leq r \leq l - 1\} \cup \{(i_l, i_l + 1)\}$$

$$= \{\sigma_{i_l} \ldots \sigma_{i_{r+1}}(i_r, i_r + 1) \mid 1 \leq r \leq l\},$$

as it is stated.

$\square$

We are now in a position to prove the following important result:

1.3.29 The Exchange Lemma *If* $(i_1, \ldots, i_l), (j_1, \ldots, j_l)$ *are elements of* $R(\pi)$, *then there exist* $k \leq l = l(\pi)$ *such that*

$$(j_1, i_1, \ldots, \hat{i}_k, \ldots, i_l) \in R(\pi),$$

where $\hat{i}_k$ *means that* i_k *is left out.*

Proof: We know that $I(\pi^{-1}) = \{\sigma_{i_1} \ldots \sigma_{i_{r-1}}(i_r, i_r + 1) \mid 1 \leq r \leq l\}$, and hence there exists an r such that

$$(j_1, j_1 + 1) = \sigma_{i_1} \ldots \sigma_{i_{r-1}}(i_r, i_r + 1).$$

But this implies (since σ_{j_1} *transposes* j_1 and $j_1 + 1$):

$$\sigma_{j_1} = \sigma_{i_1} \ldots \sigma_{i_{r-1}}\sigma_{i_r}(\sigma_{i_1} \ldots \sigma_{i_{r-1}})^{-1},$$

and so $\sigma_{j_1}\sigma_{i_1} \ldots \sigma_{i_{r-1}} = \sigma_{i_1} \ldots \sigma_{i_{r-1}}\sigma_{i_r}$, which proves the statement.

$\square$

This result will be used much later in order to introduce an important class of polynomials, the Schubert polynomials. They correspond to the permutations and form an important basis of the polynomial ring $\cup_{n>0}\mathbb{Z}[z_1, \ldots, x_n]$. They will be defined with the aid of a differential operator that corresponds to a reduced decomposition, and the Exchange Lemma will be used in order to prove that this operator is independent of the chosen reduced decomposition. Moreover, they form a natural generalization of the so-called Schur polynomials which are important both for the enumeration theory of symmetry classes of mappings and for the representation theory of symmetric groups.

Exercises

E 1.3.1 Prove lemma 1.3.1.

E 1.3.2 Show that the group $C_{\underline{m}} := \langle (1\ldots m) \rangle$ contains, for each divisor d of m exactly one subgroup U of order d. Furthermore prove that this subgroup contains $\phi(d)$ elements consisting of d–cycles only, and that these are all the generators of U, if $\phi(-)$ denotes the *Euler function*

$$\phi(d) := |\{i \in \underline{d} \mid \gcd(d,i) = 1\}|.$$

E 1.3.3 Show that, for each $m, n \in \mathbb{N}$ and $\pi \in S_{\underline{n}}$, the permutations π and π^m are conjugate, if and only if m and $n!$ are relatively prime.

E 1.3.4 Verify that $\pi, \rho \in S_{\underline{n}}$ are conjugates if and only if, for each $m \in \mathbb{N}$, $c(\pi^m) = c(\rho^m)$. Hint: solve the following system of linear equations:

$$\sum_l \gcd(m,l)(a_l(\pi) - a_l(\rho)) = 0.$$

E 1.3.5 Check 1.3.20.

1.4 Complete monomial groups

We have already met the wreath product $H \wr_X G$, where G is a group acting on X while H acts on Y. Now we consider the particular case where G is a permutation group, say $G \leq S_{\underline{n}}$, and where we take for $_G X$ the natural action of G on $\underline{n}$. In this case we shorten the notation by putting

$$H \wr G := H \wr_{\underline{n}} G.$$

A particular case is $H \wr S_{\underline{n}}$, the *complete monomial group* of degree n over H. Many important groups are of this form, examples will be given in a moment. In the case when $H \leq S_{\underline{m}}$, then $H \wr G$ has the following natural embedding into $S_{\underline{mn}}$:

1.4.1 $\delta \colon S_{\underline{m}} \wr S_{\underline{n}} \hookrightarrow S_{\underline{mn}} \colon (\psi, \pi) \mapsto \begin{pmatrix} (j-1)m + i \\ (\pi j - 1)m + \psi(\pi j)i \end{pmatrix}_{i \in \underline{m}, j \in \underline{n}}.$

This can be seen as follows: Remember the direct factors $S_{\underline{m}}^j$, for $j \in \underline{n}$, of the base group $S_{\underline{m}}^*$ of $S_{\underline{m}} \wr S_{\underline{n}}$ (cf. the remark on H^x in 1.2.12).

Its image $\delta[S_m^j]$ acts on the block $\{(j-1)m+1,\ldots,jm\}$ as S_m does on $\underline{m}$, while the image $\delta[S_n']$ of the complement S_n' of the base group acts on the set of these n subsections $\{(j-1)m+1,\ldots,jm\}$ of length m of the set $\underline{mn}$ as S_n does act on $\underline{n}$. For example the element

$$(\psi,\pi) := (\psi(1),\psi(2),\psi(3),\pi) := ((12),(123),1,(23)) \in S_{\underline{3}} \wr S_{\underline{3}}$$

is mapped under δ onto

$$\underbrace{(12)(456)}_{=\delta((\psi,1))}\ \underbrace{(47)(58)(69)}_{=\delta((\iota,\pi))} = (12)(475869) \in S_{\underline{9}}.$$

The image of $H \wr G$ under δ will be denoted as follows:

1.4.2 $$H \odot G := \delta[H \wr G].$$

It is called the *plethysm* of G and H, for reasons which will become clear later. As an application of this permutation representation we obtain a description of the centralizers of elements in finite symmetric groups. To show this we note that $\delta[C_{\underline{m}} \wr S_{\underline{n}}]$, where $C_{\underline{m}} := \langle(1\ldots m)\rangle$, is just the centralizer of

$$\sigma := (1\ldots m)(m+1,\ldots,2m)\ldots((n-1)m+1,\ldots,nm) \in S_{\underline{mn}}.$$

This follows from $\delta[C_{\underline{m}}\wr S_{\underline{n}}] \subseteq C_S(\sigma)$, which is clear from 1.3.6 together with 1.4.1 and the fact that $|C_S(\sigma)| = m^n n! = |C_{\underline{m}} \wr S_{\underline{n}}|$ (cf. 1.3.7). The general case is now easy:

1.4.3 Corollary *If $\sigma \in S_{\underline{n}}$ is of type $a = (a_1,\ldots,a_n)$, then $C_S(\sigma)$ is a subgroup of $S_{\underline{n}}$ which is similar to the direct sum*

$$\oplus_i(C_{\underline{i}} \odot S_{\underline{a_i}}).$$

Similarly we can show (recall 1.1.6)

1.4.4 Corollary *The normalizer of the n–fold direct sum*

$$\oplus^n S_{\underline{m}} := S_{\underline{m}} \oplus \ldots \oplus S_{\underline{m}}, \quad n \text{ summands},$$

is conjugate to the plethysm $S_{\underline{m}} \odot S_{\underline{n}}$.

Thus centralizers of elements and normalizers of specific subgroups of symmetric groups turn out to be direct sums of complete monomial groups. Since such groups will also occur as acting groups later on, we also describe their conjugacy classes. Consider an element (ψ, π) in $H \wr S_n$ and assume that $C^1, C^2, \ldots$ are the conjugacy classes of H. If

$$\pi = \prod_{v \in c(\pi)} (j_v \ldots \pi^{l_v - 1} j_v),$$

in standard cycle notation, then we associate with its v-th cyclic factor $(j_v \ldots \pi^{l_v - 1} j_v)$ the element

1.4.5 $h_v(\psi, \pi) := \psi(j_v)\psi(\pi^{-1} j_v) \cdots \psi(\pi^{-l_v + 1} j_v) = \psi \psi_\pi \ldots \psi_{\pi^{l_v-1}}(j_v)$

of H and call it the *v-th cycleproduct of* (ψ, π) or the cycleproduct *associated* to $(j_v \ldots \pi^{l_v - 1} j_v)$ with respect to (ψ, π). In this way we obtain a total of $c(\pi)$ cycleproducts, $a_k(\pi)$ of them arising from the cyclic factors of π which are of length k. Now let $a_{ik}(\psi, \pi)$ be the number of these cycleproducts which are associated to a k-cycle of π and which belong to the conjugacy class C^i of H (note that we did *not* say "let $a_{ik}(\psi, \pi)$ be the number of *different* cycleproducts"). We put these natural numbers together into the matrix

$$a(\psi, \pi) := (a_{ik}(\psi, \pi)),$$

This matrix has n columns (k is the column index) and as many rows as there are conjugacy classes in H (i is the row index). Its entries satisfy the following conditions:

1.4.6 $a_{ik}(\psi, \pi) \in \mathbb{N}, \quad \sum_i a_{ik}(\psi, \pi) = a_k(\pi), \quad \sum_{i,k} k \cdot a_{ik}(\psi, \pi) = n.$

We call this matrix $a(\psi, \pi)$ the *type* of (ψ, π) and we say that (ψ, π) is *of type* $a(\psi, \pi)$.

1.4.7 Lemma *The conjugacy classes of complete monomial groups $H \wr S_n$ have the following properties:*

- $C^{H \wr S_n}(\psi', \pi') = C^{H \wr S_n}(\psi, \pi)$ *if and only if* $a(\psi', \pi') = a(\psi, \pi)$.

- *The order of the conjugacy class of elements of type* (a_{ik}) *in* $H \wr S_n$, *H finite, is equal to*

$$|H|^n n! / \prod_{i,k} a_{ik}! (k|H|/|C^i|)^{a_{ik}}.$$

- *Each matrix (b_{ik}) with n columns and as many rows as H has conjugacy classes, the elements of which satisfy*

$$b_{ik} \in \mathbb{N}, \sum_{i,k} k \cdot b_{ik} = n,$$

occurs as the type of an element $(\psi, \pi) \in H \wr S_{\underline{n}}$.

- *If H is a permutation group and $\alpha := \alpha(h_v(\psi, \pi))$, then the cycle partition $\alpha(\delta(\psi, \pi))$, where δ denotes the permutation representation of 1.4.1, is equal to*

$$\sum_v l_v \cdot \alpha(h_v(\psi, \pi)),$$

where $l_v \cdot \alpha, \alpha := \alpha(h_v(\psi, \pi))$, is defined to be $(l_v \cdot \alpha_1, l_v \cdot \alpha_2, \ldots)$, and where $\sum_v \ldots$ means that the proper partition has to be formed that consists of all the parts of all the summands $l_v \cdot \alpha(h_v(\psi, \pi))$.

Proof: A first remark concerns the cycleproducts introduced in 1.4.5. Since in each group G the products xy and yx of two elements are conjugate, we have that $h_v(\psi, \pi)$ is conjugate to

$$\psi \psi_\pi \ldots \psi_{\pi^{l_v-1}}(\pi^z j_v),$$

for each integer z.

The second remark is, that for each $\pi' \in S_{\underline{n}}$ and every $\psi' \in H^{\underline{n}}$,

$$a(\psi, \pi) = a((\iota, \pi')(\psi, \pi)(\iota, \pi')^{-1}) = a((\psi', 1)(\psi, \pi)(\psi', 1)^{-1}).$$

This follows from the fact that both $(\psi_{\pi'}, \pi'\pi\pi'^{-1})$ and $(\psi'\psi\psi_\pi'^{-1}, \pi)$ are of type $a(\psi, \pi)$.

A third remark is that $a(\psi, \pi) = a(\psi', \pi')$ implies the existence of an element $\pi'' \in S_{\underline{n}}$ which satisfies $\pi = \pi''\pi'\pi''^{-1}$, and for which the cycleproducts $h_v(\psi, \pi)$ and $h_v(\psi'_{\pi''}, \pi)$ are conjugate.

It is not difficult to check these remarks and then to derive the statement (exercise 1.4.2).

□

A numerical example is provided by $S_3 \wr S_2$. The set of proper partitions characterizing the conjugacy classes of S_2 is

$$\{\alpha \mid \alpha \vdash 2\} = \{(2), (1^2)\},$$

the set of corresponding cycle types is

$$\{a \mid a \vdash 2\} = \{(0,1),(2,0)\}.$$

Thus the types of $S_3 \wr S_2$ turn out to be

$$\begin{pmatrix} 0 & 1 \\ 0 & 0 \\ 0 & 0 \end{pmatrix}, \begin{pmatrix} 0 & 0 \\ 0 & 1 \\ 0 & 0 \end{pmatrix}, \begin{pmatrix} 0 & 0 \\ 0 & 0 \\ 0 & 1 \end{pmatrix}, \begin{pmatrix} 2 & 0 \\ 0 & 0 \\ 0 & 0 \end{pmatrix}, \begin{pmatrix} 0 & 0 \\ 2 & 0 \\ 0 & 0 \end{pmatrix},$$

$$\begin{pmatrix} 0 & 0 \\ 0 & 0 \\ 2 & 0 \end{pmatrix}, \begin{pmatrix} 1 & 0 \\ 1 & 0 \\ 0 & 0 \end{pmatrix}, \begin{pmatrix} 1 & 0 \\ 0 & 0 \\ 1 & 0 \end{pmatrix}, \begin{pmatrix} 0 & 0 \\ 1 & 0 \\ 1 & 0 \end{pmatrix}.$$

The orders of the conjugacy classes are 6,18,12,1,9,4,6,4,12. We now describe an interesting action of $S_m \wr S_n$ which is in fact an action of the form ${}_G Y^X$.

1.4.8 Example The action of $S_m \wr S_n$ on $\underline{mn}$ is obviously similar to the following action of $S_m \wr S_n$ on the set $\underline{m} \times \underline{n}$:

$$S_{\underline{m}} \wr S_{\underline{n}} \times (\underline{m} \times \underline{n}) \to \underline{m} \times \underline{n} : ((\psi,\pi),(i,j)) \mapsto (\psi(\pi j)i, \pi j).$$

The corresponding permutation group on $\underline{m} \times \underline{n}$ will be denoted by

$$S_{\underline{n}}[S_{\underline{m}}]$$

and called the *composition* of $S_{\underline{n}}$ and $S_{\underline{m}}$, while

$$G[H]$$

will be used for the permutation group on $Y \times X$, induced by the natural action of $H \wr_X G$ on $Y \times X$.

The action of the wreath product $S_m \wr S_n$ on $\underline{m} \times \underline{n}$ induces a natural action of $S_m \wr S_n$ on the set

$$Y^X := 2^{\underline{m} \times \underline{n}} = \{(a_{ij}) \mid a_{ij} \in \{0,1\}, i \in \underline{m}, j \in \underline{n}\},$$

i.e. on the set of 0-1-matrices consisting of m rows and n columns:

$$S_{\underline{m}} \wr S_{\underline{n}} \times 2^{\underline{m} \times \underline{n}} : ((\psi,\pi),(a_{ij})) \mapsto (a_{\psi^{-1}(j)i,\pi^{-1}j}).$$

Since $(\psi,\pi) = (\psi,1)(\iota,\pi)$, we can do this in two steps:

$$(a_{ij}) \longmapsto (a_{i,\pi^{-1}j}) \longmapsto (a_{\psi^{-1}(j)i,\pi^{-1}j}).$$

Hence we can first of all permute the columns of (a_{ij}) in such a way that the numbers of 1's in the columns of the resulting matrix is nonincreasing from left to right: $\sum_i a_{i,\pi^{-1}1} \geq \sum_i a_{i,\pi^{-1}2} \geq \dots$ And after having carried out this permutation with a suitable π, we can find a $\psi \in S_m^*$ such that the 1's in each column are now in succinct positions from top to bottom. This proves that the orbit of (a_{ij}) under $S_{\underline{m}} \wr S_{\underline{n}}$ is characterized by an element of the form

$$\begin{pmatrix} 1 & \cdots & \cdots & \cdots & 1 \\ \vdots & & & \reflectbox{$\ddots$} & \\ 1 & \cdots & 1 & & \\ & & & & 0 \end{pmatrix} \in 2^{\underline{m} \times \underline{n}},$$

i.e. by a proper partition of $k := \sum_{i,j} a_{ij}$. Hence the orbits of $S_{\underline{m}} \wr S_{\underline{n}}$ on $2^{\underline{m} \times \underline{n}}$ are characterized by the proper partitions α, where each part $\alpha_i \leq n$ and where the total number of parts is $\leq m$:

1.4.9 Corollary *There exists a natural bijection*

$$S_{\underline{m}} \wr S_{\underline{n}} \backslash\backslash 2^{\underline{m} \times \underline{n}} \;\longrightarrow\; \{\alpha \vdash k \mid k \leq mn, \; \alpha_1 \leq n, \; \alpha_1' \leq m\}.$$

Hence an application of the Cauchy-Frobenius Lemma yields the following formula for the number of partitions of this form:

1.4.10 $\qquad |S_{\underline{m}} \wr S_{\underline{n}} \backslash\backslash 2^{\underline{m} \times \underline{n}}| = (m!^n n!)^{-1} \sum_{(\psi,\pi) \in S_{\underline{m}} \wr S_{\underline{n}}} 2^{\sum_\nu c(h_\nu(\psi,\pi))},$

which can be made more explicit by an application of 1.4.7.

$\diamond$

Exercises

E 1.4.1 Prove that the conjugacy class (in $S_{\underline{n}}$) of an even element $\pi \in S_{\underline{n}}$ splits into two $A_{\underline{n}}$–classes if and only if the lengths of the cyclic factors of π are pairwise different and odd (hint: use 1.4.3).

E 1.4.2 Fill in the details of the proof of 1.4.7.

1.5 Enumeration of symmetry classes

Our paradigmatic examples are the actions of G, H, $H \times G$ and $H \wr_x G$ on Y^X, obtained from given actions $_G X$ and $_H Y$. The orbits of these

groups are called *symmetry classes of mappings*. If we want to be
more explicit, we call them *G–classes, H–classes, H × G–classes and
H ≀$_x$ G–classes*, respectively. Their total number can be obtained by
an application of the Cauchy-Frobenius Lemma as soon as we know
the number of fixed points for each element of the respective group.
In order to derive these numbers we characterize the fixed points of
each $(\psi, g) \in H \wr_x G$ on Y^X and then we use the natural embedding
of G, H and $H \times G$ in $H \wr_x G$ as described above. Thus the following
lemma will turn out to be crucial:

1.5.1 Lemma *Consider an* $f \in Y^X$, *an element* (ψ, g) *of* $H \wr_x G$ *and
assume that*

$$\bar{g} = \prod_{v \in c(\bar{g})} (x_v \, g x_v \ldots g^{l_v - 1} x_v)$$

is the disjoint cycle decomposition of $\bar{g}$, *the permutation of* X *which
corresponds to* g.
Then f *is a fixed point of* (ψ, g) *if and only if the following two conditions hold:*

- *Each* $f(x_v)$ *is a fixed point of the cycleproduct* $h_v(\psi, g)$:

$$f(x_v) \in Y_{h_v(\psi, g)}.$$

- *The other values of* f *arise from the values* $f(x_v)$ *according to the
following equations:*

$$f(x_v) = \psi(x_v) f(g^{-1} x_v) = \psi(x_v) \psi(g^{-1} x_v) f(g^{-2} x_v) = \ldots .$$

Proof: 1.2.11 says that f is fixed under (ψ, g) if and only if its values
$f(x)$ satisfy the equations

$$f(x) = \psi(x) f(g^{-1} x) = \psi(x) \psi(g^{-1} x) f(g^{-2} x) \ldots$$
$$\ldots = \psi(x) \psi(g^{-1} x) \ldots \psi(g^{-l+1} x) f(x),$$

where l denotes the length of the cyclic factor of $\bar{g}$ containing the
point $x \in X$. Hence in particular the following must be true:

$$f(x_v) = h_v(\psi, g) f(x_v),$$

which means that $f(x_v)$ is a fixed point of $h_v(\psi, g)$, as claimed. Thus
any fixed $f \in Y^X$ clearly has the stated properties, and vice versa.

□

This, together with the Cauchy-Frobenius Lemma, yields the number
of $H \wr_x G$–classes on Y^X, and the restrictions to the subgroups G, H
and $H \times G$ yield the number of G–, H– and $H \times G$–classes on Y^X:

1.5.2 Theorem *If both $_GX$ and $_HY$ are finite actions, then we obtain the following expression for the total number of orbits of the corresponding action of $H \wr_x G$ on Y^X:*

$$|H \wr_x G \backslash\backslash Y^X| = \frac{1}{|H|^{|X|}|G|} \sum_{(\psi,g)\in H\wr_x G} \prod_{v=1}^{c(\bar{g})} |Y_{h_v(\psi,g)}|.$$

The restriction to G, H and $H \times G$ according to 1.2.13 yields:

$$|G\backslash\backslash Y^X| = \frac{1}{|G|} \sum_{g\in G} |Y|^{c(\bar{g})}, \quad |H\backslash\backslash Y^X| = \frac{1}{|H|} \sum_{h\in H} |Y_h|^{|X|},$$

and

$$|(H \times G)\backslash\backslash Y^X| = \frac{1}{|H||G|} \sum_{(h,g)\in H\times G} \prod_i |Y_{h^i}|^{a_i(\bar{g})}.$$

In order to apply these results to a specific case it remains to evaluate $c(\bar{g})$, $|Y_h|$, $|Y_{h^i}|$ and $a_i(\bar{g})$ or $|Y_{h_v}(\psi,g)|$ which still can be quite cumbersome as the following example shows.

1.5.3 Example We would like to derive from 1.5.2 a formula for the number of graphs on v vertices. Before we start doing so it should be mentioned that *this example is the second typical example which we present.* The examples 1.1.6, 1.2.4 and 1.3.12 were devoted to the introduction of group theoretical concepts, to the derivation of Sylow's Theorem and to a number theoretic result of Fermat. The only example where a suitable choice of $_GX$ and Y was made in order to define and enumerate a mathematical structure was in fact the example 1.4.8. As this example may have been a little bit artificial we admit that it is only now that we start to apply our paradigmatic actions more systematically. Let us see how suitably chosen G, X and Y can be used in order to define and enumerate the graphs on v vertices.(Later on we shall refine this method by counting these graphs according to the number of edges or according to their automorphism group. Finally we shall even use this *Ansatz* in order to construct such graphs and also to generate them uniformly at random.)The way of defining graphs as orbits of groups may at first glance seem to be circumstantial, but we shall see that this definition is very flexible since it can easily be generalized to all other kinds of graphs like multigraphs, directed graphs and so on.

- A *labelled (simple) graph* consists of a set of *vertices* and a set of *edges* joining pairs of vertices, but neither *loops* (i.e. edges joining a vertex with itself) nor multiple edges are allowed. Thus a labelled graph on v vertices can be considered (after numbering the vertices from 1 to v, say) as a map f from the set $\binom{v}{2}$ of (unordered) pairs of vertices into the set $Y := 2 = \{0,1\}$, where we put

$$f(\{i,j\}) := \begin{cases} 1 & \text{if an edge joins } i \text{ and } j, \\ 0 & \text{otherwise.} \end{cases}$$

For example, the first one of the two labelled graphs of figure 1.3 can be identified in this way with the mapping $f \colon \binom{4}{2} \to 2$ defined by

$$f \colon \begin{array}{ll} \{1,2\} \mapsto 0, & \{2,3\} \mapsto 1, \\ \{1,3\} \mapsto 0, & \{2,4\} \mapsto 0, \\ \{1,4\} \mapsto 1, & \{3,4\} \mapsto 1. \end{array}$$

- The symmetric group S_v acts on $\underline{v}$ and hence also on $\binom{v}{2}$, so that we obtain an action of S_v on $2^{\binom{v}{2}}$ which is of the form $_G(Y^X)$ as was described in 1.2.10. Two labelled graphs are called *isomorphic* if and only if they lie in the same orbit under this action, i.e. if and only if each arises from the other by renumbering the vertices, so that for example the labelled graphs of figure 1.3 are isomorphic (apply $\pi := (34) \in S_4$).

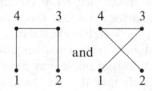

Figure 1.3: Two isomorphic labelled graphs with 4 vertices

- A *graph* Γ on v vertices is defined to be such an isomorphism class of labelled graphs. It can be visualized by taking any member of the isomorphism class and deleting the labels.This yields for the labelled graphs shown in figure 1.3 the drawings of figure 1.4. It should be clear by now what we mean by a graph, and that in our terminology a graph is *not* a pair (V, E) consisting of a set V of vertices and a set E of edges, but that a

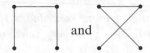

Figure 1.4: The graphs obtained from the labelled ones above

graph Γ can be *represented* by such a pair, so that, for example, the graphs of figure 1.4 are in fact *equal*.

- If we want to allow multiple edges, say up to the multiplicity k, then we again consider $X := \binom{v}{2}$, but we change Y into $Y := \{0, \dots, k\} = k + 1$. The elements of

$$Y^X = (k+1)^{\binom{v}{2}}$$

are called *labelled k–graphs*, while by *k–graphs* on v vertices we mean the orbits of $S_{\underline{v}}$ on this set.

- If we want to allow loops or multiple loops, we replace X by the union $\binom{v}{2} \cup \underline{v}$, and now $f(i) = j$, for $i \in \underline{v}$, means that the vertex with the number i carries a j-fold loop.

- If we want to consider *digraphs* (i.e. the edges are directed and neither loops nor parallel edges are allowed), we simply put

$$X := \underline{v}_i^2 := \{(i, j) \in \underline{v}^2 \mid i \neq j\},$$

the set of *injective pairs* over $\underline{v}$.

$$\diamond$$

Thus graphs, k–graphs, k–graphs with loops and also digraphs can be considered as symmetry classes of mappings. Several other structures will later on be obtained in the same way. Having *defined* the graphs this way we want to *count* them by an application of 1.5.2 which means that we have to derive a formula for $c(\bar{\pi})$, the number of cyclic factors of $\bar{\pi}$, the permutation induced by $\pi \in S_{\underline{v}}$ on the set $\binom{v}{2}$ of pairs of points, expressed in terms of the cycle structure of π. In fact we can do better, we can derive the cycle type of $\bar{\pi}$ from the cycle type of π.

1.5.4 Lemma *If $\pi \in S_{\underline{v}}$, then*

- *Each i-cycle of π, i odd, contributes to $\bar{\pi}$ exactly $(i-1)/2$ cyclic factors, each of which is an i-cycle.*

- *Each i-cycle of π, i even, contributes to $\bar{\pi}$ exactly one cycle of length $i/2$ and $(i/2) - 1$ further cycles, which are of length i.*
- *Each pair of cyclic factors of π, say an i-cycle and a j-cycle, contributes to $\bar{\pi}$ exactly $\gcd(i, j)$ cyclic factors, each of which has the length $\text{lcm}(i, j)$.*
- *All the cyclic factors of $\bar{\pi}$ arise in this way.*

Proof:
i) First let i be odd. Without loss of generality we may assume that the i-cycle in question is $(1, \ldots, i)$. Consider a positive $k \le (i - 1)/2$. Then $\bar{\pi}$ contains the following cyclic permutation of 2-subsets:

$$(\{1, k + 1\}, \{2, k + 2\}, \ldots, \{i - k, i\}, \{1, i - k + 1\}, \ldots, \{k, i\}).$$

This cycle is of length i, and the cycles of this form arising from different $k \le (i - 1)/2$ are pairwise disjoint. Furthermore these are all the cycles arising from $(1, \ldots, i)$ since, for each such k, we have, as i is odd:

$$(\{1, k + 1\}, \{2, k + 2\}, \ldots) = (\{1, i - k + 1\}, \{2, i - k + 2\}, \ldots).$$

ii) If i is even, say $i = 2j$, we may assume that the cyclic factor of π is $(1 \ldots 2j)$. It yields, for $2 \le k \le j$, the $(i/2) - 1$ different i-cycles

$$(\{1, k\}, \{2, k + 1\}, \ldots, \{i - k + 1, i\}, \{1, i - k + 2\}, \ldots, \{k - 1, i\}),$$

together with the $(i/2)$-cycle

$$(\{1, j + 1\}, \ldots, \{j, 2j\}).$$

iii) A pair of cyclic factors of π, say the pair $(1 \ldots i)(i + 1 \ldots i + j)$ contributes to $\bar{\pi}$ the following product of disjoint cycles:

$$(\{1, i + k\}, \{2, i + k + 1\}, \ldots)(\{1, i + k + 1\}, \{2, i + k + 2\}, \ldots) \ldots$$

The length of each of these cyclic factors is $\text{lcm}(i, j)$, and their number is therefore equal to $\gcd(i, j)$.
iv) is clear.

$\square$

This lemma yields the cycle structure of $\bar{\pi}$ and the desired number $c(\bar{\pi})$ of cyclic factors which we need in order to evaluate the number of graphs on v vertices by an application of the Cauchy-Frobenius Lemma:

1.5.5 Corollary *For each $\bar{\pi}$ on $\binom{v}{2}$ we have:*

- *If i is odd, then*

$$a_i(\bar{\pi}) = \frac{a_i(\pi)}{2}(i \cdot a_i(\pi) - 1) + a_{2i}(\pi) + \sum_{\substack{r<s \\ \mathrm{lcm}(r,s)=i}} a_r(\pi)a_s(\pi) \gcd(r,s).$$

- *If i is even, then*

$$a_i(\bar{\pi}) = \frac{a_i(\pi)}{2}(i \cdot a_i(\pi) - 2) + a_{2i}(\pi) + \sum_{\substack{r<s \\ \mathrm{lcm}(r,s)=i}} a_r(\pi)a_s(\pi) \gcd(r,s).$$

- *The total number of cyclic factors is*

$$c(\bar{\pi}) = \frac{1}{2}\sum_i i \cdot a_i(\pi)^2 - \frac{1}{2}\sum_{i \text{ odd}} a_i(\pi) + \sum_{r<s} a_r(\pi)a_s(\pi) \gcd(r,s).$$

Thus, by an application of the Cauchy-Frobenius Lemma, we obtain

1.5.6 Corollary *The number of k-graphs on v vertices is equal to*

$$v!^{-1} \sum_{\pi \in S_v} (k+1)^{c(\bar{\pi})},$$

where $c(\bar{\pi})$ is as above. More explicitly and in terms of cycle types of v (see 1.3.7) this number is equal to

$$\sum_{a \vdash v} \frac{(k+1)^{c_{\bar{a}}}}{\prod_i i^{a_i} a_i!}, \quad \text{where} \quad c_{\bar{a}} := \frac{1}{2}\sum_i i \cdot a_i^2 - \frac{1}{2}\sum_{i \text{ odd}} a_i + \sum_{r<s} a_r a_s \gcd(r,s).$$

A table giving the first of these numbers looks as follows:

$v\backslash k$	0	1	2	3	4
1	1	1	1	1	1
2	1	2	3	4	5
3	1	4	10	20	35
4	1	11	66	276	900
5	1	34	792	10688	90005
6	1	156	25506	1601952	43571400

According to 1.3.14 we obtain from 1.5.2 the following results:

1.5.7 Corollary *For any subgroups $G \leq S_{\underline{n}}$ and $H \leq S_{\underline{m}}$, the following congruences hold:*

$$\sum_{\pi \in G} m^{c(\pi)} \equiv 0 \ (|G|), \quad \sum_{h \in H} a_1(h)^n \equiv 0 \ (|H|),$$

and also

$$\sum_{(\rho,\pi) \in H \times G} \prod_{i=1}^{n} a_1(\rho^i)^{a_i(\pi)} \equiv 0 \ (|H||G|),$$

as well as

$$\sum_{(\psi,\pi) \in H \wr G} \prod_{v=1}^{c(\pi)} a_1(h_v(\psi,\pi)) \equiv 0 \ (|H|^n|G|).$$

Further congruences show up in the enumeration of group elements with prescribed properties. This theory of enumeration in finite groups is, besides the enumeration of chemical graphs, one of the main sources for the theory of enumeration which we are discussing here. A prominent example taken from this complex of problems is the following one due to Frobenius: The number of solutions of the equation $x^n = 1$ in a finite group G is divisible by n, if n divides the order of G. There are many proofs of this result and also many generalizations. Later on we return to this problem, at present we can only discuss a particular case which can be treated with the tools we already have at hand.

1.5.8 Example Let g denote an element of a finite group which forms its own conjugacy class and consider a prime number p, which divides $|G|$. We want to show that the number of solutions $x \in G$ of the equation $x^p = g$ is divisible by p. In order to prove this we consider the action of C_p on the set $Y^X := G^{\underline{p}}$. The orbits are of length 1 or p. An orbit is of length 1 if and only if it consists of a single and therefore of a constant mapping $(g',\ldots,g')$, say. We now restrict our attention to the following subset $M \subseteq G^{\underline{p}}$:

$$M := \{(g_1,\ldots,g_p) \mid g_1 \cdots g_p = g\}.$$

As g forms its own conjugacy class, we obtain a subaction of C_p on M (for example $g_1 \cdots g_p$ is conjugate to $g_p g_1 \cdots g_{p-1}$). Hence the desired number k of solutions of $x^p = g$ is equal to the number of orbits of length 1 in M. Now we consider the number l of orbits of length p in M. It satisfies the equation $k + pl = |M|$. As each equation $g_1 g' = g$

has a unique solution g_1 in G, we moreover have that $|M| = |G|^{p-1}$. Thus

$$k \equiv k + pl = |M| \equiv 0 \ (p),$$

which completes the proof. We note in passing that the *center* of G consists of the elements which form their own conjugacy class, so that we have proved the following:

1.5.9 Corollary *If the prime p divides the order of the group G, then the number of p-th roots of each element in the center of G is divisible by p. In particular the number of p-th roots of the unit element 1 of G has this property (and it is nonzero, since 1 is a p-th root of 1), and hence G contains elements of order p.*

This result can be used in order to give an inductive proof of Sylow's Theorem which we proved in example 1.2.4.

Exercises

E 1.5.1 Prove, by considering suitable actions, the following facts:

- $\forall \, n \in \mathbb{N}^* : \ \sum_{d|n} \phi(d) = n$.
- $\forall$ prime $p : \ (p-1)! \equiv -1 \ (p)$ (Wilson).
- $\forall z \in \mathbf{Z}, p$ prime, $n \in \mathbb{N}^* : \ z^{(p^n)} \equiv z^{(p^{n-1})} \ (p^n)$.
- $\forall z \in \mathbf{Z}, n \in \mathbb{N}^*$ such that $\gcd(z,n) - 1 : \ z^{\phi(n)} \equiv 1 \ (n)$ (Euler).

1.6 The Involution Principle

We have evaluated the number of graphs on v vertices by examining a certain action of the form $_G Y^X$. We shall now give an example of the form $_{H \times G} Y^X$, i.e. a power group action. Afterwards we shall see how these two examples can be combined in order to prove an existence theorem for a certain class of graphs. While doing so we shall meet an interesting and useful counting principle which uses suitable actions of S_2, the smallest nontrivial group.

Two labelled graphs $f, \tilde{f} \in 2^{\binom{v}{2}}$ are called *complementary* if and only if

$$\tilde{f}(\{i,j\}) = 0 \iff f(\{i,j\}) = 1.$$

Correspondingly we say that two graphs, i.e. isomorphism classes

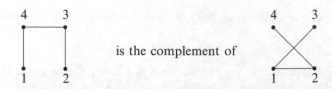

Figure 1.5: Two complementary labelled graphs

of labelled ones, are *complementary* graphs if and only if one class arises from the other by forming the complements. The example of figure 1.5 shows that graphs may very well be *selfcomplementary*, and hence we ask for the number of selfcomplementary graphs on v vertices. In order to prepare the derivation of this number, we notice that the classes which we obtain by putting a graph and its complement together in one class are just the orbits of the group $H \times G := S_2 \times S_{\underline{v}}$ on the set $Y^X := 2^{\binom{v}{2}}$ (recall 1.2.10). According to 1.5.2 the number of these orbits is equal to

$$\frac{1}{2 \cdot v!} \sum_{(\rho,\pi)\in S_2 \times S_{\underline{v}}} \prod_{i=1}^{\binom{v}{2}} |2_{\rho^i}|^{a_i(\bar{\pi})}.$$

But $|2_{\rho^i}|$, the number of fixed points of $\rho^i, \rho \in S_2$, acting on the set 2, is either 2 or zero. Hence we separate the sum over the $(\rho,\pi) \in S_2 \times S_{\underline{v}}$ into two sums depending on $\rho \in S_2$ and get the following expression for the number of these orbits:

1.6.1 $$|(S_2 \times S_{\underline{v}})\backslash\!\backslash 2^{\binom{v}{2}}| = \frac{1}{2 \cdot v!}\left(\sum_\pi 2^{c(\bar{\pi})} + {\sum_\pi}' 2^{c(\bar{\pi})}\right),$$

where $\sum_\pi$ means the sum over all the elements of $S_{\underline{v}}$, while $\sum_\pi'$ means the sum over all the elements π of $S_{\underline{v}}$ such that $\bar{\pi}$ does not contain a cycle of odd length, i.e. $a_{2i+1}(\bar{\pi}) = 0$, for each i.

In order to derive from this equation the total number of selfcomplementary graphs on v vertices we use an easy argument which we have already met when we introduced the notions of enantiomeric pairs and selfenantiomeric orbits. A group of order 2 consisting of the identity map and the "complementation" acts on the set of graphs. This action is chiral if $v \geq 2$, and hence the desired number of selfcomplementary graphs is twice the number given in 1.6.1 minus the number in 1.5.6. We have obtained

1.6.2 Corollary *The number of selfcomplementary graphs on v vertices is equal to*

$$\frac{1}{v!}\sum_{\pi}' 2^{c(\bar{\pi})} = \sum_{a}' \frac{2^{c_{\bar{a}}}}{\prod_i i^{a_i} a_i!},$$

where $c_{\bar{a}}$ is as in 1.5.6, and where $\sum_a'$ denotes the sum over all the cycle types a such that for each element π with this cycle type, the corresponding $\bar{\pi}$ does not contain any cycle of odd length.

This leads to an existence theorem (cf. exercise 1.6.1):

1.6.3 Theorem *Selfcomplementary graphs on v vertices exist if and only if v is congruent to 0 or 1 modulo 4.*

Proof: By corollary 1.6.2 a selfcomplementary graph exists if and only if there are $\pi \in S_v$ such that $\bar{\pi}$ does not contain any cycle of odd length. Now, if neither $v \equiv 0\,(4)$ nor $v \equiv 1\,(4)$, then $\binom{v}{2}$ is odd so that each $\bar{\pi}, \pi \in S_v$, must contain a cyclic factor of odd length. On the other hand, if $v \equiv 0\,(4)$, then to the full cycle $\pi := (1 \ldots v) \in S_v$ there corresponds a permutation $\bar{\pi}$ which, by 1.5.4, does not contain a cyclic factor of odd length. Finally, in the case when $v \equiv 1\,(4)$, we consider $\pi := (1 \ldots v - 1)(v)$. Again by 1.5.4, $\bar{\pi}$ does not contain any cyclic factor of odd length.   □

Before we generalize this method of complementation we should mention the following fact which is very easy to check:

1.6.4 Lemma *In each case when a direct product $H \times G$ acts on a set M, we obtain both a natural action of H on the set of orbits of G:*

$$H \times (G\backslash\backslash M) \to G\backslash\backslash M : (h, G(m)) \mapsto G(hm),$$

and a natural action of G on the set of orbits of H:

$$G \times (H\backslash\backslash M) \to H\backslash\backslash M : (g, H(m)) \mapsto H(gm).$$

Moreover the orbit of $G(m) \in G\backslash\backslash M$ under H is the set consisting of the orbits of G on M that form $(H \times G)(m)$, while the orbit of $H(m) \in H\backslash\backslash M$ under G is the set consisting of the orbits of H on M that form $(H \times G)(m)$, and therefore the following identity holds:

$$|H\backslash\backslash(G\backslash\backslash M)| = |G\backslash\backslash(H\backslash\backslash M)| = |(H \times G)\backslash\backslash M|.$$

In particular each action of the form $_{H\times G}Y^X$ can be considered as an action of H on $G\backslash\backslash Y^X$ or as an action of G on $H\backslash\backslash Y^X$. Hence each such action of $S_2 \times G$ on 2^X gives rise to an action of S_2 on $G\backslash\backslash 2^X$ and leads us to the discussion of the Involution Principle.

We call a group element $\tau \neq 1$ an *involution* if and only if $\tau^2 = 1$. The Involution Principle is a method of counting objects by simply defining a nice involution τ on a suitably chosen set M and using the fact that $S_2 \simeq \{1, \tau\}$ has orbits of length 1 (the selfenantiomeric orbits) and of length 2 (which form the enantiomeric pairs) only. A typical example is the complementation τ of graphs which is, for $v \geq 2$, an involution on the set of graphs on v vertices. An even easier case is described in

1.6.5 Examples We wish to prove that the number of divisors of $n \in \mathbb{N}^*$ is odd if and only if n is a square. In order to do this we consider the set $M := \{d \in \mathbb{N} \mid d \ divides \ n\}$ of these divisors and define

$$\tau : M \to M : d \mapsto n/d.$$

This mapping is an involution, if $n > 1$, and obviously $|M|$ is odd if and only if τ has a fixed point, i.e. if and only if there exists a divisor d such that $d = n/d$, or, in other words, if and only if $n = d^2$.

A less trivial example is the following proof (due to D. Zagier) of the fact that every prime number which is congruent 1 modulo 4 can be expressed as a sum of two squares of positive natural numbers. Consider the set

$$S := \{(x, y, z) \in (\mathbb{N}^*)^3 \mid x^2 + 4yz = p\}.$$

The following map is an involution on S (exercise 1.6.4):

$$\tau : (x, y, z) \mapsto \begin{cases} (x + 2z, z, y - x - z) & \text{if } x < y - z \\ (2y - x, y, x - y + z) & \text{if } y - z < x < 2y \ . \\ (x - 2y, x - y + z, y) & \text{if } x > 2y \end{cases}$$

This involution has exactly one fixed point, namely $(1, 1, k)$, if $p = 4k + 1$, therefore $|S|$ must be odd, and consequently the involution

$$\sigma : (x, y, z) \mapsto (x, z, y)$$

possesses a fixed point, too, which shows that $p = x^2 + 4y^2$, a sum of two squares.

$\diamond$

We look closer at actions of involutions. The following remark is trivial but very helpful: Let $\tau \in S_M$ be an involution which has the following reversion property with respect to the subsets $T, U \subseteq M$:

1.6.6 $$m \in T \iff \tau m \in U.$$

Then the restriction of τ to T establishes a bijection between T and U. We shall apply this to disjoint decompositions $M = M^+ \dot\cup M^-$ of M into subsets $M^\pm$. Each such disjoint decomposition gives rise to a *sign function* on M:

$$\text{sign}(m) := \begin{cases} 1 & m \in M^+, \\ -1 & m \in M^-. \end{cases}$$

1.6.7 The Involution Principle *Let* $M = M^+ \dot\cup M^-$ *be a disjoint decomposition of a finite set M and let $\tau \in S_M$ be a* sign reversing *involution:*

$$\forall \ m \notin M_\tau: \ \text{sign}(\tau m) = -\text{sign}(m).$$

Then the the restriction of τ to $M^+ \backslash M_\tau$ is a bijection onto $M^- \backslash M_\tau$. Moreover

$$\sum_{m \in M} \text{sign}(m) = \sum_{m \in M_\tau} \text{sign}(m).$$

If in addition $M_\tau \subseteq M^+$, *then*

$$\sum_{m \in M} \text{sign}(m) = |M_\tau| = |M^+| - |M^-|.$$

Proof: $\sum_{m \in M} \text{sign}(m)$ is equal to

$$\sum_{m \in M_\tau} \text{sign}(m) + \underbrace{\sum_{m \in M^+ \backslash M_\tau} \text{sign}(m) + \sum_{m \in M^- \backslash M_\tau} \text{sign}(m)}_{=0, by \ 1.6.6}.$$

$\square$

A beautiful application is provided by

1.6.8 Example Let A denote a finite set and let $P_1, \dots, P_n$ be any given properties. We want to express the number of elements of A which have *none* of these properties in terms of numbers of elements which have *some* of these properties. In order to do this we indicate by $P_i(a)$

the fact that $a \in A$ has the property P_i, and for an index set $I \subseteq \underline{n}$ we put

$$A_I := \{a \mid \forall \, i \in I : P_i(a)\}, \text{ in particular } A_\emptyset = A.$$

Furthermore we put

$$A^* := \{a \mid \nexists i : P_i(a)\},$$

and it is our aim to express $|A^*|$ in terms of the $|A_I|$. The set on which we shall define an involution is

$$M := \{(a, I) \mid I \subseteq \underline{n}, a \in A_I\}.$$

A disjoint decomposition of this set is $M = M^+ \cup M^-$, where

$$M^+ := \{(a, I) \mid |I| \text{ even}\}, \text{ and } M^- := M \backslash M^+.$$

Now we introduce, for $a \notin A^*$, the number $s(a) := \min\{i \mid P_i(a)\} \in \underline{n}$, and define τ on M as follows:

$$\tau(a, I) := \begin{cases} (a, I \cup \{s(a)\}) & \text{if } a \notin A^*, s(a) \notin I, \\ (a, I \backslash \{s(a)\}) & \text{if } a \notin A^*, s(a) \in I, \\ (a, I) & \text{if } a \in A^*. \end{cases}$$

Obviously $1 \neq \tau \in S_A$ provided that $A^* \neq A$. Furthermore $\tau^2 = 1$ and τ is sign–reversing, so that from 1.6.7 we obtain

$$|A^*| = |M_\tau| = |M^+| - |M^-| = \sum_{(a,I) \in M^+} 1 - \sum_{(a,I) \in M^-} 1$$

$$= \sum_{|I| \text{ even}} |A_I| - \sum_{|I| \text{ odd}} |A_I| = \sum_{I \subseteq \underline{n}} (-1)^{|I|} |A_I|.$$

Thus we have proved

1.6.9 The Principle of Inclusion and Exclusion *Let A be a finite set and $P_1, \ldots, P_n$ any properties, while A_I denotes the set of elements of A having each of the properties $P_i, i \in I \subseteq \underline{n}$. Then the order of the subset A^* of elements having none of these properties is*

$$|A^*| = \sum_{I \subseteq \underline{n}} (-1)^{|I|} |A_I|.$$

In situations where *two involutions* act we can use the following result which allows to replace certain identities of orders by bijections:

1.6.10 The Garsia–Milne bijection *We assume that*

$$M = M^+ \dot\cup M^-, \quad N = N^+ \dot\cup N^-$$

are disjoint decompositions of the finite sets M and N, that $\phi: M \to N$ is a sign-preserving bijection, and that $\sigma \in S_M, \tau \in S_N$ are sign-reversing involutions such that $M_\sigma \subseteq M^+, N_\tau \subseteq N^+$. Then the following mapping is a bijection:

$$\gamma: M_\sigma \to N_\tau: m \mapsto \sigma^*(\tau^*\sigma^*)^{k(m)}(m),$$

where

$$k(m) := \min\{k \in \mathbb{N} \mid \sigma^*(\tau^*\sigma^*)^k(m) \in N_\tau\}, \quad \sigma^* := \phi\sigma, \tau^* := \phi^{-1}\tau.$$

Proof: Easy checks give the following implications:

$$m \in M_\sigma \cup M^- \Rightarrow \sigma^*(m) \in N^+, n \in N^+\backslash N_\tau \Rightarrow \tau^*(n) \in M^-,$$

and as an immediate consequence, for each natural number k:

$$\sigma^*(\tau^*\sigma^*)^k(m) \in N^+\backslash N_\tau$$

implies that

$$(\tau^*\sigma^*)^{k+1}(m) \in M^-, \sigma^*(\tau^*\sigma^*)^{k+1}(m) \in N^+.$$

We now prove the existence of $k(m)$ indirectly. Consider $m \in M_\sigma$. If $k(m)$ does not exist, then the implications mentioned above yield that $\sigma^*(\tau^*\sigma^*)^k(m) \in N^+\backslash N_\tau$, for each natural k. But this set is supposed to be finite. Hence there would be $i, j \in \mathbb{N}, i \neq j$, such that $\sigma^*(\tau^*\sigma^*)^j(m) = \sigma^*(\tau^*\sigma^*)^i(m)$, and thus (assume $j > i$): $(\tau^*\sigma^*)^{j-i}(m) = m \in M_\sigma$, a contradiction to the earlier implications since $M_\sigma \subseteq M^+$.

Finally we mention that γ is injective for the following reason: Assume $m, m' \in M_\sigma$, for which $\gamma(m) = \gamma(m')$. They satisfy

$$\sigma^*(\tau^*\sigma^*)^{k(m)}(m) = \sigma^*(\tau^*\sigma^*)^{k(m')}(m'),$$

and hence also (assuming $k(m') - k(m) \geq 0$)

$$(\tau^*\sigma^*)^{k(m')-k(m)}(m') = m \in M_\sigma.$$

Thus either $k(m') = k(m)$, which is equivalent to $m = m'$, or there exists a $j < k(m') - k(m)$ such that

$$\sigma^*(\tau^*\sigma^*)^j(m') \in N_\tau,$$

since otherwise we had $(\tau^*\sigma^*)^{k(m')-k(m)}(m') \in M^-$. This contradicts to the minimality of $k(m')$.

$\square$

An application to certain inclusion–exclusion situations runs as follows. Consider two families $\mathscr{A} := \{A_1, \ldots, A_n\}$ and $\mathscr{B} := \{B_1, \ldots, B_n\}$ of subsets of two finite sets A and B. For each $I \subseteq \underline{n}$ we put

$$A_I := \bigcap_{i \in I} A_i, B_I := \bigcap_{i \in I} B_i, A^* := A \backslash \bigcup_{i \in \underline{n}} A_i, B^* := B \backslash \bigcup_{i \in \underline{n}} B_i.$$

The Principle of Inclusion and Exclusion yields

$$|A^*| = \sum_{I \subseteq \underline{n}} (-1)^{|I|} |A_I|, \ |B^*| = \sum_{I \subseteq \underline{n}} (-1)^{|I|} |B_I|.$$

In the case when $|A_I| = |B_I|$, for each $I \subseteq \underline{n}$, these two families $\mathscr{A}$ and $\mathscr{B}$ are called *sieve–equivalent*, a property which implies $|A^*| = |B^*|$. Now we assume that this holds and that furthermore we are given, for each $I \subseteq \underline{n}$, a bijection

$$\phi_I : A_I \to B_I.$$

Then the Garsia–Milne construction in fact allows us to sharpen the identity $|A^*| = |B^*|$ by replacing it by a bijection

1.6.11 $\gamma : A^* \to B^*,$

since we need only put

$$M := \{(a, I) \mid a \in A, \forall i \in I : a \in A_i\}, \ M^+ := \{(a, I) \mid |I| \ even\},$$

$$N := \{(b, I) \mid b \in B, \forall i \in I : b \in B_i\}, \ N^+ := \{(b, I) \mid |I| \ even\}.$$

A sign preserving bijection is

$$\phi : M \to N : (a, I) \mapsto (\phi_I(a), I),$$

and the involutions σ, τ are as in the proof of the Principle of Inclusion and Exclusion. Another consequence of the Garsia–Milne bijection is (exercise 1.6.5):

1.6.12 The Two Involutions' Principle *If $M = M^+ \dot{\cup} M^-$ is a disjoint decomposition of the finite set M, and $\sigma, \tau \in S_M$ are sign-reversing involutions such that $M_\sigma, M_\tau \subseteq M^+$, then each orbit of $G := \langle \sigma, \tau \rangle$*

either consists of a fixed point of G alone, or it contains exactly one fixed point of σ and exactly one fixed point of τ, or it contains neither a fixed point of σ nor a fixed point of τ. This means in particular that there is a canonical bijection between M_σ and M_τ, namely the γ that maps $m \in M_\sigma$ onto the fixed point of τ that lies in the orbit G(m) of m.

Exercises

E 1.6.1 Prove 1.6.3 directly.

E 1.6.2 Assume X to be a finite set with subsets $X_1, \ldots, X_n$. Use the Principle of Inclusion and Exclusion in order to derive the number of elements of X which lie in precisely m of these subsets X_i.

E 1.6.3 Express the value $\phi(n)$ of the Euler function ϕ in terms of n and its prime divisors.

E 1.6.4 Check the details of the second example in 1.6.5.

E 1.6.5 Prove 1.6.12.

1.7   Special symmetry classes

We now return to Y^X and consider its subsets consisting of the injective and the surjective maps f only:

$$Y_i^X := \{f \in Y^X \mid f \text{ injective}\} \text{ and } Y_s^X := \{f \in Y^X \mid f \text{ surjective}\}.$$

It is clear that each of these sets is both a G–set and an H–set and therefore it is also an $H \times G$–set, but it will not in general be an $H \wr_x G$–set. The corresponding orbits of G, H and $H \times G$ on Y_i^X are called *injective* symmetry classes, while those on Y_s^X will be called *surjective* symmetry classes. We should like to determine their number. In order to do this we describe the fixed points of $(h, g) \in H \times G$ on these sets to prepare an application of the Cauchy-Frobenius Lemma. A first remark shows how the fixed points of (h, g) on Y^X can be constructed with the aid of $\bar{h}$ and $\bar{g}$, the permutations induced by h on Y and by g on X (use 1.5.1):

1.7.1 Corollary *If* $\bar{g} = \prod_v (x_v \ldots g^{l_v-1} x_v)$, *then* $f \in Y^X$ *is fixed under* (h, g) *if and only if the following two conditions are satisfied:*

$$f(x_v) \in Y_{h^{l_v}},$$

and the other values of f *arise from the values* $f(x_v)$ *according to*

$$f(x_v) = hf(g^{-1} x_v) = h^2 f(g^{-2} x_v) = \ldots .$$

This together with 1.3.11 yields:

1.7.2 Corollary *The fixed points of* (h, g) *are the* $f \in Y^X$ *which can be obtained in the following way:*

- *To each cyclic factor of* $\bar{g}$, *let* l *denote its length, we associate a cyclic factor of* $\bar{h}$ *of length* d *dividing* l.

- *If* x *is a point in this cyclic factor of* $\bar{g}$ *and* y *a point in the chosen cyclic factor of* $\bar{h}$, *then put*

$$f(x) := y, f(gx) := hy, f(g^2 x) := h^2 y, \ldots .$$

Such an f is injective if and only if the mapping described in the first item of 1.7.2 is injective and corresponding cyclic factors of $\bar{g}$ and $\bar{h}$ have the same length. The number of such mappings is

$$\prod_j \binom{a_j(\bar{h})}{a_j(\bar{g})} a_j(\bar{g})!,$$

while the second item of 1.7.2 says that we have to multiply this number by $\prod_j j^{a_j(\bar{g})}$ in order to get the number $|Y^X_{i,(h,g)}|$ of fixed points of (h, g) on Y^X_i. Thus we have proved

1.7.3 Corollary *The number of fixed points of* (h, g) *on* Y^X_i *is*

$$|Y^X_{i,(h,g)}| = \prod_j \binom{a_j(\bar{h})}{a_j(\bar{g})} j^{a_j(\bar{g})} a_j(\bar{g})!,$$

and hence, by restriction, the numbers of fixed points of g *and of* h *are:*

$$|Y^X_{i,g}| = \begin{cases} \binom{|Y|}{|X|} |X|! & \text{if } \bar{g} = 1, \\ 0 & \text{otherwise,} \end{cases} \quad \text{and} \quad |Y^X_{i,h}| = \binom{a_1(\bar{h})}{|X|} |X|!.$$

An application of the Cauchy-Frobenius Lemma yields the desired number of injective symmetry classes:

1.7.4 Theorem *The number of injective $H \times G$-classes is*

$$|(H \times G)\backslash\backslash Y_i^X| = \frac{1}{|H||G|} \sum_{(h,g)} \prod_j \binom{a_j(\bar{h})}{a_j(\bar{g})} j^{a_j(\bar{g})} a_j(\bar{g})!,$$

so that we obtain by restriction the number of injective G-classes

$$|G\backslash\backslash Y_i^X| = \frac{|X|!}{|\bar{G}|}\binom{|Y|}{|X|} = \binom{|Y|}{|X|}|S_X/\bar{G}|,$$

and the number of injective H-classes

$$|H\backslash\backslash Y_i^X| = \frac{|X|!}{|H|} \sum_{k=|X|}^{|Y|} |\{h \in H \mid a_1(\bar{h}) = k\}|\binom{k}{|X|}.$$

$\square$

In order to derive the number of surjective fixed points of (h, g) we use the preceeding corollaries together with an application of the Principle of Inclusion and Exclusion in order to get rid of the nonsurjective fixed points. We denote by Y_v the set of points $y \in Y$ contained in the v-th cyclic factor of $\bar{h}$ and put, for each index set $I \subseteq \underline{c(\bar{h})}$:

$$Y_{(h,g),I}^X := \{f \in Y_{(h,g)}^X \mid \forall\, v \in I : f^{-1}[Y_v] = \emptyset\}.$$

Then, by the Principle of Inclusion and Exclusion, we obtain for the desired number of surjective fixed points of (h, g) the following expression:

$$|Y_{s,(h,g)}^X| = |Y_{(h,g)}^{X*}| = \sum_{I \subseteq \underline{c(\bar{h})}} (-1)^{|I|}|Y_{(h,g),I}^X|$$

$$= \sum_{I \subseteq \underline{c(\bar{h})}} (-1)^{c(\bar{h})-|I|}|Y_{(h,g),\underline{c(\bar{h})}\backslash I}^X|.$$

Now we recall that

$$Y_{(h,g),\underline{c(\bar{h})}\backslash I}^X = \{f \in Y_{(h,g)}^X \mid \forall\, v \notin I : f^{-1}[Y_v] = \emptyset\}.$$

This set can be identified with $\widetilde{Y}^{X}_{(\tilde{h},g)}$, where $\tilde{h}$ denotes the product of the cyclic factors of $\bar{h}$ the numbers of which lie in I, and where $\widetilde{Y}$ is the set of points contained in these cyclic factors. Thus

$$|Y^{X}_{(h,g),\underline{c(\bar{h})}\setminus I}| = |\widetilde{Y}^{X}_{(\tilde{h},g)}| = \prod_{j} |\widetilde{Y}_{\tilde{h}^j}|^{a_j(\bar{g})}.$$

We can make this more explicit by an application of 1.3.11 which yields:

1.7.5 $$|\widetilde{Y}_{\tilde{h}^j}| = a_1(\tilde{h}^j) = \sum_{d|j} d \cdot a_d(\tilde{h}).$$

Putting these things together we conclude

1.7.6 Corollary *The number of surjective fixed points of (h,g) is*

$$|Y^{X}_{s,(h,g)}| = \sum_{k=1}^{c(\bar{h})} (-1)^{c(\bar{h})-k} \sum_{a} \prod_{i=1}^{|Y|} \binom{a_i(\bar{h})}{a_i} \prod_{j=1}^{|X|} \left(\sum_{d|j} d \cdot a_d \right)^{a_j(\bar{g})},$$

where the middle sum is taken over all the sequences $a = (a_1,\ldots,a_{|Y|})$ of natural numbers a_j such that $\sum a_j = k$ (they correspond to all possible choices of $\tilde{h}$ out of h, where a_i of the chosen cyclic factors of $\tilde{h}$ are i–cycles). Hence the numbers of surjective fixed points of g and of h amount to:

$$|Y^{X}_{s,g}| = \sum_{k=1}^{|Y|} (-1)^{|Y|-k} \binom{|Y|}{k} k^{c(\bar{g})},$$

and

$$|Y^{X}_{s,h}| = \sum_{k=1}^{c(\bar{h})} (-1)^{c(\bar{h})-k} \sum_{a} \left(\prod_{i} \binom{a_i(\bar{h})}{a_i}\right) a_1^{|X|},$$

where the sum is taken over all the sequences $(a_1,\ldots,a_{|Y|})$, $a_i \in \mathbb{N}$ and $\sum a_i = k$.

An application of the Cauchy-Frobenius Lemma finally yields the desired numbers of surjective symmetry classes:

1.7.7 Theorem *The number $|(H \times G)\backslash\backslash Y^{X}_{s}|$ of surjective $H \times G$–classes is*

$$\frac{1}{|H||G|} \sum_{(h,g)} \sum_{k=1}^{c(\bar{h})} (-1)^{c(\bar{h})-k} \sum_{a} \prod_{i=1}^{|Y|} \binom{a_i(\bar{h})}{a_i} \prod_{j=1}^{|X|} \left(\sum_{d|j} d \cdot a_d \right)^{a_j(\bar{g})},$$

where the inner sum is taken over the sequences $a = (a_1, \ldots a_{|Y|})$ *described in the corollary above. This implies, by restriction, the equations*

$$|G \backslash\backslash Y_s^X| = \frac{1}{|G|} \sum_g \sum_{k=1}^{|Y|} (-1)^{|Y|-k} \binom{|Y|}{k} k^{c(\bar{g})},$$

and

$$|H \backslash\backslash Y_s^X| = \frac{1}{|H|} \sum_h \sum_{k=1}^{c(\bar{h})} (-1)^{c(\bar{h})-k} \sum_a (\prod_i \binom{a_i(\bar{h})}{a_i}) a_1^{|X|},$$

where the last sum is to be taken over all the sequences $a = (a_1, \ldots, a_{|Y|})$ *such that* $a_i \in \mathbb{N}$ *and* $\sum a_i = k$.

These considerations lead to various combinatorial numbers so that a few remarks concerning these are in order. For example, $Y_{s,g}^X$ is the set of surjective mappings $f \in Y^X$ which are constant on the $c(\bar{g})$ cyclic factors of $\bar{g}$. Hence this set can be identified with the set $Y_s^{c(\bar{g})}$. More generally we consider the set $\underline{m}_s^n$ and define the numbers $S(n, m)$ by

$$m! S(n, m) := |\underline{m}_s^n|, \quad \text{where } m, n \in \mathbb{N}.$$

These $S(n, m)$ are called the *Stirling numbers* of the *second kind*. If n is used as row index and m as column index, then the upper left hand corner of the table of Stirling numbers of the second kind is as follows:

1.7.8 $\qquad (S(n, m)) = \begin{pmatrix} 1 & & & & & \\ 0 & 1 & & & & \\ 0 & 1 & 1 & & & \\ 0 & 1 & 3 & 1 & & \\ 0 & 1 & 7 & 6 & 1 & \\ 0 & 1 & 15 & 25 & 10 & 1 \\ \vdots & & & & & \ddots \end{pmatrix}.$

By definition $m! S(n, m)$ is equal to the number of *ordered* set partitions $(\underline{n}^{(1)}, \ldots, \underline{n}^{(m)})$ of $\underline{n}$ into m *blocks*, i.e. into m nonempty subsets $\underline{n}^{(i)}$. This is clear since each such ordered partition can be identified with $f : \underline{n} \to \underline{m}$ where $f^{-1}[\{i\}] := \underline{n}^{(i)}, i \in \underline{m}$. Thus $S(n, m)$ is the number of set partitions $\{\underline{n}^{(1)}, \ldots, \underline{n}^{(m)}\}$ of the set $\underline{n}$ into m blocks, and hence B_n, the number of *all* the set partitions of $\underline{n}$ satisfies the equation

1.7.9 $$B_n = \sum_{k=0}^n S(n, k).$$

These numbers B_n are called *Bell numbers*. Another consequence of the definition of Stirling numbers of the second kind and 1.7.6 is

$$|Y|!S(c(\bar{g}), |Y|) = |Y_{s,g}^X| = \sum_{k=1}^{|Y|}(-1)^{|Y|-k}\binom{|Y|}{k}k^{c(\bar{g})},$$

which implies:

1.7.10 Stirling's Formula *For $m > 0$ and any natural number n we have:*

$$S(n, m) = \frac{1}{m!}\sum_{k=1}^{m}(-1)^{m-k}\binom{m}{k}k^n.$$

Another series of combinatorial numbers shows up if we rewrite 1.7.7 in the following form:

1.7.11 $$|G \backslash\!\backslash Y_s^X| = \frac{|Y|!}{|G|}\sum_{k=1}^{|X|}S(k, |Y|)|\{g \in G \mid c(\bar{g}) = k\}|.$$

We put

$$r(n, k) := |\{\pi \in S_{\underline{n}} \mid c(\pi) = k\}|,$$

and call these the *signless* Stirling numbers of the *first kind*. They satisfy the following recursion formula, since in $\pi \in S_{\underline{n}}$ the point n either forms a 1–cycle or does not:

1.7.12 Lemma *For $n, k > 1$ we have*

$$r(n, k) = r(n-1, k-1) + (n-1)r(n-1, k)$$

while the initial values are $r(0,0) = 1$ and $r(n,0) = r(0,k) = 0$, for $n, k > 0$.

The upper left hand corner of a table containing these numbers $r(n, k)$, for $n, k \in \mathbb{N}$, is as follows

1.7.13 $$(r(n,k)) = \begin{pmatrix} 1 & & & & & \\ 0 & 1 & & & & \\ 0 & 1 & 1 & & & \\ 0 & 2 & 3 & 1 & & \\ 0 & 6 & 11 & 6 & 1 & \\ 0 & 24 & 50 & 35 & 10 & 1 \\ \vdots & & & & & \ddots \end{pmatrix}.$$

We now return to the number $|S_X \backslash\backslash Y_s^X|$. The exercise 1.7.1 together with the identity 1.7.11 yields

1.7.14 $$\frac{|Y|!}{|X|!} \sum_{k=1}^{|X|} r(|X|,k) S(k,|Y|) = \binom{|X|-1}{|Y|-1}.$$

Another series of combinatorial numbers arises when we count certain injective symmetry classes, since 1.7.4 implies

1.7.15 $$|S_Y \backslash\backslash Y_i^X| = \frac{|X|!}{|Y|!} \sum_{k=|X|}^{|Y|} t(|Y|,k) \binom{k}{|X|},$$

where $t(n,k) := |\{\pi \in S_{\underline{n}} \mid a_1(\pi) = k\}|$. It is easy to derive these numbers from the *rencontre numbers* $R(n) := t(n,0)$, since obviously the following is true:

1.7.16 $$t(n,k) = \binom{n}{k} R(n-k).$$

This can be made more explicit by an application of exercise 1.7.2 which yields

1.7.17 $$R(n) = n! \sum_{k=0}^{n} \frac{(-1)^k}{k!}.$$

Now we use that, for $|Y| \geq |X|, |S_Y \backslash\backslash Y_i^X| = 1$, so that by the last three equations:

1.7.18 $$1 = \sum_{k=|X|}^{|Y|} \frac{1}{(k-|X|)!} \sum_{j=0}^{|Y|-k} \frac{(-1)^j}{j!}, \text{ if } |Y| \geq |X|.$$

It is in fact an important and interesting task of enumeration theory to derive identities in this way since they are understood as soon as they are seen to describe a combinatorial situation. Another example is the identity

1.7.19 Lemma *For natural numbers n and k the following identities hold:*

$$\sum_{m=1}^{k} \binom{k}{m}\binom{n-1}{m-1} = \binom{n+k-1}{n} = \frac{1}{n!} \sum_{\pi \in S_{\underline{n}}} k^{c(\pi)}.$$

Proof: Exercise 1.7.1 implies that, for $m \leq k$,

$$\binom{k}{m}\binom{n-1}{m-1}$$

is equal to the number of symmetry classes of $S_{\underline{n}}$ on $\underline{k}^{\underline{n}}$, the elements of which satisfy $|f[\underline{n}]| = m$. Thus the left hand side is $|S_{\underline{n}} \backslash\backslash \underline{k}^{\underline{n}}|$. But the orbit of $f \in \underline{k}^{\underline{n}}$ under $S_{\underline{n}}$ is characterized by the orders of the inverse images $|f^{-1}[\{i\}]|$, $i \in \underline{k}$. Hence the number of these orbits is equal to the number of k–tuples $(n_1, \ldots, n_k)$, $n_i \in \mathbb{N}$, and $\sum n_i = n$, therefore the first identity follows from exercise 1.7.3. The last equation is already clear from 1.5.2.

$\square$

Exercises

E 1.7.1 Prove that $|S_{\underline{n}} \backslash\backslash \underline{m}^{\underline{n}}_{\underline{s}}| = \binom{n-1}{m-1}$.

E 1.7.2 Use the Principle of Inclusion and Exclusion in order to prove 1.7.17.

E 1.7.3 Show that the number of k–tuples $(n_1, \ldots, n_k)$ such that $n_i \in \mathbb{N}$ and $\sum n_i = n$ is equal to

$$\binom{n+k-1}{n}.$$

E 1.7.4 Prove that the Stirling numbers of the second kind satisfy the equation

$$x^n = \sum_{k=0}^{n} S(n, k)[x]_k,$$

where $[x]_k := x(x-1) \cdot \ldots \cdot (x-k+1)$.

Chapter 2

Weights

Now we refine our methods in order to enumerate orbits with prescribed properties. We introduce a weight function on $_GX$, i.e. a mapping from X into a commutative ring which is constant on the orbits of G on X, and the Cauchy-Frobenius Lemma will be refined in order to count orbits with prescribed weight. For example we shall be able to enumerate graphs by their number of edges. This leads us to certain generating functions, the so-called cycle indicator polynomials. The enumeration of rooted trees amounts to the consideration of sums of cycle indicator polynomials and leads to recursive methods. These recursions can be used even for constructive methods, and they stimulate the formalization of the calculation of generating functions.

Afterwards we generalize the enumeration of symmetry classes by introducing a combinatorial situation which covers both the notion of symmetry class (which was in fact Pólya's approach to the enumeration of graphs) and the situation which J.H. Redfield studied in order to enumerate superpositions of graphs.

Finally we shall discuss a categorical approach to the evaluation of generating functions, the theory of species. It yields one of the various systematic approaches to decompositions of structures (like decomposing permutations into cycles, graphs into connected components, and so on).

2.1   Enumeration by weight

In the preceding chapter group actions were introduced, the Cauchy-Frobenius Lemma was proved, and we studied certain actions of groups on sets of the form Y^X in some detail. We saw that various structures like graphs and partitions can be defined as orbits on such sets in a natural way so that we already have a method at hand to evaluate the *total number* of such structures. The question arises how these methods can be refined in such a way that we can also derive the *number of orbits with certain prescribed properties* like, for example, the number of graphs on v vertices which have e edges. The answer to many such questions can be given by introducing a *weight* which mostly will be a mapping from the set on which the group is acting into a polynomial ring over $\mathbb{Q}$. The final result will be a *generating function* for the enumeration problem in question, i.e. we shall obtain a polynomial which has the desired numbers of orbits as coefficients of its different monomial summands. The basic tool is

2.1.1 The Cauchy-Frobenius Lemma, weighted form *Let $_GX$ denote a finite action and $w\colon X \to R$ a map from X into a commutative ring R containing $\mathbb{Q}$ as a subring. If w is constant on the orbits of G on X, then we have, for any transversal $\mathscr{T}$ of the orbits:*

$$\sum_{t\in\mathscr{T}} w(t) = \frac{1}{|G|}\sum_{g\in G}\sum_{x\in X_g} w(x) = \frac{1}{|\bar{G}|}\sum_{\bar{g}\in\bar{G}}\sum_{x\in X_{\bar{g}}} w(x).$$

Proof: The following equations are clear from the foregoing, except maybe the last one which uses the assumption that w is constant on the orbits:

$$\sum_{g\in G}\sum_{x\in X_g} w(x) = \sum_{x}\sum_{g\in G_x} w(x)$$

$$= \sum_{x}|G_x|w(x) = |G|\sum_{x}|G(x)|^{-1}w(x) = |G|\sum_{t\in\mathscr{T}} w(t).$$

This proves the first of the stated equations, the second follows by an application of the homomorphism theorem.

$\square$

This result implies 1.1.11 (put $w\colon x \mapsto 1$), which we shall sometimes call the *constant form* of the Cauchy-Frobenius Lemma. In order to apply 2.1.1 to the enumeration of symmetry classes of mappings f in Y^X we introduce, for a given mapping $W\colon Y \to R$, R a commutative ring with $\mathbb{Q}$ as a subring, the *multiplicative weight* $w: Y^X \to R$, defined by

2.1.2
$$w(f) := \prod_{x \in X} W(f(x)),$$

and notice that for any finite actions $_G X$ and $_H Y$ the following is true:

2.1.3 Corollary *If W is constant on the orbits of H on Y, then w is constant on the orbits of $H \wr_x G$, $H \times G$, H and G on Y^X. Moreover, for any W, the corresponding multiplicative weight function w is constant on the orbits of G on Y^X.*

Thus 2.1.1 can be applied as soon as we have evaluated the sum of the weights of those f which are fixed under $(\psi, g) \in H \wr_x G$. But this sum of weights follows directly from the characterization of the fixed points of (ψ, g) given in 1.5.1:

2.1.4 Corollary *Using the same notation as in 1.5.1, for (ψ, g) in $H \wr_x G$, a function $W: Y \to R$ constant on the orbits of H, and the corresponding multiplicative weight $w: Y^X \to R$, we obtain the equation*

$$\sum_{f \in Y^X_{(\psi,g)}} w(f) = \prod_v \sum_{y \in Y_{h_v(\psi,g)}} W(y)^{l_v}.$$

Now an application of the weighted form of the Cauchy-Frobenius Lemma to 2.1.3 yields the desired generating function for the enumeration of symmetry classes by weight:

2.1.5 Theorem *Let $_G X$ and $_H Y$ be finite actions, $W: Y \to R$ a mapping into a commutative ring containing $\mathbb{Q}$ as a subring, and denote by w the corresponding multiplicative weight function on Y^X.*

- *If W is constant on the orbits of H on Y, then w is constant on the orbits of $H \wr_x G$ on Y^X, and, for each transversal $\mathcal{T}$ of these orbits, we have*

$$\sum_{t \in \mathcal{T}} w(t) = \frac{1}{|H|^{|X|}|G|} \sum_{(\psi,g) \in H \wr_x G} \prod_{v=1}^{c(\bar{g})} \sum_{y \in Y_{h_v(\psi,g)}} W(y)^{l_v}.$$

Moreover w is also constant on the orbits of $H \times G$ and H, so that, by restriction, we obtain for the sum of the weights of the *elements in a transversal the expressions*

$$\frac{1}{|H||G|} \sum_{(h,g)\in H\times G} \prod_{i=1}^{|X|} \left(\sum_{y\in Y_{h^i}} W(y)^i \right)^{a_i(\bar{g})},$$

and

$$\frac{1}{|H|} \sum_{h\in H} \left(\sum_{y\in Y_h} W(y) \right)^{|X|}.$$

- *For any $W: Y \to R$ the corresponding multiplicative weight function $w: Y^X \to R$ is constant on the orbits of G on Y^X, and the sum of its values on a transversal of the orbits is equal to*

$$\frac{1}{|G|} \sum_{g\in G} \prod_{i=1}^{|X|} \left(\sum_{y\in Y} W(y)^i \right)^{a_i(\bar{g})}.$$

The most general weight function is obtained when we take for W a mapping which sends each $y \in Y$ to a separate indeterminate of a polynomial ring. For the sake of notational simplicity we can do this by taking the elements $y \in Y$ themselves as indeterminates and putting $W: Y \to \mathbb{Q}[Y]: y \mapsto y$, where $\mathbb{Q}[Y]$ denotes the polynomial ring over $\mathbb{Q}$ in the set Y of commuting indeterminates. This yields the multiplicative weight $w(f) = \Pi_x f(x)$, a monomial in $\mathbb{Q}[Y]$. If we define the *content* of $f \in Y^X$ to be the mapping

2.1.6 $\qquad\qquad c(f,-): Y \to \mathbb{N}: y \mapsto |f^{-1}[\{y\}]|,$

i.e. $c(f, y)$ is the multiplicity with which f takes the value y, then we get

2.1.7 Corollary *The number of G—classes on Y^X, the elements of which have the same content as $f \in Y^X$, is equal to the coefficient of the monomial $\Pi_y y^{c(f,y)}$ in the polynomial*

$$\frac{1}{|G|} \sum_{g\in G} \prod_{i=1}^{|X|} \left(\sum_{y\in Y} y^i \right)^{a_i(\bar{g})}.$$

A nice example is the solution of the so–called *necklace problem*:

2.1.8 Example We ask for the different necklaces with n beads in up to m colours and given content. In order to bring this problem within reach of unromantic mathematics, we consider such a necklace a colouring of the vertices of a regular n–gon, i.e. as an $f \in \underline{m}^{\underline{n}}$. Two such necklaces or colourings are different if and only if none of them can be obtained from the other one by a rotation. Hence we are faced with an action of the form $_G Y^X$, namely the natural action of the cyclic group $G := C_{\underline{n}}$ on the set $Y^X := \underline{m}^{\underline{n}}$. (In case we want to allow reflections, we have to consider $G := D_{\underline{n}}$, the dihedral group.) A particular case was already discussed in 1.3.12, where we obtained the total number of orbits in the special case when n is prime. Now we are in a position to count these orbits by content. In order to do this for general m and n we take from exercise 1.3.2 the cycle structure of the elements of $C_{\underline{n}}$ and obtain, by an application of 2.1.7, the desired solution of the necklace problem:

2.1.9 Corollary *The number of different necklaces containing b_i beads of the i–th colour, $i \in \underline{m}$, is the coefficient of $y_1^{b_1} \dots y_m^{b_m}$ in the polynomial*

$$\frac{1}{n} \sum_{d \mid n} \phi(d)(y_1^d + \dots + y_m^d)^{n/d},$$

where ϕ denotes the Euler function (see exercise 1.3.2).

For a numerical example we take $m := 2$ and $n := 5$ and obtain the generating function

$$\frac{1}{5}((y_1 + y_2)^5 + 4(y_1^5 + y_2^5)) = y_1^5 + y_1^4 y_2 + 2y_1^3 y_2^2 + 2y_1^2 y_2^3 + y_1 y_2^4 + y_2^5.$$

Recall that the monomial summand $2y_1^3 y_2^2$ means that there are exactly two different necklaces consisting of 5 beads three of which are of the first colour and two of which are of the second colour. Figure 2.1 shows four of the eight different necklaces, the remaining ones are obtained by simply exchanging the two colours.

$$\Diamond$$

The result 2.1.7 has an important consequence which can be used for a systematic study of certain congruences:

2.1.10 Corollary *For each finite action $_G X$ and any $m \in \mathbb{N}$ each coefficient of a monomial summand in the generating function is divisible by*

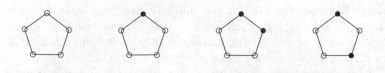

Figure 2.1: One half of the different necklaces

$|G|$, *or, in formal terms:*

$$\sum_{g\in G}\prod_{i=1}^{|X|}\left(\sum_{v=1}^{m}y_v^i\right)^{a_i(\bar{g})}\equiv 0\quad(|G|).$$

Besides the Cauchy-Frobenius Lemma also the Involution Principle admits a generalization to a weighted form:

2.1.11 The Involution Principle, weighted form *Assume that τ is a sign-reversing involution acting on the finite set $X = X^+\dot{\cup}X^-$ and that $w\colon X \to R$ is a weight function which is constant on the orbits of τ. Then*

$$\sum_{x\in X}\text{sign}(x)w(x) = \sum_{x\in X_\tau}\text{sign}(x)w(x).$$

The proof is trivial but the applications are not as is shown by

2.1.12 Example We would like to prove the so–called *q–binomial theorem*. It says that, for any $q \in \mathbb{R}$ and $n \in \mathbb{N}^*$, the following polynomial identity holds:

$$(x-1)(x-q)\dots(x-q^{n-1}) = \sum_{k=0}^{n}\begin{bmatrix}n\\k\end{bmatrix}_q q^{\binom{n-k}{2}}(-1)^{n-k}x^k,$$

where, for $n, k \in \mathbb{N}$, the rational function $\begin{bmatrix}n\\k\end{bmatrix}$ is defined by

$$\begin{bmatrix}n\\k\end{bmatrix} = \begin{cases} [n]![k]!^{-1}[n-k]!^{-1} & \text{if } 0 \le k \le n,\\ 0 & \text{otherwise,}\end{cases}$$

and

$$[0]! := 1,\ [n]! := [n][n-1]\dots[1],\ \text{for } n \ge 1.$$

while, for $n \ge 1$:

$$[n] := 1 + x + \dots + x^{n-1},$$

and finally the *q–binomial number* is defined to be the value of the *binomial function* $\begin{bmatrix} n \\ k \end{bmatrix}$ at q:

$$\begin{bmatrix} n \\ k \end{bmatrix}_q := \begin{bmatrix} n \\ k \end{bmatrix}(q), \text{ in particular } \begin{bmatrix} n \\ k \end{bmatrix}_1 = \begin{bmatrix} n \\ k \end{bmatrix}(1) = \binom{n}{k}.$$

We consider the identity we want to prove as an identity of polynomials in x over $\mathbb{R}$. This single identity is equivalent to the following system of identities:

$$\forall\, n > l \geq 0: \sum_{k=0}^{n} \begin{bmatrix} n \\ k \end{bmatrix}_q q^{\binom{n-k}{2}}(-1)^{n-k}(q^l)^k = 0.$$

We prove this system by an application of the weighted form of the Involution Principle. The set on which we shall define an involution is

$$X := \{(I,J) \mid \underline{n} = I \dot\cup J\},$$

which we decompose into

$$X^+ := \{(I,J) \in X \mid |J| \text{ even}\}, \quad X^- := X \backslash X^+.$$

The involution which we use is defined, for a fixed $l \in n$, by

$$\tau(I,J) := \begin{cases} (I \backslash \{n - l\}, J \cup \{n - l\}) & \text{if } n - l \in I, \\ (I \cup \{n - l\}, J \backslash \{n - l\}) & \text{if } n - l \notin I. \end{cases}$$

A weight function is introduced by

$$w(I,J) := q^{\binom{|J|}{2} + i(I,J) + l \cdot |I|},$$

where $i(I,J)$ means the number of *inversions between I and J*, i.e. the number of pairs $(i,j) \in I \times J$ such that $i > j$. It is clear that τ is a sign–reversing involution on X, and $X_\tau = \emptyset$. It remains to check that w is constant on the orbits of τ. Clearly $i(I \backslash \{n - l\}, J \cup \{n - l\})$ is equal to

$$i(I,J) - i(\{n - l\}, J) + i(I \backslash \{n - l\}, \{n - l\}) = i(I,J) + l - |J|.$$

This gives

$$w(I \backslash \{n - l\}, J \cup \{n - l\}) = q^{\binom{|J|+1}{2} + i(I,J) + l \cdot |I| - |J|} = w(I,J).$$

We are now in a position to apply 2.1.11 which yields, as $X_\tau = \emptyset$, that 0 is equal to

$$\sum_{(I,J)} (-1)^{|J|} q^{\binom{|J|}{2} + i\,(I,J) + l\cdot|I|} = \sum_{k=0}^{n} (-1)^{n-k} q^{\binom{n-k}{2} + k\cdot l} \sum_{\substack{(I,J) \\ |J|=n-k}} q^{i\,(I,J)},$$

so that it remains to prove

2.1.13
$$\begin{bmatrix} n \\ k \end{bmatrix}_q = \sum_{\substack{(I,J) \\ |J|=n-k}} q^{i\,(I,J)},$$

an identity that follows from exercise 2.1.4.

Exercises

E 2.1.1 Prove the following combinatorial principle: If X and Y are finite sets and R is a commutative ring, and $\varphi: Y \times X \to R$, then

$$\sum_{f \in Y^X} \prod_{x \in X} \varphi(f(x), x) = \prod_{x \in X} \sum_{y \in Y} \varphi(y, x).$$

E 2.1.2 Derive 2.1.7 directly, using the fact that $f \in Y^X$ is fixed under $g \in G$ if and only if f is constant on the cyclic factors of $\bar{g}$.

E 2.1.3 Prove by induction that

$$\sum_{\pi \in S_{\underline{n}}} q^{l(\pi)} = [n]!.$$

E 2.1.4 Derive 2.1.13 from exercise 2.1.3 by considering a transversal of the left cosets of $S_{\underline{k}} \oplus S_{\underline{n}\backslash\underline{k}}$. (Hint: Show that the permutations π in $S_{\underline{n}}$ which are increasing both on $\underline{k}$ and $\underline{n}\backslash\underline{k}$ form such a transversal.)

2.2   Cycle indicator polynomials

We have seen in 2.1.7 that the generating function for the enumeration of the G–classes on Y^X by weight is equal to

$$\frac{1}{|G|} \sum_{g \in G} \prod_{i=1}^{|X|} \left(\sum_{y \in Y} y^i \right)^{a_i(\bar{g})}.$$

This polynomial can be obtained from the polynomial

$$C(G, X) := \frac{1}{|G|} \sum_{g \in G} \prod_{i=1}^{|X|} z_i^{a_i(\bar{g})} \in \mathbb{Q}[z_1, \ldots, z_{|X|}]$$

by simply replacing the indeterminate z_i by the polynomial $\sum_y y^i$. It is therefore the polynomial $C(G, X)$ which really matters. We call this polynomial the *cycle indicator polynomial* or the *cycle index* of $_G X$, since it displays the cycle structure of the elements $\bar{g} \in \bar{G}$. (But it should be mentioned that $C(G, X) = C(H, X)$ does *not* mean that $\bar{G}$ and $\bar{H}$ are isomorphic. There are counterexamples known: for example, the regular representation of the nonabelian group of order p^3, p an odd prime number, has the same cycle indicator polynomial as the regular representation of the abelian group $C_p \times C_p \times C_p$ (exercise 2.2.3.) In the case when we wish to display its indeterminates we shall write $C(G, X; z_1, \ldots, z_{|X|})$, and if we replace z_i by $r_i \in \mathbb{Q}$, we simply write $C(G, X; r_1, \ldots, r_{|X|})$. Hence we obtain, for example (cf. 1.5.2):

2.2.1 Corollary *The number of G–classes on* Y^X *is equal to*

$$C(G, X; |Y|, \ldots, |Y|).$$

In order to generalize the substitution process mentioned above which yields the generating function from $C(G, X)$, we put, for any polynomial p in $\mathbb{Q}[u_1, \ldots, u_m]$,

$$C(G, X \mid p(u_1, \ldots, u_m)) = \frac{1}{|G|} \sum_{g \in G} \prod_{i=1}^{|X|} p(u_1^i, \ldots, u_m^i)^{a_i(\bar{g})} \in \mathbb{Q}[u_1, \ldots],$$

and call this process *Pólya–substitution*. Using this notation we can rephrase corollary 2.1.7 as follows:

2.2.2 Pólya's Theorem *The generating function for the enumeration of G–classes on* Y^X *by content can be obtained from the cycle indicator of* $_G X$ *by Pólya–substituting* $\sum_{y \in Y} y$ *into the cycle indicator polynomial* $C(G, X)$. *Hence this generating function is equal to*

$$C\left(G, X \mid \sum_{y \in Y} y\right).$$

In order to count G–classes by content it therefore remains to evaluate
the cycle indicator of $_GX$. A few examples should be welcome:

2.2.3 Examples of cycle indicator polynomials

- The cycle indicator of the identity subgroup of S_n and its natural
action on $\underline{n}$ is

$$C(\{1\}, \underline{n}) = z_1^n.$$

- The cycle indicator of the natural action of the cyclic group $C_{\underline{n}}$
on $\underline{n}$ is (recall 2.1.9)

$$C(C_{\underline{n}}, \underline{n}) = \frac{1}{n} \sum_{d \mid n} \phi(d) z_d^{n/d}.$$

- The cycle indicator of the natural action of the dihedral group
$D_{\underline{n}}$ of order $2n$ on the set $\underline{n}$ (which can be considered as being
the set of vertices of the regular n–gon, of which D_n is the
symmetry group) satisfies

$$C(D_{\underline{n}}, \underline{n}) = \frac{1}{2} C(C_{\underline{n}}, \underline{n}) + \begin{cases} \frac{1}{2} z_1 z_2^{(n-1)/2} & \text{if } n \text{ is odd,} \\ \frac{1}{4} (z_2^{n/2} + z_1^2 z_2^{(n-2)/2}) & \text{if } n \text{ is even.} \end{cases}$$

This follows from the fact that the rotations form a cyclic
subgroup of order n, while the remaining reflections either leave
exactly one vertex fixed (in the case when n is odd) or two
vertices or none (in the case when n is even), and group the
remaining vertices into pairs of vertices that are mapped onto
each other.

- Furthermore we have the following cycle indicators of the natural actions of S_n and $A_{\underline{n}}$ (cf. 1.3.7 and exercise 1.4.1):

$$C(S_{\underline{n}}, \underline{n}) = \sum_{a \vdash n} \prod_k \frac{1}{a_k!} \left(\frac{z_k}{k} \right)^{a_k},$$

$$C(A_{\underline{n}}, \underline{n}) = \sum_{a \vdash n} (1 + (-1)^{a_2 + a_4 + \cdots}) \prod_k \frac{1}{a_k!} \left(\frac{z_k}{k} \right)^{a_k}.$$

$\diamond$

For the graphs on 4 vertices we use the cycle index (exercise 2.2.1)

$$2.2.4 \qquad C\left(S_{\underline{4}}, \binom{4}{2}\right) = \frac{1}{24}(z_1^6 + 9 z_1^2 z_2^2 + 8 z_3^2 + 6 z_2 z_4),$$

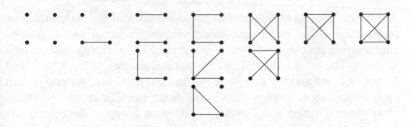

Figure 2.2: The graphs on 4 points

which is obtained from 1.5.5. It yields the generating function

$$C(S_{\underline{4}}, \binom{4}{2} \mid y_0 + y_1) = y_0^6 + y_0^5 y_1 + 2y_0^4 y_1^2 + 3y_0^3 y_1^3 + 2y_0^2 y_1^4 + y_0 y_1^5 + y_1^6,$$

in accordance with figure 2.2. In order to make life easier we can replace $y_0 + \ldots + y_{m-1}$ by $1 + y_1 + \ldots + y_{m-1}$, and in the case when $|Y| = 2$ we can even take $1 + y$ instead of $y_0 + y_1$ or $1 + y_1$, so that, for example, the generating function for the graphs on 4 vertices by their number of edges takes the following form:

$$C(S_{\underline{4}}, \binom{4}{2} \mid 1 + y) = 1 + y + 2y^2 + 3y^3 + 2y^4 + y^5 + y^6.$$

Here the coefficient of y^e is equal to the number of graphs on 4 vertices which possess exactly e edges, so that we obtain (recall 1.5.6 and 1.6.2):

2.2.5 Corollary *The total number of graphs on v vertices is equal to*

$$C(S_{\underline{v}}, \binom{v}{2}; 2, \ldots, 2),$$

while the number of selfcomplementary graphs on v vertices is equal to

$$C(S_{\underline{v}}, \binom{v}{2}; 0, 2, 0, 2, \ldots).$$

The number of graphs on v vertices which contain e edges is the coefficient of y^e in the polynomial

$$C(S_{\underline{v}}, \binom{v}{2} \mid 1 + y).$$

These examples have shown that the evaluation of the cycle indicator polynomial is an important step towards the solution of various enumeration problems, so that a few remarks concerning this are well in order. The cycle indicators of the natural actions of $S_{\underline{n}}$, $A_{\underline{n}}$, $C_{\underline{n}}$, and $D_{\underline{n}}$ are at hand and we therefore put the question how we can obtain cycle indicators of groups, which are direct sums or certain products of symmetric, alternating, cyclic or dihedral groups. More generally we want to know how the cycle indicator of a sum or a product can be obtained from the cycle indicators of the summands or factors, depending of course on the action in question. The following first remarks are clear from the definitions 1.2.6 and 1.2.7 of direct sum and cartesian product:

2.2.6 Lemma *Let $_GX$ and $_HY$ denote finite actions. We have*

$$C(G \times H, X \dot\cup Y) = C(G, X) \cdot C(H, Y),$$

and

$$C(G \times H, X \times Y) = \frac{1}{|G||H|} \sum_{(g,h)} \prod_{i,k=1}^{|X||Y|} z_{lcm(i,k)}^{gcd(i,k)a_i(\bar{g})a_k(\bar{h})}.$$

Further important constructions are the plethysm $H \odot G$ which we introduced in 1.4.2, and the composition which was introduced in 1.4.8. They are defined as permutation groups induced by *similar actions* of $H \wr_x G$, and so the corresponding cycle indicator polynomials are the same:

2.2.7 $$C(G[H], Y \times X) = C(H \odot G, |Y||X|).$$

From the description of the conjugacy classes of elements of complete monomial groups given in 1.4.7 we obtain for $C(H \odot G, |Y||X|)$ the following *plethysm of cycle indicators* (recall 1.4.7, in particular its last item):

2.2.8 $$C(H, Y) \odot C(G, X) := \frac{1}{|G|} \sum_g \prod_{k=1}^{|X|} \left(\frac{1}{|H|} \sum_h \prod_{i=1}^{|Y|} z_{i \cdot k}^{a_i(\bar{h})} \right)^{a_k(\bar{g})}.$$

Finally we show how the cycle indicator polynomial $C(G, X)$ can be obtained from the character $\chi: g \mapsto |X_g|$ of the action $_GX$ in question. In order to do this we have to evaluate the numbers $a_i(\bar{g}), i \in \mathbb{N}$, for each $g \in G$, and we shall do this by inverting the equations

2.2.9 $$\chi(g^k) = a_1(\bar{g^k}) = a_1(\bar{g}^k) = \sum_{d|k} d \cdot a_d(\bar{g})$$

(cf. 1.3.11 for the last equation). The inversion procedure uses the number theoretic Moebius function and the corresponding inversion theorem, but as we are going to use also other Moebius functions later on we shall describe this inversion method in a slightly more general context than is actually needed here.

We start doing so by introducing the notion of *incidence algebra*. Let $(P, \leq)$ denote a *poset* (partially ordered set). Its partial order $\leq$ allows us to introduce *intervals* $[p, q] := \{r \in P \mid p \leq r \leq q\}$. If all these intervals are finite, then $(P, \leq)$ is called a *locally finite* poset. Assuming this and denoting by $\mathbb{F}$ a field, we can turn the set

$$I_{\mathbb{F}}(P) := \{\varphi : P^2 \to \mathbb{F} \mid \varphi(p, q) = 0 \text{ unless } p \leq q\}$$

of all the *incidence functions* into an $\mathbb{F}$–algebra. The following addition and scalar multiplication define a vector space structure:

$$(\varphi + \psi)(p, q) := \varphi(p, q) + \psi(p, q) , \ (\rho\varphi)(p, q) := \rho \cdot \varphi(p, q), \ \rho \in \mathbb{F},$$

while the local finiteness allows to define the *convolution* product by

$$(\varphi \star \psi)(p, q) := \sum_{r \in [p, q]} \varphi(p, r)\psi(r, q).$$

This makes $I_{\mathbb{F}}(P)$ into a ring (exercise 2.2.5). The identity element is the Kronecker δ–*function*

$$\delta(p, q) := \begin{cases} 1 & \text{if } p = q \\ 0 & \text{otherwise.} \end{cases}$$

As scalar multiplication and convolution satisfy

$$\rho(\varphi \star \psi) = (\rho\varphi) \star \psi = \varphi \star (\rho\psi),$$

this ring is even an $\mathbb{F}$–*algebra*, the *incidence algebra* over $\mathbb{F}$ of $(P, \leq)$. It is important to characterize its invertible elements, i.e. the φ in $I_{\mathbb{F}}(P)$ for which there exists a $\psi \in I_{\mathbb{F}}(P)$ such that $\psi \star \varphi = \delta$ and also $\varphi \star \psi = \delta$. We obtain these incidence functions by an easy argument from linear algebra that allows to identify the incidence functions with upper triangular matrices as follows. In the case when P is finite, we can embed the partial order into a total order (i.e. we can number the $p \in P$ in a way such that $p_i < p_k$ implies $i < k$). This yields a bijection between $I_{\mathbb{F}}(P)$ and the set of upper triangular matrices over $\mathbb{F}$ which respects addition and scalar multiplication. The convolution product corresponds to the matrix product of the associated matrices

$$\varphi \mapsto \Phi := (\varphi(p_i, p_k)),$$

and so φ is invertible if and only if the values $\varphi(p, p)$ are nonzero. But this is true also in the more general case when we only assume $(P, \leq)$ to be locally finite, since then we can easily show that the incidence function recursively defined in the second item of the following lemma is in fact an inverse with respect to the convolution product:

2.2.10 Lemma *For each locally finite partial order $(P, \leq)$ and any $\varphi \in I_{\mathbb{F}}(P)$ the following is true:*

- *φ is invertible if and only if, for each $p \in P$, we have*

$$\varphi(p, p) \neq 0.$$

- *If φ is invertible, then φ^{-1} satisfies $\varphi^{-1}(p, p) = \varphi(p, p)^{-1}$, and*

$$\varphi^{-1}(p, q) = -\varphi(q, q)^{-1} \sum_{r \in [p,q)} \varphi^{-1}(p, r)\varphi(r, q)$$

$$= -\varphi(p, p)^{-1} \sum_{r \in (p,q]} \varphi(p, r)\varphi^{-1}(r, q),$$

where as usual $[p, q)$ and $(p, q]$ denote half open intervals.

A specific invertible incidence function is the *zeta function* which describes the partial order in question:

$$\zeta(p, q) := \begin{cases} 1 & \text{if } p \leq q, \\ 0 & \text{otherwise.} \end{cases}$$

Its inverse is called the *Moebius function* of $(P, \leq)$: $\mu := \zeta^{-1}$, for which we obtain from the preceeding lemma the following recursions:

$$2.2.11 \qquad \mu(p, q) = -\sum_{r \in [p,q)} \mu(p, r) = -\sum_{r \in (p,q]} \mu(r, q).$$

This close connection between the zeta and the Moebius function provides a very useful inversion theorem which we introduce next. In a poset $(P, \leq)$ the sets $\{q \in P \mid q \leq p\}$ are called the *principal (order–)ideals* of P, while the sets $\{q \in P \mid q \geq p\}$ are called the *principal filters*. The inversion theorem now reads as follows:

2.2.12 The Moebius Inversion *Let* $(P, \leq)$ *denote a locally finite poset and let* F *and* G *denote mappings from* P *into the field* $\mathbb{F}$. *Then*

- *if all the principal ideals of* P *are finite, we have the following equivalence of systems of equations:*

$$\forall p : G(p) = \sum_{q \leq p} F(q) \iff \forall p : F(p) = \sum_{q \leq p} G(q)\mu(q, p).$$

- *If all the principal filters of* P *are finite, we have the following equivalence of systems of equations:*

$$\forall p : G(p) = \sum_{q \geq p} F(q) \iff \forall p : F(p) = \sum_{q \geq p} \mu(p, q)G(q).$$

Proof: We prove the first statement, the second one follows analogously. We add to P an element 0 such that $0 < p$, for each $p \in P$, obtaining a new poset $(\bar{P} = P \cup \{0\}, \leq)$. As all the principal ideals of $(P, \leq)$ are supposed to be finite, $(\bar{P}, \leq)$ is a locally finite poset. Now we associate to F and G the incidence functions $\varphi\psi \in I_{\mathbb{F}}(\bar{P})$ defined by

$$\varphi(p, q) := \begin{cases} F(q) & \text{if } p = 0 \text{ and } q > 0, \\ 0 & \text{otherwise,} \end{cases}$$

$$\psi(p, q) := \begin{cases} G(q) & \text{if } p = 0 \text{ and } q > 0, \\ 0 & \text{otherwise.} \end{cases}$$

The system of equations $G(p) = \sum_{q \leq p} F(q)$ is equivalent to the identity $\psi = \varphi \star \zeta$, which again is equivalent to $\psi \star \mu = \varphi$, and this is nothing but the system of equations $F(p) = \sum_{q \leq p} G(q)\mu(q, p)$.

$\square$

A particular locally finite poset is $(\mathbb{N}^*, |)$, the set of positive natural numbers together with divisibility as its partial order. The corresponding μ is called the *number theoretic* Moebius function. Instead of $\mu(p, q)$ one can write $\mu(q/p)$ in this case since the intervals $[p, q]$ and $[r, s]$ are order isomorphic if $q/p = s/r$, and so $\mu(p, q) = \mu(r, s)$, by the above mentioned recursion. Thus we obtain, by an application of 2.2.12 and 2.2.9:

2.2.13 Corollary *For each finite action* $_GX$ *the following equivalent systems of equations hold:*

$$\forall k : a_1(\bar{g}^k) = \sum_{d | k} d \cdot a_d(\bar{g}) \quad and \quad \forall k : a_k(\bar{g}) = \frac{1}{k} \sum_{d | k} \mu(k/d)a_1(\bar{g}^d),$$

where μ denotes the number theoretic Moebius function. In particular we obtain the following expression of the cycle indicator of $_GX$ in terms of the character χ of $_GX$:

$$C(G, X) = \frac{1}{|G|} \sum_g \prod_i z_i^{i^{-1}\Sigma_{d|i}\mu(i/d)\chi(g^d)}.$$

In order to apply this result, we need to know the values of the number theoretic Moebius function. As ζ is defined by the partial order, the same holds for the Moebius function, and hence the Moebius function is the same for order isomorphic posets. Thus the values of the Moebius function on $(\mathbb{N}^*, |)$ can be evaluated by noting that the Moebius function is multiplicative and that an interval $[d, n]$, where d divides n, is order isomorphic to the cartesian product

2.2.14 $$[1, p_1^{k_1}] \times \ldots \times [1, p_r^{k_r}],$$

if n/d has the prime number decomposition $n/d = p_1^{k_1} \cdot \ldots \cdot p_r^{k_r}$, where the p_i are different prime numbers and the $k_i \geq 1$. Thus, for the number theoretic Moebius function we have (exercise 2.2.6):

$$\mu(n/d) := \mu(d, n) = \mu(1, n/d) = \prod_{i=1}^r \mu(1, p_i^{k_i}).$$

But from 2.2.11 we can deduce that $\mu(1) = 1, \mu(p) = -1$, if p is prime, and $\mu(p^r) = 0$, if $r > 1$. This together with 2.2.14 finally yields:

2.2.15 $$\mu(n) = \begin{cases} 1 & \text{if } n = 1, \\ (-1)^r & \text{if } n \text{ is a product of } r \text{ different primes,} \\ 0 & \text{otherwise.} \end{cases}$$

2.2.16 Examples

- The *exterior cycle index* of $\bar{G} \leq S_X$ is defined to be the cycle indicator of the natural action of S_X on the set of left cosets $S_X/\bar{G}$. The permutation character of this action is (exercise 2.2.7)

$$\chi(\pi) = \frac{|X|! \, |C^S(\pi) \cap \bar{G}|}{|\bar{G}| \, |C^S(\pi)|}.$$

This together with an application of 2.2.13 yields the exterior cycle index

$$C(S_X, S_X/\bar{G})$$

of $\bar{G}$.

- The character of S_X on the set $\binom{X}{k}$ of all the k–subsets of X is

$$\chi(\pi) = \sum_{b \vdash k} \prod_{i=1}^{k} \binom{a_i(\pi)}{b_i},$$

since a k–subset is fixed under π if and only if it is the union of cyclically permuted points. Hence we can apply 2.2.13 in order to evaluate $C(G, \binom{X}{k}) = C(\bar{G}, \binom{X}{k})$. A particular case is $C(S_v, \binom{v}{2})$ which we need for the enumeration of graphs on v vertices, and which is obtained from 1.5.5:

$$\chi(\bar{\pi}) = \binom{a_1(\pi)}{2} + a_2(\pi).$$

$\diamond$

Exercises

E 2.2.1 Check the equation 2.2.4.

E 2.2.2 Verify the details of 2.2.10.

E 2.2.3 Evaluate the cycle indicator polynomial of the action of the group $C_p \times C_p \times C_p$, p being an odd prime, on itself by left multiplication. Evaluate also the cycle indicator polynomial of the action of the nonabelian group of order p^3 on itself by left multiplication.

E 2.2.4 Express the cycle indicator $C(S_n, \underline{n})$ in terms of the polynomials $C(S_k, \underline{k}), 1 \le k \le n$.

E 2.2.5 Check that addition and convolution in fact define a ring structure on the set $I_{\mathbb{F}}(P)$ of incidence functions.

E 2.2.6 Let $(L, \wedge, \vee)$ denote a lattice and $(L, \le)$ the corresponding poset. We call $f \in I_{\mathbb{F}}(L)$ *multiplicative* if and only if, for each x, y in L, an order isomorphism

$$[x \wedge y, x \vee y] \simeq [x \wedge y, x] \times [x \wedge y, y]$$

implies that

$$f(x \wedge y, x \vee y) = f(x \wedge y, x) f(x \wedge y, y).$$

- Prove that the invertible multiplicative $f \in I_{\mathbb{F}}(L)$ form a group.
- Show that the zeta function (and hence also the Moebius function) is multiplicative.
- Verify 2.2.14 and 2.2.15.

E 2.2.7 Prove 2.2.16.

E 2.2.8 Evaluate the characters of the natural actions of S_X on $X^{\underline{n}}$ and on $X_i^{\underline{n}}$.

2.3 Sums of cycle indicators, recursive methods

If A_X denotes the alternating group on the finite set X then, by 2.1.7, the coefficient of the monomial $\Pi_y y^{c(f,y)}$ in $C(A_X, X \mid \sum y)$ is equal to the number of A_X–classes of mappings with the same content as f. If we exclude the trivial case $|X| = 1$, then the A_X–class of f differs from its S_X–class if and only if its stabilizers $(S_X)_f$ and $(A_X)_f$ are equal, and if these classes differ, then the S_X–class of f consists of *two* A_X–classes.

The stabilizer of $f \in Y^X$ in S_X is the following direct sum of the symmetric groups on the inverse images of the $y \in Y$:

2.3.1 $$(S_X)_f = \bigoplus_y S_{X_y}, \text{ where } X_y := f^{-1}[\{y\}].$$

The stabilizer of f in A_X is the intersection of $(S_X)_f$ with A_X. As each noninjective f is left fixed by a transposition while each injective f has the identity subgroup as its stabilizer, we obtain

2.3.2 Corollary *The stabilizers of $f \in Y^X$ in S_X and in A_X are the same, or, equivalently, they both are equal to the identity subgroup, if and only if f is injective.*

Thus the difference of cycle indicators of alternating and symmetric groups has the following useful interpretation (recall figure 1.2):

2.3.3 Corollary *For $|X| > 1$ the polynomial*

$$C(A_X, X \mid \sum y) - C(S_X, X \mid \sum y)$$

is the generating function for the enumeration of the injective S_X–classes on Y^X by weight.

Corresponding results hold for cyclic and dihedral groups. Also these arguments can be considered as a certain kind of involution principle. In fact we obtain in the same way the following generalization of 2.3.3 (recall 1.3.18):

2.3.4 Corollary *If $_GX$ denotes a chiral action, then*

$$C(G^+, X \mid \sum y) - C(G, X \mid \sum y)$$

is the generating function for the enumeration by weight of the G–classes on Y^X which split over G^+.

Besides these differences of cycle indicator polynomials we can form sums of cycle indicator polynomials of series of groups, e.g. we obtain (by simply comparing coefficients) the equation

$$2.3.5 \qquad \sum_{n=0}^{\infty} C(S_{\underline{n}}, \underline{n}) = \exp \sum_{k=1}^{\infty} \frac{z_k}{k} \in \mathbb{Q}[\![z_1, z_2, \ldots]\!],$$

if $C(S_{\underline{0}}, \underline{0} \mid p(u)) := 1$ and where $\mathbb{Q}[\![z_1, z_2, \ldots]\!]$ denotes the ring of formal power series over $\mathbb{Q}$ in the indeterminates $z_1, z_2, \ldots$. An immediate consequence is

$$2.3.6 \qquad \sum_{n=0}^{\infty} C(S_{\underline{n}}, \underline{n} \mid p(u)) = \exp \sum_{k=1}^{\infty} \frac{1}{k} p(u^k) \in \mathbb{Q}[\![u]\!],$$

This sum is of great interest since it can be used for a recursion method which we are going to describe next.

2.3.7 Example A graph is called a *tree* if and only if it is connected and does not contain any cycle. A tree with a single distinguished vertex is called a *rooted* tree. Figure 2.3 shows the smallest rooted trees. The root is distinguished by indicating it as a circle while the other vertices are indicated by a bullet.

If $r(x)$ denotes the generating function for the enumeration of rooted trees by their number of vertices, then figure 2.3 shows that

$$r(x) = x + x^2 + 2x^3 + 4x^4 + \ldots.$$

We claim that this formal power series satisfies a recursion formula in terms of cycle indicator polynomials of symmetric groups.

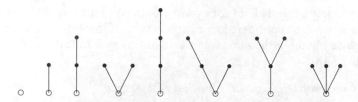

Figure 2.3: The smallest rooted trees

2.3.8 Lemma $r(x) = x \sum_{n=0}^{\infty} C(S_{\underline{n}}, \underline{n} \mid r(x))$.

Proof: It is clear that the generating function for the enumeration of rooted trees is equal to the sum over all $n \in \mathbb{N}$ of the generating functions of rooted trees with root degree n, i.e. where the root is incident with exactly n edges. It therefore remains to evaluate the generating function for the enumeration of trees with root degree n.

Denote by $\mathscr{R}$ the set of all the rooted trees. A rooted tree with root degree n can be considered as an orbit of $S_{\underline{n}}$ on the set $\mathscr{R}^{\underline{n}}$. If we now give an element of $\mathscr{R}$ the weight x^v, where v denotes the number of vertices of the rooted tree in question, then we obtain the power series $xC(S_{\underline{n}}, \underline{n} \mid r(x))$ which therefore is the desired generating function for the enumeration of rooted trees with root degree n by their number of vertices. This completes the proof.

□

An application of the above exponential expressions 2.3.5 and 2.3.6 for the sum of the cycle indicator polynomials of finite symmetric groups as an exponential formal power series allows to rewrite the recursion formula for the generating function of the rooted trees in the following way:

2.3.9 Corollary *The formal power series $r(x)$ which generates the numbers of rooted trees by number of vertices satisfies the recursion formula*

$$r(x) = x \cdot \exp \sum_{1}^{\infty} \frac{r(x^k)}{k}.$$

This recursion together with a suitable program system, like MAPLE or MACSYMA, allows to evaluate the smallest numbers of rooted trees, some of which are shown in the following table:

n	b_n	n	b_n
1	1	11	1842
2	1	12	4766
3	2	13	12486
4	4	14	32973
5	9	15	87811
6	20	16	235381
7	48	17	634847
8	115	18	1721159
9	286	19	4688676
10	719	20	12826228

$\diamondsuit$

Similar arguments apply in each case when the structure in question consists of a certain and well defined number of structures of the same kind. Lower down we shall see how a systematic theory can be developed which covers this and many other cases (there are various approaches, the books are full of them, for example the book of Goulden/Jackson gives an approach that covers very many cases in a different and more elementary way compared to the theory of species which is briefly indicated down below).

2.3.10 Example Each graph is a disjoint union of *connected* graphs (a graph is called *connected* if and only if from each of its vertices we can reach any other vertex by walking along suitably chosen edges). These connected subgraphs are well defined, and they are called the *connected components*. Thus the generating function $g(x) = \sum_v g_v x^v$ of the graphs and the generating function $c(x) = \sum_v c_v x^v$ for the connected graphs are related as follows:

$$2.3.11 \qquad g(x) = \sum_{n=0}^{\infty} C(S_{\underline{n}}, \underline{n} \mid c(x)) = \exp \sum_{k=1}^{\infty} \frac{c(x^k)}{k}.$$

As we already know that

$$g_v = \frac{1}{v!} \sum_{\pi \in S_{\underline{v}}} 2^{c(\overline{\pi})},$$

we can use 2.3.11 in order to evaluate the entries of the following
table:

v	g_v	c_v
1	1	1
2	2	1
3	4	2
4	11	6
5	34	21
6	156	112
7	1044	853
8	12346	11117
9	274668	261080
10	12005168	11716571

$\diamondsuit$

Further examples show up in the sciences. It was already briefly
mentioned that the origins of this theory of enumeration lie in chemistry and the problem of isomerism. A few remarks concerning the
history are therefore in order. It was already in the 18th century when
Alexander von Humboldt conjectured that there might be chemical substances which are composed by the same set of atoms but
have differend properties. In his book with the title "Versuche über
die gereizte Muskel- und Nervenfaser, nebst Vermutungen über den
chemischen Prozeß in der Tier- und Pflanzenwelt", published in 1797,
he writes (on page 128 of volume I):

> Drei Körper a, b und c können aus *gleichen* Quantitäten
> Sauerstoff, Wasserstoff, Kohlenstoff, Stickstoff und Me-
> tall zusammengesetzt und in ihrer Natur doch unendlich
> *verschieden* seyn.

But it needed a quarter of a century to develop the anaytical methods
that allowed to find out what the atomic constituents of a chemical molecule are. These methods were developed in particular by
J. L. Gay–Lussac and J. von Liebig, who were the first to prove von
Humboldt's conjecture to be true. Here is a sentence taken from a
paper of Gay–Lussac that describes their discovery:

> comme ces deux acides son très différents, il faudrait pour
> expliquer leur différence admettre entre leurs éléments un
> mode de combinaison différent. C'est un objet qui appelle
> un nouveau examen.

It needed some time to realize that a new phenomenon was discovered, J. J. Berzelius gave it the name *isomerism*. Chemists tried to find out what the reason is by sketching molecules. Here are three of these attempts to draw the molecule of C_2H_5OH: The first attempt is due to Couper:

$$C \begin{cases} O \cdots OH \\ H_2 \end{cases}$$

$$\vdots$$

$$C \qquad \cdots H_3$$

The next one is the way how Loschmidt drew this molecule:

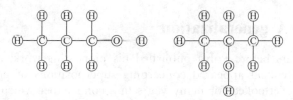

The breakthrough towards a solution of this problem is due to Alexander Crum Brown, who used a variation of Loschmidt's method by putting the circles of atoms that are assumed to be connected somehow apart but joining them by edges in order to emphasize the connection. Here are his drawings for the alcohol C_3H_7OH:

This introduction of *molecular graphs* solved the problem of isomerism by showing that there may exist different graphs that correspond to a given chemical formula (which prescribes in fact the degree sequence, which is the sequence of valencies of the atoms in the given formula). Moreover it gave rise to the development of graph theory (there are of course also other birthdays of graph theory known, for example Euler's solution of the Königsberg bridge problem, and Kirchhoff's invention of electric circuits as well as Hamiltons game called "trip around the world"), and it stimulated the *combinatorial theory of enumeration* since the question of chemical isomerism is at first glance equivalent to the problem of *constructing all the graphs which are connected and which have a given edge degree sequence.* Let us consider, for example, the chemical formula C_3H_7OH again, or, more generally the formula $C_nH_{2n+1}OH$. The problem is to construct all the graphs which correspond to each of these formulae, i.e. all the graphs that consist of n vertices of degree 4 (the carbon atoms are of that valency) together with $2n + 2$ vertices of degree 1 (the hydrogen) and one of degree 2 (the oxygen) which must have a neighbour of degree 1 (so that a hydroxyl group $-OH$ occurs). This problem amounts to the construction of rooted trees, as, by a well–known result of graph theory, such degree sequences can be satisfied by trees only (the cyclomatic number is zero in this case). The root represents the substructure $\equiv C - O - H$, so that the root degree is ≤ 3. Consider the two examples shown above which correspond to the formula C_3H_7OH. As the carbon atoms are of valency 4, we can make life easier by neglecting the hydrogen atoms, so that the *skeletons* remain, which correspond to the rooted trees with 3 vertices. From each one of these structures we can reconstruct the original molecular graph and hence the desired generating function $a(x)$ for the numbers of alcohols satisfies the recursion

2.3.12 $$a(x) = x \sum_{n=0}^{3} C(S_{\underline{n}}, \underline{n} \mid a(x)).$$

2.4   A generalization

Ten years before Pólya published his pioneering work, a paper by J. H. Redfield appeared concerning superpositions of graphs. But it was overlooked for many years (a second paper which went even further was rejected and printed only recently after it had been discovered among his mathematical papers). It is difficult to read, but it already contains the main results on enumeration by weight, moreover it presents a more general approach which we are going to describe next. It will not be necessary to give a formal definition of *superposition* , since the reader will clearly see what is meant from an example, and we shall examine a more general situation later on anyway. Two graphs on 5 vertices together with one (out of 4) superpositions of these graphs are shown in figure 2.4. The edges of one of the two superimposed graphs are dotted.

Now we introduce an enumeration problem, a special case of which is the enumeration of superpositions of graphs. Consider, for given

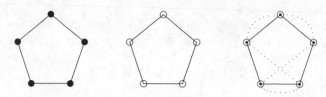

Figure 2.4: Two graphs on 5 vertices and a superposition

$m, n \in \mathbb{N}^*$, the set M of all the $n \times m$–matrices $A = (a_{ik})$ which contain in each row all the elements of $\underline{m}$, i.e. each row of $A \in M$ is an injective m–tuple over $\underline{m}$. Now we establish on M an equivalence relation $\sim_c$ by saying that $A, A' \in M$ are *column equivalent* if A' arises from A by applying a suitable column permutation σ:

$$(a_{ik}) \sim_c (a'_{ik}) \quad :\Longleftrightarrow \quad \exists \, \sigma \in \sum \; \forall \, i, k \colon \; a'_{ik} = a_{i, \sigma^{-1}k}.$$

The equivalence class of (a_{ik}) will be denoted by $(a_{ik})_c$, and we put

$$M_c := \{ (a_{ik})_c \mid (a_{ik}) \in M \}.$$

It is clear that

2.4.1 $$|M| = m!^n, \text{ and } |M_c| = m!^{n-1}.$$

Assume that we are given subgroups $H_1, \ldots, H_n \leq \sum$. Their direct product acts on M_c as follows:

2.4.2 $$(\times_i H_i) \times M_c \to M_c \colon ((\pi_1, \ldots, \pi_n), (a_{ik})_c) \mapsto (\pi_i a_{ik})_c,$$

and we ask for the number of orbits. One of the most important results of Redfield's paper is the proof of the fact that the number of superpositions of n graphs with m vertices and automorphism groups $H_1, \ldots, H_n$ is equal to

2.4.3 $$|(\times_i H_i) \backslash\!\backslash M_c|.$$

Since we are not particularly interested in this number of graphs, we go further and formulate and solve a counting problem which generalizes both Redfield's superposition problem and the enumeration of symmetry classes of mappings. To begin with we note that $f \in \underline{m}^{\underline{n}}$ can be identified with the one column matrix

$$\begin{pmatrix} f(1) \\ \vdots \\ f(n) \end{pmatrix}.$$

In addition we recall the action 1.2.11 of the exponentiation group. For subgroups $H \leq \sum, G \leq S_{\underline{n}}$, the image $\tilde{f} := (\psi, \pi)f$, for (ψ, π) in $H \wr G$, satisfies

$$\begin{pmatrix} \tilde{f}(1) \\ \vdots \\ \tilde{f}(n) \end{pmatrix} = \begin{pmatrix} \psi(1)f(\pi^{-1}1) \\ \vdots \\ \psi(n)f(\pi^{-1}n) \end{pmatrix}.$$

We compare this with Redfield's approach and seek for a generalization which covers this and the former approach. We are led to the following *Ansatz*. Consider, instead of $n \times m$–matrices, the $n \times s$–matrices A, for a fixed $s \in \underline{m}$, where each row of A is an injective s–tuple over $\underline{m}$:

$$M^{<s>} := \{A \in \underline{m}^{\underline{n} \times \underline{s}} \mid \text{each row lies in } \underline{m}_i^{\underline{s}}\}.$$

The order of this set is obviously

$$|M^{<s>}| = \left(\binom{m}{s} s! \right)^n = ([m]_s)^n, [m]_s := m(m-1)\cdots(m-s+1).$$

In order to introduce a suitable group which acts on $M^{<s>}$, we define the following *generalized wreath product* . Assume that $G \leq S_{\underline{n}}$ has the orbits $\omega_1, \ldots, \omega_r \subseteq \underline{n}$. We put, for $H_i \leq S_{\underline{m}}, i \in \underline{r}$,

$$(\times_{i=1}^r H_i) \wr G := \{(\psi, \pi) \mid \psi \in (\cup_i H_i)^{\underline{n}}, \pi \in G, i \in \omega_j \Rightarrow \psi(i) \in H_j\}.$$

The multiplication is still defined by $(\psi, \pi)(\varphi, \rho) := (\psi \varphi_\pi, \pi \rho)$, and this group acts on $M^{<s>}$ in the following way:

2.4.4 $(\times_i H_i) \wr G \times M^{<s>} \to M^{<s>} : ((\psi, \pi), (a_{ik})) \mapsto (\psi(i)a_{\pi^{-1}i,k})$.

As we have just seen, the particular case $s := 1$ yields the exponentiation group action on $\underline{m}^{\underline{n}}$. In order to cover also Redfield's column equivalence relation we furthermore introduce the corresponding action of $S_{\underline{s}}$:

2.4.5 $S_{\underline{s}} \times M^{<s>} \to M^{<s>} : (\sigma, (a_{ik})) \mapsto (a_{i,\sigma^{-1}k})$,

and note that these two actions commute:

2.4.6 $(\psi, \pi)\sigma A = \sigma(\psi, \pi)A.$

Hence we have in fact obtained an action of the direct product:

$$(\times_i H_i) \wr G \times S_{\underline{s}} \times M^{<s>} \to M^{<s>},$$

defined by

$$(((\psi, \pi), \sigma), (a_{ik})) \mapsto (\psi(i) a_{\pi^{-1}i, \sigma^{-1}k}).$$

The character of this action is given in

2.4.7 Lemma

$$a_1((\psi, \pi), \sigma) = \prod_{v=1}^{c(\pi)} \prod_{k=1}^{s} \binom{a_k(h_v(\psi, \pi))}{a_k(\sigma^{l_v})} a_k(\sigma^{l_v})! k^{a_k(\sigma^{l_v})}.$$

Proof: We start by considering the particular case $n = 1$, in which the set $M^{<s>}$ is just the set of injective s-tuples over $\underline{m}$, while the wreath product $((\times_i H_i) \wr G) \times S_{\underline{s}}$ is isomorphic to the direct product $H_1 \times S_{\underline{s}}$. Hence, for this case, we obtain the assertion from 1.7.3. For the general case $n \geq 1$ we remark that A is a fixed point of $((\psi, \pi), \sigma)$ if and only if its elements satisfy the equations

$$a_{ik} = \psi(i) a_{\pi^{-1}i, \sigma^{-1}k}.$$

Hence, for each $t \in \mathbb{N}^*$, the following is true:

2.4.8 $$a_{ik} = \psi \psi_\pi \ldots \psi_{\pi^{t-1}}(i) a_{\pi^{-t}i, \sigma^{-t}k}.$$

Now we consider a fixed $j \in \underline{n}$, and l, the length of its cyclic factor in π, which satisfy:

2.4.9 $$\forall k \in s: a_{jk} = \psi \psi_\pi \ldots \psi_{\pi^{l-1}}(j) a_{j, \sigma^{-l}k}.$$

Equation 2.4.8 means that the rows, the numbers i of which belong to the cycle containing j, are completely determined by the entries of the j-th row. Furthermore the j-th row of A, considered as an element of $\underline{m}_i^s$, must be a fixed point of

$$(\psi \psi_\pi \ldots \psi_{\pi^{l-1}}(j), \sigma^l),$$

by equation 2.4.9. In order to evaluate the number of fixed points of $((\psi, \pi), \sigma)$, we consider the standard cycle notation for π, say

$$\pi = \prod_{v=1}^{c(\pi)} (j_v \ldots \pi^{l_v-1}(j_v)).$$

For each one of its cyclic factors $(j_v \ldots \pi^{l_v-1}(j_v))$ we can freely choose an injective s-tuple over $\underline{m}$ among the fixed points of $(h_v(\psi, \pi), \sigma^{l_v})$. If we now form the product over all the cycles of π, taking the number of fixed points of $(h_v(\psi, \pi), \sigma^{l_v})$ as the factor corresponding to the v-th cyclic factor, then we obtain the desired number, and this proves the statement, as can be seen from the foregoing argument in the case $n = 1$.

$\square$

In order to derive Redfield's results from this more general one, we need another tool:

2.4.10 de Bruijn's Lemma *Assume that X is both a $G-$ and an H–set, and that we have*

$$\forall g \in G, h \in H \; \exists h' \in H \; \forall x: \; g(hx) = h'(gx).$$

Then G acts on $H \backslash\backslash X$ as follows:

$$G \times (H \backslash\backslash X) \to H \backslash\backslash X : (g, H(x)) \mapsto H(gx),$$

and the character of this action is

$$a_1(g) := |(H \backslash\backslash X)_g| = \frac{1}{|H|} \sum_{h \in H} |X_{gh}| =: \frac{1}{|H|} \sum_{h \in H} a_1(gh).$$

Proof: It is easy to check that $(g, H(x)) \mapsto H(gx)$ is an action. Furthermore we have that

$$\sum_h |X_{gh}| = \sum_{h \in H} \sum_{x \in X_{gh}} 1$$

$$= \sum_{x: gH(x) = H(x)} \sum_{h: hx = g^{-1}x} 1 = \sum_{x: gH(x) = H(x)} |H_x|$$

$$= |H| \sum_{x: gH(x) = H(x)} |H(x)|^{-1} = |H| \sum_{\omega \in H \backslash\backslash X : g\omega = \omega} 1 = |H| |(H \backslash\backslash X)_g|.$$

$\square$

In order to derive from this the character of the action 2.4.2 we use 2.4.7 and 2.4.10 which give

$$2.4.11 \qquad a_1((\pi_1, \ldots, \pi_n)) = \frac{1}{m!} \sum_{\sigma} \prod_{v=1}^{n} \prod_{k=1}^{m} \binom{a_k(\pi_v)}{a_k(\sigma)} a_k(\sigma)! k^{a_k(\sigma)},$$

where the sum is taken over the $\sigma \in \sum$. Now we observe that the summand on the right hand side is nonzero only if all the π_v are of the same cycle type as σ, in which case the double product takes the value

$$\left(\prod_k a_k(\sigma)!k^{a_k(\sigma)} \right)^n.$$

Applying this to 2.4.11 we get

$$a_1((\pi_1,\dots,\pi_n)) = \begin{cases} \left(\prod_k a_k!k^{a_k}\right)^{n-1} & \text{if each } a(\pi_v) = (a_1,\dots,a_n), \\ 0 & \text{otherwise.} \end{cases}$$

This result allows to express the number of orbits of $\times H_i$ on M_c in terms of the cycle indicator polynomials of the H_i. We introduce Redfield's so–called *cap operation* $\cap$ on the set $\mathbb{Q}[Y]$ of polynomials over $\mathbb{Q}$ in the set $Y := \{y_1,\dots,y_m\}$ of indeterminates. It is defined to be the linear extension of the following operation on monomials. Using the abbreviation $Y^b := y_1^{b_1}\cdots y_m^{b_m}$, for $b := (b_1,\dots,b_m)$, where $b_i \in \mathbb{N}$, we put:

$$\underbrace{Y^c \cap Y^d \cap \dots \cap Y^e}_{n \text{ terms}} = \begin{cases} \left(\prod_k a_k!k^{a_k}\right)^{n-1} & c_i = d_i = \dots = e_i = a_i, \\ 0 & \text{otherwise.} \end{cases}$$

This together with 2.4.11 yields

2.4.12 Redfield's Counting Theorem *The number of orbits of the direct product on the set of equivalence classes of matrices is equal to the cap product of the corresponding cycle indicator polynomials:*

$$|(\times_{i=1}^n H_i) \backslash\backslash M_c| = \bigcap_i C(H_i, \underline{m}).$$

In order to provide an example we consider the dihedral group on 5 points and put $H_1 := H_2 := D_{\underline{5}}$. This group $D_{\underline{5}}$ is the automorphism group of the graphs of Figure 2.4. The cycle indicator polynomial of this group is (use 2.2.3) $C(D_{\underline{5}}, \underline{5}) = \frac{1}{10}(y_1^5 + 4y_5 + 5y_1 y_2^2)$. Hence, according to Redfield's theorem, we obtain for the number of superpositions of two such graphs:

$$C(D_{\underline{5}},\underline{5}) \cap C(D_{\underline{5}},\underline{5}) = \frac{1}{10}(y_1^5 + 4y_5 + 5y_1 y_2^2) \cap \frac{1}{10}(y_1^5 + 4y_5 + 5y_1 y_2^2)$$

$$= \frac{1}{100}(y_1^5 \cap y_1^5 + 16(y_5 \cap y_5) + 25(y_1 y_2^2 \cap y_1 y_2^2))$$

$$= \frac{1}{100}(5! + 16 \cdot 5 + 25 \cdot 8) = 4,$$

which means that there are exactly 4 superpositions of two such graphs (see exercise 2.4.1). We can easily generalize this example since we know the cycle structure of the elements in dihedral groups (see 2.2.3). For example, if p denotes an odd prime, then the cap product of the cycle indicator polynomials of $D_{\underline{p}}$ is equal to

$$\frac{1}{4p^2}\left(p! + (p-1)^2 \cdot p + p^2((p-1)/2)!2^{(p-1)/2}\right).$$

An immediate consequence is

2.4.13 Corollary *Each prime $p > 3$ satifies the congruence*

$$(p-1)! + p(p-2) + 1 \equiv \quad (4p).$$

Exercises

E 2.4.1 Draw the four different superpositions of the two pentagonal graphs shown in Figure 2.4.

2.5 The Decomposition Theorem

Redfield's theorem 2.4.12 allows to express the solutions of many enumeration problems as cap products of cycle indicator polynomials. We consider a few examples.

2.5.1 Lemma *The number of orbits of H^G on $\underline{n}_i^{\underline{n}}$, where $H, G \leq S_{\underline{n}}$, is equal to the cap–product*

$$C(H,\underline{n}) \cap C(G,\underline{n}).$$

Proof: The set of bijections $\underline{n}_i^{\underline{n}}$ can be identified with the set M_c of classes of column equivalent $2 \times n$–matrices containing injective n–tuples over $\underline{n}$ as rows, so that Redfield's theorem yields the statement. $\quad\square$

Noticing that bijections are permutations, we can reformulate 2.5.1 as follows:

2.5.2 Corollary *The cap product $C(H,\underline{n}) \cap C(G,\underline{n})$ is equal to the number of classes of elements $\sigma \in S_{\underline{n}}$ with respect to the following equivalence relation:*

$$\sigma_1 \sim \sigma_2 \iff \exists \pi \in H, \rho \in G: \sigma_1 = \pi\sigma_2\rho^{-1}.$$

In other words, this cap product is equal to the number of (H, G)–double cosets in S_n. More explicitly, in terms of intersections of conjugacy classes C^a of the symmetric group S_n with H and G, this cap product is equal to

$$\frac{1}{|H||G|} \sum_{a \vdash n} |C^a \cap H||C^a \cap G| \prod_k a_k! k^{a_k}$$

$$= \frac{n!}{|H||G|} \sum_{a \vdash n} \frac{|C^a \cap H||C^a \cap G|}{|C^a|}.$$

An expression for the number of graphs can also be obtained from Redfield's Counting Theorem as follows. A labelled graph with v vertices and e edges can be considered as an injective mapping f from $\binom{v}{2}$ to $\binom{v}{2}$, where the i-th pair of vertices is connected by an edge if and only if $f(i) \leq e$. This together with 2.5.1 gives:

2.5.3 Corollary *The number of graphs with v vertices and e edges is equal to the cap product*

$$C(S_v, \binom{v}{2}) \cap C(S_e \oplus S_{\binom{v}{2} \setminus e}).$$

More generally we obtain for the number of G–classes on n^n, which consist of mappings with prescribed content the following result:

2.5.4 Corollary *The number of G–classes of content $(b_1, \ldots, b_m)$ on m^n is equal to the cap product*

$$C(G, n) \cap C(S_{b_1} \oplus \ldots \oplus S_{b_m}, n).$$

We shall return to this later. Tools from linear representation theory will allow a further elucidation of Redfield's methods and results. Furthermore we can derive an algorithm for a redundancy free construction of representatives of the G–classes on Y^X from 2.5.3.
Besides this useful cap operation Redfield introduced a *cup operation* $\cup$, defined to be the linear extension of the following operation on monomials:

$$Y^c \cup \ldots \cup Y^d := (Y^c \cap \ldots \cap Y^d)Y^d.$$

It clearly has the following property:

2.5.5 Lemma *The cap product $C(H, n) \cap C(G, n)$ is equal to the sum of the coefficients in the cup product $C(H, n) \cup C(G, n)$.*

4 Kerber

This shows that it should be useful to examine cup products of cycle
indicator polynomials. In fact it is possible to write each such cup
product as a sum of cycle indicators of stabilizers. We shall prove this
result of Redfield with the aid of the following lemma:

2.5.6 Redfield's Lemma *Let $_GX$ be a finite action, $\omega_1, \ldots, \omega_r$ its orbits,
$x_i \in \omega_i$ and $\chi: G \to \mathbb{Q}[Y]$ a class function. Then we have for the
stabilizers $G_i := G_{x_i}$ of these representatives that*

$$\frac{1}{|G|} \sum_{g \in G} \chi(g) |X_g| = \sum_{i=1}^{r} \frac{1}{|G_i|} \sum_{g \in G_i} \chi(g).$$

Proof:

$$|G| \sum_i \frac{1}{|G_i|} \sum_{g \in G_i} \chi(g) = \sum_i |\omega_i| \sum_{g \in G_i} \chi(g)$$

$$= \sum_{x \in X} \sum_{g \in G_x} \chi(g) = \sum_g \chi(g) |X_g|.$$

$\square$

We are now in a position to prove the main theorem of Redfield's
first paper:

2.5.7 Redfield's Decomposition Theorem *Assume that we are given sub-
groups $H_1, \ldots, H_m$ of S_n and an action of $\times_i H_i$ on M_c. Let $\omega_1, \ldots, \omega_r$
denote the orbits, choose representatives $A_i \in \omega_i$, and denote by G_i their
stabilizers. Then each G_i is conjugate in $\times^m S_n$ to a subgroup of the diagonal $\Delta(\times^m S_n)$, and the cup product of the cycle indicator polynomials
of the H_i can be decomposed with the aid of the G_i as follows:*

$$C(H_1, \underline{n}) \cup \ldots \cup C(H_m, \underline{n}) = \sum_{i=1}^{r} \frac{1}{|G_i|} \sum_{(\pi_1, \ldots, \pi_m) \in G_i} \prod_{k=1}^{n} y_k^{a_k(\pi_1)}.$$

Proof: Recall the action in question:

$$(\times_i H_i) \times M_c \to M_c : ((\pi_1, \ldots, \pi_m), (a_{ik})_c) \mapsto (\pi_i a_{ik})_c.$$

Then A is a matrix, the rows of which are injective n–tuples over $\underline{n}$,
i.e. they can be identified with elements of S_n, and hence M can be
identified with $\times^m S_n$. The equivalence relation $\sim_c$ can therefore be
expressed in group theoretical terms as follows. If $A \in M$ is identified
with $(\rho_1, \ldots, \rho_m), B \in M$ with $(\rho_1', \ldots, \rho_m')$, then

$$A \sim_c B \iff \exists \sigma \in S_{\underline{n}}: (\rho_1', \ldots, \rho_m') = (\rho_1 \sigma, \ldots, \rho_m \sigma).$$

Thus the equivalence class A_c can be identified with the following left coset of the diagonal subgroup:

$$\{(\rho_1\sigma,\dots,\rho_m\sigma) \mid \sigma \in S_{\underline{n}}\} = (\rho_1,\dots,\rho_m)\Delta(\times^m S_{\underline{n}}).$$

Analogously we can rewrite Redfield's action of $\times_i H_i$ on M_c as follows:

$$((\pi_1,\dots,\pi_m),(\rho_1,\dots,\rho_m)_c) \mapsto (\pi_1\rho_1,\dots,\pi_m\rho_m)_c.$$

The stabilizer of $A_c = (\rho_1,\dots,\rho_m)_c$ is the subgroup

$$H_1 \times \cdots \times H_m \cap (\rho_1,\dots,\rho_m)\Delta(\times^m S_{\underline{n}})(\rho_1,\dots,\rho_m)^{-1},$$

and hence is conjugate to a subgroup of the diagonal, as is claimed. In order to prove the second part of the assertion, we first of all note that by the definition of the cup operation we have that

2.5.8
$$\bigcup_{i=1}^m C(H_i,\underline{n}) = \frac{1}{\prod_i |H_i|} \sum \underbrace{\left(\prod_k a_k! k^{a_k}\right)^{m-1}}_{=a_1((\pi_1,\dots,\pi_m))} \prod_k y_k^{a_k},$$

where the sum is taken over all the $(\pi,\dots,\pi_m) \in \times_i H_i$ such that $a(\pi_1) = \dots = a(\pi_m) = (a_1,\dots,a_n)$. In order to show that this cup product can be decomposed as claimed, we apply Redfield's Lemma 2.5.6. We therefore introduce the class function $\chi \colon \times_i H_i \to \mathbb{Q}[Y]$, defined by

$$\chi((\pi_1,\dots,\pi_m)) := \begin{cases} \prod_k y_k^{a_k} & \text{for each } i \in \underline{m} \colon a(\pi_i) = (a_1,\dots,a_n), \\ 0 & \text{otherwise.} \end{cases}$$

Then 2.5.8 together with 2.5.6 yields the statement. $\qquad\square$

Putting $m := 1$, we obtain the following decomposition of the cycle indicator polynomial according to the stabilizers of the orbits:

2.5.9 Corollary *Consider $H \le S_{\underline{n}}$ with orbits $\omega_1,\dots,\omega_r$ on Y^X, representatives $f_i \in \omega_i$ and stabilizers G_i of these representatives. Then the cycle indicator polynomial $C(H,\underline{n})$ is equal to the following sum:*

$$C(H,\underline{n}) = \sum_{i=1}^r \frac{1}{|G_i|} \sum_{\pi \in G_i} \prod_{k=1}^n y_k^{a_k(\pi)}.$$

2.5.10 Examples Let us also consider a few examples of the particular case $m := 2$. Redfield's Decomposition Theorem yields

$$C(H_1, \underline{n}) \cup C(H_2, \underline{n}) = \sum_{i=1} \frac{1}{|G_i|} \sum_{(\pi_1, \pi_2) \in G_i} \prod_k y_k^{a_k(\pi_1)}.$$

The mapping

2.5.11 $\varphi: M_c \to S_{\underline{n}}: (\rho_1, \rho_2)_c \mapsto \rho_1 \rho_2^{-1}$

is clearly a bijection, and it has the property

$$\varphi((\pi_1, \pi_2)(\rho_1, \rho_2)_c) = \pi_1 \rho_1 \rho_2^{-1} \pi_2^{-1},$$

which means that the orbit of $(\rho_1, \rho_2)_c$ is mapped onto the (H_1, H_2)–double coset $H_1 \rho_1 \rho_2^{-1} H_2$. The stabilizer of $(\rho, 1)_c, \rho \in S_{\underline{n}}$, is conjugate to the intersection $(\rho^{-1} H_1 \rho \times H_2) \cap \Delta(S_{\underline{n}} \times S_{\underline{n}})$, and we have obtained:

2.5.12 Corollary If $\{\pi_1, \ldots, \pi_r\}$ is a transversal of the (H_1, H_2)–double cosets of $S_{\underline{n}}$, then, by Redfield's Decomposition Theorem, we have

$$C(H_1, \underline{n}) \cup C(H_2, \underline{n}) = \sum_{i=1}^{r} C(\pi_i^{-1} H_1 \pi_i \cap H_2, \underline{n}).$$

Special cases are

2.5.13 $C(A_{\underline{n}}, \underline{n}) \cup C(A_{\underline{n}}, \underline{n}) = |A_{\underline{n}} \backslash S_{\underline{n}} / A_{\underline{n}}| \cdot C(A_{\underline{n}}, \underline{n}),$

and (exercise 2.5.1)

2.5.14 $C(S_{n-1}, \underline{n}) \cup C(S_{n-1}, \underline{n}) = C(S_{n-1}, \underline{n}) + C(S_{n-2}, \underline{n}).$

$\diamond$

Redfield's Decomposition Theorem shows that a good knowledge of the conjugacy classes of subgroups of $\Delta(\times^m S_{\underline{n}})$ is important. We can obtain the desired information from a transversal of the left cosets of the normalizer of $\Delta(\times^m S_{\underline{n}})$ in $\times^m S_{\underline{n}}$. In order to get such a transversal we derive the following theorem which describes, for an arbitrary finite G, the lattice of subgroups in between $\Delta(\times^m G)$ and $\times^m G$. Then we shall evaluate, for particular cases, the normalizer of $\Delta(\times^m G)$ and consider applications.

2.5.15 Theorem *Let G be a finite group and $l \in \mathbb{N}^*$. The lattice of subgroups of $\times^l G$, the normalizer of which contains $\Delta(\times^l G)$, is isomorphic to the lattice of subgroups in between $\Delta(\times^{l+1} G)$ and $\times^{l+1} G$. A lattice isomorphism is provided by the mapping*

$$U \mapsto (U|G) := \{(u_1 g, \ldots, u_l g, g) \mid (u_1, \ldots, u_l) \in U, g \in G\}.$$

Proof: It is easy to check that $U \mapsto (U|G)$ is of the desired form and injective. We have to show that it is surjective and that it respects the lattice operations. In order to do this we consider the action of $(\times^{l+1} G)$ on $\times (\times^l G)$, defined by

$$((g_1, \ldots, g_{l+1}), (g_1', \ldots, g_l')) \mapsto (\ldots, g_i g_i' g_{l+1}^{-1}, \ldots).$$

This action is clearly transitive, and the stabilizer of the identity element 1 is $\Delta(\times^{l+1} G)$. Consider a subgroup H, where

$$\Delta(\times^{l+1} G) \leq H \leq \times^{l+1} G,$$

and the orbit ω of 1 under H, i.e. consider $\omega := H((1, \ldots, 1))$. For any $(g_1', \ldots, g_l') \in \omega$ there exists an element $(h_1, \ldots, h_{l+1}) \in H$ such that $(g_1', \ldots, g_l') = (h_1 h_{l+1}^{-1}, \ldots, h_l h_{l+1}^{-1})$. And as H contains the diagonal subgroup $\Delta(\times^{l+1} G)$, we have that

$$(h_1, \ldots, h_l, 1) \in H \iff (h_1, \ldots, h_l) \in \omega.$$

Using this remark it is easy to check that ω is a subgroup of $\times^l G$, the normalizer of which in $\times^l G$ contains the diagonal of $\times^l G$, and that furthermore $H = (\omega|G)$ holds. Hence the mapping $U \mapsto (U|G)$ is not only injective but also surjective and compatible with the lattice structure.

$\square$

This theorem has the following consequence:

2.5.16 Corollary *The lattice of subgroups in between $\Delta(G \times G)$ and $G \times G$, where G is a finite group, is isomorphic to the lattice of normal subgroups of G.*

Recall now the definition of $Z(G)$, the *center* of G:

$$Z(G) := \{h \in G \mid hg = gh, \text{ for each } g \in G\}.$$

One easily checks that

2.5.17 $$Z(\times^m G) = \times^m Z(G).$$

2.5.18 Theorem *The normalizer of* $\Delta(\times^{l+1}G)$ *in* $\times^{l+1}G$ *is the subgroup*
$$(Z(\times^{l}G)|G) = \{(g_1 g, \ldots, g_l g, g) \mid g_i \in Z(G), g \in G\}.$$

Proof: It is obvious, that $(Z(\times^{l}G)|G)$ is a subgroup of the normalizer. Consider $(h_1, \ldots, h_l) \notin Z(\times^{l}G)$. There exist $i \in \underline{l}$ and $g \in G$ such that $h_i g h_i^{-1} \neq g$. The last component of
$$h^* := (h_1, \ldots, h_l, 1)(g, \ldots, g)(h_1, \ldots, h_l, 1)^{-1}$$

shows that $h^* \notin \Delta(\times^{l+1}G)$. But each subgroup between $\Delta(\times^{l+1}G)$ and $\times^{l+1}G$ is of the form $(U|G)$ described in theorem 2.5.16. In particular the normalizer of $\Delta(\times^{l+1}G)$ has this form, and therefore it is the normalizer of a subgroup of $(Z(\times^{l}G)|G)$.

$\square$

As the normalizer $N_G(U)$ of $U \leq G$ is the stabilizer of U under the conjugation operation of G on the subgroup lattice $L(G)$, a knowledge of a transversal of the left cosets of $N_G(U)$ in G suffices to describe the conjugacy class of U. If $\{g_1, \ldots, g_r\}$ is such a transversal, then
$$\widetilde{U} = \{g_1 U g_1^{-1}, \ldots, g_r U g_r^{-1}\}.$$

Consider, for example, the symmetric group S_n. For $n > 2$, the center of S_n consists of 1 only, so that the diagonal subgroup $\Delta(\times^{l+1}S_n)$ is equal to its normalizer in $\times^{l+1}S_n$. A transversal of the left cosets of the diagonal subgroup of $\times^{l+1}S_n$ is
$$\{(\pi_1, \ldots, \pi_l, 1) \mid (\pi_1, \ldots, \pi_l) \in \times^{l}S_n\}.$$

Exercises

E 2.5.1 Prove 2.5.14.

E 2.5.2 Prove that
$$\underbrace{C(S_{n-1}, \underline{n}) \cup \ldots \cup C(S_{n-1}, \underline{n})}_{m \text{ factors}} = \sum_{k=1}^{m} S(m, k) C(S_{n-k}, \underline{n}),$$

where $S(m, k)$ denotes a Stirling number of the second kind.
Hint: Prove first the following result of Foulkes: For each subgroup $H \leq S_{\underline{n}}$
$$C(H, \underline{n}) \cup \ldots \cup C(H, \underline{n}) = \frac{1}{n!} \sum_{a \vdash n} \left(\frac{n! |C^a \cap H|}{|H| |C^a|} \right)^m \prod_{k} x_k^{a_k}.$$

holds. Use the fact that $x^m = \sum_{k=0}^{m} S(m, k)(x)_k$.

2.6 Species

There are many ways to formalize the evaluation of generating functions and canonic constructions using recursion, disjoint union, cartesian product formation and other set theoretic procedures. A good survey over many of these methods gives the book by Goulden and Jackson. Another method makes use of the notion of species, it will be described next.

Consider the category $\mathcal{F}$ of *finite sets with bijections*. It consists of the two classes $\mathrm{Obj}(\mathcal{F})$ of *objects* $M, N, \ldots$, the finite sets, and the class $\mathrm{Mor}(\mathcal{F})$ of *morphisms* $f, g, \ldots$, which are the bijections between finite sets. $\mathrm{Mor}(M, N)$ denotes the set of morphisms between the sets M and N:

$$\mathrm{Mor}(M, N) := \{f : M \to N \mid f \text{ is a bijection}\}.$$

(Note that the categorical definition of mappings identifies $f : M \to N$ with the *triple* $(M, \{(m, f(m)) \mid m \in M\}, N)$, and hence, if $(M, N) \neq (M', N')$, then $\mathrm{Mor}(M, N) \cap \mathrm{Mor}(M', N') = \emptyset$.) Moreover the definition of category assumes a multiplication

$$\circ : \mathrm{Mor}(L, M) \times \mathrm{Mor}(M, N) \to \mathrm{Mor}(L, N) : (f, g) \mapsto g \circ f,$$

which is associative. In our case this is of course the usual composition of mappings. Furthermore the definition of category requires a neutral element $1_M \in \mathrm{Mor}(M, M)$ (neutral with respect to the multiplication mentioned above), it is the identity mapping here.

A *species* A is a (covariant) functor on $\mathcal{F}$. This means the following: A consists of a mapping from $\mathrm{Obj}(\mathcal{F})$ to $\mathrm{Obj}(\mathcal{F})$, which we also denote by A, for sake of simplicity of notation, together with a mapping from $\mathrm{Mor}(\mathcal{F})$ to $\mathrm{Mor}(\mathcal{F})$ which will be denoted by A, too:

$$A : \mathrm{Obj}(\mathcal{F}) \to \mathrm{Obj}(\mathcal{F}) : M \mapsto A(M),$$

and

$$A : \mathrm{Mor}(\mathcal{F}) \to \mathrm{Mor}(\mathcal{F}) : f \mapsto A(f),$$

where $A(f) \in \mathrm{Mor}(A(M), A(N))$, and such that

$$A(g \circ f) = A(g) \circ A(f), \text{ and } A(1_M) = 1_{A(M)}.$$

The set $A(M)$ is called the set of *labelled A–structures* on M, $A(f)$ is called the *transport of A–structures along f*. The elements of M are called *points*, and the elements $\alpha \in A(M)$ are called *elements of A*, which is abbreviated by $\alpha \in A$. Let us consider a bunch of examples before we go into details.

2.6.1 Examples

- The species *labelled graphs G* is defined by

$$G(M) := \{\gamma \mid \gamma \text{ labelled graph with vertex set } M\},$$

and $G(f)$ maps $\gamma \in G(M)$ onto

$$\gamma' := G(f)(\gamma),$$

where γ' arises from γ by simply replacing the label $m \in M$ by the label $f(m) \in N$, for each bijection f between M and N.

- The species *permutations S* is defined by mapping M onto the symmetric group S_M on M:

$$S(M) := S_M = \{\pi : M \to M \mid \pi \text{ is bijective}\},$$

and $S(f)$ is defined to be *renumbering according to f*, which means that, for each $\pi \in S_M$, we have

$$S(f)(\pi) := f \circ \pi \circ f^{-1} \in S_N, \text{ for } f \in Mor(M, N).$$

- The species *linear orders L* maps M onto the set of all the $|M|!$ linear orders on M:

$$L(M) := \{(m_{i_1} < \ldots < m_{i_{|M|}}) \mid m_{i_\nu} \in M, m_{i_\nu} \neq m_{i_\mu}, \nu \neq \mu\}.$$

The morphism $L(f)$ means simply replacing m by $f(m)$:

$$L(f)(m_{i_1} < \ldots < m_{i_{|M|}}) := (f(m_{i_1}) < \ldots < f(m_{i_{|M|}})).$$

- The species *set E* is defined by

$$E(M) := \{M\}, \ E(f)(M) := f(M).$$

- The *empty species* $\emptyset$ maps each M onto the empty set and therefore $\emptyset(f)$ must always be the empty mapping.

- The species *empty set 1* maps the set $\emptyset$ onto $\{\emptyset\}$, and all the other M onto $\emptyset$, so that each morphism $f \neq \emptyset$ is mapped onto the empty mapping $\emptyset$, while the empty mapping, being an element of $Mor(\emptyset, \emptyset)$, is mapped onto the identity mapping on $\{\emptyset\}$.

- The species *singleton* X is defined by

$$X(M) := \begin{cases} \{m\} & \text{if } M = \{m\} \\ \emptyset & \text{otherwise,} \end{cases} \qquad X(f) := \begin{cases} 1_M & \text{if } M = \{m\} \\ \emptyset & \text{otherwise.} \end{cases}$$

- The species *endofunctions* Φ maps M onto M^M, while, for each f in $Mor(M, N)$ we put

$$\Phi(f)(\varphi) := f \circ \varphi \circ f^{-1} \in N^N, \text{ for each } \varphi \in M^M.$$

- The species Φ_0, the *endofunctions with fixed point,* maps M onto

$$\Phi_0(M) := \{\varphi \in M^M \mid \exists m \in M : \varphi(m) = m\},$$

while $\Phi_0(f)(\varphi) = f \circ \varphi \circ f^{-1}$, as before.

- The species *idempotent endofunctions* K maps M onto the following subset of $\Phi(M)$:

$$K(M) := \{\varphi \in M^M \mid \varphi^2 = \varphi\},$$

and again it has $K(f) := f \circ \varphi \circ f^{-1}$.

$$\diamond$$

Let us return to the consideration of a general species A again. We recall that it maps a morphism $f : M \to N$ onto $A(f)$, which is a bijection from $A(M)$ onto $A(N)$. We may therefore call $A(f)$ a *relabeling* of the α in $A(M)$, so that the A–structures on N arise from the A–structures on M by relabeling. *Thus it suffices (up to relabeling) to define A on each of the sets $\underline{n}$, where $n \in \mathbb{N}$.*

2.6.2 Examples The species *labelled trees* T maps $\underline{n}$ onto the set

$$T(\underline{n}) := \{\gamma \mid \gamma \text{ tree with vertex set } \underline{n}\},$$

and $\gamma' = T(f)(\gamma)$ is the tree obtained from γ by replacing the label $i \in \underline{n}$ by $f(i) \in N$, if $f \in Mor(\underline{n}, N)$. Correspondingly the species *labelled rooted trees* T_0 is defined by

$$T_0(\underline{n}) := \{\tau := (\gamma, i) \mid \gamma \in T(\underline{n}), i \in \underline{n}\},$$

the element i of (γ, i) is called the *root* of τ.

$$\diamond$$

Using this fact that it suffices, up to relabeling, to describe $A(\underline{n})$, we introduce, for each species A, the corresponding generating function called the *cardinality* of A:

$$A(x) := \sum_{n \in \mathbb{N}} |A(\underline{n})| \frac{x^n}{n!}.$$

2.6.3 Examples For the cardinalities of the preceding examples we have:

$$G(x) = \sum_n 2^{\binom{n}{2}} \frac{x^n}{n!}, \ S(x) = L(x) = \frac{1}{1-x}, \ E(x) = e^x,$$

$$\emptyset(x) = 0, \ 1(x) = 1, \ X(x) = x, \ \Phi(x) = \sum_n n^n \frac{x^n}{n!}.$$

$\diamond$

Correspondingly two species A and B are called *equipotent*, if and only if $A(x) = B(x)$. We abbreviate this by writing

$$A \sim B.$$

A stronger condition is *isomorphy*, for short:

$$A \simeq B,$$

in which we require canonic bijections $\Theta_M : A(M) \to B(M)$ which satisfy

$$B(f) \circ \Theta_M = \Theta_N \circ A(f), \ \text{for each } f \in \mathrm{Mor}(M, N).$$

It is clear that the following holds:

2.6.4 $A \simeq B \Longrightarrow A \sim B.$

The converse is not true, as it is shown by

2.6.5 Example Clearly the species S of permutations and the species L of linear orders are equipotent. Let us assume that there exist bijections $\Theta_{\underline{n}} : S(\underline{n}) \to L(\underline{n})$, which satisfy

$$L(f) \circ \Theta_{\underline{n}} = \Theta_{\underline{n}} \circ S(f),$$

for each bijection $f : \underline{n} \to \underline{n}$. Consider an $n > 1$, a bijection f which is not the identity mapping, and apply both sides of the identity to $\pi := 1 \in S_n = S(\underline{n})$. The left hand side yields, if

$$\Theta_{\underline{n}}(\pi) =: (i_1 < \ldots < i_n) \in L(\underline{n}),$$

that

$$(L(f) \circ \Theta_{\underline{n}})(\pi) = L(f)(i_1 < \ldots < i_n) = (f(i_1) < \ldots < f(i_n)),$$

while an application of the right hand side gives

$$(\Theta_{\underline{n}} \circ S(f))(\pi) = \Theta_{\underline{n}}(f \circ \pi \circ f^{-1}) = \Theta_{\underline{n}}(1)$$

$$= (i_1 < \ldots < i_n) \neq (f(i_1) < \ldots < f(i_n)).$$

$$\diamond$$

We shall now use set theoretic operations in order to introduce on the isomorphism classes of species a semiring structure. The operation of *addition* is defined by disjoint union as follows:

$$(A + B)(\underline{n}) := A(\underline{n}) \dot\cup B(\underline{n}).$$

The species $A + B$, called the *species sum* of A and B, or simply the *sum* of A and B, has as its set of transport on $\underline{n}$ the disjoint union of the set of mappings $A(f)$ and $B(f)$, where f in both cases runs through the bijective $f : \underline{n} \to \underline{n}$. The multiplication uses the cartesian product:

$$(A \cdot B)(\underline{n}) := \bigcup_{M \dot\cup N = \underline{n}} A(M) \times B(N) = \bigcup_{M \subseteq \underline{n}} A(M) \times B(\underline{n} \setminus M).$$

Since a set R together with operations $+$ and $\cdot$ is called a *semiring* if and only if both $(R, +)$ and $(R, \cdot)$ are commutative semigroups, 0 is neutral with respect to $+$, 1 is neutral with respect to $\cdot$, $0r = 0$, for each $r \in R$, and the distributivity law $(r + s)t = rt + rs$ holds, we obtain

2.6.6 Lemma *The isomorphism classes of species form a semiring with respect to addition and multiplication. The neutral element with respect to addition is the empty species $\emptyset$ while the neutral element with respect to multiplication is the species empty set 1.*

The necessary checks are straightforward. But there are several other important operations on species. Before we start defining these let us introduce a helpful notation which allows us to illustrate the various situations. In order to sketch an A–structure $\alpha \in A(\underline{4})$, say, we write

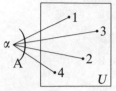   represents $\alpha \in A[U]$, where $U := \underline{4}$.

the α and the box maybe left out, so that an element of $(A + B)(\underline{4})$ is of the following form:

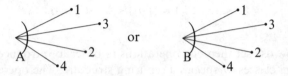

while an element of $(A \cdot B)(\underline{5})$ looks as follows:

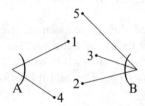

for example, an element of $(S \cdot G)(\underline{7})$ is such a pair $(\pi\gamma)$, where π is a permutation, say $(135) \in S_M$, $M := \{1, 3, 5\}$, and γ is a labelled graph on $N = \{2, 4, 6, 7\}$, with edge set $\{\{2, 3\}, \{3, 5\}\}$. We use this notation also in order to illustrate the *plethysm* $B \odot A$, defined as follows:

$$(B \odot A)(\underline{n}) := \bigcup_{p = \{p_1, \dots, p_m\}} \prod_{i=1}^{m} B(\underline{p_i}) \times A(\underline{m}),$$

where the disjoint union is taken over all the set partitions p of $\underline{n}$. For example, an element of $B \odot A(\underline{6})$, arising from the partition $p := \{\{1, 4, 5\}, \{2, 6\}, \{3\}\}$ looks as follows:

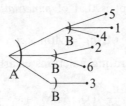

The plethysm of structures has many interesting properties, for example the singleton X is neutral with respect to plethysm:

2.6.7 $$A \simeq X \odot A \simeq A \odot X.$$

Proof: We obtain from the definition of plethysm that

$$(X \odot A)(\underline{n}) = \bigcup_p \prod_{i=1}^m X(\underline{p_i}) \times A(\underline{m}),$$

but $X(\underline{p_i})$ is empty except when $|p_i| = 1$, so that this union is in fact taken over the single partition $p = \{\{1\}, \ldots, \{n\}\}$ of $\underline{n}$, and therefore

$$(X \odot A)(\underline{n}) = A(\underline{n}).$$

It is quite often helpful to recognize species as plethysms of species. For example, if C denotes the species of cyclic permutations, i.e.

$$C(\underline{n}) := \{\sigma \in S(\underline{n}) \mid \forall\, 0 < j < n : \sigma^j 1 \neq 1\},$$

then obviously

$$S \simeq C \odot E,$$

since each permutation is a union of its disjoint cyclic factors. This motivates us to say that, in case $A \simeq B \odot E$, B is the species of *connected* A–structures. An example is the decomposition of labelled graphs into their connected components:

$$G \simeq Z \odot E,$$

where Z denotes the species *connected graphs*.
Another interesting notion is that of the *derivative*. It associates with A the species A', which is obtained by adding to the set $\underline{n}$ a further and anonymous element, we indicate it by $*$, and then applying A:

$$A'(\underline{n}) := A(\underline{n}^+), \text{ where } \underline{n}^+ := \underline{n} \cup \{*\}.$$

A further helpful concept is that of *punctuation*, where A is mapped onto

$$A_\bullet(\underline{n}) := A(\underline{n}) \times \underline{n}.$$

The corresponding generating functions clearly satisfy

2.6.8 $$A'(x) = \frac{d}{dx} A(x), \quad A_\bullet(x) = x \cdot \frac{d}{dx} A(x).$$

So far each element $\alpha \in A$ is a *labelled* structure, for example a labelled graph. In order to get rid of the labeling we have of course to introduce the canonical action

$$S_{\underline{n}} \times A(\underline{n}) \to A(\underline{n}) : (\sigma, \alpha) \mapsto A(\sigma)\alpha.$$

An orbit is called a *type* of A–structure. Furthermore we denote by $\mathcal{T}_{\underline{n}}(A)$ a transversal of $S_{\underline{n}} \backslash\backslash A(\underline{n})$, so that we obtain a transversal

$$\mathcal{T}(A) := \bigcup_{n \in \mathbb{N}} \mathcal{T}_{\underline{n}}(A)$$

of all the types of A–structures. The set

$$\widetilde{A}(\underline{n}) := \{(\sigma, \alpha) \mid \alpha \in A(\underline{n}), \sigma \in S_{\underline{n}} : A(\sigma)\alpha = \alpha\}$$

is called the species *associated* with A. Its generating function $\widetilde{A}$ is

$$\widetilde{A}(x) := \sum_{n \in \mathbb{N}} |\mathcal{T}_{\underline{n}}(A)| x^n.$$

And hence the ordinary generating function for the A–types is the exponential generating function for the species $\widetilde{A}$.

Now we would like to apply to species what we know about cycle indicator polynomials. For this purpose we introduce the following formal power series:

$$Z_A := Z_A(x_1, x_2, \ldots) := \sum_{\alpha \in \mathcal{T}(A)} C((S_{\underline{n}})_\alpha, \underline{n}; x_1, x_2, \ldots),$$

where $(S_{\underline{n}})_\alpha$ denotes the stabilizer of $\alpha \in A(\underline{n})$ in $S_{\underline{n}}$. Hence, for example (exercise 2.6.1):

2.6.9 $$Z_X = x_1, \quad Z_E = \exp(\sum_i \frac{x_i}{i}), \quad Z_L = \frac{1}{1 - x_1}, \quad Z_S = \prod_i \frac{1}{1 - x_i}.$$

Since

$$C((S_{\underline{n}})_\alpha, \underline{n}; x_1, 0, \ldots) = \frac{1}{|(S_{\underline{n}})_\alpha|} x_1^n,$$

and

$$C((S_{\underline{n}})_\alpha, \underline{n}; x, x^2, x^3, \ldots) = x^n,$$

we obtain

2.6.10 $\quad Z_A(x, 0, \ldots) = A(x), \text{ and } Z_A(x, x^2, x^3, \ldots) = \widetilde{A}(x).$

Exercises

E 2.6.1 Prove 2.6.9.

Chapter 3

Marks

We now consider another refinement (due to Burnside) of the Cauchy-Frobenius Lemma. It allows to enumerate orbits the elements of which have a given conjugacy class of subgroups as stabilizers. In particular it allows us to count orbits by their lengths. The problem is that for applications of this lemma we have to know certain matrices, the table of marks and its inverse, the calculation of which needs quite a good knowledge of the lattice $L(G)$ of subgroups of G. Fortunately there are program systems at hand (like the Aachen subgroup lattice program and CAYLEY) that allow to treat a lot of nontrivial cases successfully.

Then we consider finite actions $_GX$, where X is a poset and where G respects the order: $x < x' \Rightarrow gx < gx'$, i.e. G acts as a group of automorphisms on $(X, \leq)$. This yields generalizations of several notions introduced in the preceding chapter and it gives further insight. In particular the Burnside ring will be introduced and we shall find an interesting explanation for the table of marks.

3.1 Counting by stabilizer class

The preceding chapter was devoted to the enumeration of orbits by weight, a problem that can be solved by an easy refinement of the Cauchy-Frobenius Lemma. In the present chapter we shall introduce another variation of this lemma in order to count orbits by stabilizer class. Recall that the elements of an orbit have as their stabilizers a conjugacy class $\tilde{U}$ of subgroups of G. We say that $\tilde{U}$ is the *type* of this orbit. The *set* of orbits of type $\tilde{U}$, for a given subgroup U of G, is called the $\tilde{U}$–*stratum* and indicated by

$$\tilde{U} \backslash\backslash\backslash X.$$

First we consider the lattice $L(G)$ of subgroups of G. The group G is supposed to be finite and hence $L(G)$ is a locally finite poset with respect to the inclusion order $\leq$ and we shall be able to apply in particular the Moebius Inversion. We assume that the subgroups U^i of G are numbered in such a way that

3.1.1 $U^i \leq U^k \implies i \leq k.$

In this case the *zeta–matrix* as well as the *Moebius–matrix* of G, defined by

$$\zeta(G) := \left(\zeta(U^i, U^k)\right), \text{ and } \mu(G) := \left(\mu(U^i, U^k)\right) = \zeta(G)^{-1},$$

are upper triangular. Let us consider an easy example: $G := S_3$. This group has the lattice of subgroups shown in figure 3.1,

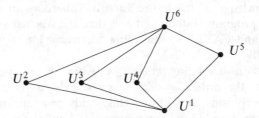

Figure 3.1: The subgroup lattice of S_3

where $U^1 = \langle 1 \rangle$, $U^2 = \langle (12) \rangle$, $U^3 = \langle (13) \rangle$, $U^4 = \langle (23) \rangle$, $U^5 = \langle (123) \rangle$, and $U^6 = S_3$. Thus

$$\zeta(S_3) = \begin{pmatrix} 1 & 1 & 1 & 1 & 1 & 1 \\ & 1 & 0 & 0 & 0 & 1 \\ & & 1 & 0 & 0 & 1 \\ & & & 1 & 0 & 1 \\ & & & & 1 & 1 \\ & & & & & 1 \end{pmatrix},$$

and so

$$\mu(S_{\underline{3}}) = \begin{pmatrix} 1 & -1 & -1 & -1 & -1 & 3 \\ & 1 & 0 & 0 & 0 & -1 \\ & & 1 & 0 & 0 & -1 \\ & & & 1 & 0 & -1 \\ & & & & 1 & -1 \\ & & & & & 1 \end{pmatrix}.$$

In order to calculate $|\widetilde{U} \backslash\!\backslash\!\backslash X|$, we consider, for the finite action $_G X$ and $U \leq G$, the sets

$$X_U := \{x \mid \forall g \in U \colon gx = x\}.$$

Burnside called the order $|X_U|$ of this set the *mark* of U on X. We express it in terms of lengths of strata:

$$|X_U| = \sum_{x : U \leq G_x} 1 = \sum_{V : U \leq V \leq G} \sum_{x : V = G_x} 1 = \sum_{V : U \leq V \leq G} \frac{1}{|\widetilde{V}|} \sum_{x : G_x \in \widetilde{V}} 1$$

$$= \sum_{V : U \leq V \leq G} \frac{|G/V|}{|\widetilde{V}|} \sum_{t \in \mathcal{T} : G_t \in \widetilde{V}} 1 = \sum_{V : U \leq V \leq G} \frac{|G/V|}{|\widetilde{V}|} |\widetilde{V} \backslash\!\backslash\!\backslash X|,$$

$$= \sum_V \zeta(U, V) \frac{|G/V|}{|\widetilde{V}|} |\widetilde{V} \backslash\!\backslash\!\backslash X|,$$

where $\mathcal{T}$ denotes a transversal of the orbits of G on X. By Moebius Inversion this equation is equivalent to:

3.1.2 $$|\widetilde{U} \backslash\!\backslash\!\backslash X| = \frac{|\widetilde{U}|}{|G/U|} \sum_V \mu(U, V) |X_V|.$$

In order to simplify this expression we consider the set $\widetilde{L}(G)$ consisting of the conjugacy classes of subgroups of G:

$$\widetilde{L}(G) := \{\widetilde{U}_1, \ldots, \widetilde{U}_d\}, \text{ with representatives } U_i \in \widetilde{U}_i.$$

(U^i should not be mixed up with U_i!) Putting

3.1.3 $$b_{ik} := \frac{|\widetilde{U}_i|}{|G/U_i|} \sum_{V \in \widetilde{U}_k} \mu(U_i, V), \text{ and } B(G) := (b_{ik}),$$

we can now reformulate 3.1.2 in terms of this matrix $B(G)$, which I call the *Burnside matrix* of G (in fact Burnside considered the inverse of $B(G)$ and called it the table of marks; we shall return to this matrix later). It is in fact the following lemma (and *not* the lemma of Cauchy-Frobenius that is quite often named after Burnside, see the remarks on history in the chapter containing the comments and references) which is

3.1.4 Burnside's Lemma *If $_GX$ is a finite action, then the vector of the lengths $|\widetilde{U}_i\backslash\!\backslash\!\backslash X|$ of the strata of G on X satisfies the equation*

$$\begin{pmatrix} \vdots \\ |\widetilde{U}_i\backslash\!\backslash\!\backslash X| \\ \vdots \end{pmatrix} = B(G) \cdot \begin{pmatrix} \vdots \\ |X_{U_i}| \\ \vdots \end{pmatrix}.$$

We can apply this now in order to enumerate the G–classes on Y^X by type. Since $f \in Y^X$ is fixed under each $g \in U_i$ if and only if f is constant on each orbit of U_i on X, we obtain:

3.1.5 Corollary *The number of symmetry classes of G on Y^X of type $\widetilde{U}_i$ is the i-th entry of the one column matrix*

$$B(G) \cdot \begin{pmatrix} \vdots \\ |Y|^{|U_i\backslash\!\backslash X|} \\ \vdots \end{pmatrix}.$$

Thus, for example, the number of k–graphs on v vertices which are of type $\widetilde{U}_j$, U_j a subgroup of $S_{\underline{v}}$, is the element in the j-th row of the matrix

$$B(S_{\underline{v}}) \cdot \begin{pmatrix} \vdots \\ (k+1)^{|U_i\backslash\binom{\underline{v}}{2}|} \\ \vdots \end{pmatrix}.$$

For $v := 4$, an application of the Burnside matrix shown in the appendix yields the table 3.1. The last column of this table shows among other things that there exist altogether 900 4–graphs on 4 vertices, and that exactly 465 of them are of type $\widetilde{U}_1$. Furthermore we note that the fourth, the sixth and the tenth row of this table consist of zeros only, which stimulates the question whether this also holds for bigger k. These rows belong to $U_4 \simeq A_{\underline{3}}, U_6 \simeq C_{\underline{4}}$ and $U_{10} \simeq A_{\underline{4}}$. A shorter formulation of this question reads as follows: Do $A_{\underline{3}}, C_{\underline{4}}$ or $A_{\underline{4}}$ occur as automorphism groups of multigraphs? More generally:

type\$\backslash k$	0	1	2	3	4
$\tilde{U}_1$	0	0	11	100	465
$\tilde{U}_2$	0	2	21	84	230
$\tilde{U}_3$	0	1	9	36	100
$\tilde{U}_4$	0	0	0	0	0
$\tilde{U}_5$	0	2	9	24	50
$\tilde{U}_6$	0	0	0	0	0
$\tilde{U}_7$	0	0	1	4	10
$\tilde{U}_8$	0	2	6	12	20
$\tilde{U}_9$	0	2	6	12	20
$\tilde{U}_{10}$	0	0	0	0	0
$\tilde{U}_{11}$	1	2	3	4	5
$\sum$	1	11	66	276	900

Table 3.1: Multigraphs on 4 vertices, counted by type

Which subgroups of G occur as stabilizers of mappings $f \in Y^X$? In order to answer this question we recall 2.3.1 which says that the stabilizer of f in the symmetric group S_X is the subgroup

$$(S_X)_f = \bigoplus_{y \in Y} S_{X_y}.$$

This implies

3.1.6 Corollary *The stabilizers of the $f \in Y^X$ are the subgroups $U \le G$, the corresponding permutation group $\bar{U}$ of which satisfies*

$$\bar{U} = S_\alpha \cap \bar{G},$$

where $\bar{G}$ corresponds to G, and S_α is the direct sum of the symmetric groups on the orbits of U:

$$S_\alpha := \bigoplus_{\omega \in U \backslash\backslash X} S_\omega.$$

We can now answer one of the questions posed above concerning automorphism groups of graphs.

3.1.7 Corollary *The alternating group A_v does not occur as an automorphism group of a multigraph on v vertices, if $v \geq 3$.*

Proof: The assumption $\bar{A}_v = S_\alpha \cap \bar{S}_v$ yields, as A_v acts transitively on $\binom{v}{2}$, that S_α is the full symmetric group on $\binom{v}{2}$, and hence $\bar{A}_v = \bar{S}_v$, which is a contradiction if $v > 2$.

$\square$

A similar result holds for the cyclic group C_v (see exercise 3.1.2) and the alternating subgroup A_{v-1} (exercise 3.1.3). Another immediate consequence of 3.1.2 is an expression for the number of orbits of prescribed length. Using the abbreviation, for $U, V \leq G$:

3.1.8 $$\mu(U, \widetilde{V}) := \sum_{W \in \widetilde{V}} \mu(U, W),$$

we derive from 3.1.2

3.1.9 Corollary *If $_G X$ is a finite action, then the number of orbits of length k of G on X is equal to*

$$\frac{1}{k} \sum_{i:|G/U_i|=k} |\widetilde{U}_i| \sum_j \mu(U_i, \widetilde{U}_j)|X_{U_j}|,$$

and in particular the number of primitive *orbits , i.e. of orbits of the (maximal) length $|G|$, is equal to*

$$\frac{1}{|G|} \sum_j \mu(1, \widetilde{U}_j)|X_{U_j}|.$$

We consider a well known example from Galois theory.

3.1.10 Example Consider the finite field $GF(q), q := p^m, p$ a prime number, and its extension field $GF(q^n)$ of degree n. By Galois theory its Galois group G is generated by the *Frobenius isomorphism*

$$\sigma : GF(q^n) \to GF(q^n) : x \mapsto x^q,$$

which is of order n:

$$G = \langle \sigma \rangle = \{1, \sigma, \ldots, \sigma^{n-1}\} \simeq C_n.$$

Moreover $GF(q^n)$ possesses a *normal basis*, which means that there exist $x \in GF(q^n)$ such that $\{x, \sigma x, \ldots, \sigma^{n-1} x\}$ is a $GF(q)$–basis of

$GF(q^n)$. Expressing the elements of $GF(q^n)$ in terms of this basis as $GF(q)$–linear combinations

$$\sum_{i=1}^{n} f(i)\sigma^i x, \ f(i) \in GF(q),$$

we can identify them with vectors $f = (f(1),\dots,f(n)) \in \underline{q}^{\underline{n}}$ on which the Galois group generator σ acts as a cyclic shift. Hence the existence of a normal basis shows that the action of the Galois group G on $GF(q^n)$ is isomorphic to the canonical action of the cyclic group $C_{\underline{n}}$ on $\underline{q}^{\underline{n}}$. Denoting by $G\backslash\!\backslash_{|G|}X$ the set of orbits of (maximal) length $|G|$, we now evaluate the number

$$|G\backslash\!\backslash_{|G|}GF(q^n)| = |C_{\underline{n}}\backslash\!\backslash_n \underline{q}^{\underline{n}}|$$

of orbits of maximal length n of the Galois group. As the cyclic group $C_{\underline{n}}$ has a subgroup lattice isomorphic to the lattice of divisors d of n, the Moebius function μ of $L(C_{\underline{n}})$ is the number theoretic Moebius function. Moreover the unique subgroup of order d, where d is a divisor of n, in the cyclic group $C_{\underline{n}}$ is generated by the power $(1\dots n)^{n/d}$ of the full cycle and, by 1.3.11, this power consists of n/d disjoint cycles, each of which has the length d. Furthermore $f \in \underline{q}^{\underline{n}}$ is fixed under this subgroup $\langle(1\dots n)^{n/d}\rangle$ if and only if f is constant on the disjoint cyclic factors of $(1\dots n)^{n/d}$. Hence, by 3.1.9, we obtain

3.1.11 $\qquad |G\backslash\!\backslash_{|G|}GF(q^n)| = |C_{\underline{n}}\backslash\!\backslash_n \underline{q}^{\underline{n}}| = \dfrac{1}{n}\sum_{d|n}\mu(d)q^{n/d},$

where μ denotes the number theoretic Moebius function. Note that this number of primitive orbits is also equal to the number of irreducible monic polynomials with zeros in $GF(q^n)$ and coefficients in $GF(q)$, since by Galois theory a root of a polynomial is mapped onto a root by each element of the Galois group.

$\diamond$

More generally, we can consider the orbits of maximal length of $C_{\underline{n}}$ on $\underline{m}^{\underline{n}}$. The numbers

$$l_{mn} := |C_{\underline{n}}\backslash\!\backslash_n \underline{m}^{\underline{n}}| = \dfrac{1}{n}\sum_{d|n}\mu(d)m^{n/d}$$

are called *Dedekind numbers*. Some of the smaller ones are shown in the following table:

$m \backslash n$	1	2	3	4	5
1	1	0	0	0	0
2	2	1	2	3	6
3	3	3	8	18	48
4	4	6	20	60	204
5	5	10	40	150	624

The $f \in \underline{m}^{\underline{n}}$ can be considered as *words*

$$f = f(1) \ldots f(n)$$

of *length n* over the *alphabet* $\underline{m}$. The *lexicographically smallest* elements in the orbits (for short: $f \leq C_n(f)$) of length n of $C_{\underline{n}}$ on $\underline{m}^{\underline{n}}$ form the *canonic transversal*

$$L_n(\underline{m}) := \{ f \in \underline{m}^{\underline{n}} \mid |C_{\underline{n}}(f)| = n, f \leq C_{\underline{n}}(f) \};$$

its elements are called the *Lyndon words* of length n over the alphabet $\underline{m}$. The union of all these sets

$$L(\underline{m}) := \bigcup_n L_n(\underline{m})$$

is called the *Lyndon set* over the alphabet $\underline{m}$.

Now we consider an arbitrary word $f \in \underline{m}^{\underline{n}}$. As each letter $i \in \underline{m}$ forms a Lyndon word of length 1, there exists a uniquely determined longest left factor $l_1(f) = f(1) \ldots$ of f which is a Lyndon word. The same holds for the remaining part w of $f = l_1(f)w$, and hence there is a unique decomposition

3.1.12 $f = l_1(f) l_2(f) \ldots l_{\lambda(f)}(f)$

of f into Lyndon words such that in the right part $l_i(f) \ldots l_{\lambda(f)}(f)$ the Lyndon word $l_i(f)$ is the maximal left Lyndon factor. This decomposition is called the *Lyndon decomposition* of f, and the number $\lambda(f)$ of factors is called the *Lyndon length* of f. Even more, the Lyndon decomposition can also be described as follows (exercise 3.1.4)

3.1.13 Lyndon's Theorem *The factors $l_i(f)$ of the decomposition 3.1.12 defined above are lexicographically nonincreasing:*

$$l_1(f) \geq l_2(f) \geq \ldots \geq l_{\lambda(f)}(f).$$

Conversely, each decomposition into nonincreasing Lyndon words is the decomposition 3.1.12 introduced above.

Using the Lyndon length we can define the following generating function:

$$l_n(x, m) := \sum_{f \in \underline{m}^n} x^{\lambda(f)},$$

which generates the numbers of words of length n over $\underline{m}$ with prescribed Lyndon length. V. Strehl has recently noticed and proved the remarkable fact that this function is symmetric in x and m. For example

$$l_3(x, m) = \frac{1}{3!}(x^3 m^3 + 3(x^3 m^2 + x^2 m^3 - x^2 m^2) + 2(x^3 m + m^3 x) - 2xm).$$

In order to prove this it is enough to show that, for all k, m, n in $\mathbb{N}^*$, the identity $l_n(k, m) = l_n(m, k)$ is true. We consider a second alphabet $\underline{k}$, say, and the corresponding set $\underline{k}^*$ of all the words over $\underline{k}$. Let $\Phi(m, k)$ denote the set of all the mappings $\phi: L(\underline{m}) \to \underline{k}^*$ such that all but a finite number of values $\phi(f)$ are equal to the empty word $\varepsilon \in \underline{k}^*$. We map ϕ onto $\hat{\phi}: L(\underline{k}) \to \underline{m}^*$, defined as follows: Let $\hat{f} \in L(\underline{k})$ occur in the Lyndon decompositions of $\phi(f_i)$, say with the multiplicity $m(\phi(f_i), \hat{f})$. We can assume without restriction that $f_i \geq f_{i+1}$, for each i. Then put

$$\hat{\phi}(\hat{f}) := f_1 \cdots \underbrace{f_i \cdots f_j}_{m(\phi(f_i), \hat{f})} \cdots f_n.$$

Let us consider an example. Assume that $\phi: L(\underline{3}) \to \underline{2}^*$ has the following nonempty images (we separate Lyndon factors by dots):

$$\phi(12) = 2 \cdot 12, \quad \phi(113) = 12 \cdot 1 \cdot 1, \quad \phi(2) = 2 \cdot 12 \cdot 1,$$

then $\hat{\phi}$ has just the following nonempty images:

$$\hat{\phi}(1) = 2 \cdot 113 \cdot 113, \quad \hat{\phi}(12) = 2 \cdot 12 \cdot 113, \quad \hat{\phi}(2) = 2 \cdot 12.$$

It is clear that ϕ can be reconstructed from $\hat{\phi}$, and Lyndon's Theorem assures that this is true also in general. Hence $\phi \mapsto \hat{\phi}$ is a bijection between $\Phi(m, k)$ and $\Phi(k, m)$. Now we introduce a *norm* by putting

$$\|\phi\| := \sum_{f \in L(\underline{m})} |f| |\phi(f)|,$$

where $|w|$ denotes the length (number of letters) of the word w. An important property of the norm is the identity

$$\|\phi\| = \sum_{f \in L(\underline{m})} |f| \sum_{\hat{f} \in L(\underline{k})} |\hat{f}| \cdot m(\phi(f), \hat{f}) = \|\hat{\phi}\|,$$

where the last equation holds since $m(\phi(f), \hat{f}) = m(\hat{\phi}(\hat{f}), f)$, by construction of $\hat{f}$.

3.1.14 Lemma (Strehl) *For all* $k, m, n \in \mathbb{N}^*$ *we have the identity*

$$l_n(k, m) = l_n(m, k).$$

Proof: Consider $f \in \underline{m}^n$ and the corresponding subset $\Lambda_f \subseteq \Phi(\underline{m}, \underline{k})$, consisting of the following ϕ: $\phi(f') = \varepsilon$ if and only if the Lyndon word f' is not a factor of f, while otherwise $\phi(f') \in \underline{k}^{m(f, f')}$. Easy checks show that $|\Lambda_f| = k^{\lambda(f)}$ and

$$\phi \in \bigcup_{f \in \underline{m}^n} \Lambda_f \iff \|\phi\| = n,$$

which allows to complete the proof:

$$l_n(k, m) = \sum_{f \in \underline{m}^n} k^{\lambda(f)} = |\{\phi \in \Phi(\underline{m}, \underline{k}) \mid \|\phi\| = n\}|$$

$$= |\{\hat{\phi} \in \Phi(\underline{k}, \underline{m}) \mid \|\hat{\phi}\| = n\}| = \sum_{\hat{f} \in \underline{k}^n} m^{\lambda(\hat{f})} = l_n(m, k).$$

$\square$

Now we use a further indeterminate z in order to define the formal power series

$$L(x, m) := \sum_n l_n(x, m) z^n.$$

Lyndon's Theorem shows that the following is true:

$$L(x, m) = \prod_n \left(\frac{1}{1 - k \cdot z^n} \right)^{l_{mn}},$$

so that we obtain the following surprising result:

$$\prod_n \left(\frac{1}{1 - k \cdot z^n} \right)^{l_{mn}} = \prod_n \left(\frac{1}{1 - m \cdot z^n} \right)^{l_{kn}},$$

which implies in particular (put $k := 1$ and note that $l_{1n} = 1$ if $n = 1$, and $l_{1n} = 0$, otherwise):

3.1.15 The cyclotomic identity *For all* $k, m, n \in \mathbb{N}^*$ *and the Dedekind numbers* $l_{mn} = \frac{1}{n} \sum_{d|n} \mu(d) m^{n/d}$ *we have the identity*

$$\prod_n \left(\frac{1}{1-z^n} \right)^{l_{mn}} = \frac{1}{1-m \cdot z}.$$

Exercises

E 3.1.1 Prove the following identity for the elements of the Burnside matrix:

$$b_{ik} = \mu(\widetilde{U}_i, U_k) \frac{|\widetilde{U}_k|}{|G/U_i|}, \quad \text{where } \mu(\widetilde{U}_i, U_k) := \sum_{V \in \widetilde{U}_i} \mu(V, U_k).$$

E 3.1.2 Prove that the cyclic group $C_{\underline{v}}$ does not occur as an automorphism group of a multigraph on v vertices, if $v \geq 2$.

E 3.1.3 Prove that the subgroup A_{v-1} of A_v does not occur as an automorphism group of a multigraph on v vertices, if $v \geq 3$.

E 3.1.4 Prove 3.1.13.

3.2 Tables of marks and Burnside matrices

We have seen the significance of the Burnside matrix for the enumeration of orbits by type. The inverse of this matrix was introduced by Burnside (1911) and called the *table of marks*. Sometimes it is also called the *supercharacter table* for a reason which will become clear later. We denote this matrix by

$$M(G) := (m_{ik}) := B(G)^{-1},$$

and state:

3.2.1 Lemma

$$m_{ik} = \frac{|G/U_k|}{|\widetilde{U}_k|} \zeta(U_i, \widetilde{U}_k) = \frac{|G/U_k|}{|\widetilde{U}_i|} \zeta(\widetilde{U}_i, U_k) \in \mathbb{N},$$

where $\zeta(\widetilde{U}, V) := \sum_{W \in \widetilde{U}} \zeta(W, V)$ *and* $\zeta(U, \widetilde{V})$ *is defined in a corresponding way.*

Proof: We start by proving the last of the two identities. It follows directly from the equation

3.2.2 $$|\widetilde{U}_i|\zeta(U_i, \widetilde{U}_k) = |\widetilde{U}_k|\zeta(\widetilde{U}_i, U_k),$$

an identity which is immediate from the definition of the zeta function. The first of the stated identities is now obtained as follows:

$$\sum_j b_{ij} \frac{|G/U_k|}{|\widetilde{U}_k|}\zeta(U_j, \widetilde{U}_k) = \frac{|\widetilde{U}_i|}{|G/U_i|}\sum_j \mu(U_i, \widetilde{U}_j)\frac{|G/U_k|}{|\widetilde{U}_k|}\zeta(U_j, \widetilde{U}_k)$$

$$= \frac{|\widetilde{U}_i||U_i|}{|\widetilde{U}_k||U_k|}\sum_{W\in\widetilde{U}_k}\underbrace{\sum_j\sum_{V\in\widetilde{U}_j}\mu(U_i, V)\zeta(V, W)}_{=\delta_{U_i,W}} = \delta_{ik}.$$

The final claim that $m_{ik} \in \mathbb{N}$ follows from the first identity since the order of a conjugacy class of a subgroup is equal to the index of the normalizer, thus

3.2.3 $$\frac{|G/U_k|}{|\widetilde{U}_k|} = \frac{|N_G(U_k)|}{|U_k|} \in \mathbb{N}.$$

□

This lemma shows that the entries of $M(G)$ describe the poset

$$(\widetilde{L}(G), \leq)$$

which consists of the conjugacy classes $\widetilde{U}_i$ of subgroups, $1 \leq i \leq d$, together with the partial order

3.2.4 $$\widetilde{U}_i \leq \widetilde{U}_k \;:\Longleftrightarrow\; \exists\, U \in \widetilde{U}_i, V \in \widetilde{U}_k : \, U \leq V.$$

Lemma 3.2.1 implies that

3.2.5 $$m_{ik} \neq 0 \iff \widetilde{U}_i \leq \widetilde{U}_k.$$

Burnside called $M(G)$ the table of marks for the following reason:

3.2.6 Lemma *The entry m_{ik} is the number of left cosets of U_k in G which remain fixed under left multiplication by the elements of U_i.*

Proof:

$$|\{gU_k \mid \forall x \in U_i : xgU_k = gU_k\}| = \frac{1}{|U_k|}|\{g \in G \mid g^{-1}U_ig \leq U_k\}|$$

$$= \frac{|G|}{|U_k||\tilde{U}_i|} |\{V \in \tilde{U}_i \mid V \leq U_k\}| = \frac{|G/U_k|}{|\tilde{U}_i|} \zeta(\tilde{U}_i, U_k) = m_{ik}.$$

Hence m_{ik} is, so to speak, the *mark* which U_i leaves when it is acting on the left cosets of U_k. We now derive further properties of these elements. As G is assumed to be finite, we can choose a numbering of the conjugacy classes $\tilde{U}_i$ such that the following holds:

3.2.7 $$|U_i| < |U_k| \implies i < k.$$

This guarantees in particular that the partial order is respected:

3.2.8 $$\tilde{U}_i \leq \tilde{U}_k \implies i \leq k.$$

Under the assumptions of 3.2.7, $M(G)$ is upper triangular, $U_1 = \{1\}$, while, since d is the number of conjugacy classes of subgroups, $U_d = G$, and so the table of marks takes the following form:

3.2.9 $$M(G) = \begin{pmatrix} |G| & \cdots & |G/U_k| & \cdots & 1 \\ & \ddots & & * & \vdots \\ & & |N_G(U_i)/U_i| & & \vdots \\ & 0 & & \ddots & \vdots \\ & & & & 1 \end{pmatrix}.$$

Other consequences of 3.2.1 are divisibility properties:

3.2.10 Lemma *If $\tilde{U}_i < \tilde{U}_k$, then $m_{ik} = m_{kk}\zeta(U_i, \tilde{U}_k)$, and so m_{kk} divides all the m_{ik} in the same column.*

Moreover, certain nonzero elements in a column form a monotonous sequence, for $m_{ik} \neq 0 \neq m_{jk}$ means that $\tilde{U}_i \leq \tilde{U}_k \geq \tilde{U}_j$. If in addition $\tilde{U}_i \leq \tilde{U}_j$ holds, which implies that $i \leq j$, then we have

$$\tilde{U}_i \leq \tilde{U}_j \leq \tilde{U}_k.$$

As we may assume $U_i \leq U_j$ without restriction, we obtain:

$$gU_jg^{-1} \leq U_k \implies gU_ig^{-1} \leq U_k,$$

so that an application of

3.2.11 $$m_{ik} = \frac{1}{|U_k|} |\{g \in G \mid gU_ig^{-1} \leq U_k\}|$$

finally yields

3.2.12 Corollary *If $\tilde{U}_i \leq \tilde{U}_j \leq \tilde{U}_k$, then the corresponding elements in the k-th column of the table of marks of G satisfy*

$$m_{ik} \geq m_{jk} \geq m_{kk}.$$

The evaluation of the table of marks is usually quite difficult since one has to know $L(G)$, its Hasse diagram, and the orders of the U_i and their normalizers. Fortunately there exists the Aachen subgroup lattice program by V. Felsch, incorporated also in the program system CAYLEY, which for example was used to evaluate the tables in the Appendix.

Burnside's original motivation for introducing the table of marks was the problem of decomposing a given action into its orbits or, in other words, to decompose a permutation representation into its *transitive constituents*. The question was whether it suffices to consider only the *character* of the action $_GX$, i.e. the function $\chi: g \mapsto |X_g|$. In order to explain character theoretically what is meant by the decomposition of the action $_GX$ into its transitive constituents we first recall that there exists a natural equivalence relation on the set of actions of G on finite sets. Two actions, $_GX$ and $_GY$, say, were called *similar* if and only if there exists a bijection $\varphi: X \to Y$ which is *G–invariant*, i.e. for which the following holds:

$$\forall \, x \in X, g \in G : \quad \varphi(gx) = g\varphi(x).$$

We know from 1.1.15 that there are exactly as many similarity classes of transitive actions as there are conjugacy classes of subgroups. An immediate implication is

3.2.13 Lemma *The set $\{ _G(G/U_i) \mid 1 \leq i \leq d\}$ is a transversal of the similarity classes of transitive actions of G.*

Proof: The actions $_G(G/U_i)$ and $_G(G/U_k)$, $i \neq k$, are not similar, since the respective stabilizers are U_i and U_k, which are different.

$\square$

3.2.14 Corollary *The characters*

$$\chi_i: G \to \mathbb{C}: g \mapsto |(G/U_i)_g|,$$

of the actions $_G(G/U_i), U_i \in \tilde{U}_i, 1 \leq i \leq d$, are the transitive characters of G. These characters have the following values (recall that $C^G(g)$ denotes the conjugacy class and $C_G(g)$ the centralizer of g):

$$\chi_i(g) \;=\; \frac{|G|}{|U_i|} \frac{|C^G(g) \cap U_i|}{|C^G(g)|}.$$

Proof: Consider a transversal $\mathcal{T}$ of the left cosets of U_i. By definition of χ_i, we have

$$\chi_i(g) = |\{t \in T \mid gtU_i = tU_i\}| = |\{t \in T \mid t^{-1}gt \in U_i\}|$$

$$= |\{g' \in G \mid g'gg'^{-1} \in U_i\}| \frac{1}{|U_i|} = \frac{|C^G(g) \cap U_i|}{|U_i|}|C_G(g)|,$$

and the result follows since $|G/C_G(g)| = |C^G(g)|$.

$\sqcap$

Burnside saw that a knowledge of the character χ of $_GX$ together with a table of the χ_i does *not* suffice to decompose χ into its transitive constituents. Such a decomposition is equivalent to the evaluation of the coefficients $n_i \in \mathbb{N}$ in the equation

$$\chi = \sum_{i=1}^{d} n_i \chi_i,$$

where n_i is the number of orbits of G on X similar to $_G(G/U_i)$, as G–sets.

Later on we shall provide an example which shows that *this linear combination is not uniquely determined. But it turns out that replacing the χ_i by the rows of the table of marks we get a unique linear combination.* We first show that the χ_i form part of the table of marks.

3.2.15 Lemma *If $U_i = \langle g \rangle$ is a cyclic subgroup of G and χ_k the character of $_G(G/U_k)$, then $m_{ik} = \chi_k(g)$.*

Proof: By an application of 3.2.11 we obtain

$$m_{ik} = \frac{1}{|U_k|}|\{g' \in G \mid g'gg'^{-1} \in U_k\}| = \chi_k(g).$$

$\square$

This is the reason why $M(G)$ is sometimes called the table of *super-characters* of G, and it also shows that it is helpful to indicate the columns of $M(G)$ which belong to cyclic subgroups so that we can easily identify the transitive characters from $M(G)$. For example the table of marks of S_4 is

$$3.2.16 \quad M(S_{\underline{4}}) = \begin{pmatrix}
24 & 12 & 12 & 8 & 6 & 6 & 6 & 4 & 3 & 2 & 1 \\
 & 2 & . & . & 2 & . & . & 2 & 1 & . & 1 \\
 & & 4 & . & 2 & 2 & 6 & . & 3 & 2 & 1 \\
 & & & 2 & . & . & . & 1 & . & 2 & 1 \\
 & & & & 2 & . & . & . & 1 & . & 1 \\
 & & & & & 2 & . & . & 1 & . & 1 \\
 & & & & & & 6 & . & 3 & 2 & 1 \\
 & & & & & & & 1 & . & . & 1 \\
 & & & & & & & & 1 & . & 1 \\
 & & & & & & & & & 2 & 1 \\
 & & & & & & & & & & 1
\end{pmatrix}
\begin{matrix}
\leftarrow \\ \leftarrow \\ \leftarrow \\ \leftarrow \\ \\ \leftarrow \\ \\ \\ \\ \\ \end{matrix}$$

a table which corresponds to the following numbering of subgroups U_i:

$$U_1 = \langle 1 \rangle, \ U_2 = \langle (24) \rangle, \ U_3 = \langle (13)(24) \rangle, \ U_4 = \langle (132) \rangle,$$

$$U_5 = \langle (13),(24) \rangle, \ U_6 = \langle (1234) \rangle, \ U_7 = \langle (12)(34),(14)(23) \rangle,$$

$$U_8 = \langle (132),(13) \rangle, \ U_9 = \langle (1234),(24) \rangle, \ U_{10} = \langle (132),(142) \rangle,$$

$$U_{11} = \langle (1324),(1342) \rangle.$$

The rows which correspond to cyclic groups are marked by an arrow $\leftarrow$, and hence the table of transitive permutation characters of S_4 is as follows:

	(1^4)	$(1^2 2)$	(2^2)	(13)	(4)
χ_1	24	.	.	.	.
χ_2	12	2	.	.	.
χ_3	12	.	4	.	.
χ_4	8	.	.	2	.
χ_5	6	2	2	.	.
χ_6	6	.	2	.	2
χ_7	6	.	6	.	.
χ_8	4	2	.	1	.
χ_9	3	1	3	.	1
χ_{10}	2	.	2	2	.
χ_{11}	1	1	1	1	1

A few words on the entries b_{ik} of the Burnside matrix $B(G) = M(G)^{-1}$ are in order since in fact it is this matrix which we usually apply for enumerative purposes (see section 3.1). By the definition of b_{ik} we have

3.2.17 $$b_{ik} \in \mathbb{Q}.$$

If again ϕ denotes the Euler function, then we have for the row and column sums of $B(G)$:

3.2.18 Lemma *The column sums of the Burnside matrix $B(G)$ of a finite group G satisfy*

$$\sum_i b_{lk} = \begin{cases} \phi(|U_k|)/|N_G(U_k)| & \text{if } U_k \text{ is cyclic,} \\ 0 & \text{otherwise,} \end{cases}$$

while the row sums are equal to

$$\sum_k b_{ik} = \begin{cases} 1 & \text{if } U_i = G \\ 0 & \text{otherwise.} \end{cases}$$

Hence the sum of all the elements of the Burnside matrix is

$$\sum_{i,k} b_{ik} = 1.$$

Proof: We put

$$x_k := \begin{cases} \phi(|U_k|)/|N_G(U_k)| & \text{if } U_k \text{ is cyclic,} \\ 0 & \text{otherwise.} \end{cases}$$

Then we note that it is sufficient to prove:

$$1 = \sum_j x_j m_{ji}. \qquad (\star)$$

This is true since multiplication of both sides by b_{ik} and summation over i yields what we want to prove, namely

$$\sum_i b_{ik} = \sum_j x_j \underbrace{\sum_i m_{ji} b_{ik}}_{= \delta_{jk}} = x_k.$$

For the remaining verification of $(\star)$ we use

$$\sum_j x_j m_{ji} = \sum_{U_j \text{cyclic}} \frac{\phi(|U_j|)}{|N_G(U_j)|} \frac{|N_G(U_j)|}{|U_i|} |\{U \in \tilde{U}_j \mid U \le U_i\}|$$

$$= \frac{1}{|U_i|} \sum_{U_j \text{cyclic}} \phi(|U_j|)|\{U \in \tilde{U}_j \mid U \leq U_i\}|.$$

The right hand side is equal to 1, for each $g \in U_i$ generates a cyclic subgroup $\langle g \rangle$, this subgroup is contained in a class $\tilde{U}_j$, where U_j is cyclic, and, being cyclic, it possesses exactly $\phi(|\langle g \rangle|) = \phi(|U_j|)$ different generators by exercise 3.2.1. Therefore the sum is just $|U_i|$.

The statement that the row sums are equal to 0 except for the last row, where it is 1 can be obtained simply by considering a trivial action of G. Take a one element set X and let G act *trivially* on it

$$G \times \{x\} \rightarrow \{x\} : (g, x) \mapsto gx := x.$$

Then the only orbit $\{x\}$ is of type $\tilde{G}$, so that Burnside's Lemma yields the equation

$$B(G) \cdot \begin{pmatrix} 1 \\ \vdots \\ 1 \\ 1 \end{pmatrix} = \begin{pmatrix} 0 \\ \vdots \\ 0 \\ 1 \end{pmatrix},$$

from which the statement follows.

The total sum of entries is therefore equal to 1, and this completes the proof.

$\square$

As $M(G)$ is upper triangular if the numbering of the conjugacy classes of subgroups satisfies 3.1.1, also $B(G)$, its inverse, is upper triangular. Furthermore several of its entries can be made explicit in terms of the Moebius function of the lattice of subgroups $L(G)$ (recall 1.1.8):

3.2.19 Corollary *If the numbering of the conjugacy classes of subgroups of G satisfies 3.1.1, then we have for the Burnside matrix of G:*

$$B(G) = \begin{pmatrix} \frac{1}{|G|} & \cdots & \frac{\mu(1,U_k)}{|N_G(U_k)|} & \cdots & \frac{\mu(1,G)}{|G|} \\ & \ddots & & * & \vdots \\ & & \frac{|U_i|}{|N_G(U_i)|} & & \frac{\mu(U_i,G)}{|N_G(U_i)/U_i|} \\ & 0 & & \ddots & \vdots \\ & & & & 1 \end{pmatrix}.$$

From the definitions of m_{ik} and b_{ik} we obtain interesting relations between various elements or products of elements of these two matrices, e.g. that the following products are rational integral:

3.2.20 $m_{ik}b_{kj} = \zeta(U_i, \tilde{U}_k)\mu(U_k, \tilde{U}_j) \in \mathbb{Z}.$

Exercises

E 3.2.1 Show that the number of generators of a cyclic group of order n is equal to $\phi(n)$.

3.3 Weighted enumeration by stabilizer class

The proof of the weighted form 2.1.1 of the Cauchy-Frobenius Lemma was as easy as the proof of its constant form 1.1.11; the same holds for the corresponding form of Burnside's Lemma:

3.3.1 Burnside's Lemma, weighted form *Let* $_GX$ *denote a finite action and* $w: X \to R$ *a function from X into a commutative ring R which contains* $\mathbb{Q}$ *as a subring. If w is constant on the orbits of X, then we have, for a transversal T of the orbits and the vector of the sums of weights of transversals of strata* $\widetilde{U}_i \backslash\!\backslash\!\backslash X$ *of G on X, the equation*

$$
\begin{pmatrix} \vdots \\ \sum_{t:G_t \in \widetilde{U}_i} w(t) \\ \vdots \end{pmatrix} = B(G) \cdot \begin{pmatrix} \vdots \\ \sum_{x:U_i \le G_x} w(x) \\ \vdots \end{pmatrix}.
$$

This weighted form of Burnside's Lemma was, as far as I know, first stated and proved in P. Stockmeyer's thesis. He provided applications of the following immediate consequence to the enumeration of graphs (resp. symmetry classes of mappings) by weight and type:

3.3.2 Corollary *The generating function for the enumeration of G– classes on Y^X of type $\widetilde{U}_j$ by weight* $w: f \mapsto \prod f(x) \in \mathbb{Q}[Y]$ *is the j-th row of the following one column matrix:*

$$
B(G) \cdot \begin{pmatrix} \vdots \\ \prod_{v=1}^{|U_i \backslash\!\backslash X|} \sum_y y^{l_v(U_i)} \\ \vdots \end{pmatrix},
$$

where $l_v(U_i)$ denotes the length of the v-th orbit of U_i on X.

Thus, for example, we obtain for the graphs on $v = 4$ vertices the column (with respect to the same numbering of the conjugacy classes of subgroups which we already used above):

$$B(S_{\underline{4}}) \cdot \begin{pmatrix} (y_0 + y_1)^6 \\ (y_0 + y_1)^2(y_0^2 + y_1^2)^2 \\ (y_0 + y_1)^2(y_0^2 + y_1^2)^2 \\ (y_0^3 + y_1^3)^2 \\ (y_0 + y_1)^2(y_0^4 + y_1^4) \\ (y_0^4 + y_1^4)(y_0^2 + y_1^2) \\ (y_0^2 + y_1^2)^3 \\ (y_0^3 + y_1^3)^2 \\ (y_0^4 + y_1^4)(y_0^2 + y_1^2) \\ y_0^6 + y_1^6 \\ y_0^6 + y_1^6 \end{pmatrix} = \begin{pmatrix} 0 \\ y_0^4 y_1^2 + y_0^2 y_1^4 \\ y_0^3 y_1^3 \\ 0 \\ y_0^5 y_1 + y_0 y_1^5 \\ 0 \\ 0 \\ 2y_0^3 y_1^3 \\ y_0^4 y_1^2 + y_0^2 y_1^4 \\ 0 \\ y_0^6 + y_1^6 \end{pmatrix}.$$

This refines the second column of table 3.1 by showing, for example, that the two graphs of type $\widetilde{U}_8$ both contain exactly 3 edges. A further example is the action of a finite group G on the set $Y^X := \underline{m}^G$ induced by the regular action $_GG$ of G on itself. According to 3.3.2 we obtain the generating function for the orbits of type $\widetilde{U}_i$ by weight:

$$\sum_k b_{ik} \prod_{v=1}^{|U_k \backslash\backslash G|} \sum_{j \in \underline{m}} y_j^{l_v(U_k)}.$$

The orbits of U_k on G are the right cosets of U_k, hence $|U_k \backslash\backslash G| = |G/U_k|$ and $l_v(U_k) = |U_k|$, so that we have proved

3.3.3 Corollary *The coefficient of the monomial* $y_1^{r_1} \ldots y_m^{r_m}$ *in the polynomial*

$$\sum_k b_{ik} \left(\sum_{j \in \underline{m}} y_j^{|U_k|} \right)^{|G/U_i|}$$

is equal to the number of orbits of type $\widetilde{U}_i$ *of G on the set* $\underline{m}^G$ *which are of content* $(r_1, \ldots, r_m)$.

Now we note that, for $f \in \underline{m}^G$, U is a subgroup of the stabilizer if and only if f is constant on the right cosets of U in G. Hence the stabilizer G_f is just the *maximal subgroup* of G such that f is constant on its right cosets. We consider the particular case $m := 2$, where $\underline{m}^G$ can be identified with the *subsets* of G. We derive from 3.3.3 the result:

3.3.4 Corollary *The coefficient of* $y_1^r y_2^{|G|-r}$ *in the polynomial*

$$|G/U_i| \sum_k b_{ik} \left(y_1^{|U_k|} + y_2^{|U_k|} \right)^{|G/U_i|}$$

is equal to the number of subsets $S \subseteq G$ *of order* r *with the property that the maximal subgroup* $U \leq G$ *such that* S *is a union of right cosets of* U *in* G, *belongs to* $\widetilde{U}_i$.

The application of the weighted form of Burnside's Lemma to $_G Y^X$ can be made more explicit by using an interesting generalization of the cycle indicator polynomial which will be described next.

The sum of weights of a transversal $\mathcal{T}$ of the stratum of $U \leq G$ satisfies, according to 3.3.1, the following equation:

$$3.3.5 \qquad \sum_{t : G_t \in \widetilde{U}} w(t) = \frac{|\widetilde{U}|}{|G/U|} \sum_k \sum_{V \in \widetilde{U}_k} \mu(U, V) \sum_{x : U_k \leq G_x} w(x).$$

We would like to evaluate the last sum on the right hand side. In order to do this we note (exercise 3.3.4):

3.3.6 Lemma *The normalizer* $N_G(U)$ *is the maximal subgroup of* G *that leaves each* U–*orbit fixed or maps it onto another* U–*orbit.*

In particular $N_G(U)$ acts on $U \backslash\backslash X$, and therefore the generating function for the corresponding enumeration by weight can be obtained from the corresponding cycle indicator polynomial

$$C(N_G(U), U \backslash\backslash X) = \frac{1}{|N_G(U)|} \sum_{g \in N_G(U)} \prod_{i=1}^{|U \backslash\backslash X|} z_i^{a_i(g)}.$$

Now we use that U lies in the kernel of this action, so that we can replace $N_G(U)$ by $N_G(U)/U$ and therefore restrict the summation to the left cosets of U in its normalizer, obtaining

$$C(N_G(U), U \backslash\backslash X) = \frac{1}{|N_G(U)/U|} \sum_{gU \in N_G(U)/U} \prod_{i=1}^{|U \backslash\backslash X|} z_i^{a_i(gU)}.$$

Moreover we can restrict the range of the product, since an element $g \in N_G(U)/U$ contains an i–cycle if and only if the generated subgroup

$\langle gU \rangle$ has an orbit of length i, hence each such i must divide the order of the acting group. This gives

$$C(N_G(U), U \backslash\backslash X) = \frac{1}{|N_G(U)/U|} \sum_{gU} \prod_{i \mid |N_G(U)/U|} Z_I^{a_i(gU)}.$$

Let us return to X now. The union of the elements of an orbit of $gU \in N_G(U)/U$ on $U \backslash\backslash X$ (as subset of X) is a union of orbits of U. This shows that the generating function for the enumeration of orbits of type $\widetilde{V}$, where $\widetilde{V} \geq \widetilde{U}$, can be obtained from the polynomial

$$Q(U, X) := \frac{1}{|N_G(U)/U|} \sum_{gU} \prod_{\substack{j \mid |U| \\ k \mid |N_G(U)/U|}} z_{j \cdot k}^{a_{j \cdot k}(\langle gU \rangle)}$$

by Pólya–substituting $\sum_y y$. ($a_{j \cdot k}(\langle gU \rangle)$ means the number of orbits of length $j \cdot k$ of the subgroup generated by gU.) This proves

3.3.7 Theorem (Rosenfeld) *The generating function for the enumeration of orbits of type $\widetilde{U}$ of G on Y^X by weight*

$$w: Y^X \to \mathbb{Q}[Y]: f \mapsto \prod_{x \in X} f(x)$$

is equal to

$$\frac{|\widetilde{U}|}{|G/U|} \sum_{V \geq U} \mu(U, V) Q(V, X \mid \sum_{y \in Y} y).$$

From 3.3.5 we can also allow to derive interesting number theoretic congruences, since it implies

3.3.8 $$\sum_k \sum_{V \in \widetilde{U}_k} \mu(U, V) \sum_{x: U_k \leq G_x} w(x) \equiv 0 \left(\frac{|G/U|}{|\widetilde{U}|} \right).$$

A particular case of this is (put $U := \{1\}$):

3.3.9 $$\sum_k \sum_{V \in \widetilde{U}_k} \mu(1, V) \sum_{x: U_k \leq G_x} w(x) \equiv 0 \; (|G|).$$

3.3.10 Example Applying 3.3.9 to actions of the form ${}_G(Y^X)$ and the corresponding multiplicative weight we obtain (recall 3.3.2):

3.3.11 $$\sum_{U \leq G} \mu(1, U) \prod_{v=1}^{|U \backslash\backslash X|} \sum_{y \in Y} y^{l_v(U)} \equiv 0 \; (|G|).$$

In the case when G is the cyclic group of order p^m, acting on $\underline{p^m}$, this congruence reads as follows:

3.3.12
$$\left(\sum y\right)^{(p^m)} \equiv \left(\sum y^p\right)^{(p^{m-1})} \quad (p^m).$$

Being a congruence between coefficients of corresponding monomial summands, this shows that for multinomial coefficients the following is true:

3.3.13
$$\binom{p^m}{n_1, \ldots, n_{|Y|}} \equiv \binom{p^{m-1}}{n_1/p, \ldots, n_{|Y|}/p} \quad (p^m),$$

where, by convention, a multinomial coefficient containing a non integral n_i/p is zero. This can be iterated, in order to get

$$\binom{p^m}{n_1, \ldots, n_{|Y|}} \equiv \binom{p^{m-k}}{n_1/p^k, \ldots, n_{|Y|}/p^k} \quad (p^{m-k+1})$$

$$\equiv 0 \quad (p^{m-k}),$$

if p^k is the greatest common divisor of $\{n_1, \ldots, n_{|Y|}, p^m\}$.

$\diamond$

The problem with applications of Burnside's Lemma to finite actions $_GX$ is that they need the Burnside matrix $B(G)$ of G which assumes a detailed knowledge of the subgroup lattice $L(G)$, and this information is not easy to obtain. For example in the case of the symmetric groups S_n, the maximal n for which we can get $B(S_n)$ by using sophisticated program systems is $n = 8$ or, maybe, $n = 9$. Most of this information is redundant if we are dealing with a single action $_GX$ since only a few of these subgroups occur as stabilizers of elements $x \in X$. Let us discuss these subgroups of G and the corresponding set partitions of X in some detail. Consider the set

$$L(G) := \{U \mid U \leq G\},$$

of subgroups of G, ordered by inclusion: $(L(G), \leq)$, together with the set

$$SP(X) := \{p \mid p \text{ is a set partition of } X\}$$

of set partitions $p = \{p_1, \ldots\}$ of X, ordered by *refinement*:

$$p \leq q : \iff \forall \, p_i \in p \; \exists \, q_j \in q: \, p_i \subseteq q_j.$$

We introduce the following mappings between these two sets:

$$per: L(G) \to SP(X): U \mapsto U \backslash\backslash X, \ stab: SP(X) \to L(G): p \mapsto G_p,$$

where $G_p := \{g \in G \mid \forall i: g[p_i] = p_i\}$ is the *stabilizer* of p. The partition $per(U) = U \backslash\backslash X$ is called the *period* of U. These mappings are monotone:

$$U \le V \Rightarrow U \backslash\backslash X \le V \backslash\backslash X, \ p \le q \Rightarrow G_p \le G_q,$$

and their compositions satisfy:

$$U \le (stab \circ per)(U), \ p \ge (per \circ stab)(p).$$

This means (cf. exercises 3.3.2 and 3.3.3) that *per* is a *Galois function*, that *stab ∘ per* is a *closure operator* on $L(G)$, and that *per ∘ stab* is a *coclosure operator* on $SP(X)$. Correspondingly we have for the *quotients*, i.e. the set $\bar{L}(G)$ of closed elements, and the set $\overline{SP}(X)$ of coclosed elements, respectively:

3.3.14 $\bar{L}(G) = stab[SP(X)], \ \overline{SP}(X) = per[L(G)].$

Moreover these quotients are isomorphic (as posets):

3.3.15 $\bar{L}(G) \simeq \overline{SP}(X).$

3.3.16 Example A very easy case is provided by the natural action of the symmetric group $G := S_n$, on the set $X := \underline{n}$. The stabilizer of a partition $p \in SP(\underline{n})$ is obviously the direct sum $\oplus_i S_{p_i}$ of the symmetric groups S_{p_i} on the blocks p_i of p. The closed elements, which form the quotient $\bar{L}(S_n)$, are these direct sums, which are called the *Young subgroups* of S_n. On the other hand, each element of $SP(\underline{n})$ is coclosed, and so we have:

$$\bar{L}(S_n) \simeq SP(X).$$

In words: the lattice of Young subgroups of S_n is isomorphic to the lattice of partitions of $\underline{n}$. This shows that in order to examine the natural action of S_n on $\underline{n}$, it suffices to consider the lattice $SP(\underline{n})$ of partitions or the lattice of Young subgroups.

$\diamond$

Now we use these notions in order to introduce *periods of mappings* . The *partition* $p(f)$ of $f \in Y^X$ has as its blocks the subsets on which f is constant:

$$p(f) := \{f^{-1}[\{y\}] \mid y \in f[X]\}.$$

The coclosure of $p(f)$ is called the *period of f*:

$$per(f) := (per \circ stab)(p(f)) = per(G_{p(f)}) = G_{p(f)} \backslash\backslash X.$$

Less formally: $per(f)$ is the coarsest partition of the form $U \backslash\backslash X$ such that f is constant on each block. Now recall the multiplicative weight function

$$w: Y^X \to \mathbb{Q}[Y]: f \mapsto \prod_{x \in X} f(x).$$

We shall use it in order to define two interesting mappings on the set of *periods of $_G X$*:

$$P(_G X) := \overline{SP}(X) = \{p \in SP(X) \mid p = (per \circ stab)(p)\}$$

$$= per[L(G)] = \{U \backslash\backslash X \mid U \le G\}.$$

These mappings are:

$$A: P(_G X) \to \mathbb{Q}[Y]: p \mapsto \sum_{f: per(f) = p} w(f),$$

and

$$B: P(_G X) \to \mathbb{Q}[Y]: p \mapsto \sum_{f: per(f) \le p} w(f).$$

They satisy the following equation:

3.3.17
$$B(p) = \sum_q \mu(q, p) A(q),$$

which means that for each period p of G on X the following is true:

3.3.18
$$\sum_{f: per(f) \le p} w(f) = \sum_{q \in P(_G X)} \mu(q, p) \sum_{f: per(f) = q} w(f).$$

This improves the methods offered by the weighted form of Burnside's Lemma, since on the right hand side there are considerably fewer summands.

Exercises

E 3.3.1 Prove that for natural numbers n and the number theoretic Moebius function μ the following is true:

$$\sum_{t \mid n} \mu(t) \binom{n/t}{n_1/t, \ldots, n_{|Y|}/t} \equiv 0 \ (n).$$

E 3.3.2 Let $(M, \leq)$ and $(N, \leq)$ denote partially ordered sets and consider a pair (α, β) of mappings $\alpha: M \to N$ and $\beta: N \to M$. Then (α, β) is called a *Galois connection* if and only if α and β are antitone, and

$$(\beta \circ \alpha)(m) \geq m, \ (\alpha \circ \beta)(n) \geq n.$$

Prove that in this case the following is true:

- $\alpha \circ \beta \circ \alpha = \alpha$, and $\beta \circ \alpha \circ \beta = \beta$.

- $\alpha \circ \beta$ and $\beta \circ \alpha$ are *closure operators*:

  - $m \leq (\beta \circ \alpha)(m)$, and $n \leq (\alpha \circ \beta)(n)$,

  - $m \leq m' \Rightarrow (\beta \circ \alpha)(m) \leq (\beta \circ \alpha)(m')$,

  - $n \leq n' \Rightarrow (\alpha \circ \beta)(n) \leq (\alpha \circ \beta)(n')$,

  - $(\alpha \circ \beta)^2 = \alpha \circ \beta$, and $(\beta \circ \alpha)^2 = \beta \circ \alpha$.

- For the subsets of *closed elements* (i.e. the m, n with the property $m = (\beta \circ \alpha)(m), n = (\alpha \circ \beta)(n)$) we have

  $$\bar{M} = \beta[N], \ \bar{N} = \alpha[M].$$

- $\bar{M}$ and $\bar{N}$ are antiisomorphic, with α and β as inverse mappings.

E 3.3.3 Let $(M, \leq)$ and $(N, \leq)$ denote partially ordered sets. A mapping $\alpha: M \to N$ is called a *Galois function* if there exists a mapping β from N to M such that both these mappings are monotone, while

$$(\beta \circ \alpha)(m) \geq m, \text{ and } (\alpha \circ \beta)(n) \leq n.$$

Prove that in this case the following is true:

- $\beta \circ \alpha$ is a closure operator on M, while $\alpha \circ \beta$ is a *coclosure operator* on n, which means:

  $$n \geq (\alpha \circ \beta)(n), n \leq n' \Rightarrow (\alpha \circ \beta)(n) \leq (\alpha \circ \beta)(n'), (\alpha \circ \beta)^2 = \alpha \circ \beta.$$

- $\alpha[M]$ is the set of *coclosed elements* (i.e. the set of n such that $n = (\alpha \circ \beta)(n)$).

- The set $\bar{M}$ of coclosed elements of M and the set $\bar{N}$ of coclosed elements of N are isomorphic with α and β as inverse mappings.

E 3.3.4 Prove lemma 3.3.6.

3.4 Actions on posets, semigroups, lattices

We have discussed the Burnside matrix and the table of marks. They belong (in a sense which will become clear later) to the subgroup lattice $L(G)$ on which G acts by conjugation:

3.4.1 $$G \times L(G) \to L(G) : (g, U) \mapsto gUg^{-1}.$$

This operation respects the partial order $\leq$ of $L(G)$:

3.4.2 $$U \leq U' \implies gUg^{-1} \leq gU'g^{-1},$$

and it respects the operations $\wedge$ and $\vee$ on $L(G)$:

$$g(U \wedge U')g^{-1} = g(U \cap U')g^{-1} = gUg^{-1} \wedge gU'g^{-1},$$

$$g(U \vee U')g^{-1} = g\langle U \cup U' \rangle g^{-1} = gUg^{-1} \vee gU'g^{-1}.$$

We therefore consider actions of finite groups which respect a partial order or a multiplication or both the operations $\wedge$ and $\vee$ of a finite lattice. In other words, we are going to consider *actions of finite groups as groups of automorphisms of posets, semigroups and lattices*, in the following sense. Let $(X, \leq)$ denote a poset. The group G acts on X as a group of *automorphisms* if and only if the following holds:

3.4.3 $$\forall g \in G, \ x, x' \in X \ (x \leq x' \iff gx \leq gx').$$

We shall abbreviate this by writing

$$_G(X, \leq),$$

and we shall call this a *poset action*.

3.4.4 Lemma *If $_G(X, \leq)$ denotes a finite poset action, then the following holds:*

- *Any two elements in the same orbit are incomparable.*

- *The orbits ω_i of G on X can be numbered in such a way that*

$$\omega_i \ni x \leq x' \in \omega_k \implies i \leq k.$$

- *For any orbit ω and a fixed $x \in X$, the numbers*

$$|\{x' \in \omega \mid x \leq x'\}| \ and \ |\{x' \in \omega \mid x \geq x'\}|$$

depend only on the orbit containing x and not on the chosen representative.

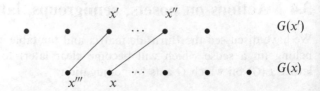

Figure 3.2: Two orbits of the poset

- *For any* $x, x' \in X$, *we have*

$$\frac{|\{x'' \in X \mid x \le x'' \in G(x')\}|}{|\{x''' \in X \mid x' \ge x''' \in G(x)\}|} = \frac{|G(x')|}{|G(x)|}.$$

Proof:

i) If $x \in X$ were comparable with $gx \ne x$, say (without restriction) $x < gx$, then we have

$$x < gx < g^2 x < \ldots < g^{-1} x < x,$$

which is a contradiction.

ii) Suppose $x_1, x_2 \in \omega_i, x'_1, x'_2 \in \omega_k, i \ne k$. Assume that $x_1 < x'_1$ and that x_2 and x'_2 are comparable. Then $x_2 > x'_2$ would yield, for suitable $g, g' \in G$: $gx_1 = x_2 > x'_2 = g'x'_1$, and hence also $x_1 > g^{-1}g'x'_1$, which implies the contradiction $x'_1 > g^{-1}g'x'_1$. Thus the partial order can be embedded into a total order that respects the partial order:

$$\underbrace{x_1, x_2, \ldots, x_{|\omega_1|}}_{\in\, \omega_1}, \underbrace{x_{|\omega_1|+1}, \ldots, x_{|\omega_1|+|\omega_2|}}_{\in\, \omega_2}, \ldots, \text{where } x_i < x_k \Rightarrow i < k.$$

iii) is clear from 3.4.3

iv) follows from a trivial "double count". We consider the bipartite graph consisting of the two orbits $G(x)$ and $G(x')$, where comparable elements are joint by an edge (see Figure 3.2).

□

A lattice $(L, \wedge, \vee)$ defines a poset $(L, \le)$ and besides this it yields two *semigroups* $(L, \wedge)$ and $(L, \vee)$, as both these compositions are associative by the definition of a lattice.

3.4.5 Lemma *Let* $(L, \wedge, \vee)$ *denote a lattice on which a finite group* G *acts. The following three conditions are equivalent:*

- $\forall\, x, x', g : x < x' \Longrightarrow gx < gx',$

- $\forall\, x, x', g\, :\; g(x \wedge x') = gx \wedge gx'$,
- $\forall\, x, x', g\, :\; g(x \vee x') = gx \vee gx'$.

Proof:

i)$\Rightarrow$ ii): As $x \wedge x'$ is less than or equal to both x and x', we obtain from i) that $g(x \wedge x')$ is less than or equal to both gx and gx'. This yields

$$g(x \wedge x') \leq gx \wedge gx'. \tag{$\star$}$$

If now $g(x \wedge x')$ were strictly less than $gx \wedge gx'$, we also have by i):

$$g^2(x \wedge x') < g(gx \wedge gx') \leq g^2x \wedge g^2x',$$

where the last inequality comes from ($\star$). Hence, for each $n \in \mathbb{N}$, we obtain

$$g^n(x \wedge x') < g^nx \wedge g^nx',$$

which yields a contradiction by putting $n := |\langle g \rangle|$. Thus $g(x \wedge x') = gx \wedge gx'$ must hold.

i)$\Rightarrow$ iii) follows quite analogously.

ii)$\Rightarrow$ i): The assumption $x < x'$ yields $x \wedge x' = x$, so that $g(x \wedge x') = gx$, and hence, by ii), $gx \leq gx'$. This implies $gx < gx'$, as $x \neq x'$.

iii)$\Rightarrow$ i) follows similarly.

$\square$

Lemma 3.4.5 means that we may either check if the action respects the partial order or one of the two compositions $\wedge$ or $\vee$. In each of these cases we shall use either the notation $_G(L, \leq)$ or we shall indicate this situation by

$$_G(L, \wedge, \vee)$$

and call such actions *lattice actions*. An immediate consequence of 3.4.4 is

3.4.6 Corollary *If* $_G(L, \wedge, \vee)$ *denotes a finite lattice action, then, for any orbit* ω *and a fixed* $x \in L$, *the numbers*

$$|\{x' \in \omega \mid x \leq x'\}| \text{ and } |\{x' \in \omega \mid x \geq x'\}|$$

depend only on the orbit containing x *and not on the chosen representative* x. *Thus, having numbered the orbits in the way described in 3.4.4, we can introduce the numbers*

$$a_{ik}^\wedge := |\{x' \in \omega_k \mid x \leq x'\}| \text{ and } a_{ik}^\vee := |\{x' \in \omega_k \mid x \geq x'\}|,$$

where x is an element of ω_i. The $a_{ik}^\wedge$ form an upper triangular matrix $A^\wedge := (a_{ik}^\wedge)$, while the $a_{ik}^\vee$ form a lower triangular matrix $A^\vee := (a_{ik}^\vee)$. The main diagonals consist of ones, and hence both these matrices are invertible over $\mathbb{Z}$. Furthermore the elements of these matrices are related by the equations

$$|\omega_i| \cdot a_{ik}^\wedge = |\omega_k| \cdot a_{ki}^\vee.$$

Now we consider the more general case, where a group G acts as a group of automorphisms on a *semigroup* $(X, \cdot)$, i.e. we assume that the action also satisfies

$$\forall\, x, x', g : \; g(x \cdot x') = gx \cdot gx'.$$

Such actions are called *semigroup actions* and they are indicated by

$$_G(X, \cdot).$$

We denote the orbits of G on X by

$$\omega_1, \ldots, \omega_d.$$

A trivial but important remark is (exercise 3.4.1):

3.4.7 Lemma *For each $i, j, k \in \underline{d}$ and any $z, z' \in \omega_k$ we have*

$$|\{(x, x') \in \omega_i \times \omega_j \mid x \cdot x' = z\}| = |\{(x, x') \in \omega_i \times \omega_j \mid x \cdot x' = z'\}|.$$

In other words: The number of solutions $(x, x') \in \omega_i \times \omega_j$ of $x \cdot x' = z, z \in \omega_k$, does *not* depend on the chosen z but only on its orbit. We can therefore denote this number by

3.4.8 $$\qquad a_{ijk} := |\{(x, x') \in \omega_i \times \omega_j \mid x \cdot x' = z\}|,$$

for a fixed $z \in \omega_k$. (The reader should note the upper index "$\cdot$" which indicates the multiplication in question, and which therefore is *not* a fly blow.)

We next introduce a ring which has these numbers as its structure constants. To do this we start from the *semigroup ring* of X over Z, which is the set

$$\mathbb{Z}^X = \{f \mid f : X \to \mathbb{Z}\},$$

together with addition and multiplication defined by:

$$(f + f')(x) := f(x) + f'(x), \quad (f \star f')(x) := \sum_{x' \cdot x'' = x} f(x') f'(x'').$$

We denote the resulting *ring* by $\mathbb{Z}^{X,\cdot}$. Its elements will be written as "formal sums"

$$f = \sum_{x \in X} f_x x, \quad \text{where } f_x := f(x).$$

If, in addition, we are given an action $_G X$, then we call the f that are fixed under each $g \in G$, for short: the $f \in \mathbb{Z}_G^X$, the *G–invariants* or the *G–invariant mappings* (recall the notation X_G introduced in the first section). They form an important subring (exercise 3.4.2), the main properties of which are gathered in the following lemma:

3.4.9 Lemma

- The *G–invariants* $f \in \mathbb{Z}^X$ form the subring:

$$\mathbb{Z}_G^{X,\cdot} := \{f : X \to \mathbb{Z} \mid \forall g \in G : f = f \circ g^{-1}\}.$$

- This subring has as a $\mathbb{Z}$–basis the orbit sums

$$\underline{\omega_i} := \sum_{x \in \omega_i} x \in \mathbb{Z}_G^{X,\cdot}.$$

- The structure constants of $\mathbb{Z}_G^{X,\cdot}$ are the a_{ijk} defined in 3.4.8, i.e. we have for the product of basis elements

$$\underline{\omega_i} \cdot \underline{\omega_j} = \sum_k a_{ijk} \, \underline{\omega_k}.$$

In this way each action of a finite group G on a finite lattice $(L, \wedge, \vee)$ as a group of lattice automorphisms yields the two rings $\mathbb{Z}^{L,\wedge}$ and $\mathbb{Z}^{L,\vee}$ together with their subrings

$$\mathbb{Z}_G^{L,\wedge} \text{ and } \mathbb{Z}_G^{L,\vee},$$

the multiplicative structure of which is described by the constants

$$a_{ijk}^\wedge := |\{(x,x') \in \omega_i \times \omega_j \mid x \wedge x' = z\}|,$$

$$a_{ijk}^\vee := |\{(x,x') \in \omega_i \times \omega_j \mid x \vee x' = z\}|,$$

for a fixed $z \in \omega_k$.

A paradigmatic example is formed by the subgroup lattice $L := L(G)$ and the action of G on it by conjugation. We are now in a position to state and prove the main theorem of this section (W. Plesken):

3.4.10 Theorem *Let* $_G(L, \wedge, \vee)$ *denote a finite lattice action of G. Assume that* $\omega_1, \ldots, \omega_d$ *are the orbits,* $\underline{\omega}_1, \ldots, \underline{\omega}_d$ *their sums, numbered according to 3.4.4. Then*

- *The mapping*

$$\underline{\omega}_k \mapsto \begin{pmatrix} a^\wedge_{1k} \\ \vdots \\ a^\wedge_{dk} \end{pmatrix}$$

  defines a ring isomorphism between $\mathbb{Z}_G^{L, \wedge}$ *and* $\mathbb{Z}^{\underline{d}}$, *while*

- *the mapping*

$$\underline{\omega}_k \mapsto \begin{pmatrix} a^\vee_{1k} \\ \vdots \\ a^\vee_{dk} \end{pmatrix}$$

  defines a ring isomorphism between $\mathbb{Z}_G^{L, \vee}$ *and* $\mathbb{Z}^{\underline{d}}$,

where $\mathbb{Z}^{\underline{d}}$ *is equipped with pointwise addition and multiplication.*

Proof: In order to check the homomorphy first, we consider the product $a^\wedge_i \cdot a^\wedge_j$ of the i–th and j–th column of $A^\wedge$. We want to verify that it satisfies $a^\wedge_i \cdot a^\wedge_j = \sum_k a^\wedge_{ijk} a^\wedge_k$. From the definition of $a^\wedge_{li}$ we obtain (for a fixed $x \in \omega_l$):

$$a^\wedge_{li} \cdot a^\wedge_{lj} = |\{y \in \omega_i \mid y \geq x\}| \cdot |\{z \in \omega_j \mid z \geq x\}|$$

$$= |\{(y, z) \in \omega_i \times \omega_j \mid x \leq (y \wedge z)\}| = \sum_k a^\wedge_{ijk} a^\wedge_{lk},$$

which proves homomorphy. In order to check the isomorphy we use that both $A^\wedge := (a^\wedge_{ik})$ and $A^\vee := (a^\vee_{ik})$ are triangular by 3.4.6 and contain only 1's along their main diagonal (and hence are invertible over $\mathbb{Z}$). This shows that the above mappings are even $\mathbb{Z}$–isomorphisms, which completes the proof of the first statement, the second one follows analogously.

$\square$

These results show the fundamental importance of the *columns* of $A^\wedge$. But the *rows* also have interesting properties (see exercise 3.4.3).

Exercises

E 3.4.1 Prove 3.4.7.

E 3.4.2 Check the first statement of 3.4.9.

E 3.4.3 Prove that the matrices $A_i^\wedge := (a_{ijk}^\wedge)$ have the rows of $A^\wedge$ as eigenvectors. What are the eigenvalues?

3.5 Examples

Decorative lattices on which finite groups act as groups of automorphisms are formed by the faces, edges and vertices of the regular polyhedra: the tetrahedron, the cube, the octahedron, the dodecahedron and the icosahedron. Let us consider the easiest case, the *tetrahedron* (Figure 3.3). Its four faces, six edges and four vertices

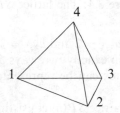

Figure 3.3: The tetrahedron

together with T itself and $\emptyset$ form a lattice L of order 16, which is ordered by the incidence relation. It is obvious that the alternating group A_4 acts on L and respects incidence, i.e. it acts on L as a group of automorphisms. The corresponding matrices $A^\wedge$ and $A^\vee$ are the following ones:

$$A^\wedge = \begin{pmatrix} 1 & 4 & 6 & 4 & 1 \\ & 1 & 3 & 3 & 1 \\ & & 1 & 2 & 1 \\ & & & 1 & 1 \\ & & & & 1 \end{pmatrix}, \quad A^\vee = \begin{pmatrix} 1 & & & & \\ 1 & 1 & & & \\ 1 & 2 & 1 & & \\ 1 & 3 & 3 & 1 & \\ 1 & 4 & 6 & 4 & 1 \end{pmatrix}.$$

A product of columns is e.g.

$$a_3^\wedge \cdot a_4^\wedge = \begin{pmatrix} 24 \\ 9 \\ 2 \\ 0 \\ 0 \end{pmatrix} = 2a_3^\wedge + 3a_2^\wedge.$$

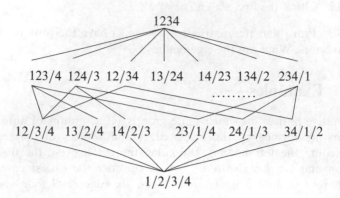

Figure 3.4: The lattice $SP(\underline{4})$

This identity shows that $a^{\wedge}_{343} = 2$ and $a^{\wedge}_{342} = 3$, which means that each edge can be represented in exactly two ways as the infimum of a facet and an edge, while a vertex can be represented in exactly three ways as such an infimum.

Our next example is the lattice $SP(\underline{n})$ consisting of the *set partitions* of $\underline{n} = \{1,\dots,n\}$, ordered by *refinement*. This lattice is called the *partition lattice* of $\underline{n}$, the particular case $SP(\underline{4})$ is ·shown in Figure 3.4, where the distribution of the four elements into blocks is indicated by "/".

If we order the lengths of the blocks of $p \in SP(\underline{n})$ into a nonincreasing sequence α, then we obtain a proper partition

$$\alpha(p) = (\alpha_1, \alpha_2, \dots) \vdash n,$$

which we call the *type* of p. The following facts are easily checked (exercise 3.5.1):

3.5.1 Lemma *For the natural action of $S_{\underline{n}}$ on $SP(\underline{n})$ we have:*

- *$S_{\underline{n}}$ acts as a group of automorphisms on $SP(\underline{n})$:*

$$p \le p' \iff \pi p \le \pi p'.$$

- *The lattice $(SP(\underline{n}), \le)$ is isomorphic to the sublattice of $L(S_{\underline{n}})$ consisting of the stabilizers of the set partitions.*

- *The orbits of $S_{\underline{n}}$ on $SP(\underline{n})$ are the subsets of partitions of the same type:*

$$S_{\underline{n}}(p) = S_{\underline{n}}(p') \iff \alpha(p) = \alpha(p').$$

The matrices $A^\wedge$ and $A^\vee$ of $SP(\underline{4})$ are

$$A^\wedge = \begin{pmatrix} 1 & 6 & 3 & 4 & 1 \\ & 1 & 1 & 2 & 1 \\ & & 1 & 0 & 1 \\ & & & 1 & 1 \\ & & & & 1 \end{pmatrix}, \quad A^\vee = \begin{pmatrix} 1 & & & & \\ 1 & 1 & & & \\ 1 & 2 & 1 & & \\ 1 & 3 & 0 & 1 & \\ 1 & 6 & 3 & 4 & 1 \end{pmatrix}.$$

Again the products of columns yield interesting enumerative results, for example

$$a_2^\vee \cdot a_3^\vee = \begin{pmatrix} 0 \\ 0 \\ 2 \\ 0 \\ 18 \end{pmatrix} = 2a_3^\vee + 12a_5^\vee$$

shows that there are exactly two ways of representing a set partition of type (2^2) of $\underline{4}$ as supremum $p \vee p'$ of a partition p of type $(2, 1^2)$ and a partition p' of type (2^2). The equation shows furthermore that the set partition 1234 of type (4) can be represented in exactly 12 ways as the supremum $p \vee p'$, where $\alpha(p) = (2, 1^2)$ and $\alpha(p') = (2^2)$. This can be checked easily in Figure 3.4. The lattice $SP(\underline{n})$ possesses a *rank function* (for the basic notions of lattice theory see e.g. the book by Aigner), the rank of $p \in SP(\underline{n})$ is

3.5.2 $r(p) = n - l(p),$

where $l(p)$ means the *length* of p i.e. the number of blocks. The order of the $(n - k)$-th *level* of $SP(\underline{n})$, from the bottom upwards, i.e. the number of set partitions of $\underline{n}$ consisting of k blocks, is the Stirling number of the second kind $S(n, k)$ (cf. 1.7.8):

3.5.3 $|\{p \in SP(\underline{n}) \mid r(p) = n - k\}| = S(n, k).$

Correspondingly the total order $|SP(\underline{n})|$ of this lattice is the n-th Bell number (recall 1.7.9):

3.5.4 $|SP(\underline{n})| = B_n.$

Further important finite lattices are the subspace lattices of finite vector spaces. We denote by

$$\mathscr{L}(d, q)$$

the lattice of subspaces of the d–dimensional vector space $V :=$ $GF(q)^{\underline{d}}$ over the Galois field $GF(q)$. The general linear group $GL(V)$, which is $GL_d(q)$, acts on it as a group of automorphisms, and the orbits are clearly formed by the subspaces of the same dimension. The rank function is

3.5.5 $$r(U) = \dim U,$$

and hence the order of the $(d - k)$-th level of $\mathcal{L}(d, q)$ is equal to the number of k–dimensional subspaces of $V = GF(q)^{\underline{d}}$. For technical reasons we put $d = m + n$ and state:

3.5.6 Lemma *For natural numbers m and n, where $0 < n$, the number of subspaces $U \leq GF(q)^{\underline{m+n}}$ of dimension n is equal to*

$$\frac{(q^{m+n} - 1) \cdot \ldots \cdot (q^{m+1} - 1)}{(q^n - 1) \cdot \ldots \cdot (q - 1)} = \begin{bmatrix} m + n \\ n \end{bmatrix}_q.$$

Proof: It is easy to see that the number of n–tuples consisting of linearly independent elements of $GF(q)^{\underline{m+n}}$ is equal to

$$(q^{m+n} - 1)(q^{m+n} - q) \cdot \ldots \cdot (q^{m+n} - q^{n-1}).$$

In the same way we see that the number of different bases of $GF(q)^{\underline{n}}$ is equal to

$$(q^n - 1)(q^n - q) \cdot \ldots \cdot (q^n - q^{n-1}).$$

Hence the number of subspaces of dimension n is equal to the quotient of these two cardinalities and the statement is obtained by cancelling powers of q and recalling the definition of q–binomial numbers from 2.1.12.

$\square$

Now we introduce the so–called *Gaussian polynomials*:

3.5.7 $$G_{mn} := \sum_{k=0}^{mn} p(k; m, n) x^k,$$

where $p(k; m, n)$ is defined to be the number of proper partitions $\alpha \vdash k$ into at most m parts $\alpha_i > 0$ and subject to the condition that each $\alpha_i \leq n$.

3.5.8 Lemma

$$G_{mn} = \begin{bmatrix} m + n \\ n \end{bmatrix}.$$

Proof: First, note that

$$\begin{bmatrix} m+n \\ n \end{bmatrix} = x^n \begin{bmatrix} (m-1)+n \\ n \end{bmatrix} + \begin{bmatrix} m+(n-1) \\ n-1 \end{bmatrix};$$

this is immediate from the definition of the binomial function. Moreover we have that

$$\begin{bmatrix} m+0 \\ 0 \end{bmatrix} = \begin{bmatrix} 0+n \\ n \end{bmatrix} = 1 = G_{m0} = G_{0n}.$$

It therefore suffices to show that the G_{mn} satisfy the recursion

3.5.9 $\qquad G_{mn} = x^n G_{m-1,n} + G_{m,n-1}$, if $0 < m, n$.

In order to prove this we apply the following identity for $k \geq n$: Putting $p(r; s, t) := 0$, if $r < 0$, we have

$$p(k; m, n) = p(k - n; m - 1, n) + p(k; m, n - 1).$$

(The first summand on the right hand side is just the number of proper partitions α of k such that $\alpha_1 = n$ and the number of parts is smaller than m. The second summand is the number of $\alpha \vdash k$ such that $\alpha_1 < n$ while the number of parts is less than or equal to m.) This identity yields

$$G_{mn} = \sum_{k=0}^{mn} p(k - n; m - 1, n)x^k + \sum_{k=0}^{mn} p(k; m, n - 1)x^k.$$

But $p(k-n; m-1, n) = 0$ if $k > mn$, and $p(k; m, n-1) = 0$ if $k > m(n-1)$. Thus we may procede as follows:

$$G_{mn} = \sum_{k=n}^{mn} p(k - n; m - 1, n)x^k + \sum_{k=0}^{m(n-1)} p(k; m, n - 1)x^k$$

$$= x^n \sum_{k=n}^{mn} p(k - n; m - 1, n)x^{k-n} + G_{m,n-1} = x^n G_{m-1,n} + G_{m,n-1}.$$

$\qquad\qquad\qquad\qquad\qquad\qquad\qquad\qquad\qquad\qquad\qquad\qquad\qquad\qquad\qquad\square$

We have proved

3.5.10 Corollary *For natural numbers m, n and prime powers q*

$$G_{mn}(q) = \begin{bmatrix} m+n \\ n \end{bmatrix}_q = \sum_{k=0}^{mn} p(k; m, n) q^k$$

is equal to the order of the n-th level of the subspace lattice $\mathcal{L}(m+n, q)$.

This yields the entries of $A^\vee$ and the entries of $A^\wedge$ are obtained similarly or by an application of 3.4.6:

3.5.11 Corollary *For the lattice* $\mathcal{L}(d, q)$ *we have*

$$A^\wedge = \left(\begin{bmatrix} d-i \\ k-i \end{bmatrix}_q \right)_{i,k \in \underline{d}}, \quad A^\vee = \left(\begin{bmatrix} i \\ k \end{bmatrix}_q \right)_{i,k \in \underline{d}}.$$

We can obtain the matrix $A^\vee$ for each prime power q by simply evaluating at q the matrix

3.5.12 $A := \left(\begin{bmatrix} i \\ k \end{bmatrix} \right).$

Its upper left hand corner is

$$A = \begin{pmatrix} 1 \\ G_{10} & G_{01} \\ G_{20} & G_{11} & G_{02} \\ G_{30} & G_{21} & G_{12} & G_{03} \\ G_{40} & G_{31} & G_{22} & G_{13} & G_{04} \\ \cdots & \cdots & \cdots & \cdots & \cdots & \cdots \end{pmatrix}$$

$$= \begin{pmatrix} 1 \\ 1 & 1 \\ 1 & 1+x & 1 \\ 1 & 1+x+x^2 & 1+x+x^2 & 1 \\ 1 & 1+x+x^2+x^3 & 1+x+2x^2+x^3+x^4 & \cdots & 1 \\ \cdots & \cdots & \cdots & \cdots \end{pmatrix}.$$

Exercises

E 3.5.1 Prove 3.5.1.

E 3.5.2 Show that the matrix $A^\vee$ of the lattice $SP(\underline{n})$ can be evaluated recursively.

E 3.5.3 Evaluate the matrices $A^\wedge$ and $A^\vee$ for the cube and the icosahedron, on which the groups S_4 and A_5 act, respectively.

E 3.5.4 Evaluate these matrices for the action of S_n on the lattice formed by the subsets of $\underline{n}$.

3.6 The Burnside ring

We saw how symmetry classes of mappings can be counted by weight and stabilizer class using the *Burnside matrix* which is the inverse of the table of marks. Moreover we met actions of groups on lattices $(L, \wedge, \vee)$, and the corresponding subrings $\mathbb{Z}_G^{L,\wedge}$ and $\mathbb{Z}_G^{L,\vee}$ of the semigroup rings $\mathbb{Z}^{L,\wedge}$ and $\mathbb{Z}^{L,\vee}$, where the matrices $A^\wedge = (a_{ik}^\wedge)$ and $A^\vee = (a_{ik}^\vee)$ played a central role. We now build a bridge between these two topics by introducing the Burnside ring $\Omega(G)$ of G which can be embedded into $\mathbb{Z}_G^{L(G),\wedge}$, the matrix $A^\wedge$ of which is closely connected with the table of marks. In order to do this we indicate first how a complete set of transitive G–sets can be obtained (exercise 3.6.1):

3.6.1 Lemma *Let G denote a finite group with its conjugacy classes of subgroups $\tilde{U}_1, \ldots, \tilde{U}_d$ and representatives $U_i \in \tilde{U}_i$. Then*

- *The sets $G/U_i := \{gU_i \mid g \in G\}, i \in \underline{d}$, consisting of the left cosets gU_i of the subgroups U_i of G are G–sets with respect to the operation $g : xU_i \mapsto gxU_i$.*

- *These G–sets are transitive and pairwise not similar.*

- *$\{G/U_1, \ldots, G/U_d\}$ is a complete system of transitive but pairwise dissimilar G–sets.*

Switching to the similarity classes

$$\overline{G/U_i} := \{X \mid X \text{ a } G\text{-set and } {}_GX \approx {}_G(G/U_i)\},$$

we obtain the *complete system* $\Omega := \{\overline{G/U}_1, \ldots, \overline{G/U}_d\}$ of G–similarity classes of transitive G–sets. Consider the free abelian group

$$\mathbb{Z}^\Omega := \{\psi \mid \psi : \Omega \to \mathbb{Z}\}, \text{ where } (\psi + \psi')(\overline{G/U_i}) := \psi(\overline{G/U_i}) + \psi'(\overline{G/U_i}).$$

We shall as usual display the $\psi \in \mathbb{Z}^\Omega$ as "formal sums"

$$\psi = \sum_{i=1}^d z_i \cdot \overline{G/U_i}, \text{ where } z_i := \psi(\overline{G/U_i}) \in \mathbb{Z}.$$

The addition of the two formal sums

$$\overline{G/U_i} := 1_{\mathbb{Z}} \cdot \overline{G/U_i} \text{ and } \overline{G/U_k} := 1_{\mathbb{Z}} \cdot \overline{G/U_k}$$

in $\mathbb{Z}^\Omega$ can be interpreted as first taking the disjoint union of G/U_i and G/U_k and afterwards switching to the G–similarity class $\overline{X}$ of the resulting G–set X:

$$\overline{G/U_i} + \overline{G/U_k} = \overline{G/U_i \dot\cup G/U_k}.$$

This is clear from the fact that each G–set possesses a unique decomposition into orbits (but note that also in the case when $i = k$ we have to form the *disjoint* union, e.g. $|G/U_i \dot\cup G/U_i| = 2|G/U_i|$). Hence *each G–set X and its similarity class $\overline{X}$ can be identified in this way with a uniquely determined element of the subset $\mathbb{N}^\Omega \subseteq \mathbb{Z}^\Omega$*:

$$3.6.2 \qquad\qquad \overline{X} = \sum_{i=1}^{d} |\widetilde{U}_i \backslash\!\backslash X| \cdot \overline{G/U_i}.$$

Furthermore we can introduce on $\mathbb{Z}^\Omega$ a multiplication as linear extension of

$$\overline{G/U_i} \cdot \overline{G/U_j} := \sum_k b_{ijk} \overline{G/U_k}, \text{ if } \overline{G/U_i \times G/U_j} = \sum_k b_{ijk} \overline{G/U_k}.$$

Soon we shall see that this in fact yields a well defined multiplication. The corresponding structure constant b_{ijk} is equal to the number of orbits of G on $G/U_i \times G/U_j$ (with respect to the natural action $g(x,y) := (gx, gy)$) that belong to the class $\overline{G/U_k}$.

For example, the conjugacy classes of subgroups in $G := S_{\underline{3}}$ are represented by the subgroups

$$U_1 := \{1\}, \ U_2 := S_{\underline{2}}, \ U_3 := A_{\underline{3}}, \ U_4 := S_{\underline{3}},$$

and so we obtain the following transversal of the similarity classes of transitive $S_{\underline{3}}$–sets:

$$G/U_1 = S_{\underline{3}}/\{1\}, \ G/U_2 = S_{\underline{3}}/S_{\underline{2}}, \ G/U_3 = S_{\underline{3}}/A_{\underline{3}}, \ G/U_4 = S_{\underline{3}}/S_{\underline{3}},$$

which are of order 6,3,2,1, respectively. It is easy to check that $S_{\underline{3}}$ acts, for example, transitively on $G/U_2 \times G/U_3$, so we obtain (already by checking cardinalities) that

$$\overline{G/U_2} \cdot \overline{G/U_3} = \overline{G/U_2 \times G/U_3} = \overline{G/U_1}.$$

3.6.3 Theorem *The following mapping defines an embedding of the ring* $(\mathbb{Z}^{\Omega}, +, \cdot)$ *into the ring* $\mathbb{Z}_G^{L(G),\wedge}$:

$$\mathbb{Z}^{\Omega} \hookrightarrow \mathbb{Z}_G^{L(G),\wedge} : \overline{G/U_i} \mapsto |N_G(U_i) : U_i| u_i,$$

where

$$u_i := \sum_{U \in \widetilde{U}_i} U \in \mathbb{Z}_G^{L(G),\wedge}.$$

Proof: The structure constants of $\mathbb{Z}^{\Omega}$ were denoted by b_{ijk}, while the structure constants of $\mathbb{Z}_G^{L(G),\wedge}$ are the $a_{ijk}^{\wedge}$ introduced in 3.4.9. It therefore remains to prove the following equation:

$$b_{ijk} = \frac{|N_G(U_i)/U_i||N_G(U_j)/U_j|}{|N_G(U_k)/U_k|} a_{ijk}^{\wedge}.$$

Since $|\widetilde{U}_k| = |G/N_G(U_k)|$ we have

$$b_{ijk} = \frac{1}{|G/U_k|} |\{(x,y) \in G/U_i \times G/U_j \mid G_{(x,y)} \in \widetilde{U}_k\}|$$

$$= \frac{|\widetilde{U}_k|}{|G/U_k|} |\{(x,y) \in G/U_i \times G/U_j \mid G_{(x,y)} = G_x \cap G_y = U_k\}|$$

$$= \frac{|U_k|}{|N_G(U_k)|} |\{(U,V) \in \widetilde{U}_i \times \widetilde{U}_j \mid U \cap V = U_k\}| \frac{|N_G(U_i)||N_G(U_j)|}{|U_i||U_j|}$$

$$= \frac{|N_G(U_i)/U_i||N_G(U_j)/U_j|}{|N_G(U_k)/U_k|} a_{ijk}^{\wedge}.$$

$\square$

This shows in particular that

$$\Omega(G) := (\mathbb{Z}^{\Omega}, +, \cdot)$$

is a ring which we call the *Burnside ring* of G. The table of marks $M(G)$ of G is closely related to the table $A^{\wedge} = (a_{ik}^{\wedge})$ of $\mathbb{Z}_G^{L(G),\wedge}$:

3.6.4 Theorem *The matrix $A^{\wedge}$ of $\mathbb{Z}_G^{L(G),\wedge}$ and the table $M(G)$ of marks of G satisfy the equation*

$$M(G) = A^{\wedge} \cdot \begin{pmatrix} \ddots & & 0 \\ & |N_G(U_k)/U_k| & \\ 0 & & \ddots \end{pmatrix}.$$

Proof: Using 3.2.1 and 3.4.6 we obtain:

$$m_{ik} = \frac{|G/U_k|}{|\widetilde{U}_k|}|\{V \in \widetilde{U}_k \mid U_i \le V\}| = |N_G(U_k)/U_k|a_{ik}^{\wedge}.$$

$\square$

We have just seen how the Burnside ring $\Omega(G)$ can be embedded into $\mathbb{Z}_G^{L(G),\wedge}$, and we already know from 3.4.10 that $\mathbb{Z}_G^{L(G),\wedge}$ is isomorphic to $\mathbb{Z}^{\underline{d}}$ via $u_i \mapsto a_i^{\wedge}$ so that we finally obtain

3.6.5 Corollary *The following mapping linearly extends to an embedding of rings:*

$$\varepsilon : \Omega(G) \hookrightarrow \mathbb{Z}^{\underline{d}} : \overline{G/U_k} \mapsto \mu_k := \begin{pmatrix} m_{1k} \\ \vdots \\ m_{dk} \end{pmatrix}.$$

We call these columns μ_k of $M(G)$ the *marks* of G.

In this way *we can identify the finite G–sets with the* $\mathbb{N}$*–linear combinations of the marks of G*. As 3.6.5 describes an embedding of rings, to the product in $\Omega(G)$ there corresponds the pointwise product in $\mathbb{Z}^{\underline{d}}$:

3.6.6 $\varepsilon(\overline{G/U_i \cdot G/U_j}) = \mu_i \cdot \mu_j.$

Restricting attention to the *i*-th coordinate we obtain the mapping

$$\varepsilon_i : \Omega(G) \to \mathbb{Z} : \overline{X} \mapsto |X_{U_i}|,$$

and 3.6.5 says that ε_i is a homomorphism. Correspondingly we obtain, for *any* subgroup U of G, a *canonical homomorphism*

$$\varepsilon_U : \Omega(G) \to \mathbb{Z} : \overline{X} \mapsto |X_U|.$$

But note that the number of U–invariants $\varepsilon_U(\overline{X}) = |X_U|$ is *not* the desired coefficient of $\overline{G/U}$, when we express $\overline{X}$ as a $\mathbb{Z}$–linear combination of similarity classes $\overline{G/U_i}$ of transitive G–sets:

$$\overline{X} = \sum_{i=1}^{d} |\widetilde{U}_i \backslash\!\backslash\!\backslash X| \cdot \overline{G/U_i}.$$

But there is a certain case when $|\widetilde{U}_i \backslash\!\backslash\!\backslash X|$ can be obtained directly from $\varepsilon_U(\overline{X})$: The equation 3.1.2 shows that the following is true:

3.6.7 Lemma *The subgroup* $U \in \tilde{U}_i$ *is maximal such that* $\varepsilon_U(\overline{X}) \neq 0$ *if and only if it is maximal such that* $|\tilde{U}_i \backslash\backslash\backslash X| \neq 0$, *and in this case we have*

$$\varepsilon_U(\overline{X}) = |X_U| = |\tilde{U}\backslash\backslash\backslash X||N_G(U)/U|.$$

Let us apply this to an example. Later on we shall use it in the proof of an astonishing theorem that leads to important applications.

3.6.8 Example Consider the set of mappings f from G to $\underline{n}$ which are of fixed weight t (we now use as weight the sum of the values!):

$$\underline{n}_t^G := \{f : G \to \underline{n} \mid \sum f(g) = t\}.$$

It is easy to check that $f \in \underline{n}_t^G$ remains fixed under each $g \in U$ if and only if f is constant on the right cosets of U. Hence such an invariant f takes each of its values with a multiplicity that is divisible by $|U|$, therefore $|U|$ divides t, and the invariants $f \in \underline{n}_t^G$ are in one-to-one correspondence with the elements of $\underline{n}_{t/|U|}^{G/U}$. The order of this last set follows from exercise 1.7.3, and so we obtain

$$\varepsilon_U(\overline{\underline{n}_t^G}) = \binom{|G/U| + t/|U| - 1}{t/|U|}.$$

In particular, if $|U| = t$, then $\varepsilon_U(\overline{\underline{n}_t^G}) = |G/U|$, and we can apply 3.6.7, obtaining

$$U \in \tilde{U}_i, |U| = t \Longrightarrow |\tilde{U}_i \backslash\backslash\backslash \underline{n}_t^G| = |\tilde{U}_i|.$$

In the case when the acting group is cyclic, these particular elements form a basis of the Burnside ring (see exercise 3.6.2 for another basis):

3.6.9 Lemma *The Burnside ring* $\Omega(C_n)$ *has the following* $\mathbb{Z}$–*basis:*

$$\{\overline{\underline{n}_t^{C_n}} \mid t \text{ divides } n\}.$$

Proof: We denote by $C(s)$ the unique subgroup of order s in C_n, for each divisor s of n. The matrix (n_{st}) of the coefficients in

$$\overline{\underline{n}_t^{C_n}} = \sum_{s|n} n_{st} \overline{C_n/C(s)}$$

is triangular with ones along their main diagonal, and hence invertible over $\mathbb{Z}$, which proves the statement.   ◇

We recall that

$$\varepsilon_{U_i}(\overline{G/U_k}) = \varepsilon_i(\overline{G/U_k}) = m_{ik},$$

and so $\varepsilon_U = \varepsilon_V$ if and only if U and V are conjugate. Moreover,

$$\varepsilon_i(\overline{X}) = \varepsilon_i(\sum_k |\tilde{U}_k \backslash\!\backslash\!\backslash X| \overline{G/U_k}) = \sum_k |\tilde{U}_k \backslash\!\backslash\!\backslash X| m_{ik},$$

which shows that the desired numbers $|\tilde{U}_k \backslash\!\backslash\!\backslash X|$ can be obtained from the numbers $\varepsilon_i(\overline{X})$, since the table of marks is not singular. Hence we have proved

3.6.10 Corollary *We can identify the element $\overline{X}$ of the Burnside ring $\Omega(G)$ with the mapping $U \mapsto \varepsilon_U(\overline{X})$, obtaining an embedding of $\Omega(G)$ into the following ring which is called the* ghost ring *of G:*

$$\tilde{\Omega}(G) := \mathbb{Z}_{\sim}^{L(G)} := \{f \in \mathbb{Z}^{L(G)} \mid f \text{ constant on each conjugacy class}\}.$$

The ghost ring $\tilde{\Omega}(C_n)$ of the cyclic group is equal to the Burnside ring of C_n, since C_n is abelian. Moreover, as C_n contains just one subgroup of order t, for each divisor t of n, both rings can be identified in a canonical way with $\mathbb{Z}^{T(n)}$, if $T(n)$ denotes the set of divisors of n. This leads to a canonic map into the ghost ring of G via the function *card* that maps $U \in L(G)$ onto its cardinality:

$$\alpha: \mathbb{Z}^{T(|G|)} \to \mathbb{Z}_{\sim}^{L(G)}: f \mapsto f \circ card.$$

The crucial point is that this map is a *ring homomorphism*, which is clear from the following: First of all we know from 3.6.8 that, if $n := |G|$, then, if $C(|G|)$ denotes the cyclic group of order $|G|$:

$$\varepsilon_U(\underline{n}_t^G) = \varepsilon_{C(|U|)}(\underline{n}_t^{C(|G|)}).$$

This together with 3.6.7 implies

$$\alpha(\underline{n}_t^{C(|G|)}) = \underline{n}_t^G.$$

Finally we use that ε is a ring homomorphism, and therefore the following map must extend to a ring homomorphism:

$$\underline{n}_t^{C(|G|)} \mapsto \underline{n}_t^G.$$

Thus we have proved the following important result:

3.6.11 Theorem (Dress, Siebeneicher, Yoshida) *If G is a finite group of order n, then*

$$\alpha : \Omega(C(|G|)) \to \Omega(G) : f \mapsto f \circ card,$$

is a ring homomorphism such that, for each finite $C(|G|)$–set X and any subgroup U of G we have

$$\varepsilon_U(\alpha(\overline{X})) = \varepsilon_{C(|U|)}(\overline{X}).$$

For example,

$$\varepsilon_{C(t')}(\overline{C_{\underline{n}}/C(n/t)}) = \begin{cases} t & \text{if } C(t') \subseteq C(n/t) \\ 0 & \text{otherwise.} \end{cases}$$

Hence, by the theorem,

$$\varepsilon_U(\alpha(\overline{C_{\underline{n}}/C(n/t)})) = \begin{cases} t & \text{if } t \text{ divides } |G|/|U| \\ 0 & \text{otherwise.} \end{cases}$$

An application of 3.6.7 now shows that

$$|\widetilde{U}_i \backslash\!\backslash\!\backslash \alpha(\overline{C_{\underline{n}}/C(n/t)})| = \begin{cases} |\widetilde{U}| & \text{if } t = |G/U| \\ 0 & \text{if } t \text{ does not divide } |G|/|U|. \end{cases}$$

3.6.12 Corollary *For each divisor t of $|G|$ there exists a G–set X_t, for which*

$$\varepsilon_U(\overline{X_t}) = \begin{cases} t & \text{if } t \text{ divides } |G/U| \\ 0 & \text{otherwise,} \end{cases}$$

and therefore

$$|\widetilde{U}_i \backslash\!\backslash\!\backslash X_t| = \begin{cases} |\widetilde{U}_i| & \text{if } t = |G/U_i| \\ 0 & \text{if } t \text{ does not divide } |G/U_i|. \end{cases}$$

This G–set X_t is of order t.

Beautiful applications are the following proofs (due to B. Wagner and Dress/Siebeneicher/Yoshida) of Sylow's theorems: From 3.6.12 we derive that

$$t = \sum_{i: t \text{ divides } |G/U_i|} |\widetilde{U}_i \backslash\!\backslash\!\backslash X_t||G/U_i| \in \sum_{i: t \text{ divides } |G/U_i|} \mathbb{Z} \cdot |G/U_i|.$$

This shows that t is the greatest common divisor of the indices $|G/U_i|$ which are divisible by t. Hence, if $|G|$ is t times a prime power p^r, *there must exist a subgroup of order p^r.*

Dividing this equation by t and then reducing modulo p we obtain

$$1 \equiv |\{U \leq G \mid |U| = p^r\}| \ (p),$$

obtaining that *the number of subgroups of order p^r is congruent 1 modulo p*. The remaining Sylow theorem that each p–subgroup is subconjugate to each p–Sylow subgroup is left as exercise 3.6.4.

Exercises

E 3.6.1 Prove 3.6.1.

E 3.6.2 Show that also the following set is a $\mathbb{Z}$–basis of $\Omega(C_{\underline{n}})$:

$$\{ \overline{\binom{C_{\underline{n}}}{t}} \mid t \text{ divides } n \}.$$

E 3.6.3 Prove that for G–sets X of p–groups G the following congruence is true (if $U_d = G$):

$$\varepsilon_1(\overline{X}) \equiv n_d(\overline{X}) = \varepsilon_G(\overline{X}) \ (p).$$

E 3.6.4 Use exercise 3.6.3 in order to derive that, for any p–Sylow subgroup P and each p–subgroup U, there exists a subgroup V of P which is conjugate to U. (Hint: Consider a p–subgroup V, a subgroup U for which p does not divide $|G/U|$, and examine $\varepsilon_V(\overline{G/U})$.)

Chapter 4

Representations

It will turn out to be useful to refine the preceding considerations of permutation representations. We consider linear representations on corresponding vector spaces and decompose them into their irreducible constituents. Having done this we can use all what is known on ordinary irreducible representations of finite groups, in particular we can use the results on ordinary representation theory of symmetric groups which will give us further insight into the problems.

For this purpose a self–contained introduction to the theory of ordinary representations of finite groups is given. Afterwards a problem–oriented introduction to the representation theory of finite symmetric groups is provided. It is based on symmetric and alternating group actions which yield two sequences of set theoretic bijections, so that the fundamental results can be formulated in terms of orbits, in terms of double cosets, in terms of matrices with natural entries and prescribed row and column sums, in terms of standard tableaux, and, last not least, in terms of standard bitableaux, which are polynomials.

This approach is carried through until we reach the point, where irreducible matrix representations can be evaluated. They allow to calculate symmetry adapted bases for vector spaces on which finite group representations act. The corresponding decompositions of vector spaces are analogous to the decomposition of sets on which finite groups act into their orbits.

4.1   Linear representations

We embed the notion of finite action into a more general concept
in order to reach a position which allows a finer analysis. Orbits
will be replaced by subspaces of a vector space and these may then
decompose into smaller subspaces.

Recall that a finite action $_G X$ is essentially the same as a certain
permutation representation of G on X, namely the homomorphism

$$\delta : G \to S_X : g \mapsto (x \mapsto gx)$$

from G into the symmetric group S_X on X.

Now we consider, for an arbitrary field $\mathbb{F}$, the free vector space over $\mathbb{F}$
with basis X, i.e. we consider $\mathbb{F}^X = \{f : X \to \mathbb{F}\}$. The linear mapping

$$D(g) : \mathbb{F}^X \to \mathbb{F}^X : f \mapsto f \circ g^{-1}$$

generalizes $\delta(g)$ since $D(g)$ permutes the basis X in the same way as
$\delta(g)$ does with the set X. After having numbered the basis elements
$x_1, \ldots, x_{|X|}$, we obtain a matrix which represents this linear mapping:

$$\mathbf{D}(g) := (d_{ik}(g)), \text{ where } d_{ik}(g) := \begin{cases} 1 & \text{if } gx_k = x_i, \\ 0 & \text{otherwise.} \end{cases}$$

(Such matrices are called *permutation matrices* since they describe
permutations of the basis.)

This shows that the notions of finite group action and that of permutation representation are particular cases of the general concept of
linear representation of finite groups, for a *linear representation D* of
G over a field $\mathbb{F}$ is defined to be a homomorphism D from G into
the group $GL(V)$ of invertible linear mappings of a finite dimensional
vector space V over $\mathbb{F}$ onto itself. The vector space V is called the
representation space and its dimension d is also called the *dimension*
of D.

Two representations $D : G \to GL(V)$ and $D' : G \to GL(V')$ of G over $\mathbb{F}$
are considered to be essentially the same and are called *equivalent* if
and only if there exists an invertible linear $T : V \to V'$ such that

$$\forall \, g \in G : \; TD(g) = D'(g)T.$$

Each choice of a basis $B = \{b_1, \ldots, b_d\}$ yields invertible matrices
$\mathbf{D}(g)$ which describe the $D(g)$ with respect to B. Therefore a *matrix
representation $\mathbf{D}$* of G over $\mathbb{F}$ is defined to be a homomorphism from

G into a *general linear group* $GL(d,\mathbb{F})$, the group consisting of all the invertible matrices over $\mathbb{F}$ with d rows and columns. It is clear that conversely each matrix representation $\mathbf{D}:G \to GL(d,\mathbb{F})$ yields a representation $D:G \to GL(V)$, V being the d–dimensional vector space $\mathbb{F}^{\underline{d}}$ over $\mathbb{F}$. Equivalence of matrix representations is defined correspondingly, so that we are free to consider either representations or matrix representations. Which concept we choose will depend on the situation in question.

We already have a wealth of examples at hand since each finite action $_GX$ yields a representation as described above. The trivial representation of G arising from the *trivial action* $_G\{x\}$ of G on a one element set $\{x\}$, where $gx := x$, is called the *identity representation* and it is indicated as follows:

$$IG: G \to GL(\mathbb{F}): g \mapsto id_{\mathbb{F}},$$

where $\mathbb{F}$ is the 1–dimensional vector space over $\mathbb{F}$.

Furthermore there are several ways to get new representations from old ones. For example $D:G \to GL(V)$ and $D':G \to GL(V')$ yield the *sum* $D + D'$ which we can define by giving a corresponding matrix representation $\mathbf{D} + \mathbf{D}'$, arising from $\mathbf{D}$ and $\mathbf{D}'$ as follows:

$$(\mathbf{D} + \mathbf{D}')(g) := \begin{pmatrix} \mathbf{D}(g) & 0 \\ 0 & \mathbf{D}'(g) \end{pmatrix}.$$

We can also form the *inner tensor product* $D \otimes D'$, corresponding to $\mathbf{D} \otimes \mathbf{D}'$ which is defined by

$$(\mathbf{D} \otimes \mathbf{D}')(g) := \begin{pmatrix} d_{11}(g)\mathbf{D}'(g) & d_{12}(g)\mathbf{D}'(g) & \cdots \\ d_{21}(g)\mathbf{D}'(g) & d_{22}(g)\mathbf{D}'(g) & \cdots \\ \cdots & \cdots & \cdots \end{pmatrix}.$$

This matrix is called the *Kronecker product* of the matrices $\mathbf{D}(g)$ and $\mathbf{D}'(g)$ and it is denoted by $\mathbf{D}(g) \otimes \mathbf{D}'(g)$. This product of matrices can also be used to define the *outer tensor product* $D\#D'$ of D of G and D' of G', which is a representation of the direct product $G \times G'$ and which has as one of its corresponding matrix representations the matrix representation $\mathbf{D}\#\mathbf{D}'$, the representing matrices $(\mathbf{D}\#\mathbf{D}')(g,g')$ of which are defined to be

$$\mathbf{D}(g) \otimes \mathbf{D}'(g') := \begin{pmatrix} d_{11}(g)\mathbf{D}'(g') & d_{12}(g)\mathbf{D}'(g') & \cdots \\ d_{21}(g)\mathbf{D}'(g') & d_{22}(g)\mathbf{D}'(g') & \cdots \\ \cdots & \cdots & \cdots \end{pmatrix}.$$

Besides these constructions we can get a representation $D \downarrow H$ of $H \leq G$ by restricting a representation D of G to the subgroup H:

$$D \downarrow H(h) := D(h)$$

is called the *restriction* of D to H. Conversely we can *induce* from a representation D of a subgroup $H \leq G$ obtaining the *induced representation* $D \uparrow G$ of G as follows: Take a corresponding matrix representation $\mathbf{D}$ of H and consider a decomposition of G into left cosets of H, say

$$G = \bigcup_{i=1}^{|G/H|} g_i H.$$

Then we put

$$\mathbf{D} \uparrow G(g) := \begin{pmatrix} & \vdots & \\ \cdots & \dot{\mathbf{D}}(g_i^{-1} g g_k) & \cdots \\ & \vdots & \end{pmatrix},$$

where

$$\dot{\mathbf{D}}(g_i^{-1} g g_k) := \begin{cases} \mathbf{D}(g_i^{-1} g g_k) & \text{if } g_i^{-1} g g_k \in H, \\ \text{zero matrix} & \text{otherwise.} \end{cases}$$

For our purposes here it is very important to notice that *the particular representation* $IH \uparrow G$ *of* G, *induced by the identity representation* IH *of the subgroup* $H \leq G$, *is equivalent to the representation* D *of* G *which corresponds to the action* $_G(G/H)$ as is described at the beginning of this section. This follows from the fact that $g g_k H = g_i H$ is equivalent to $g_i^{-1} g g_k \in H$. Further constructions will be discussed later.

The representation $D: G \to GL(V)$ and also V is called *reducible* if and only if there exists a subspace W such that $\{0_V\} \neq W \neq V$ and

$$\forall g \in G : D(g)[W] = W,$$

i.e. if and only if there exists a nontrivial *G–invariant subspace* W of V. Otherwise D and V are called *irreducible* . The restriction of D to such an invariant subspace W of V is denoted by

$$D|_W.$$

It is a representation of G and called a *subrepresentation* of D. We can choose a basis $B = \{b_1, \ldots, b_d\}$ of V which is *adapted* to W, i.e.

the subset $\{b_1,\ldots,b_e\} \subseteq B$ is a basis of W. The corresponding matrix representation $\mathbf{D}$ then takes the form

$$\mathbf{D}(g) = \begin{pmatrix} \mathbf{D}_1(g) & \star \\ 0 & \mathbf{D}_2(g) \end{pmatrix},$$

where $\mathbf{D}_1 : g \mapsto \mathbf{D}_1(g)$ is an e–dimensional matrix representation of G which is in fact the restriction of $\mathbf{D}$ to W:

$$\mathbf{D}_1 = \mathbf{D}|_W.$$

But also $\mathbf{D}_2$ is a matrix representation of G, namely on the factor space V/W. The representation $\mathbf{D}_2$ is irreducible if and only if W is a maximal invariant subspace of V and hence, since d is finite, we can find a finite chain of subspaces W_i of V such that

$$V = W_0 \supset W_1 \supset \ldots \supset W_k = \{0_V\},$$

and where W_i is a maximal invariant subspace of $W_{i-1}, 1 \leq i \leq k+1$. The matrix representation $\mathbf{D}^{(i)}$ of G corresponding to W_{i-1}/W_i is irreducible, and for a suitable basis B of V, $\mathbf{D}$ takes the form

$$\mathbf{D}(g) = \begin{pmatrix} \mathbf{D}^{(k)}(g) & & & \star \\ & \ddots & & \\ 0 & & \ddots & \\ & & & \mathbf{D}^{(1)}(g) \end{pmatrix}.$$

The $D^{(i)}$ are uniquely determined up to equivalence and order of occurrence, they are called the *irreducible constituents* of D. This follows from the *Jordan–Hölder Theorem* for any D and any ground field $\mathbb{F}$. We do not give a proof of this theorem since for the particular case in which we are interested, there is an easier proof.

From now on we restrict our attention to linear representations of finite groups G over the complex field $\mathbb{C}$. Such representations are called ordinary representations of G.

Our first observation concerns the decomposition of ordinary representations into irreducible representations. We show that such decompositions are direct decompositions for a suitable choice of basis. Let $D : G \to GL(V)$ denote an ordinary representation of G on V. As we know already from linear algebra, each finite dimensional vector space V over $\mathbb{C}$ carries, for any basis $B = \{b_1, \ldots, b_d\}$, the hermitian inner product

$$\langle -, - \rangle : V^2 \to \mathbb{C} : (u, v) \mapsto \sum u_i \bar{v}_i.$$

Using such an inner product on V and the representation D of G on V, we can define

$$(- \mid -) : V^2 \to \mathbb{C} : (u, v) \mapsto \sum_g \langle D(g)u, D(g)v \rangle.$$

It is easy to check that this is also an hermitian inner product, and that it has the further property

4.1.1 $\forall\, g \in G\ \forall\, u, v \in V : (u \mid v) = (D(g)u \mid D(g)v).$

This has the remarkable consequence that the orthogonal complement $W^\perp$ (with respect to $(- \mid -)$) of a G–invariant subspace W of V is also G–invariant. Since $v \neq 0$ implies that $(v \mid v) \neq 0$ it follows that the sum $W + W^\perp$ is direct, and so a basis of V which is adapted to this decomposition $V = W \oplus W^\perp$ yields a matrix representation corresponding to D which *splits* :

$$\mathbf{D}(g) = \begin{pmatrix} \mathbf{D}_1(g) & 0 \\ 0 & \mathbf{D}_2(g) \end{pmatrix}.$$

where $\mathbf{D}_1 = \mathbf{D}|_W, \mathbf{D}_2 = \mathbf{D}|_{W^\perp}$. This proves

4.1.2 Maschke's Theorem *Each ordinary representation of a finite group splits into a direct sum of irreducible representations.*

Furthermore we can construct a basis of V which is orthonormal with respect to $(- \mid -)$. It is easy to check that a corresponding matrix representation $\mathbf{D}$ consists of unitary matrices $\mathbf{D}(g)$. Thus we have also proved

4.1.3 Theorem *Each ordinary representation of a finite group is equivalent to a unitary matrix representation.*

Our next aim is to prove that a decomposition of an ordinary representation into irreducible ones, which is direct by Maschke's Theorem, is also unique in the sense that the irreducible constituents $D^{(i)}$ are uniquely determined up to equivalence and order of occurrence. We first prove

4.1.4 Schur's Lemma *Let* $D: G \to GL(V)$ *and* $D': G \to GL(V')$ *denote ordinary irreducible representations of G and assume that* $T: V \to V'$ *is an* intertwining *operator, which means a linear mapping satisfying* $TD(g) = D'(g)T$, *for each* $g \in G$. *Then the following is true:*

- *If D is not equivalent to* D', *then* $T = 0$.
- *If D is equal to* D', *then T is a multiple of the identity mapping.*
- *If D is equivalent to* D', *say* $D'(g) = SD(g)S^{-1}$, *for each g and a suitable* $\mathbb{C}$–*isomorphism* $S: V \simeq V'$, *then T is a multiple of S.*

Proof: It is easy to check that both the kernel and the image of T are G–invariant subspaces of V and V', respectively. Hence
i) if $T \neq 0$, then $T[V] = V'$, since D' is irreducible, and therefore D is equivalent to D'.
ii) Let us now assume that $D = D'$, so that T is an endomorphism of $V = V'$. As $\mathbb{C}$ is the ground field, there exists an eigenvalue of T, say λ. Thus $T' := T - \lambda \cdot id$ has a nonzero kernel. Because of $T'D(g) = D'(g)T'$, for every $g \in G$, and the irreduciblity of V, this kernel, being G–invariant and nonzero, must be V, so that $T' = 0$ and consequently $T = \lambda \cdot id$.
iii) Finally if D is equivalent to D', say $D'(g) = SD(g)S^{-1}$, then we have that $T^{-1}SD(g)S^{-1}T = D(g)$, for each g, and so, by ii), $T^{-1}S$ is a multiple of the identity mapping, which completes the proof.
□

We can construct such an intertwining operator T from every linear mapping $t: V \to V'$ simply by putting

$$T := \frac{1}{|G|} \sum_{g \in G} D'(g^{-1})tD(g),$$

since $D'(x^{-1})TD(x) = T$, for each $x \in G$. In terms of elements of representing matrices we have:

$$T_{il} = \frac{1}{|G|} \sum_{g} \sum_{j,k} d'_{ij}(g^{-1})t_{jk}d_{kl}(g).$$

Thus Schur's Lemma gives:

4.1.5 Schur's Relations *For any* $t_{jk} \in \mathbb{C}$ *and ordinary irreducible matrix representations* **D** *and* **D′** *of G we have, for any* i, l *and* $d := dim D$:

$$\frac{1}{|G|} \sum_{g} \sum_{j,k} d'_{ij}(g^{-1})t_{jk}d_{kl}(g) = \begin{cases} 0 & \mathbf{D}, \mathbf{D'} \text{ inequivalent}, \\ \delta_{il}d^{-1} \sum_j t_{jj} & \text{if } \mathbf{D} = \mathbf{D'}. \end{cases}$$

Exercises

E 4.1.1 Find out where in the above proof of Maschke's theorem we made use of the fact that the groundfield is of characteristic 0.

E 4.1.2 Show that the mapping

$$\mathbf{D}: C_{\underline{p}} \to GL(2, GF(p)): (1 \ldots p)^i \mapsto \begin{pmatrix} 1 & 1 \\ 0 & 1 \end{pmatrix}^i,$$

p a prime, defines a reducible matrix representation which does not split.

E 4.1.3 Assume that the normal subgroup N of a finite group G is contained in the kernel of the representation D of G.

- Check that $\widetilde{D}(Ng) := D(g)$ defines a representation of the factor group G/N.
- Prove that $\widetilde{D}$ is irreducible if and only if D is.

E 4.1.4 Let G denote a finite group. Its *commutator subgroup* G' is defined to be the subgroup *generated* by the *commutators*, i.e. by the elements of the form $xyx^{-1}y^{-1}$, for $x, y \in G$.

- Prove that G' is the smallest normal subgroup of G such that the corresponding factor group is abelian.
- Show that G' is the kernel intersection of the 1-dimensional representations of G.
- Verify that $|G/G'|$ is the number of 1–dimensional representations of G.

E 4.1.5 Prove that $A_{\underline{n}}$ is the commutator subgroup of $S_{\underline{n}}$ and moreover that each element of $A_{\underline{n}}$ is itself a commutator.

E 4.1.6 How many onedimensional representations of $S_{\underline{n}}$ exist?

E 4.1.7 Use the fact that $A_{\underline{n}}$ is the only nontrivial proper normal subgroup of $S_{\underline{n}}$, if $n \neq 4$, in order to show that each irreducible representation of $S_{\underline{n}}$, $n \neq 4$, of dimension $\neq 1$ is *faithful*, i.e. it has kernel $\{1\}$.

E 4.1.8 Show that for subgroups U and H of a finite group G such that $U \leq H$ and any representation D of U we have

$$D \uparrow G = (D \uparrow H) \uparrow G$$

(in short: the induction of representations is *transitive*, a notion which must not be confused with the transitivity of actions).

4.2 Ordinary characters of finite groups

·We now apply the preceding results to

$$\chi^D : G \to \mathbb{C} : g \mapsto \operatorname{tr} D(g) = \sum_i d_{ii}(g),$$

which maps $g \in G$ onto the trace of $D(g)$. The map χ^D is called the *character* of D. In fact D is characterized by its character in the sense that we shall be able to derive from it the irreducible constituents of D, which in turn characterize D.

4.2.1 Lemma *For any finite groups G, G'', ordinary representations D, D' of G and D'' of G'' and their characters we have:*

- $\chi^D(1_G) = d = \dim D$, $\chi^D(g^{-1}) = \overline{\chi^D(g)}$, *the complex conjugate of* $\chi^D(g)$, *and $\chi^D(g)$ is a sum of complex roots of unity.*

- $\chi^D(gg'g^{-1}) = \chi^D(g')$, *for any $g, g' \in G$, i.e. χ^D is constant on each conjugacy class of elements of G, in short: χ^D is a "class function".*

- $\chi^D = \chi^{D'}$, *if D is equivalent to D'.*

- $\chi^{D \dotplus D'} = \chi^D + \chi^{D'}$, *i.e. $\chi^{D \dotplus D'}(g) = \chi^D(g) + \chi^{D'}(g)$.*

- $\chi^{D \otimes D'} = \chi^D \chi^{D'}$, *i.e. $\chi^{D \otimes D'}(g) = \chi^D(g) \chi^{D'}(g)$.*

- $\chi^{D \# D''} = \chi^D \chi^{D''}$, *i.e. $\chi^{D \# D''}(g, g'') = \chi^D(g) \chi^{D''}(g'')$.*

Proof: These statements are trivial except for the second and third part of the first statement. The second part follows from 4.1.3. For the third part we use the fact that $D(1) = D(g^{|\langle g \rangle|}) = D(g)^{|\langle g \rangle|}$ and that the eigenvalues of a power of a matrix are the powers of the eigenvalues of the matrix. □

We define a hermitian inner product on the space $\mathbb{C}^G$ consisting of all the complex valued functions on G, as follows

$$[\varphi \mid \psi] := \frac{1}{|G|} \sum_g \varphi(g)\overline{\psi(g)}.$$

Applying it to irreducible characters, we get the following remarkable result:

4.2.2 Theorem *The ordinary irreducible characters of G form an orthonormal set with respect to* $[- \mid -]$.

Proof: 4.1.5 yields

$$[\chi^D \mid \chi^{D'}] = \sum_{i,k} \frac{1}{|G|} \sum_g d_{ii}(g)d'_{kk}(g^{-1}) = \begin{cases} 1 & \text{if } D, D' \text{ equivalent,} \\ 0 & \text{otherwise.} \end{cases}$$

$\square$

If χ^D is the character of the ordinary representation D, and if $D = D^{(k)} + \ldots + D^{(1)}$ is the decomposition of D into irreducible representations $D^{(j)}$, where exactly a_i of the $D^{(j)}$ are equivalent to an ordinary irreducible representation D_i of G, then, by 4.2.2, this multiplicity is the inner product $[\chi^D \mid \chi^{D_i}] = [\sum a_j\chi^{D_j} \mid \chi^{D_i}] = a_i$. Thus we have proved

4.2.3 Theorem *If D is an ordinary representation of G and D_i an ordinary irreducible representation, then for any decomposition of D into irreducible constituents, the number (D, D_i) of constituents equivalent to D_i is equal to the inner product of the corresponding characters:*

$$(D, D_i) = [\chi^D \mid \chi^{D_i}].$$

This multiplicity of D_i in D is therefore uniquely determined, and so there is essentially one such decomposition only and the multiplicities of the irreducible constituents of D, and hence also χ^D, characterize the equivalence class of D.

We can therefore write

$$D = n_1 D_1 + \ldots + n_r D_r,$$

where n_i is the multiplicity of the irreducible representation D_i in D. It remains to determine the D_i and to show how many of them exist. For this purpose we consider the *regular representation* (cf. 1.1.6) which is induced by the identity representation of the identity subgroup, and which corresponds to the action of G on G via left multiplication:

$$R := I\{1\} \uparrow G.$$

It has the character

$$\chi^R(g) = \begin{cases} |G| & \text{if } g = 1_G, \\ 0 & \text{otherwise.} \end{cases}$$

An application of 4.2.3 to this character yields:

4.2.4 Corollary *The multiplicity of the irreducible representation D_i of G in the regular representation is equal to the dimension d_i of D_i:*

$$(R, D_i) = d_i.$$

We are now in a position to evaluate the number of (equivalence classes of) ordinary irreducible representations of G. Lemma 4.2.1 together with theorem 4.2.2 shows that there are at most as many ordinary irreducible representations as there are classes of conjugate elements in G. We would like to show that this is the exact number. In order to do this we introduce, for each representation $D: G \to GL(V)$ and any $\varphi: G \to \mathbb{C}$ the following linear mapping on V:

$$D^\varphi := \sum_g \overline{\varphi(g)} D(g).$$

4.2.5 Lemma *If D is irreducible and φ a class function, then*

$$D^\varphi = \frac{|G|}{d} [\chi^D \mid \varphi] \cdot \text{id.}$$

Proof: A direct calculation shows that D^φ commutes with every $D(g)$, so that $D^\varphi = \lambda \cdot id$, by Schur's Lemma. But

$$\lambda \cdot d = \text{tr } (D^\varphi) = \sum_g \overline{\varphi(g)} \text{tr } (D(g)) = |G| [\chi^D \mid \varphi].$$

$\square$

4.2.6 Theorem *The space $CF(G, \mathbb{C})$ of all the complex valued class functions on G has the ordinary irreducible characters of G as an orthogonal basis. Hence the number of conjugacy classes of elements of G, i.e. the dimension of $CF(G, \mathbb{C})$, is equal to the number of ordinary irreducible characters of G.*

Proof: By 4.2.2 it remains to prove that the subspace V of $CF(G, \mathbb{C})$ generated by the ordinary irreducible characters is in fact equal to $CF(G, \mathbb{C})$. Let φ be in the orthogonal complement $V^\perp$ of V. Then, by 4.2.5, $D^\varphi = 0$, for each irreducible representation D. Thus, for the regular representation R of G, we have $R^\varphi = \sum_i d_i D_i^\varphi = 0$, the zero mapping. But, on the other hand, as R is a mapping from G into $GL(\mathbb{C}^G)$, the general linear group of the vector space $\mathbb{C}^G$, and since $\mathbb{C}^G$ has the elements of G as a basis, we obtain:

$$R^\varphi 1_G = \sum_g \overline{\varphi(g)} R(g) 1_G = \sum_g \overline{\varphi(g)} g.$$

We therefore obtain $\overline{\varphi(g)} = 0$, for each $g \in G$, and so $V^\perp = \{0\}$ and $V = CF(G, \mathbb{C})$.

□

In the sequel we shall denote the ordinary irreducible characters of G by ζ^i and we shall mean by ζ_k^i the value of ζ^i on the k-th conjugacy class of G. Furthermore we shall assume that ζ^1 is the character of the identity representation $D_1 = I$, and that the first conjugacy class is the one that consists of the identity element alone, so that $\zeta_1^i = d_i$, the dimension. Then the *character table*

$$Z(G) := (\zeta_k^i), 1 \le i, k \le r := \text{number of conjugacy classes},$$

contains in its first row only 1's, and in its first column the dimensions d_i of the ordinary irreducible representations:

$$Z(G) = \begin{pmatrix} d_1 = 1 & \cdots & 1 \\ \vdots & & \\ d_i & \star & \\ \vdots & & \\ d_r & & \end{pmatrix}.$$

4.2.7 The second orthogonality relation *For a finite group G, its irreducible characters $\zeta^i, i = 1, \ldots, r$, and elements $g, g' \in G$ we have*

$$\sum_{i=1}^r \zeta^i(g') \zeta^i(g^{-1}) = \begin{cases} |C_G(g)| & \text{if } g \text{ and } g' \text{ are conjugate elements,} \\ 0 & \text{otherwise.} \end{cases}$$

Proof: Consider the function $\chi: G \to \mathbb{C}$ which is characteristic for the conjugacy class $C^G(g)$ of g, i.e. which has value 1 on $C^G(g)$ and zero elsewhere. Then $\chi = \sum_i a_i \zeta^i$, where $a_i = [\chi \mid \zeta^i] = |C^G(g)| \cdot |G|^{-1} \overline{\zeta^i(g)}$. We obtain

$$\chi(g') = \sum_i a_i \zeta^i(g') = \frac{|C^G(g)|}{|G|} \sum_i \zeta^i(g') \zeta^i(g^{-1}),$$

which yields the statement.

□

Later we shall need a formula for the evaluation of the induced character. Assume that $H \leq G = \dot{\cup}_i g_i H$ and that χ is a character of H. The definition of induced representation yields

4.2.8 $\quad \chi \uparrow G(g) = \sum_i \dot\chi(g_i^{-1} g g_i),$ where $\dot\chi(g_i^{-1} g g_i) = \operatorname{tr} \dot{\mathbf{D}}(g_i^{-1} g g_i).$

We can express this in terms of conjugacy classes C_i of H and the corresponding values χ_i of χ (exercise 4.2.5):

4.2.9 $\quad \chi \uparrow G(g) = \frac{|G|}{|H|} \sum_{i: C_i \subseteq C^G(g)} \frac{|C_i|}{|C^G(g)|} \chi_i.$

An important particular case is $\chi = \chi^{IH}$, the identity character of H. We get from 4.2.9 that

4.2.10 $\quad \chi^{IH \uparrow G}(g) := \chi^{IH} \uparrow G(g) = \frac{|G||C^G(g) \cap H|}{|H||C^G(g)|}.$

Another application of 4.2.9 yields (exercise 4.2.6):

4.2.11 Frobenius' Reciprocity Law *If $H \leq G$ and if χ is a character of H and ψ is a character of G, then we have the following equality of inner products:*

$$[\chi \uparrow G \mid \psi] = [\chi \mid \psi \downarrow H].$$

Exercises

E 4.2.1 Show that a representation of a finite group G with character χ contains $g \in G$ in its kernel if and only if $\chi(g) = \chi(1_G)$.

E 4.2.2 Rephrase exercise 1.1.3 in terms of characters.

E 4.2.3 Prove that the sum of elements in each row of a character table of a finite group is a nonnegative integer.

E 4.2.4 Consider $G \leq S_{\underline{n}}$ and the set

$$\{k_1, \ldots, k_r\} := \{a_1(g) \mid g \in G \backslash \{1\}\}.$$

Show that $|G|$ divides the product $\prod_{i=1}^{r} (n - k_i)$. (Hint: The mapping $\pi \mapsto \prod (a_1(\pi) - k_i)$ is a class function on G, the inner product of which with each irreducible character lies in $\mathbb{Z}$. Such functions are called *generalized characters*.)

E 4.2.5 Prove 4.2.9.

E 4.2.6 Prove 4.2.11.

E 4.2.7 A finite action $_GX$ is called *k–fold transitive* if and only if the corresponding action $_GX_i^k$ of G on the injective k–tuples is transitive. Show that the character χ of a 2–fold transitive action $_GX$ is of the form $\chi = \zeta^1 + \xi$, where ζ^1 is the identity character and ξ is an irreducible character of G.

E 4.2.8 Use 4.2.10 together with 1.2.2 in order to show that, for each finite group G and its subgroups A and B,

$$|A \backslash G / B| = \left[\chi^{I A \uparrow G} \mid \chi^{I B \uparrow G} \right] = \left[\chi^{I A \uparrow G} \cdot \chi^{I B \uparrow G} \mid \iota \right].$$

4.3 Representations of symmetric groups

We shall characterize the ordinary irreducible representations of finite symmetric groups as constituents of certain permutation representations. In order to do this we introduce the notion of an *improper partition* λ of n, by which we mean a sequence $\lambda := (\lambda_1, \lambda_2, \ldots)$ of natural numbers λ_i such that $\sum_i \lambda_i = n$. We indicate this by writing

$$\lambda \models n.$$

Corresponding to $\lambda \models n$ let $\underline{n}^\lambda$ be a sequence of subsets $\underline{n}_i^\lambda \subseteq \underline{n}, i \in \mathbb{N}^*$, where

$$|\underline{n}_i^\lambda| = \lambda_i, \ i \in \mathbb{N}^*, \text{ and } \underline{n} = \bigcup_i \underline{n}_i^\lambda.$$

Such an $\underline{n}^\lambda$ will be called a *decomposition* of $\underline{n}$ or, more explicitly, a λ–*decomposition* of $\underline{n}$. (Note that this concept is slightly more general than that of a set–partition since now *empty* blocks are allowed.) We consider the direct sum of the symmetric groups of these blocks:

$$S(\underline{n}^\lambda) := S_{\underline{n}_1^\lambda} \oplus S_{\underline{n}_2^\lambda} \oplus \ldots := \{\pi \in S_{\underline{n}} \mid \forall i : \pi\underline{n}_i^\lambda = \underline{n}_i^\lambda\},$$

which is obviously isomorphic to the direct product $S_{\lambda_1} \times S_{\lambda_2} \times \ldots$. (Recall that $S_0 = \{1\}$.) These groups are called *Young subgroups*. We can also directly associate with $\lambda \models n$ a *canonic decomposition* $\underline{n}^\lambda$ by putting

$$\underline{n}_i^\lambda := \{\sum_{j=1}^{i-1} \lambda_j + 1, \ldots, \sum_{j=1}^{i} \lambda_j\}.$$

The corresponding Young subgroup will be called the *canonic Young subgroup* associated with λ and denoted by

$$S_\lambda.$$

It is important to realize the following consequence of 1.3.6:

4.3.1 Lemma *All the Young subgroups $S(\underline{n}^\lambda)$ arising from an improper partition λ of n and corresponding λ–decompositions $\underline{n}^\lambda$ of $\underline{n}$ are conjugate subgroups of $S_{\underline{n}}$.*

Thus all these subgroups corresponding to $\lambda \models n$ induce equivalent representations, and hence it suffices to consider the canonic Young subgroups S_α, α being a *proper* partition of n.
In the case when the numbering of the elements $\underline{n}_i^\lambda$ of $\underline{n}^\lambda$ matters, then we call the sequence $(\underline{n}^\lambda) = (\underline{n}_1^\lambda, \underline{n}_2^\lambda, \ldots)$ a λ–*flag* and denote by

$$\lambda(\underline{n})$$

the set of *all* the λ–flags over $\underline{n}$. The action

4.3.2 $$S_{\underline{n}} \times \lambda(\underline{n}) \to \lambda(\underline{n}) : (\pi, (\underline{n}^\lambda)) \mapsto (\pi\underline{n}_1^\lambda, \pi\underline{n}_2^\lambda, \ldots)$$

is transitive, and hence it is in fact $S_{\underline{n}}$–isomorphic to the action of $S_{\underline{n}}$ on the set $S_{\underline{n}}/S_\lambda$ of left cosets of S_λ in $S_{\underline{n}}$ (cf. 1.1.15):

4.3.3 $$\lambda(\underline{n}) \simeq S_{\underline{n}}/S_\lambda, \text{ as } S_{\underline{n}}\text{–sets.}$$

Thus we can apply 1.2.9 to the corresponding action of $S_{\underline{n}}$ on $\lambda(\underline{n}) \times \mu(\underline{n})$, where $\lambda, \mu \models n$, and obtain:

4.3.4 Corollary *For any* $\lambda, \mu \models n$, *the corresponding canonic decompositions* $\underline{n}^\lambda, \underline{n}^\mu$ *and their stabilizers* S_λ, S_μ *we have the natural bijection*

$$S_{\underline{n}} \backslash\backslash (\lambda(\underline{n}) \times \mu(\underline{n})) \to S_\lambda \backslash S_{\underline{n}} / S_\mu : S_{\underline{n}}(\underline{n}^\lambda, \pi \underline{n}^\mu) \mapsto S_\lambda \pi S_\mu.$$

This together with 4.3.3 yields the natural bijections

$$S_{\underline{n}} \backslash\backslash (S_{\underline{n}}/S_\lambda \times S_{\underline{n}}/S_\mu) \to S_{\underline{n}} \backslash\backslash (\lambda(\underline{n}) \times \mu(\underline{n})) \to S_\lambda \backslash S_{\underline{n}} / S_\mu.$$

The permutation representation corresponding to 4.3.2 is equivalent to $IS_\lambda \uparrow S_{\underline{n}}$ (recall the remark following the definition of induced representations). We call such a representation a *Young representation* and denote its character by

$$\xi^\lambda.$$

These characters are called *Young characters* and 4.3.1 shows that the set $\{\xi^\alpha \mid \alpha \vdash n\}$ is the *complete* set of Young characters of $S_{\underline{n}}$. Later we shall in fact show that each ordinary irreducible character of $S_{\underline{n}}$ is a uniquely determined $\mathbb{Z}$–linear combination of Young characters and we shall evaluate the coefficients. The permutation representation corresponding to the action of $S_{\underline{n}}$ on $\lambda(\underline{n}) \times \mu(\underline{n})$ is clearly equivalent to

$$IS_\lambda \uparrow S_{\underline{n}} \otimes IS_\mu \uparrow S_{\underline{n}}, \text{ with character } \xi^\lambda \xi^\mu.$$

Hence an application of exercise 4.2.8 yields, if we denote by ι the identity character:

4.3.5 Corollary *For any improper partitions* $\lambda, \mu \models n$, *the corresponding canonic Young subgroups* $S_\lambda, S_\mu \leq S_{\underline{n}}$, *the Young characters* ξ^λ, ξ^μ *and the set* $S_\lambda \backslash S_{\underline{n}} / S_\mu$ *of all the* (S_λ, S_μ)–*double cosets we have:*

$$[\xi^\lambda \mid \xi^\mu] = [\xi^\lambda \xi^\mu \mid \iota] = |S_{\underline{n}} \backslash\backslash (\lambda(\underline{n}) \times \mu(\underline{n}))| = |S_\lambda \backslash S_{\underline{n}} / S_\mu|.$$

Besides this we want to evaluate $[\xi^\lambda \xi^\mu \mid \epsilon]$, ϵ being the *alternating* or *sign* character, which maps each permutation onto its sign (cf. 1.3.15). This expression satisfies, by definition of the inner product of characters, the equation

$$[\xi^\lambda \xi^\mu \mid \epsilon] = [\xi^\lambda \xi^\mu \downarrow A_{\underline{n}} \mid \iota \downarrow A_{\underline{n}}] - [\xi^\lambda \xi^\mu \mid \iota],$$

and so it is in fact equal to the number of orbits of $S_{\underline{n}}$ on the set $\lambda(\underline{n}) \times \mu(\underline{n})$ which *split over* $A_{\underline{n}}$, i.e. which consist of several, and hence of exactly two, $A_{\underline{n}}$–orbits (recall 1.3.16). But, for $n > 1$, an $S_{\underline{n}}$–orbit splits over A_n if and only if the stabilizers of its elements are the same in both of these groups. Thus an application of 1.2.8 yields

4.3.6 $\quad [\xi^\lambda \xi^\mu \mid \epsilon] = |\{S_\lambda \pi S_\mu \in S_\lambda \backslash S_{\underline{n}} / S_\mu \mid S_\lambda \cap \pi S_\mu \pi^{-1} = \{1\}\}|.$

In order to make these results more explicit we give a more detailed description of the double cosets $S_\lambda \pi S_\mu$:

4.3.7 Coleman's Lemma *For* $\lambda, \mu \models n$ *and corresponding flags* $(\underline{n}^\lambda)$ *and* $(\underline{n}^\mu)$ *the following is true*

$$\pi \in S_\lambda \rho S_\mu \iff \forall\, i,j : |\underline{n}_i^\lambda \cap \pi \underline{n}_j^\mu| = |\underline{n}_i^\lambda \cap \rho \underline{n}_j^\mu|.$$

Proof:
i) If $\pi \in S_\lambda \rho S_\mu$, say $\pi = \sigma \rho \tau, \sigma \in S_\lambda, \tau \in S_\mu$, then, for each j,

$$\pi \underline{n}_j^\mu = \sigma \rho \tau \underline{n}_j^\mu = \sigma \rho \underline{n}_j^\mu,$$

thus for each i and j we have:

$$\underline{n}_i^\lambda \cap \pi \underline{n}_j^\mu = \underline{n}_i^\lambda \cap \sigma \rho \underline{n}_j^\mu = \sigma \left[\underline{n}_i^\lambda \cap \rho \underline{n}_j^\mu \right].$$

This yields one half of the statement since σ is a bijection.
ii) The assumption

$$\forall\, i,j : |\underline{n}_i^\lambda \cap \rho \underline{n}_j^\mu| = |\underline{n}_i^\lambda \cap \pi \underline{n}_j^\mu|$$

implies that for fixed i the subsets $\underline{n}_i^\lambda \cap \rho \underline{n}_j^\mu$ and the subsets $\underline{n}_i^\lambda \cap \pi n_j^\mu$ form two dissections of $\underline{n}_i^\lambda$ into subsets which can be collected into pairs

$$(\underline{n}_i^\lambda \cap \rho \underline{n}_j^\mu, \underline{n}_i^\lambda \cap \pi \underline{n}_j^\mu)$$

of subsets of equal order. Hence for each i there exists $\sigma_i \in S_{\underline{n}_i^\lambda}$, which satisfies

$$\forall\, j : \sigma_i \left[\underline{n}_i^\lambda \cap \rho \underline{n}_j^\mu \right] = \underline{n}_i^\lambda \cap \pi \underline{n}_j^\mu.$$

The product $\sigma := \sigma_1 \sigma_2 \ldots \in S_\lambda$ of such permutations σ_i then satisfies

$$\forall j : \sigma \rho \underline{n}_j^\mu = \pi \underline{n}_j^\mu.$$

Thus there exist $\tau \in S_\mu$ such that $\pi = \sigma \rho \tau$, as stated.
$\square$

The main point is the following direct consequence of Coleman's Lemma:

4.3.8 Corollary *If we denote by $M_{\lambda\mu}$ the set of matrices over $\mathbb{N}$ with row sums $\lambda_1, \lambda_2, \ldots$ and column sums $\mu_1, \mu_2, \ldots$, then we have the bijection*

$$S_\lambda \backslash S_{\underline{n}} / S_\mu \longrightarrow M_{\lambda\mu} : S_\lambda \rho S_\mu \mapsto (z_{ij}),$$

where $z_{ij} := |\underline{n}_i^\lambda \cap \rho \underline{n}_j^\mu|$. The restriction of this mapping to the set

$$(S_\lambda \backslash S_{\underline{n}} / S_\mu)' := \{ S_\lambda \pi S_\mu \mid S_\lambda \cap \pi S_\mu \pi^{-1} = \{1\} \}$$

of double cosets with trivial intersection has as its image the set

$$M'_{\lambda\mu} := \{ (z_{ij}) \in M_{\lambda\mu} \mid z_{ij} \in \{0, 1\} \}$$

of 0–1–matrices with row sums $\lambda_1, \lambda_2, \ldots$ and column sums $\mu_1, \mu_2, \ldots$.

Applying this to the above inner products of characters we obtain

4.3.9 Corollary *For $\lambda, \mu \models n$ we have*

$$[\xi^\lambda \mid \xi^\mu] = |M_{\lambda\mu}| \text{ and } [\xi^\lambda \mid \epsilon\xi^\mu] = |M'_{\lambda\mu}|.$$

We call the matrix (z_{ij}) the *double coset symbol* or, in short, the *dc–symbol* corresponding to $S_\lambda \rho S_\mu$.

Summarizing 4.3.4 and 4.3.8 and denoting by $(S_{\underline{n}} \backslash\backslash \lambda(\underline{n}) \times \mu(\underline{n}))'$ the set of orbits which split over the alternating group, we get the following result:

4.3.10 Corollary *For $n > 1$ and $\lambda, \mu \models n$ we have natural bijections*

$$S_{\underline{n}} \backslash\backslash S_{\underline{n}} / S_\lambda \times S_{\underline{n}} / S_\mu \rightarrow S_{\underline{n}} \backslash\backslash \lambda(\underline{n}) \times \mu(\underline{n}) \rightarrow M_{\lambda\mu},$$

and

$$(S_{\underline{n}} \backslash\backslash S_{\underline{n}} / S_\lambda \times S_{\underline{n}} / S_\mu)' \rightarrow (S_{\underline{n}} \backslash\backslash \lambda(\underline{n}) \times \mu(\underline{n}))' \rightarrow M'_{\lambda\mu},$$

according to 4.3.8.

Now we restrict attention to specific pairs (α, β) of proper partitions of n, where β is closely related to α. In order to define this particular β we illustrate α by the corresponding *Young diagram* $[\alpha]$, which consists of n nodes $\times$ placed in rows. The i-th row of $[\alpha]$ consists of α_i nodes, and all the rows start in the same column. The partition $(3, 2, 1^2)$ for example is illustrated by $[3, 2, 1^2]$ (we write $[3, 2, 1^2]$ instead of $[(3, 2, 1^2)]$) which looks as follows:

$$
\begin{array}{ccc}
\times & \times & \times \\
\times & \times & \\
\times & & \\
\times & &
\end{array}
$$

Recalling that $\alpha_i \geq \alpha_{i+1}$, we see that the lengths α_i' of the columns of $[\alpha]$ form another partition α' of n:

$$\alpha' := (\alpha_1', \alpha_2', \ldots), \quad \text{where } \alpha_i' := \sum_{j, \alpha_j \geq i} 1.$$

This partition α' is called the *partition associated with* α. The Young diagram $[\alpha']$ arises from $[\alpha]$ by simply reflecting $[\alpha]$ in its main diagonal, e.g. $[(3,2,1^2)'] = [4,2,1]$. Partitions α and Young diagrams $[\alpha]$ where $\alpha = \alpha'$ are called *self–associated*.

It is an easy exercise to see that for any such pair (α, α') of associated partitions there exists exactly one 0-1–matrix with row sums α_i and column sums α_i'; in formal terms:

4.3.11 $\qquad\qquad\qquad \forall \, \alpha \vdash n: \; |M_{\alpha\alpha'}'| = 1.$

This has the following important consequence:

4.3.12 $\qquad\qquad\qquad \forall \, \alpha \vdash n: \; [\xi^\alpha \mid \epsilon\xi^{\alpha'}] = 1.$

The representation of $S_{\underline{n}}$ which has the character $\epsilon\xi^{\alpha'}$ is the representation which is induced by the *alternating representation* A of $S_{\alpha'}$ (please check this carefully):

$$A: S_{\alpha'} \to GL(\mathbb{C}): \pi \mapsto \epsilon(\pi)id_{\mathbb{C}}.$$

Thus 4.3.12 yields (applying 4.2.2 and 4.2.3) the following result which is basic for the representation theory of the symmetric groups:

4.3.13 Theorem *For each proper partition α of n the induced representations $IS_\alpha \uparrow S_{\underline{n}}$ and $AS_{\alpha'} \uparrow S_{\underline{n}}$ of $S_{\underline{n}}$ have exactly one irreducible representation as a common constituent. They both contain this irreducible constituent with multiplicity 1.*

We denote this constituent or its equivalence class by $[\alpha]$ and its character by ζ^α, so that, by slight abuse of the intersection symbol, we have

$$[\alpha] := IS_\alpha \uparrow S_{\underline{n}} \cap AS_{\alpha'} \uparrow S_{\underline{n}}, \quad \text{with character } \zeta^\alpha.$$

As $IS_{(n)} \uparrow S_{\underline{n}} = IS_{\underline{n}}$, the identity representation, $AS_{(n)} \uparrow S_{\underline{n}} = AS_{\underline{n}}$, the alternating representation, and $IS_{(1^n)} \uparrow S_{\underline{n}} = AS_{(1^n)} \uparrow S_{\underline{n}} = RS_{\underline{n}}$, the

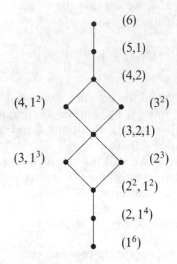

Figure 4.1: The poset $(P(6), \trianglelefteq)$

regular representation, we obtain from 4.2.4 the following particular cases:

4.3.14 $\qquad [n] = IS_{\underline{n}}, \ [1^n] = AS_{\underline{n}}, \ [\alpha'] = [1^n] \otimes [\alpha].$

It is in fact our aim to show that $\{[\alpha] \mid \alpha \vdash n\}$ is a transversal of the equivalence classes of the ordinary irreducible representations of $S_{\underline{n}}$. In order to prove this we introduce a total and a partial order on the sets

$$P(n) := \{\alpha \mid \alpha \vdash n\} \subseteq IP(n) := \{\lambda \mid \lambda \vDash n\}$$

of all the proper and all the improper partitions of n. A natural total order is the *lexicographic order*

$$\lambda < \mu \ :\Longleftrightarrow \ \exists \, i\colon \lambda_1 = \mu_1, \dots, \lambda_{i-1} = \mu_{i-1}, \lambda_i < \mu_i.$$

The partial order $\trianglelefteq$ called the *dominance order* is defined by

$$\lambda \trianglelefteq \mu \ :\Longleftrightarrow \ \forall \, i\colon \sum_1^i \lambda_v \leq \sum_1^i \mu_v.$$

It differs from the lexicographic order on $P(n)$ if and only if $n \geq 6$. The Hasse diagram of the poset $(P(6), \trianglelefteq)$ is shown in Figure 4.1.

It will be useful to characterize when $\alpha \vdash n$ is *covered* by $\beta \vdash n$, i.e. when

$$\alpha \lhd \beta \text{ and } \not\exists \gamma \vdash n \colon \alpha \lhd \gamma \lhd \beta.$$

We shall see that this can be expressed very nicely in terms of the corresponding Young diagrams $[\alpha]$ and $[\beta]$. In fact $[\beta]$ arises from $[\alpha]$ by moving one node from the end of a certain row of $[\alpha]$ upwards to the end of another row, say from the j-th row to the i-th row, see Figure 4.2. Moreover this step has to be as small a step as possible, which means that either $i = j - 1$ or $i < j - 1$ and $\alpha_i = \alpha_{i+1} = \ldots = \alpha_j$ (cf. Figure 4.3):

4.3.15 Theorem $\alpha \vdash n$ *is covered by* $\beta \vdash n$ *if and only if there exist indices* i *and* j *such that* $1 \le i < j$ *and*

- $\beta_j = \alpha_j - 1$ *and* $\beta_i = \alpha_i + 1$, *while, for* $k \ne i, j$, *we have* $\alpha_k = \beta_k$,
- $i = j - 1$, *or* $\alpha_i = \alpha_j$.

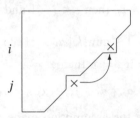

Figure 4.2: Construction of the covering partition

Proof: Assuming first that α is covered by β, we put

$$i := \min\{k \mid \alpha_k \ne \beta_k\}, \; j := \min\{t \mid \sum_1^t \alpha_k = \sum_1^t \beta_k, i < t\}.$$

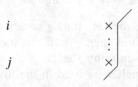

Figure 4.3: The case when $i \ne j - 1$

Then obviously

$$1 \le i < j \le n, \text{ and } \alpha_j > \beta_j \ge 0, \beta_{j+1} \ge \alpha_{j+1}.$$

If $i > 1$, then $\alpha_i < \beta_i \le \beta_{i-1} = \alpha_{i-1}$, and so in this case

$$\alpha_i + 1 \le \beta_i \le \beta_{i-1} = \alpha_{i-1}.$$

Also $\alpha_j > \beta_j \ge \beta_{j+1} \ge \alpha_{j+1}$, and therefore

$$\alpha_j - 1 \ge \alpha_{j+1}.$$

Hence in any case, whether $i > 1$ or not, we obtain

$$\alpha \lhd \gamma := (\alpha_1, \ldots, \alpha_{i-1}, \alpha_i + 1, \alpha_{i+1}, \ldots, \alpha_{j-1}, \alpha_j - 1, \alpha_{j+1}, \ldots) \unlhd \beta,$$

so that $\gamma = \beta$ by assumption, and $[\beta]$ arises from $[\alpha]$ by moving exactly one node upwards from the end of the j-th row to the end of the i-th row of $[\alpha]$.
If $i \ne j - 1$ and $\alpha_i \ne \alpha_j$, then $i < j - 1$ and $\alpha_i > \alpha_j$. We can therefore put

$$t := 1 + \min\{k \mid \alpha_k > \alpha_{k+1}, i \le k < j\}.$$

Note that $i < t \le j$. If $t = j$, then $\alpha_i = \ldots = \alpha_{j-1} > \alpha_j > 0$, and thus

$$\alpha \lhd (\alpha_1, \ldots, \alpha_{i-1}, \alpha_i + 1, \ldots, \alpha_{j-2}, \alpha_{j-1} - 1, \alpha_j, \ldots) \lhd \beta.$$

But this contradicts the assumption made that β covers α. If $t < j$, then $\alpha_i = \ldots = \alpha_{t-1} > \alpha_t \ge \ldots \ge \alpha_j > 0$, and so in this case we have

$$\alpha \lhd (\alpha_1, \ldots, \alpha_{t-1}, \alpha_t + 1, \ldots, \alpha_{j-1}, \alpha_j - 1, \alpha_{j+1}, \ldots) \lhd \beta,$$

which also contradicts the assumption.
Conversely let α, β, i and j satisfy the conditions of the theorem, and let γ be a partition of n with the property that γ covers α and $\gamma \unlhd \beta$. Then, for the parts of γ, we have:

$$\forall \, k < i : \alpha_k = \gamma_k = \beta_k, \text{ and } \forall k > j : \alpha_k = \gamma_k = \beta_k.$$

Hence, if $i = j - 1$, the fact that γ covers α implies that $\gamma_i = \alpha_i + 1$, and $\gamma_{i+1} = \alpha_i - 1$, and then $\gamma = \beta$. In the case when $i \ne j - 1$, we obtain from the assumption that $\alpha_i = \ldots = \alpha_j$. Furthermore, by the same arguments which were used in the first part of this proof, there exist k and l such that

$$\gamma_k = \alpha_k + 1, \gamma_l = \alpha_l - 1, \gamma_v = \alpha_v \text{ for } v \ne k, l.$$

But this can hold only if $k = i$ and $l = j$, for otherwise

$$\alpha_k = \gamma_k - 1 \leq \gamma_{k-1} - 1 = \alpha_{k-1} - 1 < \alpha_{k-1} = \alpha_i,$$

or

$$\alpha_l = \gamma_l + 1 \geq \gamma_{l+1} + 1 = \alpha_{l+1} + 1 > \alpha_{l+1} = \alpha_j$$

would contradict $\alpha_i = \ldots = \alpha_j$. Therefore $\gamma = \beta$ also in this case.

$\square$

We shall use this in the proof of the following very important fact:

4.3.16 Lemma *For any proper partitions* $\alpha, \beta \vdash n$ *we have:*

$$\alpha \trianglelefteq \beta \iff \beta' \trianglelefteq \alpha'.$$

Proof: If $\alpha \trianglelefteq \beta$, then there exist partitions $\alpha^v \vdash n, 0 \leq v \leq r$, which satisfy

$$\alpha = \alpha^0 \vartriangleleft \alpha^1 \vartriangleleft \ldots \vartriangleleft \alpha^r = \beta,$$

and where α^i *covers* α^{i-1}. Now 4.3.15 shows that

$$(\alpha^i)' \vartriangleleft (\alpha^{i-1})'.$$

Thus we obtain the chain of conjugate partitions

$$\beta' = (\alpha^r)' \vartriangleleft \ldots \vartriangleleft (\alpha^0)' = \alpha',$$

which shows that $\beta' \vartriangleleft \alpha'$. The converse is true by symmetry.

$\square$

Obviously $\trianglelefteq$ can be embedded into the lexicographic order:

4.3.17 $$\alpha \trianglelefteq \beta \implies \alpha \leq \beta.$$

The dominance order on $P(n)$ is defined in terms of the partial sums

$$s_i^\alpha := \sum_1^i \alpha_j$$

of the parts of α. Using these expressions we can define, for any $\alpha, \beta \vdash n$, the infimum $\alpha \wedge \beta$ by

$$\alpha \wedge \beta := \gamma, \text{ where } s_i^\gamma := \min\{s_i^\alpha, s_i^\beta\},$$

and

$$\alpha \vee \beta := (\alpha' \wedge \beta')'.$$

It is easy to check that $\alpha \vee \beta$ is the supremum and $\alpha \wedge \beta$ the infimum of α and β with respect to the dominance order, so that we have obtained (cf. 4.3.16):

4.3.18 Corollary *The dominance order $\trianglelefteq$ induces a lattice structure on $P(n)$. The mapping*

$$-' : P(n) \to P(n) : \alpha \mapsto \alpha'$$

is an order antiisomorphism on $P(n)$.

This lattice $(P(n), \wedge, \vee)$ is a very important combinatorial structure. We call it the *diagram lattice* of order n, since the name "partition lattice" would be misleading, as it is already the standard name of a different lattice structure.

We return to the matrices with prescribed row and column sums.

4.3.19 Lemma *For any proper partitions $\alpha, \beta \vdash n$ we have:*

$$|M'_{\alpha\beta'}| > 0 \implies \alpha \trianglelefteq \beta.$$

Proof: Assume that $A \in M'_{\alpha\beta'}$ and shift its nonzero entries in their rows as far to the left as possible. The resulting matrix A' contains in its first column α'_1 elements 1. Hence $\alpha'_1 \geq \beta'_1$. Moreover the first two columns of A' contain $\alpha'_1 + \alpha'_2$ entries 1, so that also $\alpha'_1 + \alpha'_2 \geq \beta'_1 + \beta'_2$, and so on. Thus $\alpha' \trianglerighteq \beta'$, which is equivalent to the assertion, by 4.3.16. $\square$

4.3.20 Lemma $[\xi^\alpha \mid \zeta^\beta] > 0$ *implies that $\alpha \trianglelefteq \beta$.*

Proof: The equation $[\epsilon\xi^{\beta'} \mid \zeta^\beta] = 1$ together with the above assumption yields that

$$0 < [\xi^\alpha \mid \epsilon\xi^{\beta'}] = |M'_{\alpha\beta'}|,$$

which implies the statement by 4.3.19.

$\square$

We are now in a position to prove the main theorem of the ordinary representation theory of finite symmetric groups:

4.3.21 Theorem *The set $\{[\alpha] \mid \alpha \vdash n\}$ is a transversal of the equivalence classes of ordinary irreducible representations of $S_{\underline{n}}$.*

Proof: We need only show that $[\alpha] = [\beta]$ implies $\alpha = \beta$, for then the cardinality of $\{[\alpha] \mid \alpha \vdash n\}$ is equal to the number of conjugacy classes of $S_{\underline{n}}$, and so this system must be complete. But if $[\alpha] = [\beta]$, we can argue in the following way:

$$(IS_\alpha \uparrow S_{\underline{n}}, [\beta]) = (IS_\alpha \uparrow S_{\underline{n}}, [\alpha])$$

$$= 1 = (IS_\beta \uparrow S_{\underline{n}}, [\beta]) = (IS_\beta \uparrow S_{\underline{n}}, [\alpha]).$$

Thus, by 4.3.20, we have both $\alpha \trianglelefteq \beta$ and $\beta \trianglelefteq \alpha$, which imply $\alpha = \beta$, and the proof is complete.

$\square$

We denote the multiplicities of the irreducible constituents of Young representations as follows:

$$\kappa_{\alpha\beta} := (IS_\alpha \uparrow S_{\underline{n}}, [\beta]) = [\xi^\alpha \mid \zeta^\beta].$$

These numbers are called the *Kostka numbers* . With respect to the *reverse lexicographic order* on $P(n)$, the matrix consisting of these multiplicities is of the following form (cf. 4.3.13 and 4.3.20):

$$4.3.22 \qquad K_n := (\kappa_{\alpha\beta}) = \begin{pmatrix} 1 & & & & \\ \vdots & \ddots & & & \\ 1 & & 1 & & \\ \vdots & & \star & \ddots & \\ 1 & \dots & f^\beta & \dots & 1 \end{pmatrix},$$

where f^β denotes the dimension of $[\beta]$. The triangular form of this *Kostka matrix* K_n has several important consequences. We denote by ζ^α_β and ξ^α_β the value of ζ^α and that of ξ^α on the conjugacy class of elements with cycle partition β. Putting these values into matrices, say

$$Z_n := (\zeta^\alpha_\beta), \quad \Xi_n := (\xi^\alpha_\beta),$$

we obtain, using the lexicographic order of the partitions:

$$4.3.23 \qquad \Xi_n = K_n Z_n, \text{ and hence } Z_n = K_n^{-1} \Xi_n.$$

As K_n^{-1} is a matrix over $\mathbb{Z}$ (see 4.3.22), this implies

4.3.24 Corollary *Each ordinary irreducible character ζ^α of $S_{\underline{n}}$ is a uniquely determined $\mathbb{Z}$–linear combination of the Young characters ξ^β, $\beta \vdash n$.*

4.3.24 shows the importance of the Kostka matrix K_n. It can be evaluated as soon as the numbers of double cosets are known:

$$4.3.25 \qquad \sum_{\gamma \vdash n} \kappa_{\alpha\gamma} \kappa_{\beta\gamma} = [\xi^\alpha \mid \xi^\beta] = |S_\alpha \backslash S_{\underline{n}} / S_\beta|,$$

while these numbers can be obtained as follows:

4.3.26 Lemma $|S_\alpha \backslash S_{\underline{n}} / S_\beta|$ *is the coefficient of the monomial*

$$x^\alpha y^\beta := x_1^{\alpha_1} x_2^{\alpha_2} \dots y_1^{\beta_1} y_2^{\beta_2} \dots$$

in the formal power series

$$\prod_{i,k \in \mathbb{N}^*} (1 - x_i y_k)^{-1} := \prod_{i,k} \left(\sum_{v=0}^{\infty} x_i^v y_k^v \right).$$

But 4.3.23 also shows that K_n^{-1} is even more important than K_n. We shall therefore give a better description of the inverse of the Kostka matrix later. It remains to describe how $\Xi_n = (\xi_\beta^\alpha)$ can be evaluated, so that we can derive the character table Z_n by an application of 4.3.23 and 4.3.26, say. The Young character ξ^α is the character of the action of S_n on the set $\alpha(\underline{n})$ of α–flags. A flag $\underline{n}^\alpha = (\underline{n}_1^\alpha, \dots, \underline{n}_h^\alpha)$ can be illustrated by the corresponding *tabloid* that contains in its i-th row the elements of the i-th block $\underline{n}_i^\alpha$ of the flag in their natural order:

$$\begin{array}{c} \overline{r_1 \dots \dots r_{\alpha_1}} \\ \overline{\dots \dots \dots} \\ \overline{t_1 \dots t_{\alpha_h}} \end{array},$$

if $\underline{n}_1^\alpha = \{r_1 < \dots < r_{\alpha_1}\}, \dots, \underline{n}_h^\alpha = \{t_1 < \dots < t_{\alpha_h}\}$. More explicitly we shall also call such a tabloid an α–*tabloid*. For example

$$\frac{\overline{124}}{35}$$

is the $(3,2)$-tabloid representing the flag $\underline{5}^{(3,2)} := \{\{1,4,2\}, \{5,3\}\}$. It is obvious that such a tabloid is fixed under $\pi \in S_n$ if and only if, for each cyclic factor of π, the points contained in it belong to the same block, or, in other words, if and only if each block $\underline{n}_i^\alpha$ is a union of orbits of π. This proves

4.3.27 Lemma *For each* $\alpha = (\alpha_1, \dots, \alpha_h) \vdash n$ *and any* $\pi \in S_n$, *the Young character value* $\xi^\alpha(\pi)$ *can be expressed in terms of multinomial coefficients as follows:*

$$\xi^\alpha(\pi) = \sum_{a^{(1)}, \dots, a^{(h)}} \prod_{i=1}^n \binom{a_i(\pi)}{a_i^{(1)}, \dots, a_i^{(h)}}.$$

Antwortkarte

**Bibliographisches Institut
& F. A. Brockhaus AG**

Werbeabteilung
Postfach 10 03 11

6800 Mannheim 1

Meine Buchhandlung:

B.I.-Hochschultaschenbücher,
Einzelwerke und Reihen

Mathematik, Informatik, Physik, Astronomie,
Philosophie, Chemie, Medizin, Ingenieur-
wissenschaften, Wirtschaftswissenschaften,
Geowissenschaften

B·I

Wissenschaftsverlag
Mannheim/Wien/Zürich

W 156

Ja, ich würde gerne mehr über Ihr Programm wissen:

☐ Mathematik ☐ Philosophie

☐ Informatik ☐ Pharmakologie/Toxikologie

☐ Physik ☐ Ingenieurwissenschaften

☐ Astronomie ☐ Geowissenschaften

☐ Disketten mit den Programmen zu den Formelsammlungen zur Numerischen Mathematik von G. Engeln-Müllges/F. Reutter (FORTRAN 77, BASIC, TURBO-PASCAL, C, MODULA 2 u.a.)

☐ Deutsche Sprache/Wörterbücher

☐ Ja, ich würde gerne regelmäßig die Verzeichnisse über die allgemeine Produktion des Verlages Bibliographisches Institut & F. A. Brockhaus erhalten.

Gewünschtes bitte ankreuzen.

Name, Vorname
_____

Straße, Hausnummer
_____

PLZ/Ort
_____

Beruf
_____

○ Dozent ○ Praktiker

○ Student ○ _____

an

○ Universität ○ Fachhochschule

○ PH ○ Technikerschule

○ _____

The sum has to be taken over the cycle types $a^{(1)} \vdash \alpha_1, \ldots, a^{(h)} \vdash \alpha_h$ which sum up to $a(\pi)$ in the following sense:

$$\sum_i a^{(i)} := \left(\sum_i a_1^{(i)}, \ldots, \sum_i a_n^{(i)} \right) = (a_1(\pi), \ldots, a_n(\pi)).$$

□

For example:

4.3.28 $\quad \xi^{(n)}(\pi) = 1, \xi^{(n-1,1)}(\pi) = a_1(\pi), \xi^{(n-2,2)}(\pi) = \binom{a_1(\pi)}{2} + a_2(\pi).$

Lemma 4.3.27 shows that each ξ^α and hence also each ζ^α is a polynomial function in the a_i. Let us consider the multinomial factors of its summands. As

$$\binom{a_i(\pi)}{a_i^{(1)}, \ldots, a_i^{(h)}} := \frac{a_i(\pi)!}{a_i^{(1)}! \ldots a_i^{(h)}!} = \binom{a_i(\pi)}{a_i^{(1)}} \binom{\sum_2^h a_i^{(j)}}{a_i^{(2)}, \ldots, a_i^{(h)}},$$

we see that $\xi^\alpha(\pi)$ is the value, at $(x_1, \ldots, x_n) := a(\pi)$, of the polynomial function $\Xi^{\hat{\alpha}}$, corresponding to the *truncated partition* $\hat{\alpha} := (\alpha_2, \alpha_3, \ldots)$, that belongs to the polynomial

$$\Xi^{\hat{\alpha}} := \sum_{a^{(2)}, \ldots, a^{(h)}} \prod_{i=1}^n \binom{\sum_2^h a_i^{(j)}}{a_i^{(2)}, \ldots, a_i^{(h)}} \binom{x_i}{\sum_2^h a_i^{(j)}} \in \mathbb{Q}[x_1, x_2, \ldots].$$

The sum has to be taken over all the cycle types $a^{(2)} \vdash \alpha_2, \ldots, a^{(h)} \vdash \alpha_h$, $\alpha_2, \ldots, \alpha_h$ being the (nonzero) parts of the truncated partition $\hat{\alpha}$. Moreover, if $\hat{\beta} = \hat{\alpha}$, $\Xi^{\hat{\beta}} = \Xi^{\hat{\alpha}}$, hence $\Xi^{\hat{\alpha}}$ gives an *infinite series* of Young characters, namely all the ξ^β for which $\beta = (\beta_1, \alpha_2, \alpha_3, \ldots)$, via

$$\xi^\beta(\pi) = \Xi^{\hat{\alpha}}(a_1(\pi), \ldots, a_m(\pi)), \text{ if } \beta \vdash m = \beta_1 + \sum_2^h \alpha_i.$$

Hence $\Xi^{\hat{\alpha}} \in \mathbb{Q}[x_1, x_2, \ldots]$ has prescribed values at infinitely many points $a = (a_1, a_2, \ldots)$, and at each such point only finitely many coordinates a_i are nonzero. This proves

4.3.29 Theorem *For each proper partition $\hat{\alpha} = (\alpha_2, \alpha_3, \ldots, \alpha_h) \vdash n$ there exists the uniquely determined polynomial*

$$\Xi^{\hat{\alpha}} := \sum_{a^{(2)}, \ldots, a^{(h)}} \prod_{i=1}^n \binom{\sum_2^h a_i^{(j)}}{a_i^{(2)}, \ldots, a_i^{(h)}} \binom{x_i}{\sum_2^h a_i^{(j)}} \in \mathbb{Q}[x_1, x_2, \ldots]$$

(where the sum is over all $a^{(2)} \vdash \alpha_2, \ldots, a^{(h)} \vdash \alpha_h$, if $\alpha_2, \ldots, \alpha_h$ are the nonzero parts of $\hat{\alpha}$) such that the corresponding polynomial function yields the values $\xi^\beta(\pi)$ of all the Young characters ξ^β, where $\beta = (\beta_1, \alpha_2, \ldots, \alpha_h)$ via

$$\xi_a^\beta = \Xi^{\hat{\alpha}}(a_1, \ldots, a_m), \ \ if \ \beta \vdash m = n + \beta_1.$$

We call these polynomials *Young polynomials*. Here are the smallest examples (cf. 4.3.28):

4.3.30 $\Xi^\emptyset = 1, \Xi^{(1)} = x_1, \Xi^{(2)} = \begin{pmatrix} x_1 \\ 2 \end{pmatrix} + x_2, \Xi^{(1^2)} = x_1(x_1 - 1).$

Many further examples of Young polynomials and the corresponding character polynomials which we shall introduce later, and which yield infinitely many irreducible characters, can be found in the appendix.

Exercises

E 4.3.1   Evaluate K_3 and K_4, Z_3 and Z_4.

4.4   Tableaux and matrices

The notion of a *tableau* is motivated by the equation $|M'_{\alpha\alpha'}| = 1$, which means that to an α–flag $(\underline{n}^\alpha)$ and an α'–flag $(\underline{n}^{\alpha'})$ there corresponds *exactly one* double coset $S(\underline{n}^\alpha)\pi S(\underline{n}^{\alpha'})$ with trivial intersection property. We want to construct a representative π of this particular double coset. In order to do this we replace the nodes in the i-th *row* of the Young diagram $[\alpha]$ by the elements of the block $\underline{n}_i^\alpha$ and take for the k-th block of $\pi(\underline{n}^{\alpha'})$ the resulting set of elements in the k-th *column*. Obviously

$$S(\underline{n}^\alpha) \cap \pi S(\underline{n}^{\alpha'})\pi^{-1} = S(\underline{n}^\alpha) \cap S(\pi(\underline{n}^{\alpha'})) = \{1\}.$$

The following example illustrates this. The flags

$$(\underline{n}^\alpha) := (\{1, 3, 4\}, \{2, 5\}), \ \ and \ \ (\underline{n}^{\alpha'}) := (\{1, 2\}, \{3, 4\}, \{5\})$$

yield the *tableau* (the exact definition will be given later)

$$\begin{array}{ccc} 3 & 1 & 4 \\ 2 & 5 & \end{array} ,$$

if we choose the permutation

$$\pi = \begin{pmatrix} 1 & 2 & 3 & 4 & 5 \\ 2 & 3 & 1 & 5 & 4 \end{pmatrix},$$

which satisfies $S(\underline{n}^\alpha) \cap \pi S(\underline{n}^{\alpha'})\pi^{-1} = \{1\}$. More formally, and in fact more generally, we can describe this process of replacing the nodes of the diagram $[\alpha]$ by a mapping as follows. The Young diagram $[\alpha]$ can be considered as a subset of $\mathbb{N}^* \times \mathbb{N}^*$:

$$[\alpha] = \bigcup_i \{(i,1), \ldots, (i, \alpha_i)\},$$

where (i, j) is the coordinate pair of the node in the i-th row and the j-th column of $[\alpha]$. Let now $\mathcal{R}$ be a nonempty *range* set. Each mapping

$$T : [\alpha] \to \mathcal{R} : (i,j) \mapsto t_{ij}$$

is called an α–*tableau* over $\mathcal{R}$. The partition $\mathrm{sh}(T) := \alpha$ is called the *shape* of T, and $t_{ij} = T((i,j))$ is called the *entry* of T at (i,j). Usually the range $\mathcal{R}$ will be a totally ordered set and we shall generally take $\mathcal{R} = \underline{n}$, if $\mathrm{sh}(T) \vdash n$. In this case we put

$$c(T) := (\lambda_1, \lambda_2, \ldots), \quad \text{where } \lambda_i := |T^{-1}[\{i\}]|,$$

and call this sequence the *content* of T. It is an improper partition of n: $c(T) \models n$. Tableaux of content (1^n) will turn out to be of particular importance for us; they are called *Young tableaux* . The example given above is in fact a Young tableau. A tableau T over $\underline{n}$ will be called *row injective* if and only if T is injective on each of its *rows*. A tableau T is called *strictly (weakly) row monotonous* if and only if, for each i, $t_{ij} < t_{i,j+1} (t_{ij} \le t_{i,j+1})$, for each j. Monotony along the columns is defined in a similar way. T is called a *standard tableau* if and only if it is weakly monotonous in its rows and strictly monotonous in its columns. The set of α–tableaux over $\underline{n}$, the set of standard α–tableaux over $\underline{n}$, the set of α–tableaux and the set of all the standard α–tableaux of content λ will be denoted by

$$T^\alpha(\underline{n}), \ ST^\alpha(\underline{n}), \ T^\alpha(\lambda), \ \text{and} \ ST^\alpha(\lambda),$$

respectively, while the set of all the Young tableaux of shape α and the set of all the standard Young tableaux of shape α will be abbreviated as follows:

$$T^\alpha := T^\alpha((1^n)), \ \text{and} \ ST^\alpha := ST^\alpha((1^n)).$$

The definition of standard tableau immediately implies that, for each $\alpha \vdash n$ and any $\lambda \models n$, we have

4.4.1 $ST^{\alpha}(\lambda) \neq \emptyset \implies \lambda \unlhd \alpha,$

where, for any $\lambda, \mu \models n$, the *dominance* of improper partitions is defined in the obvious way:

$$\lambda \unlhd \mu :\iff \forall i: \sum_{1}^{i} \lambda_{v} \leq \sum_{1}^{i} \mu_{v}.$$

We are now in a position to connect tableaux, Young characters and matrices over $\mathbb{N}$ with prescribed row and column sums. Our first step will be to establish bijections between $M_{\lambda\mu}$ and $M'_{\lambda\mu}$ and the sets

$$\bigcup_{\alpha \vdash n} ST^{\alpha}(\lambda) \times ST^{\alpha}(\mu) \text{ and } \bigcup_{\alpha \vdash n} ST^{\alpha}(\lambda) \times ST^{\alpha'}(\mu),$$

of *pairs* of standard tableaux, respectively. In order to show how this can be done, we map the matrix $Z := (z_{ij}) \in M_{\lambda\mu}$ onto the *double sequence*

$$z := \begin{pmatrix} z^1 \\ z^2 \end{pmatrix} := \begin{pmatrix} 1 \ldots 1 \, 1 \ldots 1 \ldots i \ldots i \ldots \\ \underbrace{1 \ldots 1}_{z_{11}} \underbrace{2 \ldots 2}_{z_{12}} \ldots \underbrace{j \ldots j}_{z_{ij}} \ldots \end{pmatrix}.$$

For example

$$Z := \begin{pmatrix} 0 & 0 & 2 \\ 1 & 1 & 0 \\ 3 & 0 & 0 \end{pmatrix} \longmapsto z = \begin{pmatrix} 1 & 1 & 2 & 2 & 3 & 3 & 3 \\ 3 & 3 & 1 & 2 & 1 & 1 & 1 \end{pmatrix}.$$

We note that the content $c(z^1)$ of the first row z^1 of z is λ, while $c(z^2) = \mu$. The double sequence z will now be mapped onto a pair of standard tableaux, a so–called *standard bitableau* . We start with z^2 and apply to it the *Insertion Algorithm* which yields a standard tableau, the construction of which yields then a second tableau. This algorithm is due to D.E. Knuth and it generalizes particular cases already described by G. de B. Robinson, G. Schensted and M.P. Schützenberger.

4.4.2 The Insertion Algorithm *The following method associates with each matrix over* $\mathbb{N}$, *having row sums vector* λ *and column sums vector* μ, *where* $\lambda, \mu \models n$, *a standard tableau* T *such that* $sh(T) \vdash n$ *and* $c(T) = \mu$:

Construct first the corresponding double sequence z *and then from* $z^2 = (z_1^2, z_2^2, \ldots)$ *a sequence* $T^0, T^1, \ldots, T^n$ *of tableaux as follows:*

- $T^0 := \emptyset$, *the empty tableau.*
- *For* $1 \le i \le n$ *the tableau* T^i *is obtained from the tableau* T^{i-1} *by insertion of* $r := z_i^2$ *according to the following rules:*

   1. *If the first row of* T^{i-1} *does not contain an element greater than* r, *put* r *at the end of that row.*

   2. *Otherwise take the leftmost* $s > r$ *from the first row of* T^{i-1}, *replace it by* r *and call the result* $(T^{i-1})'$. *Compare the element* s *which was "bumped" by* r *with the elements in the second row of* $(T^{i-1})'$. *If there is no* $t > s$, *then put* s *at the end of this row, otherwise bump the leftmost* $t > s$, *obtain* $(T^{i-1})''$ *and compare* t *with the elements in the third row of* $(T^{i-1})''$, *and so on, until finally the bumped element is put at the end of the next row since this row does not contain any bigger entry.*

The example z shown above yields the sequence

$$T^0 = \emptyset \mapsto T^1 = \boxed{3} \mapsto T^2 = \boxed{3 \ \ 3} \mapsto T^3 = \begin{array}{cc} 1 & 3 \\ 3 & \end{array} \mapsto T^4 = \begin{array}{cc} 1 & 2 \\ 3 & 3 \end{array}$$

$$\mapsto T^5 = \begin{array}{cc} 1 & 1 \\ 2 & 3 \\ 3 & \end{array} \mapsto T^6 = \begin{array}{ccc} 1 & 1 & 1 \\ 2 & 3 & \\ 3 & & \end{array} \mapsto T^7 = \begin{array}{cccc} 1 & 1 & 1 & 1 \\ 2 & 3 & & \\ 3 & & & \end{array} .$$

Proof of the theorem: We use induction. The tableau T^1 is obviously standard. Assume that T^{i-1} is standard. The insertion of z_i^2 yields T^i which is weakly monotonous in its rows. But T^i is also strictly monotonous in its columns, which follows easily by an indirect proof. □

We now put $T_2 := T^n$. The other tableau T_1 is obtained in parallel to the construction of T_2 by simply putting the element z_i^1 of z^1, the first row of z, into the position which is filled when obtaining T^i from T^{i-1}. Our example gives

$$T_1 = \begin{array}{cccc} 1 & 1 & 3 & 3 \\ 2 & 2 & & \\ 3 & & & \end{array} .$$

Thus we have obtained the standard bitableau

$$(T_1, T_2) = \begin{pmatrix} 1 & 1 & 3 & 3 & & 1 & 1 & 1 & 1 \\ 2 & 2 & & & & 2 & 3 & & \\ 3 & & & & , & 3 & & & \end{pmatrix},$$

which is an element of $SBT^{(4,2,1)}((2,2,3),(4,1,2))$, if we use the abbreviation

$$SBT^\alpha(\lambda,\mu) \;:=\; ST^\alpha(\lambda) \times ST^\alpha(\mu).$$

The construction of (T_1, T_2) shows that the resulting bitableau is a *standard bitableau*. Furthermore it is obvious that T_1 and T_2 are of the same shape. The stated bijectivity between $M_{\lambda\mu}$ and $\cup_\alpha SBT^\alpha(\lambda,\mu)$ follows from the fact that the double sequence z, and hence also the matrix Z can be reconstructed from (T_1, T_2) by an application of

4.4.3 The Cancellation Algorithm *If an insertion procedure according to 4.4.2 amounts to filling the box at the end of the j-th row of T^{i-1} in order to get T^i, then we can determine which number r was inserted and also we can recover T^{i-1} as follows:*

- *In the case when $j = 1$ then $r = r_1$, the element at the end of the first row of T^i.*

- *In the case when $j > 1$, then we have to consider the entry r_j which is in the position at the end of the j-th row of T^i. There exists in the $(j-1)$-th row an entry less than r_j which is as far to the right as possible. We call it r_{j-1} and exchange it with r_j. If $j > 2$ we compare r_{j-1} with the elements in the $(j-2)$-th row, exchange it with the element less than r_{j-1} which is as far as possible to the right, which we denote by r_{j-2}, and so on. We do this until finally an element r_1 remains which originates from the first row.*

The element $r := r_1$ is the element which was inserted.

An example is provided by the following tableau

$$\begin{array}{cccc} 1 & 1 & 1 & 1 \\ 2 & 3 & & \\ 3 & & & \end{array} \quad .$$

We wish to remove the element at the end of the third row. According to 4.4.3 the procedure is as follows

$$\begin{array}{cccc} 1 & 1 & 1 & 1 \\ 2 & 3 & & \\ 3 & & & \end{array} \quad \mapsto \quad \begin{array}{cccc} 1 & 1 & 1 & 1 \\ 3 & 3 & & \\ & & & \end{array} \quad \mapsto \quad \begin{array}{cccc} 1 & 1 & 1 & 2 \\ 3 & 3 & & \\ & & & \end{array}$$

so the element removed is $r = 1$. In order to reconstruct z and Z from (T_1, T_2), this cancellation is applied in the following way:

4.4.4 Theorem *The sequence of the positions which have to be cancelled is read off from T_1 as follows: From right to left we look for places containing the biggest entries and cancel these positions one after the other from T_2. Then we take the positions with the second biggest entries, and so on. These positions have to be cancelled from T_2 according to 4.4.3. The resulting pairs of entries $(z_i^1 \in T_1, z_i^2 \in T_2)$ yield the double sequence z, but in reverse order.*

For our example the first two steps are trivial, since the rightmost entries 3 occur in the first row of T_1:

$$\begin{pmatrix} 1 & 1 & 3 & 3 & & 1 & 1 & 1 & 1 \\ 2 & 2 & & & & 2 & 3 & & \\ 3 & & & , & & 3 & & & \end{pmatrix} \mapsto \begin{pmatrix} 1 & 1 & 3 & & 1 & 1 & 1 \\ 2 & 2 & & & 2 & 3 & \\ 3 & & & , & 3 & & \end{pmatrix}$$

$$\mapsto \begin{pmatrix} 1 & 1 & & 1 & 1 \\ 2 & 2 & & 2 & 3 \\ 3 & & , & 3 & \end{pmatrix} .$$

Hence these cancellations yield the pairs $(3, 1) = (z_7^1, z_7^2)$ and $(3, 1) = (z_6^1, z_6^2)$. In the next step the elements in the third row and first column have to be canceled. According to 4.4.4, we get

$$\begin{pmatrix} 1 & 1 & & 1 & 1 \\ 2 & 2 & & 2 & 3 \\ 3 & & , & 3 & \end{pmatrix} \mapsto \begin{pmatrix} 1 & 1 & & 1 & 2 \\ 2 & 2 & , & 3 & 3 \end{pmatrix},$$

and so we obtain the pair $(3, 1) = (z_5^1, z_5^2)$. In the remaining pair the rightmost element 2 of T_1 is in the second row and second column, hence we procede as follows:

$$\mapsto \begin{pmatrix} 1 & 1 & & 1 & 3 \\ 2 & & , & 3 & \end{pmatrix} \mapsto (1 \quad 1 \quad , \quad 3 \quad 3)$$

$$\mapsto (1 \quad , \quad 3) \mapsto (\emptyset \quad , \quad \emptyset).$$

This process yields the double sequence introduced above which in turn gives us the matrix Z. Hence (exercise 4.4.1) the mapping $Z \mapsto (T_1, T_2)$ is *injective*. It can be shown that, conversely, by this cancellation method we obtain from each standard bitableau $(T_1, T_2) \in ST^\alpha(\lambda) \times ST^\alpha(\mu)$ a matrix $A \in M_{\lambda\mu}$. This establishes the desired relation between matrices and bitableaux:

4.4.5 Corollary *For any* $\lambda, \mu \models n$, *the Insertion Algorithm establishes a bijection*

$$M_{\lambda\mu} \rightarrow \bigcup_{\alpha \vdash n} SBT^{\alpha}(\lambda, \mu).$$

In particular this gives the following identity, for $m_{\lambda\mu} := |M_{\lambda\mu}|$ *and* $st^{\alpha}(\lambda) := |ST^{\alpha}(\lambda)|$:

$$m_{\lambda\mu} = \sum_{\alpha \vdash n} st^{\alpha}(\lambda) st^{\alpha}(\mu).$$

It is surprising to see that this fact has the following remarkable consequence for the representation theory of symmetric groups:

4.4.6 Corollary *The Kostka numbers are equal to the numbers of standard tableaux:*

$$\kappa_{\alpha\beta} = st^{\beta}(\alpha);$$

thus Young characters decompose into irreducible characters as follows:

$$\xi^{\alpha} = \sum_{\beta} st^{\beta}(\alpha) \zeta^{\beta}.$$

In particular f^{α}, *the dimension of* $[\alpha]$, *is equal to the number* $t^{\alpha} = st^{\alpha}(1^n)$ *of standard Young tableaux of shape* α.

Proof: We note first that, with respect to the lexicographic order of the proper partitions, both the Kostka matrix Ξ_n and the matrix containing the number $st^{\beta}(\alpha)$ in the row with number α and in the column with number β have the same scalar products of rows: An application of 4.4.5 and of 4.3.9 gives:

$$\sum_{\gamma} st^{\gamma}(\alpha) st^{\gamma}(\beta) = m_{\alpha\beta} = \sum_{\gamma} \kappa_{\alpha\gamma} \kappa_{\beta\gamma}.$$

Furthermore both these matrices are upper triangular, by 4.3.22 and 4.4.1, and they have ones along their main diagonal. Thus, since their last rows are equal, an induction yields that they are elementwise equal. This also implies the statement on the dimensions (cf. 4.3.22).   □

A direct implication is obtained from 4.3.14:

$$\epsilon \xi^{\alpha} = \sum_{\gamma} st^{\gamma}(\alpha) \zeta^{\gamma'} = \sum_{\gamma} st^{\gamma'}(\alpha) \zeta^{\gamma},$$

so that

4.4.7
$$m'_{\alpha\beta} = [\xi^\beta \mid \epsilon\xi^\alpha] = \sum_{\gamma \vdash n} st^\gamma(\beta)st^{\gamma'}(\alpha).$$

With these results at hand it is now relatively easy to evaluate ordinary irreducible characters using Young characters. For example $ST^\beta((n))$ is nonempty if and only if $\beta = (n)$, in which case this set consists of the single tableau $1\dots1$. Hence we have $1 \cdot \zeta^{(n)} = \xi^{(n)}$, the identity character. This is of course obvious also from the definition of $[n]$. But what about $\zeta^{(n-r,r)}$, where $0 < r \le n/2$? As $ST^\beta((n-r,r))$, if it is nonempty, consists of the elements

$$\begin{array}{l} 1\dots\dots12\dots2 \\ 2\dots2 \end{array},$$

we derive from 4.4.6 the following decomposition:

4.4.8
$$\zeta^{(n-r,r)} = \sum_{0 \le s \le r} \zeta^{(n-s,s)}.$$

This, together with 4.3.28 gives

4.4.9
$$\zeta^{(n-1,1)}(\pi) = a_1(\pi) - 1, \zeta^{(n-2,2)} = \frac{a_1(\pi)(a_1(\pi) - 3)}{2} + a_2(\pi).$$

There exist in fact polynomial functions which yield irreducible character values if we apply them to cycle types. They do in fact depend on the truncated partition $\hat{\alpha}$ only, so that we can denote them by $Z^{\hat{\alpha}}$. Here are the smallest examples (cf. 4.3.30):

4.4.10
$$Z^\emptyset = 1, Z^{(1)} = x_1 - 1, Z^{(2)} = \frac{x_1(x_1 - 3)}{2} + x_2.$$

We shall consider the general case later.

Exercises

E 4.4.1 Give the remaining details of the proof that $Z \mapsto (T_1, T_2)$ is an injective mapping.

4.5 The Determinantal Form

In order to invert 4.4.6 by expressing the irreducible character ζ^α of S_n in terms of the Young characters ξ^β, we shall derive a basic combinatorial lemma which shows that $st^{\alpha}(\lambda)$ is an alternating sum of the numbers $m'_{\mu\nu}$. It should be mentioned already here that there exists an easier proof of this result. It is due to Littlewood (cf. his "University Algebra") and it uses Schur polynomials which we shall introduce later on. Moreover it is basically a comparison of coefficients between certain polynomials while the proof given here uses an inclusion–exclusion argument and bijections. It therefore yields in a sense more information.

For $\tau \in S_n$ and $\mu \models n$, put

$$\tau\mu := (\mu_1 + \tau 1 - 1, \mu_2 + \tau 2 - 2, \ldots, \mu_n + \tau n - n).$$

Using this notation we can consider, for each f from the set $IP(n)$ of improper partitions of n to the complex field $\mathbb{C}$, the expression

$$\sum_{\tau:\tau\lambda\models n} f(\tau\lambda),$$

where the sum has to be taken over all the $\tau \in S_n$ such that $\tau\lambda$ is an improper partition of n, i.e. for which each $\lambda_i + \tau i - i \geq 0$. The crucial result concerning expressions of this form will turn out to be

4.5.1 Doubilet's Lemma *For each $\alpha \vdash n, \lambda \models n$ the following equation holds:*

$$st^{\alpha'}(\lambda) = \sum_{\tau:\tau\alpha\models n} \epsilon(\tau)m'_{\tau\alpha,\lambda}.$$

Proof:

i) For $\tau \neq 1$ we describe a complete dissection of $M'_{\tau\alpha,\lambda}$ into pairwise disjoint subsets $C_{\tau}(t,i,j)$ and a subset B_{τ}. Then we show that the summand $\epsilon(\tau)c_{\tau}(t,i,j)$, where $c_{\tau}(t,i,j) := |C_{\tau}(t,i,j)|$, of $\epsilon(\tau)m'_{\tau\alpha,\lambda}$ cancels with $\epsilon(\tau(ij))c_{\tau(ij)}(t,i,j)$, the corresponding summand of $\epsilon(\tau(ij))m'_{\tau(ij)\alpha,\lambda}$.

    a) The decomposition of $M'_{\tau\alpha,\lambda}$: For each matrix A we denote by $s(t,i,A)$ the sum of the first t elements in its i-th row and define

$$C_{\tau} := \{A \in M'_{\tau\alpha,\lambda} \mid \exists t,i,j: i < j, s(t,i,A) - \tau i = s(t,j,A) - \tau j\}.$$

Then

$$M'_{\tau\alpha,\lambda} = C_{\tau} \,\dot{\bigcup}\, B_{\tau}, \text{ where } B_{\tau} := M'_{\tau\alpha,\lambda}\backslash C_{\tau},$$

and C_{τ} again can be decomposed into disjoint subsets $C_{\tau}(t,i,j)$, consisting of the $A \in C_{\tau}$ for which (t,i,j) is the lexicographically smallest triple such that

$$s(t,i,A) - \tau i = s(t,j,A) - \tau j. \tag{*}$$

Hence

$$M'_{\tau\alpha,\lambda} = B_\tau \,\dot\cup\, \left(\dot\cup_{t,i,j} C_\tau(t,i,j)\right).$$

Of course some of the $C_\tau(t,i,j)$ may very well be empty.

b) A bijection between $C_\tau(t,i,j)$ and $C_{\tau(ij)}(t,i,j)$: Consider $A = (a_{rs}) \in C_\tau(t,i,j)$. We exchange the first t elements of the i-th row of A with the elements in the j-th row and the same column. Let $A' := (a'_{rs})$ denote the resulting matrix. An easy check shows that A' is an element of $M'_{\tau(ij)\alpha,\lambda}$, while the minimality of (t,i,j) yields that A' is contained in $C_{\tau(ij)}(t,i,j)$. Furthermore $A \mapsto A'$ establishes a *bijection* between $C_\tau(t,i,j)$ and $C_{\tau(ij)}(t,i,j)$ since this operation is an involution.

c) We have thus obtained that each summand $\epsilon(\tau)c_\tau(t,i,j)$ of $\epsilon(\tau)m'_{\tau\alpha,\lambda}$ cancels with the corresponding summand:

$$\epsilon(\tau(ij))c_{\tau(ij)}(t,i,j) = -\epsilon(\tau)c_\tau(t,i,j),$$

which is a summand of $\epsilon(\sigma)m'_{\sigma\alpha,\lambda}$, where $\sigma := \tau(ij)$.

ii) Part i) has already shown that all the summands $\epsilon(\tau)|C_\tau|$ cancel so that it remains to examine the cases when $C_\tau \neq M'_{\tau\alpha,\lambda}$.

a) $\tau \neq 1$ implies that $C_\tau = M'_{\tau\alpha,\lambda}$: In order to prove this we have to verify that, for $\tau \neq 1$ and $A \in M'_{\tau\alpha,\lambda}$, there exists a triple (t,i,j) such that $(*)$ holds. But $\tau \neq 1$ implies the existence of $i < j$ such that $\tau i > \tau j$. Hence

$$s(0,i,A) - \tau i = -\tau i < -\tau j = s(0,j,A) - \tau j,$$

and also

$$s(\infty,i,A) - \tau i = \alpha_i - i > \alpha_j - j = s(\infty,j,A) - \tau j.$$

Now consider the sequences (x_t) and (y_t), where

$$x_t := s(t,i,A) - \tau i, \quad \text{and} \quad y_t := s(t,j,A) - \tau j.$$

As A is a 0–1–matrix, these sequences increase by 0 or 1 only. Thus $x_0 < y_0$ and $x_\infty > y_\infty$ yield the existence of t such that $x_t = y_t$ and hence $A \in C_\tau$.

b) a) together with i) yields

$$\sum_{\tau\alpha\models n} \epsilon(\tau)m'_{\tau\alpha,\lambda} = |M'_{\alpha,\lambda}\setminus C_1| = |B_1|.$$

It therefore remains to show that B_1 and $ST^{\alpha'}(\lambda)$ are bijective.

c) Consider $A \in M'_{\alpha,\lambda}\setminus C_1$, so that in particular for each t and $i < j$ we have

$$s(t, i, A) - i \neq s(t, j, A) - j.$$

We again examine the sequences (x_t) and (y_t), for which we have in this case $\tau = 1$:

$$x_0 = s(0, i, A) - i > -j = s(0, j, A) - j = y_0.$$

Thus $A \notin C_1$ implies that for each t and $i < j$ we have

$$x_t = s(t, i, A) - i > s(t, j, A) - j = y_t. \qquad (**)$$

This will help us to show that the following mapping is a bijection between B_1 and $ST^{\alpha'}(\lambda)$. We map A onto T_A, the tableau which contains in its i-th column the j's (in their natural order) for which $a_{ij} = 1$, e.g.

$$\begin{pmatrix} 1 & 0 & 1 \\ 0 & 1 & 0 \\ 0 & 0 & 0 \end{pmatrix} \mapsto \begin{matrix} 1 & 2 \\ 3 & \end{matrix} \quad and \quad \begin{pmatrix} 1 & 1 & 0 \\ 0 & 0 & 1 \\ 0 & 0 & 1 \end{pmatrix} \mapsto \begin{matrix} 1 & 3 & 3 \\ 2 & & \end{matrix}.$$

Now $A \in M'_{\alpha\lambda}$ yields that $\mathrm{sh}(T_A) = \alpha'$ and $c(T_A) = \lambda$. The strict monotony in the columns is trivial and hence it remains to check the weak monotony in the rows, which we prove indirectly, assuming that (i, j) is the lexicographically smallest pair for which this monotony is violated, i.e. for which we have $k := t_{i,j-1} > t_{i,j} =: l$. This assumption implies that $s(k, j-1, A) = s(l, j, A) = i$ and so we have, for $k > l$:

$$s(k, j - 1, A) = s(l, j, A). \qquad (***)$$

But as $a_{j-1,k} = 1$, we have

$$s(k, j - 1, A) > s(l, j - 1, A) \geq_{(**)} s(l, j, A),$$

which contradicts $(***)$.

□

The main consequence of Doubilet's Lemma now easily follows. We use the lexicographic order on $P(n)$ so that, for each $\varphi: P(n) \times P(n) \to \mathbb{C}$, we obtain a matrix $(\varphi_{\alpha\beta})$ containing the value $\varphi_{\alpha\beta} := \varphi(\alpha, \beta)$ in its α-th row and β-th column. Using this abbreviation and the notation A^t for the transpose of the matrix A, we already know that

4.5.2 $$(m'_{\alpha\beta}) = (st^\alpha(\beta))^t (st^{\alpha'}(\beta)).$$

Putting

$$\epsilon_{\alpha\beta} := \sum_{\tau:(\tau\alpha)^* = \beta} \epsilon(\tau),$$

where $(\tau\alpha)^*$ again denotes the *proper* partition obtained from $\tau\alpha$ by reordering this sequence in the case when it is an improper partition, Doubilet's Lemma together with 4.5.2 yields the crucial equation due to D. E. Littlewood:

4.5.3 The Standard Inversion $(\epsilon_{\alpha\beta})^{-1} = (st^\alpha(\beta))^t$.

Hence $(\epsilon_{\alpha\beta})$ is the inverse of the Kostka matrix and we can invert 4.4.6 obtaining

4.5.4 Corollary *For each* $\alpha \vdash n$ *we have*

$$\zeta^\alpha = \sum_{\beta \vdash n} \epsilon_{\alpha\beta} \xi^\beta = \sum_{\beta \trianglerighteq \alpha} \epsilon_{\alpha\beta} \xi^\beta,$$

is the uniquely determined $\mathbb{Z}$*–linear combination of* ζ^α *in terms of Young characters (recall 4.3.24).*

Another useful consequence of Doubilet's Lemma is

4.5.5 Corollary *For each* $\alpha \vdash n, \lambda \models n$ *and the corresponding proper partition* λ^* *obtained from* λ *by rearrangement, we have*

$$st^\alpha(\lambda) = st^\alpha(\lambda^*).$$

Our next aim is to determine a very explicit expression for the dimension f^α of $[\alpha]$. Corollary 4.5.4 has shown how its character can be expressed in determinantal form using the Young characters $\xi^{\tau\alpha}$. With the aid of the symbol # which we use for the outer tensor product and keeping in mind that $[m]$ is the identity representation of $S_{\underline{m}}$, we see that, for $\tau\alpha \models n$, $\xi^{\tau\alpha}$ is the character of the representation

$$[\alpha_1 + \tau_1 - 1][\alpha_2 + \tau2 - 2]\ldots := [\alpha_1 + \tau1 - 1]\#[\alpha_2 + \tau2 - 2]\#\ldots \uparrow S_{\underline{n}}.$$

(More generally we put, for $\alpha \models m, \beta \models n$:

$$[\alpha][\beta] \; := \; [\alpha]\#[\beta] \uparrow S_{\underline{m+n}},$$

where we mean by $[\alpha]\#[\beta]$ the irreducible representation of the subgroup $S_{\underline{m}} \oplus S_{\underline{n}}$ of $S_{\underline{m+n}}$.) This notation allows us to rephrase the first part of 4.5.4 as follows:

4.5.6 The Determinantal Form *The irreducible representation* $[\alpha], \alpha \vdash n$ *of* $S_{\underline{n}}$ *can be expressed as follows in terms of Young representations:*

$$[\alpha] = \det\left([\alpha_i + j - i]\right).$$

But this notation must be used with care, it must be interpreted in terms of characters since it contains summands with negative signs. It describes, as it was already stated, ζ^{α} as a generalized character, and since we defined summands $\xi^{\tau\alpha}$ if and only if $\tau\alpha \models n$, we have to put $\xi^{\tau\alpha} = 0$ otherwise, and also we have to set $\xi^{(0)} := 1$. An example illustrates this:

$$[3,1^2] = \det \begin{pmatrix} [3] & [4] & [5] \\ 1 & [1] & [2] \\ 0 & 1 & [1] \end{pmatrix} = [3][1][1] - [3][2] - [4][1] + [5].$$

This has to be considered as being a "virtual representation". It is preferable to consider the corresponding generalized character (cf. exercise 4.2.4):

$$\zeta^{(3,1^2)} = \xi^{(3,1,1)} - \xi^{(3,2)} - \xi^{(4,1)} + \xi^{(5)}.$$

From this determinantal form of $[\alpha]$ we can easily derive important results on the values of irreducible characters, e.g. the character of the n–cycle:

$$\text{4.5.7} \qquad \zeta^{\alpha}((1\ldots n)) = \begin{cases} (-1)^r & \text{if } \alpha = (n-r, 1^r), r \leq n-1, \\ 0 & \text{otherwise.} \end{cases}$$

Proof: The only Young subgroup S_{β} containing n–cycles is $S_{(n)} = S_{\underline{n}}$ itself. Thus $\zeta^{\alpha}((1\ldots n)) \neq 0$ implies that $\det\left([\alpha_i + j - i]\right)$ must contain an entry equal to $[n]$, and hence

$$\det([\alpha_i + j - i]) = \det \begin{pmatrix} [\alpha_1] & \cdots & [n] \\ & \ddots & \vdots \\ \star & & [\alpha_h] \end{pmatrix},$$

which implies that $\alpha = (n - (h-1), 1^{h-1})$. Furthermore in this case we get

$$\zeta^\alpha((1\ldots n)) = (-1)^{h-1}\xi^{(n)}((1\ldots n)) = (-1)^{h-1}.$$

□

Thus $\zeta^\alpha((1\ldots n))$ is nonzero if and only if $[\alpha]$ is a diagram of shape:

$$[\alpha] = [n-r, 1^r] = \begin{array}{l} \times \quad \times \quad \ldots \quad \times \\ \times \\ \vdots \\ \times \end{array} \quad .$$

Such diagrams are called *hooks* and they play a very important role in the representation theory of the symmetric groups. Hooks allow many results to be formulated in an easy manner. We define the (i,j)–*hook*

$$H_{ij}^\alpha$$

to be the following subset of $[\alpha]$: The node (i,j) itself, which we call the *corner* of this hook, together with its *arm* consisting of the nodes $(i,k), k > j$, and also the *leg* of the hook, consisting of the nodes $(l,j), l > i$. The overall number h_{ij}^α of nodes in H_{ij}^α is called the *length* of the hook, while the *leg length* is denoted by l_{ij}^α :

$$h_{ij}^\alpha = \alpha_i - j + \alpha_j' - i + 1, \quad l_{ij}^\alpha = \alpha_j' - i.$$

It is important to realize that to each hook H_{ij}^α there corresponds a uniquely determined part

$$R_{ij}^\alpha$$

of the *rim* of $[\alpha]$ which also consists of h_{ij}^α nodes and which begins with the node (i, α_i) and ends with the node (α_j', j). For example to $H_{11}^{(3,2,1^2)}$ there corresponds the part of the rim of $[3, 2, 1^2]$ which we indicated by encircled nodes:

$$\begin{array}{ll} \times & \otimes \quad \otimes \\ \otimes & \otimes \\ \otimes \\ \otimes \end{array}$$

The main fact is that the deletion of R_{ij}^α from $[\alpha]$ leaves a Young diagram, we denote it by

$$[\alpha] \backslash R_{ij}^\alpha.$$

For example: $[3,2,1^2] \backslash R_{11}^{(3,2,1^2)} = \times = [1]$.

Using this notation we can express the dimension f^α of $[\alpha]$ in terms of hook lengths as follows:

4.5.8 The Hook Formula *The dimension f^α of the ordinary irreducible representation $[\alpha]$ of $S_{\underline{n}}$ can be expressed as follows in terms of hook lengths:*

$$f^\alpha = \frac{n!}{\prod_{i,j} h_{ij}^\alpha}.$$

Proof: We apply the determinantal formula which yields

$$f^\alpha = n! \cdot \det\left(\frac{1}{(\alpha_i + j - i)!}\right)$$

with the convention that $(\alpha_i + j - i)!^{-1} := 0$, if $\alpha_i + j - i < 0$. Elementary transformations applied to this determinant yield

$$\det\left(\frac{1}{(\alpha_i + j - i)!}\right) = \frac{1}{\prod_i h_{i1}^\alpha!} \det\left(\frac{h_{i1}^\alpha!}{(\alpha_i + j - i)!}\right)$$

$$= \frac{1}{\prod_i h_{i1}^\alpha!} \det\left(\prod_{r=1}^{h-j}(h_{i1}^\alpha + r + j - h)\right).$$

Further elementary transformations of the determinant on the right hand side of this equation yield the Vandermonde determinant

$$\det\left((h_{i1}^\alpha)^{h-j}\right) = \prod_{i<j}(h_{i1}^\alpha - h_{j1}^\alpha).$$

This shows that f^α can be expressed in terms of the hooks H_{i1}^α which have their corner in the first column. It also shows that we can complete the proof by showing that for $1 \le i \le q$ we have

4.5.9
$$\prod_{j=i+1}^{h}(h_{i1}^\alpha - h_{j1}^\alpha) \prod_{v=1}^{\alpha_i} h_{iv}^\alpha = h_{i1}^\alpha!.$$

The verification of this is left as an exercise.

□

Another useful application of the determinantal form of $[\alpha]$ is the proof of the following theorem on the irreducible characters ζ^α which was already mentioned in connection with 4.3.29 when the analogous result for Young characters ξ^α was proved:

4.5.10 Specht's Theorem *For each partition* $\hat{\alpha} := (\alpha_2, \ldots, \alpha_h) \vdash n$ *there exists a uniquely determined polynomial*

$$Z^{\hat{\alpha}} = \sum_\sigma \epsilon(\sigma) \Xi^{(\alpha_2 + \sigma(2) - 2, \ldots, \alpha_h + \sigma(h) - h)} \in \mathbf{Q}[x_1, x_2, \ldots],$$

sum over all the $\sigma \in S_h$, *that yields all the values of all the irreducible characters* ζ^β *for which* $\beta = (\beta_1, \alpha_2, \ldots, \alpha_h)$ *by applying the corresponding polynomial function to the cycle type in question:*

$$\zeta^\beta(\pi) = Z^{\hat{\alpha}}(a_1(\pi), \ldots, a_m(\pi)), m := n + \beta_1.$$

Proof: The determinantal form of $[\alpha]$, $\alpha = (\alpha_1, \alpha_2, \ldots, \alpha_h) \vdash n$, yields

$$\zeta^\alpha(\pi) = \sum_\sigma \epsilon(\sigma) \zeta^{(\alpha_1 + \sigma(1) - 1, \alpha_2 + \sigma(2) - 2, \ldots, \alpha_h + \sigma(h) - h)},$$

so that the statement follows by an applications of 4.3.29.

$\square$

Since the name "Specht polynomials" is already used for a different series of polynomials we call the $Z^{\hat{\alpha}}$ *character polynomials* . Here are two further examples ($Z^\emptyset$, $Z^{(1)}$ and $Z^{(2)}$ were already shown in 4.4.10):

$$Z^{(1^2)} = \binom{x_1}{2} - \binom{x_2}{1} - \binom{x_1}{1} + 1,$$

$$Z^{(3)} = \binom{x_3}{1} + \binom{x_1}{1}\binom{x_2}{1} + \binom{x_1}{3} - \binom{x_2}{1} - \binom{x_1}{2}.$$

(I did not simplify these expressions since 4.5.10 shows that each character polynomial is in fact a $\mathbb{Z}$–linear combination of products of binomials, see also the further character polynomials given in the Appendix.)

4.6 Standard bideterminants

We have used bijections between sets of matrices and sets of pairs of standard tableaux in order to derive the ordinary irreducible representations of symmetric groups. A further bijection leads from sets of pairs of tableaux to polynomials on which the symmetric group acts in a natural way and from which we shall obtain *bases* which yield the ordinary irreducible *matrix representations*, as will be described next. Consider the ring of polynomials over $\mathbb{Z}$ in the commuting indeterminates X_{ij}, where $i, j \in \mathbb{N}^*$:

$$\mathbb{Z}[X] := \mathbb{Z}[X_{ij} \mid i, j \in \mathbb{N}^*].$$

Since we assume the indeterminates to be commutative, we can decompose $\mathbb{Z}[X]$ into submodules according to degree. In order to do this we put

$$X^Z := \prod_{i,j} X_{ij}^{z_{ij}}, \text{ for each } Z \in M_{\lambda\mu},$$

and indicate by $\mathbb{Z}_{\lambda\mu}$, where $\lambda, \mu \models n$, the $\mathbb{Z}$–span of these monomials:

$$\mathbb{Z}_{\lambda\mu} := \langle X^Z \mid Z \in M_{\lambda\mu} \rangle_{\mathbb{Z}},$$

from which we obtain the obvious decomposition

4.6.1 $$\mathbb{Z}[X] = \bigoplus_n \bigoplus_{\lambda,\mu \models n} \mathbb{Z}_{\lambda\mu}.$$

Now we introduce the following abbreviation, for $i_v, j_\mu \in \mathbb{N}^*$:

$$\begin{pmatrix} i_1 & j_1 \\ \vdots & \vdots \\ i_m & j_m \end{pmatrix} := \det \begin{pmatrix} X_{i_1 j_1} & \cdots & X_{i_m j_m} \\ \vdots & & \vdots \\ X_{i_m j_1} & \cdots & X_{i_m j_m} \end{pmatrix} \in \mathbb{Z}[X].$$

For example

$$\begin{pmatrix} 1 & 4 \\ 3 & 8 \\ 3 & 2 \end{pmatrix} = \det \begin{pmatrix} X_{14} & X_{18} & X_{12} \\ X_{34} & X_{38} & X_{32} \\ X_{34} & X_{38} & X_{32} \end{pmatrix} = 0.$$

And, for any bitableau (S, T), where S and T are tableaux of *the same shape* over $\mathbb{N}^*$, we denote by $(S \mid T)$ the product of the determinants arising from corresponding columns:

$$\begin{pmatrix} i_1 & k_1 & \cdots & j_1 & l_1 & \cdots \\ \vdots & \vdots & & \vdots & \vdots \\ \vdots & k_n & & \vdots & l_n \\ i_m & & & j_m & \end{pmatrix} = \det(X_{i_v j_\mu}) \cdot \det(X_{k_v l_\mu}) \cdot \ldots,$$

in particular

$$(i_1 \ldots k_1 \mid j_1 \ldots l_1) = X_{i_1 j_1} \cdot \ldots \cdot X_{k_1 l_1}.$$

There are natural actions of the symmetric group of $\mathbb{N}^*$ on $\mathbb{Z}[X]$ from the left and from the right:

$$\sigma f(\ldots, X_{ij}, \ldots) := f(\ldots, X_{\sigma i, j}, \ldots),$$

$$f(\ldots, X_{ij}, \ldots)\tau := f(\ldots, X_{i, \tau^{-1} j}, \ldots).$$

Clearly each of the submodules $\mathbb{Z}_{(1^n), \mu}$ is invariant under the restriction to S_n of the action from the left. The same holds for $\mathbb{Z}_{\lambda, (1^n)}$ and the action from the right. Furthermore, if $\sigma, \tau \in S_n$, then we have

4.6.2
$$\begin{pmatrix} i_{\sigma 1} & j_{\tau 1} \\ \vdots & \vdots \\ i_{\sigma n} & j_{\tau n} \end{pmatrix} = \text{sign}(\sigma\tau) \begin{pmatrix} i_1 & j_1 \\ \vdots & \vdots \\ i_n & j_n \end{pmatrix}.$$

Now we recall that a tableau S over $\mathbb{N}^*$ of shape α is a mapping. with domain

$$[\alpha] = \bigcup_i \{(i, 1), \ldots, (i, \alpha_i)\},$$

and range $\mathbb{N}^*$, namely

$$S : [\alpha] \to \mathbb{N}^* : (i, j) \mapsto s_{ij}.$$

The content of the tableau S was defined to be the following sequence of multiplicities of values:

$$c(S) = (|S^{-1}[\{1\}]|, |S^{-1}[\{2\}]|, \ldots),$$

so that $c(S) \models n$, if the shape α of S is a partition of n. Now we note that there are two canonic Young subgroups of the symmetric group

$$S_{[\alpha]}$$

on the set of nodes $(i, j) \in [\alpha]$: The *horizontal group* H_α, consisting of the *horizontal* or *row permutations* , and the *vertical group* V_α consisting of the *vertical* or *column permutations*:

$$H_\alpha := \{\pi \in S_{[\alpha]} \mid \pi \text{ leaves each } (i, j) \text{ in its row}\},$$

$$V_\alpha := \{\pi \in S_{[\alpha]} \mid \pi \text{ leaves each } (i, j) \text{ in its column}\}.$$

These subgroups of $S_{[\alpha]}$ will help us easily to describe several polynomials associated with a bitableau (S, T) consisting of two tableaux S and T of shape α: The *natural monomial* is defined to be

$$\{S \mid T\} := \prod_{(i,j) \in [\alpha]} X_{S_{ij}, T_{ij}},$$

in terms of which the corresponding bideterminant now reads as follows:

4.6.3　$(S \mid T) = \sum_{\sigma \in V_\alpha} \text{sign}(\sigma)\{S \circ \sigma \mid T\} = \sum_{\tau \in V_\alpha} \text{sign}(\tau)\{S \mid T \circ \tau\}.$

The bideterminants that correspond to *standard* bitableaux are called *standard bideterminants* , and it is our main aim to show that they form a *basis* of $\mathbb{Z}[X]$. For example

$$(21 \mid 12) = (12 \mid 12) - \left(\begin{matrix} 1 & 2 \\ 1 & 2 \end{matrix} \right).$$

In order to prove the independence of the standard bideterminants, we introduce an important result from multilinear algebra. It holds not only for diagrams $[\alpha]$ but also for arbitrary finite subsets A of $\mathbb{N}^* \times \mathbb{N}^*$, for which we can define tableaux, horizontal or vertical groups H_A or V_A, and bideterminants $(S \mid T)$ in an obvious way. For example

$$\left(\begin{matrix} & 3 & & 7 & \\ 2 & & 6 & & \\ 5 & 1 & 8 & 1 & \end{matrix} \right) := \left(\begin{matrix} 2 & 6 \\ 5 & 8 \end{matrix} \right) \cdot \left(\begin{matrix} 3 & 7 \\ 1 & 1 \end{matrix} \right).$$

4.6.4 Theorem (Clausen) *Assume that $A, B \subseteq \mathbb{N}^* \times \mathbb{N}^*$ are finite, that $\varphi : A \to B$ is a bijection, S a tableau with shape A and T a tableau with shape B. Put $\psi := \varphi^{-1}$, denote by $\mathcal{T}(\varphi)$ a transversal of*

$$\varphi V_A \varphi^{-1} / \varphi V_A \varphi^{-1} \cap V_B,$$

by $\mathcal{T}(\psi)$ a transversal of

$$\psi V_B \psi^{-1} / \psi V_B \psi^{-1} \cap V_A.$$

Then the following identity holds:

$$\sum_{\sigma \in \mathcal{T}(\psi)} \text{sign}(\sigma)(S \circ \sigma \mid T \circ \varphi) = \sum_{\tau \in \mathcal{T}(\varphi)} \text{sign}(\tau)(S \circ \psi \mid T \circ \tau).$$

Proof: We consider the sum of monomials

$$(S \mid T)_\varphi := \sum_{\sigma \in \psi V_B \psi^{-1} \cdot V_A} \mathrm{sign}(\sigma)\{S \circ \sigma \mid T \circ \varphi\},$$

which is, by 4.6.3, equal to

$$\sum_\sigma \mathrm{sign}(\sigma)\{S \mid T \circ \varphi \circ \sigma^{-1}\} = \sum_\sigma \{S \circ \varphi^{-1} \mid T \circ \varphi \circ \sigma^{-1} \circ \varphi^{-1}\}.$$

Now we note that $\sigma \mapsto \varphi \circ \sigma^{-1} \circ \varphi^{-1}$ is a bijection between $\psi V_B \psi^{-1} \cdot V_A$ and $\varphi V_A \varphi^{-1} \cdot V_B$, so that we can proceed as follows:

$$= \sum_{\tau \in \varphi V_A \varphi^{-1} \cdot V_B} \mathrm{sign}(\tau)\{S \circ \varphi^{-1} \mid T \circ \tau\} =: {}_\psi(S \mid T).$$

Moreover, as

$$\psi V_B \psi^{-1} \cdot V_A = \sum_{\eta \in \mathscr{T}(\psi)} \eta V_A,$$

we have that

$$(S \mid T)_\varphi = \sum_{\eta \in \mathscr{T}(\psi)} \mathrm{sign}(\eta) \sum_{\theta \in V_A} \mathrm{sign}(\theta)\{S \circ \eta \circ \theta \mid T \circ \varphi\}$$

$$= \sum_{\eta \in \mathscr{T}(\psi)} \mathrm{sign}(\eta)(S \circ \eta \mid T \circ \varphi),$$

which is the left hand side of the stated equality. Hence, by symmetry, ${}_\psi(S \mid T)$ is equal to the right hand side, and this completes the proof. □

4.6.5 Example Consider the tableaux

$$S := \begin{matrix} 1 \\ \vdots \\ k-1 \\ k \\ k+1 \\ \vdots \\ n \end{matrix}, \quad \text{and} \quad T := \begin{matrix} 1 \\ \vdots \\ k-1 \\ k \\ k+1 \\ \vdots \\ n \end{matrix},$$

in which case $\varphi = \psi$ is the transposition $((k,1),(k,2))$, while

$$V_A = S_{\{(1,1),\dots,(k-1,1),(k+1,1),\dots,(n,1)\}} \oplus S_{\{(k,2)\}} \simeq S_{n-1},$$

$$V_B = S_{\{(1,1),\dots,(n,1)\}} \simeq S_n.$$

Hence

$$\mathcal{T}(\varphi) = \{1\}, \quad \mathcal{T}(\psi) = \{((j,1),(k,2)) \mid j \in \underline{n}\setminus\{k\}\} \cup \{1\}.$$

Thus we obtain for the right hand side of the equation proved in 4.6.4:

$$\sum_{\tau \in \mathcal{T}(\psi)} \operatorname{sign}(\tau)(S \circ \psi \mid T \circ \tau) = (S \circ \psi \mid T \circ \tau) = \begin{pmatrix} \left. \begin{matrix} 1 \\ \vdots \\ n \end{matrix} \right| \begin{matrix} 1 \\ \vdots \\ n \end{matrix} \end{pmatrix}.$$

The left hand side is

$$\sum_{\sigma \in \mathcal{T}(\psi)} \operatorname{sign}(\sigma)(S \circ \sigma \mid T \circ \varphi) = \sum_{\sigma \in \mathcal{T}(\psi)} -(S \circ \sigma \mid T \circ \varphi),$$

where, for $\sigma := ((j,1),(k,2))$, we have (if $j \le k-1$):

$$(S \circ \sigma \mid T \circ \varphi) = \begin{pmatrix} \left. \begin{matrix} 1 \\ \vdots \\ j-1 \\ k \\ j+1 \\ \vdots \\ k-1 \\ k+1 \\ \vdots \\ n \end{matrix} \right| \begin{matrix} 1 \\ \vdots \\ j-1 \\ j \\ j+1 \\ \vdots \\ k-1 \\ k+1 \\ \vdots \\ n \end{matrix} \end{pmatrix} = (j|k) \begin{pmatrix} \left. \begin{matrix} 1 \\ \vdots \\ j-1 \\ k \\ j+1 \\ k-1 \\ k+1 \\ \vdots \\ n \end{matrix} \right| \begin{matrix} 1 \\ \vdots \\ j-1 \\ j \\ j+1 \\ k-1 \\ k+1 \\ \vdots \\ n \end{matrix} \end{pmatrix}$$

$$= (j \mid k)(-1)^{k-j-1} \begin{pmatrix} \left. \begin{matrix} 1 \\ \vdots \\ j-1 \\ j+1 \\ \vdots \\ n \end{matrix} \right| \begin{matrix} 1 \\ \vdots \\ k-1 \\ k+1 \\ \vdots \\ n \end{matrix} \end{pmatrix}.$$

This proves the well known expansion of the determinant of (X_{jk}) along the k-th column:

$$
\begin{pmatrix} 1 & 1 \\ \vdots & \vdots \\ n & n \end{pmatrix} = \sum_j (-1)^{j+k} (j \mid k) \begin{pmatrix} 1 & & 1 \\ \vdots & & \vdots \\ j-1 & & k-1 \\ j+1 & & k+1 \\ \vdots & & \vdots \\ n & & n \end{pmatrix}.
$$

It is clear that many other determinantal identities can also be obtained from the theorem proved above.

$\diamond$

We now introduce the following total order $\leq$ on $\mathbb{N}^* \times \mathbb{N}^*$, since we want to define canonic transversals:

$$(i,j) \leq (k,l) \quad :\Longleftrightarrow \quad (j > l) \vee (j = l \wedge i \leq k).$$

The smallest elements with respect to $\leq$ in their left coset form *canonic transversals* $\mathscr{C}(\varphi)$ and $\mathscr{C}(\psi)$. In order to describe them more explicitly we recall the notion of tabloid, and we remember that a tabloid represents the lexicographically smallest element of its left coset with respect to the corresponding Young subgroup. Since here we are dealing with Young subgroups, too, namely with $V_A, V_B, \varphi V_A \varphi^{-1}$, $\psi V_B \psi^{-1}$ and their intersections, their smallest representatives are the permutations that are increasing (with respect to $\leq$) on each block. Denoting by A^j and B^j the columns of A and B, we therefore obtain the following result:

$$\mathscr{C}(\varphi) = \{\pi \in S_B \mid \forall\, j,k : \pi[\varphi[A^j]] = \varphi[A^j], \pi \text{ increases on } \varphi[A^j] \cap B^k\},$$

$$\mathscr{C}(\psi) = \{\pi \in S_A \mid \forall\, j,k : \pi[\psi[B^j]] = \psi[B^j], \pi \text{ increases on } \psi[B^j] \cap A^k\}.$$

These permutations are called *shuffles* with respect to φ and ψ, respectively.

4.6.6 Example Consider $A := [2^4, 1], B := [3, 2, 1^4]$ and the following bijection $\varphi : [2^4, 1] \rightarrow [3, 2, 1^4]$, which we define by replacing $(i,j) \in$

$[3, 2, 1^4]$ by its inverse image $(r, s) := \psi((i, j)) = \varphi^{-1}((i, j))$:

$$\psi := \begin{array}{lll} (1,2) & (3,2) & (1,1) \\ (2,2) & (4,2) & \\ (2,1) & & \\ (3,1) & & \\ (4,1) & & \\ (5,1) & & \end{array} \quad.$$

Then $\psi V_B \psi^{-1} = V_{\psi[B]}$ is equal to

$$S_{\{(1,2),(2,2),(2,1),(3,1),(4,1),(5,1)\}} \oplus S_{\{(3,2),(4,2)\}} \oplus S_{\{(1,1)\}} \simeq S_{(6,2,1)},$$

and its intersection with V_A is

$$S_{\{(1,2),(2,2)\}} \oplus S_{\{(2,1),(3,1),(4,1),(5,1)\}} \oplus S_{\{(3,2),(4,2)\}} \oplus S_{\{(1,1)\}} \simeq S_{(2,4,2,1)}.$$

Thus $\mathscr{C}(\psi)$ is the set of elements of $\psi V_B \psi^{-1}$ that are increasing on each of the sets

$$\{(1, 2), (2, 2)\}, \{(2, 1), (3, 1), (4, 1), (5, 1)\}, \{(3, 2), (4, 2)\}, \{(1, 1)\}.$$

We express this symbolically in the following way (abbreviating (i, k) by ik):

$$\mathscr{C}(\psi) = \left\| \begin{array}{c} 12\ 22 \\ \nearrow \end{array} \right| \begin{array}{c} 21\ 31\ 41\ 51 \\ \nearrow \end{array} \left\| \begin{array}{c} 32\ 42 \\ \nearrow \end{array} \right\| \begin{array}{c} 11 \\ \nearrow \end{array} \right\|.$$

For example

$$\begin{pmatrix} 12 & 22 & 21 & 31 & 41 & 51 & 32 & 42 & 11 \\ 22 & 41 & 12 & 21 & 31 & 51 & 32 & 42 & 11 \end{pmatrix} \in \mathscr{C}(\psi),$$

and

$$|\mathscr{C}(\psi)| = \binom{6}{2,4} \cdot \binom{2}{2} \cdot \binom{1}{1} = 15.$$

Now we introduce a total order on the set $BT(\lambda, \mu)$ of bitableaux: Assume that $(S, T) \in BT^\alpha(\lambda, \mu)$ and $(S', T') \in BT^\beta(\lambda, \mu)$, then we define

$$(S, T) \leq (S', T') \quad :\Longleftrightarrow \quad (\alpha' > \beta') \vee (\alpha' = \beta' \wedge S * T \leq S' * T'),$$

where $S * T$ means the concatenation of the words obtained from S and T by reading one column after the other from top to bottom and from left to right:

$$S * T = s_{11} s_{21} \ldots s_{\alpha'_1, 1} s_{12} s_{22} \ldots t_{11} t_{21} \ldots,$$

and $S' * T'$ is defined correspondingly, while $S * T \leq S' * T'$ uses the lexicographic order of these words.

4.6.7 Theorem *If* $(U, V) \in BT(\lambda, \mu)$ *is not standard, then its bidetermi-nant* $(U \mid V)$ *is a* $\mathbb{Z}$*–linear combination of bideterminants corresponding to bitableaux* $(S, T) \in BT(\lambda, \mu)$ *that are strictly smaller than* (U, V).

Proof: By induction using the total order introduced above.
i) If (U, V) consists of tableaux U, V with one column only, then, since (U, V) is not standard, we obtain a unique standard tableau (S, T) by rcordering both U and V, hence $(S, T) < (U, V)$ and $(U \mid V) = \pm (S \mid T)$.
ii) Suppose that $(U, V) \in BT(\lambda, \mu)$ is not standard, that the shape α of U and V has more than one column, and that the statement is true for each nonstandard $(U', V') < (U, V)$. We note that we can make the following additional assumptions:

- Both U and V consist of injective columns, since otherwise $(U \mid V)$ is zero (in which case the statement holds).

- The columns are strictly increasing from top to bottom, since reordering within a column means only a change in sign.

Hence the first violation of the standardness looks as follows (assuming that these are the columns U^j and U^{j+1} of U):

$$
\begin{array}{ccc}
a_1 & \leq & b_1 \\
\wedge & & \wedge \\
\vdots & & \vdots \\
\wedge & & \wedge \\
a_{k-1} & \leq & b_{k-1} \\
\wedge & & \wedge \\
a_k & > & b_k \\
\wedge & & \wedge \\
\vdots & & \vdots \\
\vdots & & \wedge \\
\vdots & & b_t \\
\vdots & & \\
\wedge & & \\
a_s & &
\end{array}
$$

Correspondingely we have for the bideterminant that

$$(U \mid V) = (U^j \mid V^j)(U^{j+1} \mid V^{j+1}) \prod_{i: j \neq i \neq j+1} (U^i \mid V^i).$$

Let us consider the following bijection on the shape A of $U^j U^{j+1}$:

$$\varphi = \psi^{-1}: A \to B, \text{ defined by } \begin{matrix} (1,2) & (1,1) \\ (2,2) & (2,1) \\ \vdots & \vdots \\ (k-1,2) & (k-1,1) \\ (k+1,1) & (k,1) \\ (k+2,1) & (1,3) \\ \vdots & \vdots \\ \vdots & (t-k,3) \\ (s+1,1) & \end{matrix}.$$

Furthermore we put $S := U^j U^{j+1}$, and $T := (V^j V^{j+1}) \circ \psi$, obtaining from theorem 4.6.4 the following expression for $(S \mid T \circ \varphi)$:

$$-\sum_{1 \neq \sigma \in \mathscr{C}(\psi)} \mathrm{sign}(\sigma)(S \circ \sigma \mid T \circ \varphi) + \sum_{\tau \in \mathscr{C}(\varphi)} \mathrm{sign}(\tau)(S \circ \psi \mid T \circ \tau).$$

Let us consider each of the two sums on the right hand side separately.
a) We note that the transversal is

$$\mathscr{C}(\psi) = \left\| \begin{matrix} 11 \dots k-1, 1 \\ \nearrow \end{matrix} \right\| \begin{matrix} 12 \dots k2 \\ \nearrow \end{matrix} \left| \begin{matrix} k1 \dots s1 \\ \nearrow \end{matrix} \right\| \begin{matrix} k+1, 2 \dots t2 \\ \nearrow \end{matrix} \right\|.$$

Hence the word corresponding to $S \circ \sigma$ is of the form

$$a_1 \dots a_{k-1} w b_{k+1} \dots b_t,$$

where w is a word that is a permutation of the chain

$$b_1 < \dots < b_k < a_k < \dots < a_s.$$

Thus $S \circ \sigma < S$, if $\sigma \neq 1$, and hence $S \circ \sigma * T \circ \varphi = U^j U^{j+1} * V^j V^{j+1}$ is lexicographically smaller than $S * T \circ \varphi$.
b) For the second sum in the above equation we need only note that the image B of A, the shape of $U^j U^{j+1}$, consists of *three* columns, so

that the word $S \circ \psi * T \circ \tau$ is lexicographically smaller than the word $U^j U^{j+1} * V^j V^{j+1}$, too, and we are done.

□

In order to proceed with the proof of the independency of the standard bideterminants, we shall introduce linear operators on the set of polynomials

$$\mathbb{Z}[X]_n := \{f \in \mathbb{Z}[X] \mid f \text{ is homogeneous of degree } n\}.$$

For this purpose we construct, for each $Z = (z_{ij}) \in M_{\lambda\mu}, \lambda, \mu \models n$, two $\mathbb{Z}$–endomorphisms L_Z and R_Z of $\mathbb{Z}[X]_n$. They will be defined in terms of sets of the following type:

$$Sub_Z(U) := \{S \in T^\alpha(\mathbb{N}^*) \mid \forall i, j : z_{ij} = |S^{-1}[\{i\}] \cap U^{-1}[\{j\}]|\},$$

corresponding to $U \in T^\alpha(\mathbb{N}^*)$. Note that $Sub_Z(U)$ *is the set of all the α–tableaux S which arise from the α–tableau U over $\mathbb{N}^*$ by substituting z_{ij} entries j in U by i, for each $(i, j) \in [\alpha]$, simultaneaously and independently.* Hence in particular $Sub_Z(U) = \emptyset$, if $U \notin T^\alpha(\mu)$. We put

$$L_Z\{U \mid V\} := \sum_{S \in Sub_Z(U)} \{S \mid V\},$$

and, correspondingly,

$$R_Z\{U \mid V\} := \sum_{T \in Sub_Z(V)} \{U \mid T\}.$$

It is not difficult to check that these mappings are well defined (exercise 4.6.1), so that we can linearly extend them to $\mathbb{Z}[X]_n$. The resulting $\mathbb{Z}$–endomorphisms L_Z and R_Z are called the *left* and the *right substitution corresponding to Z.* From their definition we can easily derive that they satisfy

4.6.8 $\quad L_Z(U \mid V) = \displaystyle\sum_{S \in Sub_Z(U)} (S \mid V), R_Z(U \mid V) = \sum_{T \in Sub_Z(V)} (U \mid T).$

Now we use that we can restrict the summation to the $S \in Sub_Z(U)$ that consist of injective columns only: $L_Z(U \mid V)$ is equal to

$$\sum_{\substack{c.inj.\ S \in Sub_Z(U)}} (S \mid V), R_Z(U \mid V) = \sum_{\substack{c.inj.\ T \in Sub_Z(V)}} (U \mid T).$$

Hence, in particular, $L_Z(U \mid V) = 0$, or $R_Z(U \mid V) = 0$, if $Sub_Z(U)$ or $Sub_Z(V)$ does not contain any column injective element.

Now we restrict attention to specific matrices $Z(S)$ arising from tableaux $S \in T^\alpha(\underline{n})$ by putting $z_{ij}, i, j \in \underline{n}$, equal to the number of j occuring in the i-th row of S:

$$Z(S)_{ij} := |\{i\} \times \mathbb{N}^* \cap S^{-1}[\{j\}]|.$$

For example

$$Z \begin{pmatrix} 1 & 1 & 3 & 3 \\ 2 & 3 & 4 & \\ 4 & & & \end{pmatrix} = \begin{pmatrix} 2 & 0 & 2 & 0 \\ 0 & 1 & 1 & 1 \\ 0 & 0 & 0 & 1 \\ 0 & 0 & 0 & 0 \end{pmatrix}.$$

Using this notation we put

$$C_{ST} := L_{Z(S)} R_{Z(T)},$$

and call it the *Capelli operator associated with* (S, T). In order to reach a position where we can use these Capelli operators for a proof of the independency of the standard bideterminants, we need the following result:

4.6.9 The Sorting Lemma *Each tableau T on $\underline{n}$, the columns of which are strictly increasing from top to bottom, yields a standard tableau*

$$T^s$$

when we reorder the elements of each of its rows in the natural way.

Proof: By induction on the maximal entry m of T.

i) If $m = 1$, then $T = 1 \ldots 1 = T^s$ is standard.

ii) Assume that $m > 1$. Each m is the bottom entry of its column. We order each set of columns of the same length lexicographically according to their bottom entries. The resulting diagram is called X, and obviously $X^s = T^s$. Moreover $X \mapsto X^s$ does not move any entry m, so that we can cancel m and apply the induction assumption to the remaining rest.

□

For example

$$T := \begin{array}{cccc} 1 & 2 & 2 & 7 \\ 3 & 3 & 9 & 8 \\ 5 & 4 & 10 & \\ 8 & 5 & & \end{array} \mapsto T^s = \begin{array}{cccc} 1 & 2 & 2 & 7 \\ 3 & 3 & 8 & 9 \\ 4 & 5 & 10 & \\ 5 & 8 & & \end{array}.$$

4.6.10 Lemma *Let* S *and* T *denote* α–*tableaux,* $\alpha \vdash n$, *with strictly increasing columns. Then we have, for*

$$
T_\alpha := \begin{array}{cccc}
1 & 1 & \ldots \ldots & 1 \\
2 & 2 & \ldots & 2 \\
\ldots & \ldots & \ldots & \\
\alpha'_1 & \ldots & \alpha'_1 &
\end{array},
$$

that

$$
L_{Z(S)}(S \mid T) = (T_\alpha \mid T) \neq 0, \; R_{Z(S)}(S \mid T) = (S \mid T_\alpha) \neq 0,
$$

and hence the Capelli operator corresponding to (S, T) *satisfies*

$$
C_{ST}(S \mid T) = (T_\alpha \mid T_\alpha) \neq 0.
$$

Proof: It clearly suffices to prove the first statement. In order to do this we first remark that, for each $\sigma \in H_\alpha$, we have $Z(S) = Z(S \circ \sigma)$, and hence, since $(S \circ \sigma \mid T \circ \sigma) = (S \mid T)$,

$$
L_{Z(S)}(S \mid T) = L_{Z(S \circ \sigma)}(S \circ \sigma \mid T \circ \sigma).
$$

We can therefore assume without restriction that the maximal entries m of S occur in adjacent positions at the end of rows of equal length, and so, if S' denotes the remaining rest of S, we have that

$$
S = \left[\begin{array}{ccc}
S' & & \ddots \\
 & \ddots & m \ldots m \\
m \ldots m & & \\
\ldots & \ddots &
\end{array} \right.
$$

Moreover we can inductively assume that T_μ, μ the shape of S', is the only column injective element of $Sub_{Z(S')}(S')$. Hence each column injective element of $Sub_{Z(S)}(S)$ is obtained by replacing S' by T_μ and then replacing each entry m by the number of its row (recall the definition of $Sub_{Z(S)}(S)$!). Thus T_α is in fact the only column injective element of $Sub_{Z(S)}(S)$, and we are done.

□

Our next aim is a necessary condition for pairs of bitableaux (S, T) and (U, V), for which $C_{ST}(U \mid V) \neq 0$, and where (S, T) is assumed to be a standard bitableau. We are going to show that such pairs are related by a generalization of the dominance order. A *standard* tableau $S \in ST^\alpha(\lambda)$ can be reconstructed from the following sequence of inverse images of S:

$$\bar{S} := (S^{-1}[\{1\}], S^{-1}[\{1,2\}], \ldots, S^{-1}[\{1,\ldots,k\}]),$$

where k is maximal such that $\lambda_k \neq 0$. The coimage $S^{-1}[\{1,\ldots,i\}]$ is a subdiagram of $[\alpha]$ consisting of $\sum_1^i \lambda_j$ nodes. For example the tableau

$$S := \begin{matrix} 2 & 2 & 3 & 5 \\ 3 & 3 & 5 \\ 5 \end{matrix} \quad \in ST^{(4,3,1)}(0,2,3,0,3)$$

gives rise to the sequence

$$\bar{S} = \left(\emptyset, \ \times \ \ \times \ , \ \begin{matrix} \times & \times & \times \\ \times & \times \end{matrix} \ , \ \begin{matrix} \times & \times & \times \\ \times & \times \\ \times \end{matrix} \ , \ \begin{matrix} \times & \times & \times & \times \\ \times & \times & \times \\ \times \end{matrix} \right),$$

from which S easily can be reconstructed.

Now we use these sequences in order to define the announced *dominance order* on the set $ST(\lambda)$, by putting

$$S \trianglelefteq W :\Longleftrightarrow \bar{S} \trianglelefteq \bar{W} :\Longleftrightarrow \forall i: \ S^{-1}[\{1,\ldots,i\}] \trianglelefteq W^{-1}[\{1,\ldots,i\}].$$

Another description of this situation can be given in terms of the following matrix: For $S \in ST^\alpha(\lambda)$ we put

$$a_{pq}(S) := |\{(i,j) \in [\alpha] \mid s_{ij} \leq p, i \leq q\}|,$$

i.e. $a_{pq}(S)$ is *the number of entries $\leq p$ in the first q rows of S.*

4.6.11 Lemma *For standard tableaux S and W of same content the following is true:*

$$S \trianglelefteq W \iff \forall p,q : \ a_{pq}(S) \leq a_{pq}(W).$$

Proof: Since S is assumed to be standard, the diagram $S^{-1}[\{1,\ldots,i\}]$ is

$$[a_{i1}(S), a_{i2}(S) - a_{i1}(S), a_{i3}(S) - a_{i2}(S), \ldots].$$

Thus $S^{-1}[\{1,\ldots,i\}] \trianglelefteq W^{-1}[\{1,\ldots,i\}]$ is equivalent to $a_{iq}(S) \leq a_{iq}(W)$, for each q, and the statement follows.

This lemma shows that $\trianglelefteq$ is antisymmetric, and since it is obviously transitive, it is in fact a *partial order* on $ST(\lambda)$, we call it the *dominance order*. It can be refined as follows: We say that an A–tableau S and a B–tableau T, where $A, B \subseteq \mathbb{N}^* \times \mathbb{N}^*$, are *row–equivalent*, for short: $S \leftrightarrow T$, if they have the same column contents:

$$\forall\, i, j : |i \times \mathbb{N}^* \cap S^{-1}[\{j\}]| = |i \times \mathbb{N}^* \cap T^{-1}[\{j\}]|.$$

Correspondingly the *column equivalence* $S \updownarrow U$ is defined. And we put

$$S \Leftrightarrow\!\!\updownarrow U :\Longleftrightarrow \exists\, T : S \leftrightarrow T \updownarrow U.$$

For example

$$\begin{matrix} 1 & 1 & 2 & 2 \\ 3 & & & \end{matrix} \;\; \Leftrightarrow\!\!\updownarrow \;\; \begin{matrix} 1 & 1 & 2 & 2 & 3 \end{matrix}$$

since

$$\begin{matrix} 1 & 1 & 2 & 2 \\ 3 & & & \end{matrix} \;\; \leftrightarrow \;\; \begin{matrix} 1 & 1 & 2 & 2 \\ & & & 3 \end{matrix} \;\; \updownarrow \;\; \begin{matrix} 1 & 1 & 2 & 2 & 3 \end{matrix}.$$

The next implication is now immediate from 4.6.11:

4.6.12 $$S \Leftrightarrow\!\!\updownarrow U \Longrightarrow S \trianglelefteq U.$$

Hence $\Leftrightarrow\!\!\updownarrow$ is antisymmetric, and the transitive closure of $\Leftrightarrow\!\!\updownarrow$ is a partial order on $ST(\lambda)$, which we call the *hyperdominance order*, and we denote it by $\twoheadrightarrow$. We are now in a position to derive the following necessary condition for $C_{ST}(U \mid V) \neq 0$:

4.6.13 Lemma *If both (S, T) and (U, V) are bitableaux of content (λ, μ), then*

$$C_{ST}(U \mid V) \neq 0 \Longrightarrow S \Leftrightarrow\!\!\updownarrow U \text{ and } T \Leftrightarrow\!\!\updownarrow V.$$

Proof: It clearly suffices to prove that $L_{Z(S)}(U \mid V) \neq 0$ implies $S \Leftrightarrow\!\!\updownarrow U$. Assume that α is the shape of S and β the shape of U. An easy check yields that $Z(S) \in M_{\alpha\lambda}$. $L_{Z(S)}(U \mid V) \neq 0$ implies the existence of a $W \in Sub_{Z(S)}(U)$ which is column injective. Note that W arises from U by replacing, for each i and j, as many j by i as there are j's in the i-th row of S. But these j arising from collinear i in S, lie in different columns of W. Hence each j of S can be moved within its row to the column that it occupies in U, and the statement follows.

$\square$

We shall indicate this necessary condition as follows:

$$(S, T) \looparrowright (U, V) :\Longleftrightarrow S \looparrowright U \text{ and } T \looparrowright V,$$

and call the resulting partial order on $SBT(\lambda, \mu)$ the *hyperbidominance* order. We shall also indicate it by

$$\looparrowright .$$

Using this partial order we shall prove the following main result:

4.6.14 Theorem *For each pair* $\lambda, \mu \models n$, *the set* $SBD(\lambda, \mu)$ *of standard bideterminants* $(S \mid T)$, *where* $(S \mid T) \in ST^{\alpha}(\lambda) \times ST^{\alpha}(\mu)$, *for some* $\alpha \vdash n$, *forms a* $\mathbb{Z}$–*basis of* $\mathbb{Z}_{\lambda\mu}$:

$$\mathbb{Z}_{\lambda\mu} = \ll SBD(\lambda, \mu) \gg_{\mathbb{Z}} .$$

Proof: We first show that these standard bideterminants are linearly independent, Consider a linear relation

$$0 = \sum_{(U \mid V) \in SBD(\lambda, \mu)} a_{UV}(U \mid V),$$

and take a pair (S, T) that is maximal (with respect to hyperdominance) in the support

$$\{(U, V) \in SBD(\lambda, \mu) \mid a_{\mu\nu} \neq 0\}.$$

The corresponding Capelli operator C_{ST} yields, when applied to the linear relation, that

$$0 = a_{ST}(S \mid T) = a_{ST} \underbrace{(T_{\alpha} \mid T_{\alpha})}_{\neq 0},$$

which implies $a_{ST} = 0$. Hence the standard bideterminants are linearly independent. Now we recall theorem 4.6.7. It says that each nonstandard tableau is a linear combination of bideterminants corresponding to smaller bitableaux. But the smallest bitableaux are standard, and so they are in fact linear combinations of standard bideterminants, which shows that $SBD(\lambda, \mu)$ does generate $\mathbb{Z}_{\lambda\mu}$, and we are done.

□

Let us consider the following example in detail:

$$\mathbb{Z}_{(1^n)(1^n)}.$$

To each permutation $\pi \in S_{\underline{n}}$ we can associate the mapping

$$(S \mid T) \mapsto (\pi S \mid T)$$

and we can linearly extend it to $\mathbb{Z}_{(1^n)(1^n)}$, which yields a representation of the symmetric group. Let us order the basis $SBD(1^n, 1^n)$ consisting of the standard bideterminants via the total order $\leq$ of the corresponding set of standard bitableaux $SBT(1^n, 1^n)$ which was defined above. This total order is compatible with the (partial) hyperbidominance. In this total order the elements of the same shape form intervals, and within such an interval we have the double lexicographic order with respect to the columns, so that the elements (S, T) with the same second component T for intervals, too. We therefore put these elements into sets according to the second diagram. For $n = 4$ we obtain the following sets:

$$M_1 := \left\{ \left(\begin{array}{c|c} 1 & 1 \\ 2 & 2 \\ 3 & 3 \\ 4 & 4 \end{array} \right) \right\},$$

$$M_2 := \left\{ \left(\begin{array}{c|c} 14 & 14 \\ 2 & 2 \\ 3 & 3 \end{array} \right), \left(\begin{array}{c|c} 13 & 14 \\ 2 & 2 \\ 4 & 3 \end{array} \right), \left(\begin{array}{c|c} 12 & 14 \\ 3 & 2 \\ 4 & 3 \end{array} \right) \right\},$$

$$M_3 := \left\{ \left(\begin{array}{c|c} 14 & 13 \\ 2 & 2 \\ 3 & 4 \end{array} \right), \left(\begin{array}{c|c} 13 & 13 \\ 2 & 2 \\ 4 & 4 \end{array} \right), \left(\begin{array}{c|c} 12 & 13 \\ 3 & 2 \\ 4 & 4 \end{array} \right) \right\},$$

$$M_4 := \left\{ \left(\begin{array}{c|c} 14 & 12 \\ 2 & 3 \\ 3 & 4 \end{array} \right), \left(\begin{array}{c|c} 13 & 12 \\ 2 & 3 \\ 4 & 4 \end{array} \right), \left(\begin{array}{c|c} 12 & 12 \\ 3 & 3 \\ 4 & 4 \end{array} \right) \right\},$$

$$M_5 := \left\{ \left(\begin{array}{c|c} 13 & 13 \\ 24 & 24 \end{array} \right), \left(\begin{array}{c|c} 12 & 13 \\ 34 & 34 \end{array} \right) \right\},$$

$$M_6 := \left\{ \left(\begin{array}{c|c} 13 & 12 \\ 24 & 34 \end{array} \right), \left(\begin{array}{c|c} 12 & 12 \\ 34 & 34 \end{array} \right) \right\},$$

$$M_7 := \left\{ \left(\begin{array}{c|c} 134 & 134 \\ 2 & 2 \end{array} \right), \left(\begin{array}{c|c} 124 & 134 \\ 3 & 2 \end{array} \right), \left(\begin{array}{c|c} 123 & 134 \\ 4 & 2 \end{array} \right) \right\},$$

$$M_8 := \left\{ \left(\begin{array}{c|c} 134 & 124 \\ 2 & 3 \end{array} \right), \left(\begin{array}{c|c} 124 & 124 \\ 3 & 3 \end{array} \right), \left(\begin{array}{c|c} 123 & 124 \\ 4 & 3 \end{array} \right) \right\},$$

$$M_9 := \left\{ \left(\begin{array}{c|c} 134 & 123 \\ 2 & 4 \end{array} \right), \left(\begin{array}{c|c} 124 & 123 \\ 3 & 4 \end{array} \right), \left(\begin{array}{c|c} 123 & 123 \\ 4 & 4 \end{array} \right) \right\},$$

$$M_{10} := \left\{ \left(\ 1234 \mid 1234 \ \right) \right\}.$$

Now we denote the submodule generated by the standard bideterminants contained *in the first k of these sets* M_i by $U_k(\mathbb{Z})$,

$$U_k(\mathbb{Z}) := \ll M_1, \ldots, M_k \gg_{\mathbb{Z}},$$

obtaining the chain

$$U_1(\mathbb{Z}) \subseteq \ldots \subseteq U_r(\mathbb{Z}),$$

where r denotes the number of standard Young tableaux with n
entries. It is easy to see that each of these sumodules is invariant
under the linear extension of

$$\pi(S \mid T) := (\pi S \mid T),$$

and so each $U_k(\mathbb{Z})$ is an *invariant submodule* of $\mathbb{Z}_{(1^n)(1^n)}$ (cf. exercise 4.6.6). Moreover, if T_k denotes the right hand side standard
tableau of the bitableaux in the k-th row, then the restriction of $R_{Z(T_k)}$
to $U_k(\mathbb{Z})$, which is in fact a $S_{\underline{n}}$–homomorphism, maps $U_k(\mathbb{Z})$ onto the
Specht module

$$\mathscr{S}_\alpha(\mathbb{Z}) := \ll (S \mid T_\alpha) \mid S \in ST^\alpha(1^n) \gg_{\mathbb{Z}},$$

where α denotes the shape of T_k. The submodule $U_{k-1}(\mathbb{Z})$ lies in the
kernel of this restriction. Since the Specht module does only depend
of the shape α, it occurs f^α–times in $\mathbb{Z}_{(1^n)(1^n)}$, and hence Maschke's
theorem shows that the modules

$$\mathscr{S}_\alpha(\mathbb{Q}) := \mathbb{Q} \otimes_{\mathbb{Z}} \mathscr{S}_\alpha(\mathbb{Z})$$

form a complete system of ordinary irreducible representation modules
for $S_{\underline{n}}$. For example

$$\mathscr{S}_{(4)}(\mathbb{Q}) = \ll (\ 1234 \mid 1111\ ) \gg_{\mathbb{Q}},$$

$$\mathscr{S}_{(3,1)}(\mathbb{Q}) = \ll \left(\begin{array}{c|c} 134 & 111 \\ 2 & 2 \end{array} \right), \left(\begin{array}{c|c} 124 & 111 \\ 2 & 2 \end{array} \right), \left(\begin{array}{c|c} 123 & 111 \\ 4 & 2 \end{array} \right) \gg_{\mathbb{Q}},$$

$$\mathscr{S}_{(2^2)}(\mathbb{Q}) = \ll \left(\begin{array}{c|c} 13 & 11 \\ 24 & 22 \end{array} \right), \left(\begin{array}{c|c} 12 & 11 \\ 34 & 22 \end{array} \right) \gg_{\mathbb{Q}},$$

$$\mathscr{S}_{(2,1^2)}(\mathbb{Q}) = \ll \left(\begin{array}{c|c} 14 & 11 \\ 2 & 2 \\ 3 & 3 \end{array} \right), \left(\begin{array}{c|c} 13 & 11 \\ 2 & 2 \\ 4 & 3 \end{array} \right), \left(\begin{array}{c|c} 12 & 11 \\ 3 & 2 \\ 4 & 3 \end{array} \right) \gg_{\mathbb{Q}},$$

$$\mathscr{S}_{(1^4)}(\mathbb{Q}) = \ll \left(\begin{array}{c|c} 1 & 1 \\ 2 & 2 \\ 3 & 3 \\ 4 & 4 \end{array} \right) \gg_{\mathbb{Q}}.$$

Having these bases at hand we are now in a position to evaluate *matrix representations*. A detailed example may be in order, let us evaluate the representation afforded by $\mathscr{S}_{(3,1)}(\mathbb{Q})$. The basis elements are

$$\left(\begin{smallmatrix}134\\2\end{smallmatrix}\big|\begin{smallmatrix}111\\2\end{smallmatrix}\right) = X_{11}X_{22}X_{31}X_{41} - X_{12}X_{21}X_{31}X_{41},$$

$$\left(\begin{smallmatrix}124\\3\end{smallmatrix}\big|\begin{smallmatrix}111\\2\end{smallmatrix}\right) = X_{11}X_{21}X_{32}X_{41} - X_{12}X_{21}X_{31}X_{41},$$

$$\left(\begin{smallmatrix}123\\4\end{smallmatrix}\big|\begin{smallmatrix}111\\2\end{smallmatrix}\right) = X_{11}X_{21}X_{31}X_{42} - X_{12}X_{21}X_{31}X_{41}.$$

The action of the transposition (12) on the basis elements is as follows:

$$(12)\left(\begin{smallmatrix}134\\2\end{smallmatrix}\big|\begin{smallmatrix}111\\2\end{smallmatrix}\right) = \left(\begin{smallmatrix}234\\1\end{smallmatrix}\big|\begin{smallmatrix}111\\2\end{smallmatrix}\right) = -\left(\begin{smallmatrix}134\\2\end{smallmatrix}\big|\begin{smallmatrix}111\\2\end{smallmatrix}\right),$$

$$(12)\left(\begin{smallmatrix}124\\3\end{smallmatrix}\big|\begin{smallmatrix}111\\2\end{smallmatrix}\right) = \left(\begin{smallmatrix}214\\3\end{smallmatrix}\big|\begin{smallmatrix}111\\2\end{smallmatrix}\right) = X_{11}X_{21}X_{32}X_{41} - X_{11}X_{22}X_{31}X_{41}$$
$$= \left(\begin{smallmatrix}124\\3\end{smallmatrix}\big|\begin{smallmatrix}111\\2\end{smallmatrix}\right) - \left(\begin{smallmatrix}134\\2\end{smallmatrix}\big|\begin{smallmatrix}111\\2\end{smallmatrix}\right),$$

$$(12)\left(\begin{smallmatrix}123\\4\end{smallmatrix}\big|\begin{smallmatrix}111\\2\end{smallmatrix}\right) = \left(\begin{smallmatrix}213\\4\end{smallmatrix}\big|\begin{smallmatrix}111\\2\end{smallmatrix}\right) = X_{11}X_{21}X_{31}X_{42} - X_{11}X_{22}X_{31}X_{41}$$
$$= \left(\begin{smallmatrix}123\\4\end{smallmatrix}\big|\begin{smallmatrix}111\\2\end{smallmatrix}\right) - \left(\begin{smallmatrix}134\\2\end{smallmatrix}\big|\begin{smallmatrix}111\\2\end{smallmatrix}\right).$$

Hence this action of (12) is represented by the matrix

$$\mathbf{D}((12)) = \begin{pmatrix} -1 & -1 & -1 \\ 0 & 1 & 0 \\ 0 & 0 & 1 \end{pmatrix}.$$

The matrices representing (23) and (34) are easier to evaluate since these transpositions just permute the basis elements:

$$\mathbf{D}((23)) = \begin{pmatrix} 0 & 1 & 0 \\ 1 & 0 & 0 \\ 0 & 0 & 1 \end{pmatrix}, \quad \mathbf{D}((34)) = \begin{pmatrix} 1 & 0 & 0 \\ 0 & 0 & 1 \\ 0 & 1 & 0 \end{pmatrix}.$$

In order to check these calculations we verify the relations in order to show that we have in fact evaluated matrices that define a representation of the symmetric group in question (the regularity of the evaluated matrices is obvious): In fact an easy check shows that

$$\mathbf{D}((12))^2 = \mathbf{D}((23))^2 = \mathbf{D}((34))^2$$

$$= \mathbf{D}((12)(23))^3 = \mathbf{D}((23)(34))^3 = \begin{pmatrix} 1 & 0 & 0 \\ 0 & 1 & 0 \\ 0 & 0 & 1 \end{pmatrix}.$$

Finally we identify this representation with one of the irreducible representations introduced above by calculating the character χ, the trace function. It has the values

$$\chi(1) = 3, \ \chi((12)) = 1, \ \chi((123)) = 0, \ \chi((12)(34)) = \chi((1234)) = -1,$$

so that **D** is a matrix representation corresponding to the irreducible representation [3, 1], according to the character table shown in the appendix.

In case we want to evaluate bigger representations, we can organize the calculations as follows. We again number the elements $(S \mid T_\alpha), S \in ST^\alpha(1^n)$, according to the column lexicographic order on $ST^\alpha(1^n)$, obtaining the sequence

$$(S_1 \mid T_\alpha) < \ldots < (S_{f^\alpha} \mid T_\alpha).$$

Each $(\pi S_k \mid T_\alpha)$ is a $\mathbb{Z}$–linear combination of these standard bideterminants $(S_i \mid T_\alpha)$, say

$$(\pi S_k \mid T_\alpha) = \sum_{i=1}^{f^\alpha} d_{ik}^\alpha(\pi)(S_i \mid T_\alpha),$$

where we have to evaluate the coefficients $d_{ik}^\alpha(\pi)$, since they form the desired representing matrix $\mathbf{D}^\alpha(\pi)$. Now for each $j \leq f^\alpha$ there is the Capelli operator

$$C_i := C_{S_j T_\alpha},$$

and so

$$C_j(\pi S_k \mid T_\alpha) = \sum_i d_{ik}^\alpha(\pi) C_j(S_i \mid T_\alpha).$$

We recall that $C_j(S_i \mid T_\alpha) \neq 0$ implies that $i \leq j$, and $C_j(S_j \mid T_\alpha) = (T_\alpha \mid T_\alpha) \neq 0$. Hence the coefficient of $(S_i \mid T_\alpha)$ in $(\pi S_k \mid T_\alpha)$ is equal to the coefficient of the monomial $\{T_\alpha \mid T_\alpha\}$ in $C_i(\pi S_k \mid T_\alpha)$. We therefore indicate this coefficient as follows:

$$b_{ij} := \text{coefficient of } \{T_\alpha \mid T_\alpha\} \text{ in } C_j(S_i \mid T_\alpha).$$

The matrix consisting of these coefficients b_{ij} is therefore upper triangular, and it has ones along its main diagonal. But the main point is the equation

$$(b_{ij}) \begin{pmatrix} d_{1,k}^\alpha(\pi) \\ \vdots \\ d_{f^\alpha,k}^\alpha(\pi) \end{pmatrix} = \begin{pmatrix} b_1 \\ \vdots \\ b_{f^\alpha} \end{pmatrix},$$

where
$$b_i := \text{coefficient of } \{T_\alpha \mid T_\alpha\} \text{ in } C_i(\pi S_k \mid T_\alpha).$$

Exercises

E 4.6.1 Prove that $L_Z\{U \mid V\}$ is in fact well defined.

E 4.6.2 Verify 4.6.8.

E 4.6.3 Evaluate the order diagram of $ST(2^2, 1)$ with respect to hyperdominance.

E 4.6.4 Assume that S is a standard tableau that is hyperdominated by a tableau U which is strictly increasing down each of its columns. Show that there exist *standard* tableaux $S1, \ldots, S_r$ such that

$$S = S_1 \Leftrightarrow S_2 \Leftrightarrow \ldots \Leftrightarrow S_r \Leftrightarrow U.$$

E 4.6.5 Prove that a standard bitableau (S, T) is hyperbidominated by (U, V) with strictly increasing columns if and only if there exist standard bitableaux $(S_1, T_1), \ldots, (S_r, T_r)$ such that

$$S = S_1 \Leftrightarrow T_1 \Leftrightarrow \ldots \Leftrightarrow S_r \Leftrightarrow U, \text{ and } T = T_1 \Leftrightarrow \ldots T_r \Leftrightarrow U.$$

E 4.6.6 Prove that each of the submodules $U_k(\mathbb{Z})$ introduced above is in fact an invariant submodule for the representation defined by $\pi(S \mid T) := (\pi S \mid T)$. Show that U_k is the image of $R_{Z(T_k)}$, while U_{k-1} is the kernel of this map, when it is applied to U_k.

Chapter 5

Applications

We shall now refine our results on the enumeration of symmetry classes of mappings by applications of the preceeding results on linear representations of finite groups, in particular of symmetric groups. Conversely, we shall apply to representation theory what we know about combinatorial enumeration. A first striking example is the theory of Schur polynomials. These symmetric polynomials will be defined here with the aid of irreducible characters of the symmetric group, and later on we shall show what these polynomials count. We shall discuss the diagram lattice, using representation theory first, and afterwards we can show its significance for unimodality questions about generating functions of enumeration theory.

Then we will see that symmetrization and permutrization of representations are natural generalizations of situations which we met already in connection with the enumeration of symmetry classes of mappings. Another striking example is the so called plethysm of representations, the corresponding permutation representation case we have already met. Two very important theorems of representation theory of symmetric groups will be derived, the Littlewood–Richardson Rule and the Murnaghan–Nakayama Rule. They show how certain decompositions of induced representations can be evaluated, and how we can recursively calculuate the ordinary irrducible characters. These results can be used in connection with representations, too.

5.1   Schur polynomials

We now refine enumeration under finite group action with the aid of the preceding results on linear representations. A first remark rephrases the Cauchy-Frobenius Lemma 1.1.11 and 1.3.16 in terms of inner products of characters:

5.1.1 Corollary *For any finite action $_GX$, the corresponding permutation character $\chi:g \mapsto |X_g|$, the identity character $\iota:g \mapsto 1$ of G and the alternating character $\epsilon:g \mapsto \epsilon(\bar{g})$ of G, we have:*

- *The number of orbits of G on X is equal to $[\chi \mid \iota]$.*

- *The number of orbits which split over $G^+ := \{g \mid \epsilon(\bar{g}) = 1\}$ is equal to $[\chi \mid \epsilon]$.*

- *The number of G–orbits which are also G^+–orbits is equal to the difference $[\chi \mid \iota] - [\chi \mid \epsilon]$.*

The main applications are those which take place in the enumeration of symmetry classes of mappings by weight. In order to describe some of them we recall the definition of the cycle indicator polynomial:

$$C(G,X) = \frac{1}{|G|} \sum_{g\in G} \prod_{i=1}^{|X|} z_i^{a_i(\bar{g})} = \frac{1}{|\bar{G}|} \sum_{\bar{g}\in\bar{G}} \prod_{i=1}^{|X|} z_i^{a_i(\bar{g})}.$$

We notice that it is a sum of monomials $\prod_i z_i^{a_i(\bar{g})}$ which depend only on the cycle type $a(\bar{g}) = (a_1(\bar{g}),\dots,a_{|X|}(\bar{g}))$ of $\bar{g}$. Hence we can rewrite $C(G,X)$ using the notation C^a for the conjugacy class of S_X consisting of the elements of cycle type $a \vdash |X|$:

5.1.2 $$C(G,X) = \frac{1}{|X|!} \sum_{a\vdash|X|} \frac{|X|!}{|\bar{G}|} \frac{|C^a \cap \bar{G}|}{|C^a|} |C^a| \prod_{i=1}^{|X|} z_i^{a_i}.$$

In terms of the character $\iota_{\bar{G}} \uparrow S_X$ induced by the identity character $\iota_{\bar{G}}$ of $\bar{G}$ and its value $(\iota_{\bar{G}} \uparrow S_X)_a$ on the class of elements of type a, this is

5.1.3 $$= \frac{1}{|X|!} \sum_{a\vdash|X|} (\iota_{\bar{G}} \uparrow S_X)_a |C^a| \prod_i z_i^{a_i}.$$

Hence we introduce the *generalized* cycle indicator polynomial corresponding to $_GX$ and *the representation D of G with character χ^D*:

$$C(G,X,D) := \frac{1}{|G|} \sum_{g\in G} \chi^D(g^{-1}) \prod_{i=1}^{|X|} z_i^{a_i(\bar{g})}.$$

Using this generalization we obtain an expression for $C(G, X)$ in terms of generalized cycle indicator polynomials of the natural action of the symmetric S_X:

5.1.4 Foulkes' Lemma *For each finite action* $_G X$ *we have:*

$$C(G, X) = \sum_{\alpha \vdash |X|} (I\bar{G} \uparrow S_X, [\alpha]) C(S_X, X, [\alpha]).$$

This together with Pólya's Theorem gives the following form of the generating function for the enumeration of G classes on Y^X by weight

$$\sum_{\alpha \vdash |X|} (I\bar{G} \uparrow S_X, [\alpha]) C(S_X, X, [\alpha] \mid \sum_{y \in Y} y).$$

We therefore introduce the abbreviation, for $\alpha \vdash n$ and any set Y of indeterminates:

$$\{\alpha, Y\} := C(S_{\underline{n}}, \underline{n}, [\alpha] \mid \sum_{y \in Y} y) = \frac{1}{n!} \sum_{a \vdash n} \zeta_a^\alpha |C^a| \prod_{i=1}^n \left(\sum_{y \in Y} y^i \right)^{a_i}.$$

This polynomial, for which we sometimes simply write

$$\{\alpha\},$$

is called the *Schur polynomial* corresponding to α in the indeterminates $y \in Y$. Using this notation and the *group reduction function*

$$\mathrm{Grf}(G, Y^X) := C(G, X \mid \sum y),$$

as well as the corresponding generalization

$$\mathrm{Grf}(G, Y^X, D) := C(G, X, D \mid \sum y),$$

Pólya's Theorem now reads as follows:

5.1.5 Corollary *The generating function for the enumeration of G–classes on Y^X by weight is equal to the group reduction function*

$$\mathrm{Grf}(G, Y^X) = \sum_{\alpha \vdash |X|} (I\bar{G} \uparrow S_X, [\alpha])\{\alpha, Y\}.$$

A particular example is

5.1.6 $\mathrm{Grf}\,(A_X, Y^X) = \{(|X|), Y\} + \{(1^{|X|}), Y\},$

since clearly $I A_{\underline{n}} \uparrow S_{\underline{n}} = [n] + [1^n]$. This implies (recall 5.1.1):

5.1.7 Corollary *The generating function for the enumeration of injective S_X–classes by weight is equal to the Schur polynomial*

$$\{(1^{|X|}), Y\}.$$

These examples suffice for the moment. We recall that *using Schur polynomials we get a decomposition of the generating function and therefore of the enumeration of G–classes on Y^X*, so that it remains to show what is counted by Schur polynomials. It will turn out that this can be formulated in terms of standard tableaux.

Consider, for $\alpha \vdash n$, the natural action of S_α on $Y^{\underline{n}}$. The corresponding group reduction function is

5.1.8 $\mathrm{Grf}\,(S_\alpha, Y^{\underline{n}}) = \sum_{\beta \vdash n} st^\beta(\alpha)\{\beta, Y\}$

Another expression for this group reduction function will be obtained from

5.1.9 Lemma (Ruch) *If $_G X$ is a finite action and $\bar{G}$ the corresponding subgroup of S_X, then, for a fixed $f \in Y^X$ and its stabilizer $(S_X)_f$, the mapping*

$$\theta: S_X \to Y^X: \pi \mapsto f \circ \pi^{-1}$$

establishes a bijection between the set

$$\bar{G}\backslash S_X/(S_X)_f$$

of double cosets and the set of orbits of G on Y^X consisting of mappings with the same content $c(f, -)$ (recall 2.1.6).

Proof:
i) The inverse image of $f \circ \pi^{-1}$ is the left coset $\pi(S_X)_f$, since

$$\theta(\pi) = \theta(\rho) \iff f \circ \pi^{-1} = f \circ \rho^{-1} \iff \rho \in \pi(S_X)_f.$$

ii) $f \circ \pi^{-1}$ and $f \circ \rho^{-1}$, for $\pi, \rho \in S_X$, lie in the same orbit of G if and only if there exists $\tau \in \bar{G}$ such that $f \circ \pi^{-1} \circ \tau^{-1} = f \circ \rho^{-1}$, i.e. if and only if $\rho^{-1}\tau\pi \in (S_X)_f$, which means $\pi \in \bar{G}\rho(S_X)_f$.   □

The order of $\bar{G}\backslash S_X/(S_X)_f$ can be written as a scalar product of characters (see exercise 4.2.8), and so we obtain

5.1.10 Corollary *If* $_GX$ *is a finite action,* $\bar{G}$ *the corresponding subgroup of* S_X, $f \in Y^X$, *then the number of orbits of* G *on* Y^X *consisting of elements of content* $c(f,-)$ *is, for finite* Y, *the scalar product of the characters of the induced representations* $I\bar{G} \uparrow S_X$ *and* $I(S_X)_f \uparrow S_X$.

Using an ordered set $Y := \{y_1, \ldots, y_m\}$ and the abbreviation

$$Y^\lambda := y_1^{\lambda_1} \ldots y_m^{\lambda_m},$$

we obtain for example

5.1.11 Corollary *The group reduction function for the natural action of the Young subgroup* S_α *on* $\underline{m}^{\underline{n}}$ *is*

$$\mathrm{Grf}\,(S_\alpha, \underline{m}^{\underline{n}}) = \sum_{(\lambda_1, \ldots, \lambda_m) \models n} |S_\lambda \backslash S_{\underline{n}} / S_\alpha| Y^\lambda$$

$$= \sum_{(\lambda_1, \ldots, \lambda_m) \models n} \sum_{\beta \vdash n} st^\beta(\lambda) st^\beta(\alpha) Y^\lambda.$$

Comparing this equation with 5.1.8 we finally obtain

5.1.12 Corollary *For each finite set* Y *of indeterminates and any proper partition* $\alpha \vdash n$ *we have*

$$\{\alpha, Y\} = \sum_{(\lambda_1, \ldots, \lambda_{|Y|}) \models n} st^\alpha(\lambda) Y^\lambda.$$

In other words: Schur polynomials are the generating functions for counting standard tableaux.

We recall that $ST^\alpha(\lambda) \neq \emptyset$ implies that the number of nonzero λ_i must be at least the number of nonzero parts α_i of α. Hence we obtain

5.1.13 Corollary *For each proper partition* α *the Schur polynomial* $\{\alpha, Y\}$ *is the zero polynomial if the number of indeterminates* $y \in Y$ *is smaller than the number of nonzero parts of* α.

A further consequence of 5.1.12 is

5.1.14 Lemma *The Gaussian polynomials (cf. 3.5.7) are specializations of the Schur polynomials corresponding to one rowed partitions:*

$$\begin{bmatrix} m+n \\ n \end{bmatrix} = \{m\}(1, x, \ldots, x^n),$$

if $\{m\}$ *is taken over the set* $Y := \{y_1, \ldots, y_{n+1}\}$ *of indeterminates.*

Proof: We obtain from 5.1.12 that

$$\{m\}(1, x, \ldots, x^n) = \sum_{(\lambda_1, \ldots, \lambda_{n+1}) \models m} st^{(m)}(\lambda) x^{\Sigma_i (i-1)\lambda_i}.$$

It therefore suffices to establish a bijection

$$\bigcup_{(\lambda_1, \ldots, \lambda_{n+1}) \models m} ST^{(m)}(\lambda) \longrightarrow \{\alpha \mid \exists k \leq m \cdot n \colon \alpha \vdash k, \alpha_1' \leq m, \alpha_1 \leq n\}.$$

Such a bijection is provided by

$$T := t_1 \ldots t_m \mapsto \alpha(T) := (t_m - 1, \ldots, t_1 - 1) \vdash (\Sigma_i t_i) - m \leq m \cdot n,$$

since this mapping is the inverse of

$$(\alpha_1, \ldots, \alpha_m) \vdash k \mapsto T(\alpha) := \alpha_1 + 1 \ldots \alpha_m + 1.$$

$\square$

Another immediate corollary is 4.5.5. Since $\{\alpha, Y\}$ is symmetric, $st^\alpha(\lambda) = st^\alpha(\lambda^*)$, for any improper partition $\lambda \models n$.

We consider an example of a group reduction function. The generating function for the enumeration of graphs on 4 vertices is

$$C\left(S_{\underline{4}}^{[2]}, \binom{4}{2} \mid y_0 + y_1\right) = \sum_{\alpha \vdash 6} (IS_{\underline{4}}^{[2]} \uparrow S_{\underline{6}}, [\alpha])\{\alpha\} = \{6\} + \{4, 2\} + \{3^2\}.$$

This follows from 5.1.13 together with an application of character theory which gives

$$IS_{\underline{4}}^{[2]} \uparrow S_{\underline{6}} = [6] + [4, 2] + [3^2] + [2^3] + [2^2, 1^2] + [1^6].$$

Hence 5.1.12 shows that the group reduction function for graphs on 4 vertices is equal to the sum of monomials corresponding to the standard tableaux

$$\begin{array}{cccccc} 0 & 0 & 0 & 0 & 0 & 0, \end{array} \quad \begin{array}{cccccc} 0 & 0 & 0 & 0 & 0 & 1, \end{array} \quad \begin{array}{cccccc} 0 & 0 & 0 & 0 & 1 & 1, \end{array}$$

$$\begin{array}{cccccc} 0 & 0 & 0 & 1 & 1 & 1, \end{array} \quad \begin{array}{cccccc} 0 & 0 & 1 & 1 & 1 & 1, \end{array} \quad \begin{array}{cccccc} 0 & 1 & 1 & 1 & 1 & 1, \end{array}$$

$$\begin{array}{cccccc} 1 & 1 & 1 & 1 & 1 & 1, \end{array} \quad \begin{array}{ccc} 0 & 0 & 0 \\ 1 & 1 & \end{array} \begin{array}{ccc} 0 & 0 & 0 \\ 1 & 1 \end{array} , \quad \begin{array}{ccc} 0 & 0 & 1 \\ & 1 & \end{array} ,$$

$$\begin{array}{cccc} 0 & 0 & 1 & 1 \\ 1 & 1 & \end{array} , \quad \begin{array}{cccc} 0 & 0 & 0 \\ 1 & 1 & 1 \end{array} .$$

But until now there is no natural bijection known between the set of graphs on v vertices and the corresponding set of standard tableaux. Another interesting consequence of the bijection from double cosets and orbits allows to reformulate Redfield's cap product of cycle indicator polynomials in terms of characters (use 2.5.2 and exercise 4.2.8 again):

5.1.15 Corollary *For any two finite actions* $_G\underline{n}$ *and* $_H\underline{n}$ *the corresponding cap product of the cycle indicator polynomials is equal to the inner product of the corresponding characters of* $S_{\underline{n}}$ *induced by the identity characters:*

$$C(G,\underline{n}) \cap C(H,\underline{n}) = \left[\chi^{I\bar{G}\uparrow S_{\underline{n}}} \mid \chi^{\bar{H}\uparrow S_{\underline{n}}}\right].$$

Correspondingly we have, for more than 2 factors, that

$$C(G,\underline{n}) \cap \ldots \cap C(K,\underline{n}) = \left[\chi^{I\bar{G}\uparrow S_{\underline{n}}} \cdots \chi^{I\bar{K}\uparrow S_{\underline{n}}} \mid \chi^{IS_{\underline{n}}}\right].$$

5.2 Symmetric polynomials

We now consider Schur polynomials in a more general context. There is a natural action of S_m on the set $\mathbb{Q}[Y] := \mathbb{Q}[y_1,\ldots,y_m]$ of all the polynomials in the set of indeterminates $Y := \{y_1,\ldots,y_m\}$ over $\mathbb{Q}$. The invariants of this action are called *symmetric polynomials* (over $\mathbb{Q}$). Consider the $\mathbb{Q}$–vector space

$$\Sigma_n[Y]$$

consisting of all the symmetric polynomials that are homogeneous and of degree $n \leq m$ in the indeterminates $y_i \in Y$, together with the zero polynomial. We shall establish an isometry between $\Sigma_n[Y]$ and the vector space

$$CF(S_{\underline{n}}, \mathbb{Q})$$

consisting of the $\mathbb{Q}$–valued class functions on $S_{\underline{n}}$. In order to do this we introduce various series of symmetric polynomials. For $p \geq 1$ we set

$$e_p := \sum_{i_j < i_{j+1}} y_{i_1} \ldots y_{i_p},$$

($e_0 := 1$) and note that $e_p = 0$ if $p > m$. Now, for each $\alpha \vdash n$, introduce

$$e_\alpha := e_{\alpha_1} e_{\alpha_2} \ldots$$

and call these the *elementary symmetric* polynomials. Furthermore define:

$$h_p := \sum_{(i_1,\ldots,i_m)\models p} y_1^{i_1} \ldots y_m^{i_m}, \; h_0 := 1, \; h_\alpha := h_{\alpha_1} h_{\alpha_2} \ldots,$$

the *complete symmetric* polynomials. Another series of symmetric polynomials is formed by the

$$s_\alpha := s_{\alpha_1} s_{\alpha_2} \ldots, \text{ where } s_p := \sum_i y_i^p, \; s_0 := 1.$$

These s_p are called the *symmetric power sums*. Finally put

$$k_\alpha := \sum y_{i_1}^{\alpha_1} y_{i_2}^{\alpha_2} \ldots,$$

the *monomial symmetric* polynomials, where the sum has to be taken over all the *different* monomials $y_{i_1}^{\alpha_1} y_{i_2}^{\alpha_2} \ldots$ with *pairwise different* indices $i_j \in \underline{m}$, thus $k_\alpha = 0$, if $\alpha_1' > m$. The crucial connections between these series of symmetric polynomials are the following

5.2.1 Lemma *For each proper partition α of n we have:*

$$h_\alpha = \sum_{\beta \vdash n} m_{\alpha\beta} k_\beta, \; e_\alpha = \sum_{\beta \vdash n} m'_{\alpha\beta} k_\beta, \; k_\alpha = \sum_{\lambda \models n : \lambda^* = \alpha} y_1^{\lambda_1} y_2^{\lambda_2} \ldots,$$

and

$$\{\alpha\} = \frac{1}{n!} \sum_{\beta \vdash n} |C^\beta| \zeta_\beta^\alpha s_\beta = \sum_{\beta \vdash n} \kappa_{\beta\alpha} k_\beta,$$

so that, by inversion, we obtain

$$k_\alpha = \sum_{\beta \vdash n} \epsilon_{\beta\alpha} \{\beta\}, \; h_\alpha = \sum_{\beta \vdash n} \kappa_{\alpha\beta} \{\beta\}, \; \{\alpha\} = \sum_{\beta \vdash n} \epsilon_{\alpha\beta} h_\beta.$$

Proof: It follows from the definition of h_α that

$$h_\alpha = \sum_{(i_1,\ldots,i_m)\models\alpha_1} y_1^{i_1} y_2^{i_2} \ldots y_m^{i_m} \sum_{(j_1,\ldots,j_m)\models\alpha_2} y_1^{j_1} y_2^{j_2} \ldots y_m^{j_m} \sum \ldots.$$

Each summand of this expression corresponds to a matrix

$$M := \begin{pmatrix} i_1 & i_2 & \ldots & i_m \\ j_1 & j_2 & \ldots & j_m \\ \ldots & \ldots & \ldots & \ldots \end{pmatrix}$$

with row sums α_i. If $M \in M_{\alpha\lambda}$, then $\lambda \models n$ and the corresponding summand is $y_1^{\lambda_1} y_2^{\lambda_2} \ldots$, and so we can proceed as follows:

$$= \sum_{\lambda \models n} m_{\alpha\lambda} y_1^{\lambda_1} y_2^{\lambda_2} \cdots = \sum_{\beta \vdash n} m_{\alpha\beta} k_\beta,$$

since obviously $k_\beta = \sum_{\lambda^* = \beta} y_1^{\lambda_1} y_2^{\lambda_2} \ldots$. This proves the first statement, while the second is obtained analogously, the matrices M now being elements of $M'_{\alpha\lambda}, \lambda \models n$. The expression of k_α in terms of the monomials Y^λ is obvious. The linear combinations of $\{\alpha\}$ in terms of the s_β and of the k_α is clear from the definition of Schur polynomials and the fact that the Kostka numbers are numbers of standard tableaux, for which we know that $st^\alpha(\lambda)$ is equal to $st^\alpha(\lambda^*)$. The final row of equations is obtained by inversion.

$\square$

It is trivial that the $\{k_\alpha \mid \alpha \vdash n\}$ is a $\mathbb{Q}$–basis of $\Sigma_n[Y]$, and hence we obtain from 5.2.1:

5.2.2 Corollary *The* $s_\alpha, e_\alpha, h_\alpha, k_\alpha, \{\alpha\}$ *form* $\mathbb{Q}$–*bases of* $\Sigma_n[Y]$, *if* α *runs through the proper partitions* $(\alpha_1, \ldots, \alpha_m) \vdash n$, *where* $m := |Y|$. *Some of the intertwining matrices which lead from one basis to the others are shown in 5.2.1.*

$\square$

The following example, taken from the enumeration of symmetry classes, exhibits the relationship between the e_α and the s_α.

5.2.3 Example We recall from 5.1.7 that the generating function for the enumeration of injective S_n–classes on $Y^{\underline{n}}$ is the Schur polynomial

$$\{1^n\} = \frac{1}{n!} \sum_{a \vdash n} (-1)^{\Sigma(i-1)a_i} |C^a| \prod_i s_i^{a_i} = \sum_a \frac{(-1)^{a_2 + a_4 + \cdots}}{\prod_i i^{a_i} a_i!} \prod_i s_i^{a_i}.$$

On the other hand it is obvious from the definition of e_n that it is the generating function for the numbers of injective S_n–classes. Thus we have proved the identity

5.2.4 $$e_n = \sum_{a \vdash n} (-1)^{a_2 + a_4 + \cdots} \prod_i \frac{1}{a_i!} \left(\frac{s_i}{i} \right)^{a_i}.$$

From this identity also a recursion for the e_n follows (cf. exercise 5.2.1).

$\diamond$

We now introduce a bilinear form $\langle -, - \rangle$ on $\Sigma_n[Y]$, *Hall's inner product*, which is defined as a bilinear extension of

$$\langle h_\alpha, k_\beta \rangle := \delta_{\alpha\beta}.$$

5.2.5 Lemma $\langle -, - \rangle$ *is symmetric, and* $\langle h_\alpha, h_\beta \rangle = m_{\alpha\beta}$, *while* $\langle h_\alpha, e_\beta \rangle = m'_{\alpha\beta}$.

Proof: Using 5.2.1 we obtain

$$\langle h_\alpha, h_\beta \rangle = \langle h_\alpha, \sum_\gamma m_{\beta\gamma} k_\gamma \rangle = m_{\beta\alpha} = m_{\alpha\beta} = \langle h_\beta, h_\alpha \rangle,$$

which yields the first two statements. The third statement also follows by an application of 5.2.1.

$\square$

In seeking for an orthonormal basis with respect to Hall's inner product we note

5.2.6 Theorem *The* $\{\alpha, Y\}, \alpha \vdash n$, *form an orthonormal basis of* $\Sigma_n[Y]$ *which is interrelated with* $\{k_\alpha \mid \alpha \vdash n\}, \{h_\alpha \mid \alpha \vdash n\}$, *and* $\{e_\alpha \mid \alpha \vdash n\}$, *by matrices over* $\mathbb{Z}$.

Proof: The orthonormality follows from an application of 5.2.5:

$$\langle \{\alpha\}, \{\beta\} \rangle = \sum_{\gamma, \delta \vdash n} \epsilon_{\alpha\gamma} \epsilon_{\beta\delta} \langle h_\gamma, h_\delta \rangle = \delta_{\alpha\beta},$$

where the final equation is clear from the proof of 5.2.5. The others follow from 5.2.2.

$\square$

The only orthogonal matrices over $\mathbb{Z}$, which are invertible over $\mathbb{Z}$, are the matrices which contain in each row and in each column exactly one nonzero entry, and this entry is ± 1. Hence 5.2.6 yields that up to factors ± 1 the Schur polynomials are the only orthonormal basis of $\Sigma_n[Y]$:

5.2.7 Corollary *The Schur polynomials* $\{\alpha, Y\}, \alpha \vdash n$, *form essentially the only orthonormal basis of* $\Sigma_n[Y]$.

We are now in a position to compare the vector space $CF(S_n, \mathbb{Q})$, and its scalar product $[- \mid -]$, with $\Sigma_n[Y]$, equipped with Hall's inner product $\langle - \mid - \rangle$. Consider the *Frobenius mapping*

$$F: CF(S_n, \mathbb{Q}) \to \Sigma_n[Y] : \psi \mapsto \frac{1}{n!} \sum_{\alpha \vdash n} \psi_\alpha |C^\alpha| s_\alpha,$$

where ψ_α denotes the value of ψ on the conjugacy class C^α. Hence, for example,

5.2.8 $$F(\zeta^\alpha) = \{\alpha\}.$$

Now we point to the connection between induced characters and group reduction functions, expressed in terms of Frobenius' mapping:

5.2.9 Lemma *For each representation D of a subgroup $U \leq S_n$ we have:*

$$F(\chi^D \uparrow S_{\underline{n}}) = \text{Grf}(S_{\underline{n}}, Y^{\underline{n}}, D \uparrow S_{\underline{n}}) = \text{Grf}(U, Y^{\underline{n}}, D).$$

In particular, for each $\alpha \vdash n$ and the corresponding Young character ξ^α, we have

$$F(\xi^\alpha) = F(\xi^{\alpha_1})F(\xi^{\alpha_2})\dots = h_\alpha = e_{\alpha'},$$

and inparticular

$$h_p = \text{Grf}(S_{\underline{p}}, Y^{\underline{p}}).$$

Proof: The first statement is clear. An application of 2.2.6 gives

$$F(\xi^\alpha) = \text{Grf}(S_\alpha, Y^{\underline{n}}) = \prod_i \text{Grf}(S_{\alpha_i}, Y^{\underline{\alpha_i}}) = \prod_i F(\xi^{\alpha_i}).$$

It therefore suffices to prove that $F(\xi^{(p)}) = h_p = e_{(1^p)} = e_1 e_1 \dots$. But $h_p = e_{(1^p)}$ is clear by definition. Furthermore h_p is the sum of all the monomials of degree p while $F(\xi^{(p)}) = F(\zeta^{(p)}) = \text{Grf}(S_{\underline{p}}, Y^{\underline{p}})$, which counts the mappings $f \in Y^{\underline{p}}$ by content, and the orbits of $S_{\underline{p}}$ on this set are characterized by the weights $y_1^{i_1} \dots y_m^{i_m}$.

$\square$

We are now in a position to prove the main result of this section:

5.2.10 Theorem *The Frobenius map F is an isometry between the vector spaces $CF(S_{\underline{n}}, \mathbb{Q})$ and $\Sigma_n[Y]$.*

Proof: The Young characters ξ^α form a basis of $CF(S_{\underline{n}}, \mathbb{Q})$, so, by 5.2.9, F is an isomorphism. Furthermore

$$[\xi^\alpha \mid \xi^\beta] = m_{\alpha\beta} = \langle h_\alpha, h_\beta \rangle = \langle F(\xi^\alpha), F(\xi^\beta) \rangle,$$

and so F is even an isometry.

$\square$

It is important to realize that 5.2.10 means that we either can use characters or we can use symmetric polynomials in order to do representation theory of the symmetric group!

Exercises

E 5.2.1 Derive from 5.2.4 *Newton's identity,*

$$\sum_{l=0}^{n-1}(-1)^l e_l s_{n-l} + (-1)^n n e_n = 0.$$

5.3   The diagram lattice

Lemma 5.1.4 implies

5.3.1 Corollary *The group reduction function of a finite action $_G X$ can be expressed as follows:*

$$\mathrm{Grf}\,(G, Y^X) = \sum_{\alpha \vdash |X|} (I\bar{G} \uparrow S_X, [\alpha]) \sum_{(\beta_1,\dots,\beta_{|Y|}) \vdash |X|} \kappa_{\beta\alpha} k_\beta$$

$$= \sum_{\alpha,\beta} (I\bar{G} \uparrow S_X, [\alpha]) st^\alpha(\beta) k_\beta.$$

In order to compare the coefficients $\kappa_{\beta\alpha} = st^\alpha(\beta)$, we first derive

5.3.2 Theorem *For $\alpha, \beta \vdash n$ there exists a character $\chi_{\alpha\beta}$ of S_n such that $\xi^\beta + \chi_{\alpha\beta} = \xi^\alpha$ if and only if $\alpha \lhd \beta$.*

Proof: The existence of such a $\chi_{\alpha\beta}$ implies that $\alpha \neq \beta$ and that

$$1 = [\xi^\beta \mid \zeta^\beta] \le [\xi^\alpha \mid \zeta^\beta].$$

Hence, by 4.3.20, $\alpha \lhd \beta$ must hold. If on the other hand $\alpha \lhd \beta$, then there exists a sequence of partitions $\alpha^i \vdash n$ such that

$$\alpha = \alpha^0 \lhd \alpha^1 \lhd \dots \lhd \alpha^r = \beta,$$

where α^i covers α^{i-1}. Thus we need only prove the statement in the case when β covers α. We can therefore assume the existence of i and j which satisfy

$$0 < i < j, \ \beta_i = \alpha_i + 1, \ \beta_j = \alpha_j - 1, \ \forall\, k \neq i, j: \alpha_k = \beta_k.$$

We shall express $\chi_{\alpha\beta}$ in terms of these indices i and j. Consider the representation with character ξ^α,

$$[\alpha_1]\#[\alpha_2]\#\dots \uparrow S_{\underline{n}} = (([\alpha_i]\#[\alpha_j])\#(\#_{k\neq i,j}[\alpha_k])) \uparrow S_{\underline{n}}.$$

The Determinantal Form 4.5.6 yields

$$[\alpha_i]\#[\alpha_j] = [\alpha_i, \alpha_j] + [\alpha_i + 1][\alpha_j - 1],$$

thus we can proceed as follows (since induction is transitive):

$$[\alpha_1]\#[\alpha_2]\#\dots \uparrow S_{\underline{n}} = \big(([\alpha_i, \alpha_j] + [\alpha_i + 1][\alpha_j - 1])\#(\#[\alpha_k])\big) \uparrow S_{\underline{n}}$$

$$= \big([\alpha_i, \alpha_j]\#(\#_{k \neq i,j}[\alpha_k])\big) \uparrow S_{\underline{n}} + [\beta_1]\#[\beta_2]\#\dots \uparrow S_{\underline{n}},$$

and hence the character $\chi_{\alpha\beta}$ of the representation

$$([\alpha_i, \alpha_j]\#(\#_{k \neq i,j}[\alpha_k])) \uparrow S_{\underline{n}}$$

is equal to $\xi^\alpha - \xi^\beta$.

$\square$

An immediate consequence of this theorem, 4.4.1 and 4.5.5 is

5.3.3 Corollary *For each $\alpha \vdash n$ and $\lambda \models n$ we have*

$$ST^\alpha(\lambda) \neq \emptyset \iff \lambda^* \trianglelefteq \alpha.$$

Moreover $st^\alpha(\alpha) = 1$ and, if also $\mu \models n$, then

5.3.4 $$\lambda^* \vartriangleleft \mu^* \trianglelefteq \alpha \implies st^\alpha(\lambda) > st^\alpha(\mu) > 0.$$

In order to use this for a proof of an existence theorem on 0–1–matrices, we consider the identity

$$m'_{\alpha\beta} = [\xi^\alpha \mid \epsilon\xi^\beta].$$

Since, by 4.3.14, we have

$$\epsilon\xi^\beta = \epsilon \sum_\gamma st^\gamma(\beta)\zeta^\gamma = \sum_\gamma st^{\gamma'}(\beta)\zeta^\gamma,$$

we can deduce
5.3.5 $$m'_{\alpha\beta} = \sum_\gamma st^\gamma(\alpha)st^{\gamma'}(\beta).$$

This shows that $M'_{\alpha\beta}$ is not empty if and only if a $\gamma \vdash n$ exists such that $\alpha \trianglelefteq \gamma$ and $\gamma \trianglelefteq \beta'$, i.e. if and only if $\alpha \trianglelefteq \beta'$. An easy generalization gives the following important existence theorem:

5.3.6 Theorem (Gale–Ryser) *For any* $\lambda, \mu \models n$ *we have*

$$M'_{\lambda,\mu} \neq \emptyset \iff \lambda^* \trianglelefteq (\mu^*)'.$$

In terms of Young characters this reads as follows:

5.3.7 Theorem (Ruch–Schönhofer) *For any* $\alpha, \beta \vdash n$ *and the corresponding Young characters of* $S_{\underline{n}}$ *we have*

$$[\xi^\alpha \mid \epsilon\xi^\beta] > 0 \iff \alpha \trianglelefteq \beta'.$$

These characterizations of dominance in terms of standard tableaux, 0–1–matrices and common irreducible constituents show the importance of the diagram lattice $(P(n), \trianglelefteq)$. The following subsets I_α and F_α of this lattice are called the *principal ideal* and the *principal filter* corresponding to α:

$$I_\alpha := \{\beta \vdash n \mid \beta \trianglelefteq \alpha\}, \ F_\alpha := \{\gamma \vdash n \mid \alpha \trianglelefteq \gamma\}.$$

In terms of these the above characterizations of dominance read as follows:

5.3.8 Corollary *For each* $\alpha \vdash n$,

$$I_\alpha = \{\beta \vdash n \mid ST^\alpha(\beta) \neq \emptyset\} = \{\beta \vdash n \mid M'_{\alpha'\beta} \neq \emptyset\}$$

$$= \{\beta \vdash n \mid [\xi^\beta \mid \zeta^\alpha] > 0\} = \{\beta \vdash n \mid [\xi^{\alpha'} \mid \epsilon\xi^\beta] > 0\},$$

while

$$F_\alpha = \{\beta \vdash n \mid ST^{\alpha'}(\beta') \neq \emptyset\} = \{\beta \vdash n \mid M'_{\alpha\beta'} \neq \emptyset\}$$

$$= \{\beta \vdash n \mid [\xi^\alpha \mid \zeta^\beta] > 0\} = \{\beta \vdash n \mid [\xi^\alpha \mid \epsilon\xi^{\beta'}] > 0\}.$$

There are various other sets of partitions which are unions of principal ideals of filters in diagram lattices.

5.3.9 Example The *edge degree* of a vertex in a labelled graph Γ is the number of edges which meet in this vertex. The edge degrees of all the v vertices of a labelled graph with e edges form, after reordering (if necessary), a nonincreasing sequence $(\alpha_1, \ldots, \alpha_v)$ which gives a partition $\alpha := (\alpha_1, \alpha_2, \ldots) \vdash 2e$ after adding further $\alpha_i := 0$, $i > v$. We call this sequence the *edge degree sequence* of Γ and of the graph which is represented by Γ, and we ask for a characterization of *graphical partitions*, i.e. of partitions that occur as edge degree

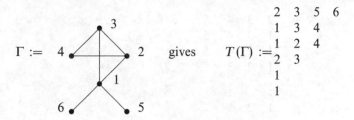

Figure 5.1: A labelled graph Γ and its tableau $T(\Gamma)$

sequences. (Recall the basic problem of combinatorial enumeration which was mentioned above, the construction of chemical isomers, which amounts to the construction of connected multigraphs with a given edge degree sequence!)

Assume that $\alpha \vdash n = 2e$ is an edge degree sequence, and that Γ has its i-th vertex of degree α_i. The labelled graph Γ can be described by a tableau $T(\Gamma)$ which contains in its i-th row the numbers of the vertices which are connected with the i-th vertex. In order to have $T(\Gamma)$ uniquely determined, we assume that the row entries are put in increasing order. An example is shown in Figure 5.1. We note that both the shape and the content of $T(\Gamma)$ is equal to α. Furthermore it is clear that

5.3.10 $$\sum_{i=1}^{j}(\alpha_i' - \alpha_i) \geq j, \ 1 \leq j \leq d(\alpha),$$

if $d(\alpha)$ denotes the length of the main diagonal of the diagram $[\alpha]$, i.e. if

$$d(\alpha) := \max\{i \mid \alpha_i \geq i\} = \max\{j \mid \alpha_j' \geq j\}.$$

5.3.11 Lemma *The partitions $\alpha \vdash n = 2e$ with the property*

$$\sum_{i=1}^{j}(\alpha_i' - \alpha_i) = j, \ 1 \leq j \leq d(\alpha),$$

are graphical partitions.

Proof: The tableau

$$
\begin{array}{cccccccc}
2 & 3 & 4 & 5 & \ldots & & \ldots & \ldots & \alpha'_1 \\
1 & 3 & 4 & 5 & \ldots & \alpha'_2 + 1 \\
1 & 2 & 4 & 5 & \ldots \\
1 & 2 & 3 & \ldots & \ldots \\
\vdots & \vdots & \vdots \\
1 & 2 \\
\vdots \\
1
\end{array}
$$

which is of this shape and content α shows the existence of a labelled graph with edge degree sequence α.

□

We shall show that these particular partitions form an antichain in $P(n)$. In fact the following more general result is true:

5.3.12 Lemma *For each sequence* $z = (z_1, \ldots)$ *of integers* z_i, *the set*

$$
P(n)_z := \{\alpha \vdash n \mid \forall j \le d(\alpha) : \Sigma_1^j (\alpha'_i - \alpha_i) = z_j\}
$$

is an antichain, i.e. the elements of this set are pairwise incomparable with respect to the dominance order.

Proof: Using an indirect proof we assume that α, $\beta \in P(n)_z$ are comparable, say $\alpha \trianglelefteq \beta$, and we shall show that this implies $\alpha = \beta$. The assumption $\alpha \trianglelefteq \beta$ yields $\alpha_1 \le \beta_1$, hence also $\alpha_1 + z_1 \le \beta_1 + z_1$, i.e. $\alpha'_1 \le \beta'_1$. But $\alpha \trianglelefteq \beta$ is the same as $\beta' \trianglelefteq \alpha'$, so that also $\beta'_1 \le \alpha'_1$ must hold, and we obtain that $\alpha'_1 = \beta'_1$, which gives $\alpha_1 = \beta_1$. Using this we can derive in the same way that also $\alpha_2 = \beta_2$, $\ldots, \alpha_{d(\alpha)} = \beta_{d(\alpha)}$.

□

Hence in particular the set $P(n)_1$, where $z := (1, 1, \ldots)$, which consists, if n is even, of graphical partitions (cf. 5.3.11), is an antichain. In order to show that the union of the principal ideals of the elements in $P(n)_1$ is the complete set of graphical partitions, we need one further result:

5.3.13 Lemma *If the graphical partition* α *covers* β, *then* β *is also graphical.*

Proof: As α covers β, there exist $i < j$ such that $\alpha_i = \beta_i + 1, \alpha_j = \beta_j - 1$, and $\alpha_k = \beta_k$, for each $k \ne i, j$. Consider a tableau $T(\Gamma)$ that describes a labelled graph with edge degree sequence α. The inequality $\beta_i \geq \beta_j$ implies that $\alpha_i \geq \alpha_j + 2$, so that there exists a vertex of Γ that is connected with the i-th vertex but not with the j-th vertex, let k be its label. The labelled graph Γ' which arises from Γ by erasing the edge that joins the i-th and the k-th vertex and adding an edge that connects the k-th and the j-th vertex obviously has edge degree sequence β, which proves the theorem.

$\square$

Thus, by 5.3.11, $P(n)_1$ consists of graphical partitions, if n is even. Furthermore, the ideals of the elements of $P(n)_1$ consist of graphical partitions, by 5.3.13. Since 5.3.10 together with 5.3.11 shows that a graphical partition α is dominated by the element $\beta \in P(n)_1$, defined by

$$\beta_1 := \alpha_1, \ldots, \beta_{d(\alpha)} := \alpha_{d(\alpha)}, \text{ and } \beta_1' := \alpha_1 + 1, \ldots, \beta_{d(\alpha)}' := \alpha_{d(\alpha)} + 1,$$

we have proved the following:

5.3.14 Theorem (Gutman–Ruch) *For even* n, *the set*

$$G(n) := \{\alpha \in P(n) \mid \exists \, \beta \in P(n)_1 : \alpha \trianglelefteq \beta\},$$

i.e. the union of the ideals generated by elments of $P(n)_1$, *is the set of graphical partitions of* n, *i.e. the set of edge degree sequences of graphs with* $n/2$ *edges.*

For example the set of graphical partitions of $n = 6$ is

$$I_{(2^3)} \cup I_{(3,1^3)} = \{(2^3), (3, 1^3), (2^2, 1^2), (2, 1^4), (1^6)\}.$$

$\diamond$

The theorem of Gutman and Ruch suggests to compare the *branching* of graphs. They say that a graph with edge degree sequence α is *more branched* than a graph with edge degree sequence β if and only if $\alpha \triangleright \beta$. In this sense the graphs with edge degree sequence $\alpha \in P(2e)_1$ are the *maximally branched* graphs with e edges. For example $\alpha := (e, 1^e)$, the edge degree sequence of the *star* with e edges, gives a maximally branched graph. In order to enumerate the elements of $P(2e)_1$, we note that $\alpha \in P(2e)_1$ is uniquely determined by the sequence $(\alpha_1, \alpha_2 - 1, \ldots, \alpha_{d(\alpha)} - (d(\alpha) - 1))$ which is strictly increasing. Furthermore each strictly decreasing sequence of natural numbers $(n_1, \ldots, n_r)$ yields an $\alpha \in P(n)_1$, n even, by putting $\alpha_1 :=$

$n_1, \alpha_2 := n_2 + 1, \ldots, \alpha_{d(\alpha)} := n_{d(\alpha)} + (d(\alpha) - 1)$, where $d(\alpha) := r$, and $\alpha'_i := \alpha_i + 1$, for $1 \le d(\alpha)$. Hence $P(2e)_1$ is of the same cardinality as the set of strictly decreasing partitions of e, which proves

5.3.15 Corollary *The number of elements in $P(2e)_1$, i.e. the number of edge degree sequences that correspond to maximally branched graphs with e edges, is the coefficient c_e in the formal power series*

$$\sum_{e \in \mathbb{N}} c_e x^e := \prod_{n \in \mathbb{N}^*} (1 + x^n) = 1 + x + x^2 + 2x^3 + 2x^4 + 3x^5 + \ldots .$$

5.4   Unimodality

In an earlier chapter we have seen that the numbers of graphs on 4 vertices which have 0,1,2,3,4,5,6 edges are 1,1,2,3,2,1,1. For the graphs on 5 vertices we obtain the sequence 1,1,2,4,6,6,6,4,2,1,1 according to the number of edges. Both these sequences weakly increase up to their middle term and then they weakly decrease, i.e. they both are *unimodal* sequences. Furthermore we notice that, if $g(v, e)$ denotes the number of graphs with v vertices and e edges, that, at least for the cases $v := 4, 5$, we have $g(v, e) = g(v, \binom{v}{2} - e)$, i.e. corresponding terms are equal and hence these two sequences are also *reciprocal*. Thus the sequences of numbers of graphs on v vertices according to their number of edges are reciprocal and unimodal, at least for the cases $v = 4$ and $v = 5$. It is our aim to show that this is true for *each v*, in fact we shall prove a much more general result on unimodal and reciprocal sequences.

The reciprocity of the sequence $g(v, e)$, for each v, is trivial by complementation of graphs:

5.4.1 $\forall v \in \mathbb{N}: \; g(v, e) = g(v, \binom{v}{2} - e)$, for each e.

In order to prove the unimodality of this sequence is we recall 5.3.1 which yields

5.4.2 $\mathrm{Grf}(G, Y^X) = \sum_{(\beta_1, \ldots, \beta_{|Y|}) \vdash n} \left[\chi^{I\bar{G} \uparrow S_X} \mid \xi^\beta \right] k_\beta.$

Since $k_\beta = \sum_{\lambda^* = \beta} Y^\lambda$, this gives

5.4.3 Corollary *The number of G–classes on* Y^X, *the elements of which are of content* $\lambda \models |X|$, *is equal to the following inner product of characters:*

$$\left[\chi^{I\bar{G}\uparrow S_X} \mid \xi^\lambda\right] = \left[\chi^{I\bar{G}\uparrow S_X} \mid \xi^{\lambda^*}\right].$$

An application of 5.3.2 to this result proves

5.4.4 Theorem *If* $\lambda, \mu \models n$ *and* $\lambda^* \lhd \mu^*$, *then the number of G–classes of content* λ *on* Y^X *is greater than or equal to the number of G–classes of content* μ.

Hence in particular each sequence of numbers of G–classes on Y^X by content is monotonous as soon as the partitions λ^* corresponding to the contents λ form a chain. An example of a chain of partitions is formed by the two–rowed partitions:

$$(|X|) \rhd (|X| - 1, 1) \rhd (|X| - 2, 2) \rhd \dots \rhd (|X| - \lfloor |X|/2 \rfloor, \lfloor |X|/2 \rfloor).$$

This gives

5.4.5 Corollary *In the case when* $|Y| = 2$, *the sequence of numbers of G–classes on* Y^X *by content is unimodal and reciprocal.*

In terms of the group reduction function this means that the sequence of the coefficients of the monomials in $C(G, X \mid y_1 + y_2)$ is unimodal. The coefficient of $y_1^{|X|-k} y_2^k$ in this polynomial is equal to the coefficient of y^k in $C(G, X \mid 1 + y)$. We therefore can also use $C(G, X \mid 1 + y)$ which is easier to write down. Let us now generalize our definitions of unimodality and reciprocity to *polynomials* in $\mathbb{R}[y]$. Consider $p = b_0 + b_1 y + \dots + b_k y^k \in \mathbb{R}[y]$. If $p = b_i y^i + b_{i+1} y^{i+1} + \dots + b_j y^j$, where $b_i \neq 0 \neq b_j$, then we call $m(p) := (i + j)/2$ the *middle* of p, while $d(p) := i + j$. Now we say that p is a *unimodal polynomial* if and only if its coefficients weakly increase up to the middle while they weakly decrease afterwards:

$$b_0 \leq b_1 \leq \dots \leq b_{\lfloor m(p) \rfloor} \geq b_{\lfloor m(p) \rfloor + 1} \geq \dots \geq b_{d(p)}.$$

Thus, for example $1 + y + 2y^2 + 2y^3 + y^4 + y^5$ and $y^3 + y^4$ are unimodal. Furthermore we call p a *reciprocal polynomial* if and only if, for each $i \leq d(p)$, we have that

$$b_i = b_{d(p)-i}.$$

Hence 5.4.5 can be rephrased as follows:

5.4.6 Corollary *For each finite action $_GX$ the polynomial $C(G, X \mid 1+y)$ is unimodal and reciprocal.*

A trivial example is formed by the identity subgroup of $S_{\underline{n}}$ which gives

$$C(\{1\}, \underline{n} \mid 1 + y) = (1 + y)^n = \sum_{k=0}^{n} \binom{n}{k} y^k.$$

Hence, as it is well known, the sequence of binomial coefficients is unimodal and reciprocal. A less trivial example follows from 1.4.8/2.2.8. If $p(k; m, n)$ denotes the number of partitions $\alpha \vdash k$ such that $\alpha'_1 \leq m$ and $\alpha_1 \leq n$, then we have, since the actions of $S_{\underline{m}} \wr S_{\underline{n}}$ on $\underline{m} \times \underline{n}$ and on $\underline{mn}$ are similar (recall 2.2.7):

$$5.4.7 \qquad \begin{bmatrix} m + n \\ n \end{bmatrix} = C(S_{\underline{m}} \odot S_{\underline{n}}, \underline{mn} \mid 1 + y) = \sum_{k=0}^{mn} p(k; m, n) y^k,$$

and so the sequence of numbers $p(k; m, n)$ and the Gaussian polynomial $\begin{bmatrix} m+n \\ n \end{bmatrix}$ are reciprocal and unimodal. If we compare this result with 5.1.14, we obtain the interesting equation

$$5.4.8 \qquad C(S_{\underline{m}} \odot S_{\underline{n}}, \underline{mn} \mid 1 + y) = \{m\}(1, y, \ldots, y^n).$$

We next aim to show that even $C(G, X \mid 1 + y + y^2 + \ldots y^k)$ is reciprocal and unimodal. In order to prove this we note (exercise 5.4.1)

5.4.9 Lemma *For the polynomials in a single indeterminate y over the field $\mathbb{R}$ of real numbers we have:*

- *$p \in \mathbb{R}[y]$ is reciprocal if and only if $p = y^{d(p)} \cdot p(y^{-1})$.*

- *Products of reciprocal polynomials are reciprocal.*

- *The sum of reciprocal unimodal polynomials p and q with the same middle $m(p) = m(q)$ is reciprocal and unimodal.*

- *Multiplying any reciprocal and unimodal polynomial by a nonnegative real number we obtain a reciprocal and unimodal polynomial.*

- *Products of reciprocal and unimodal polynomials are reciprocal and unimodal.*

Proof: The first statement is obviously valid and it implies the second, while the third and the fourth statement are trivial. In order to prove the fifth statement, we consider $p, q \in \mathbb{R}[y]$, both being unimodal and reciprocal. We can rewrite $p = b_0 + b_1 y + \ldots + b_k y^k$ in the following ways:

$$p = b_0 + b_1 y + \ldots + b_1 y^{d(p)-1} + b_0 y^{d(p)}$$

$$= b_0(1 + y + \ldots + y^{d(p)}) + (b_1 - b_0)(y + \ldots + y^{d(p)-1}) + \ldots .$$

Doing the same with $q = c_0 + \ldots + c_l y^l$, we get that pq is equal to

$$\sum_{i,j} (a_{i+1} - a_i)(b_{j+1} - b_j)(y^{i+1} + \ldots + y^{d(p)-(i+1)})(y^{j+1} + \ldots + y^{d(q)-(j+1)}).$$

Each one of these summands is reciprocal by part one, and it is not difficult to check that they are also unimodal. Since $(d(p) + d(q))/2$ is the middle of each of them, also $p \cdot q$, their sum, must be unimodal. □

We now remark that 5.1.12 yields

5.4.10 Corollary *For $Y = \{y_1, y_2\}$ we have that*

$$\{\alpha, Y\} = y_1^{\alpha_1} y_2^{\alpha_2} + y_1^{\alpha_1 - 1} y_2^{\alpha_2 + 1} + \ldots + y_1^{\alpha_2} y_2^{\alpha_1},$$

if α has at most two rows and $\{\alpha, Y\} = 0$ otherwise. Hence in particular

$$C(S_{\underline{n}}, \underline{n}, [\alpha] \mid 1 + y) = \begin{cases} y^{\alpha_2} + y^{\alpha_2 + 1} + \ldots + y^{\alpha_1} & \text{if } \alpha_3 = 0, \\ 0 & \text{otherwise.} \end{cases}$$

Thus $C(S_{\underline{n}}, \underline{n}, [\alpha] \mid 1 + y)$ is in any case reciprocal and unimodal and its coefficients are natural numbers.

In order to generalize this to $C(S_{\underline{n}}, \underline{n}, [\alpha] \mid 1 + \ldots + y^k)$, we shall express this polynomial in terms of plethysm of cycle indicator polynomials. Let us therefore introduce the plethysm of *arbitrary polynomials* first: We define $p(y_1, \ldots) \odot q(z_1, \ldots)$ to be

$$q(p(y_{1 \cdot 1}, y_{1 \cdot 2}, \ldots), \ldots, p(y_{n \cdot 1}, y_{n \cdot 2}, \ldots)).$$

We note that this definition is in accordance with 2.2.8. Using this generalization of plethysm of cycle indicator polynomials we can state that the following identity holds:

5.4.11 $C(S_{\underline{n}}, \underline{n}, [\alpha] \mid 1 + y + \ldots + y^k) = C(S_{\underline{k}}, \underline{k} \mid 1 + y) \odot C(S_{\underline{n}}, \underline{n}, [\alpha]).$

Proof: 2.2.8 implies that $C(S_{\underline{k}}, \underline{k} \mid y_1 + y_2) \odot C(S_{\underline{n}}, \underline{n}, [\alpha])$ is equal to

$$\frac{1}{n!} \sum_{\rho \in S_n} \zeta^{\alpha}(\rho^{-1}) \prod_{i=1}^{n} \underbrace{\left(\frac{1}{k!} \sum_{\pi \in S_k} \prod_{j=1}^{k} (y_1^{i \cdot j} + y_2^{i \cdot j})^{a_j(\pi)} \right)^{a_i(\rho)}}_{= y_1^{i \cdot k} + y_1^{i \cdot (k-1)} y_2^{i} + \dots + y_2^{i \cdot k}, \ by \ 5.4.10.},$$

which is the same as $C(S_{\underline{n}}, \underline{n}, [\alpha] \mid y_1^k + y_1^{k-1} y_2 + \dots + y_2^k)$, and so we obtain the statement by putting $y_1 := 1, y_2 := y$.

□

Now $C(S_{\underline{k}}, \underline{k} \mid y_1 + y_2) \odot C(S_{\underline{n}}, \underline{n}, [\alpha])$ belongs to $\Sigma_{k \cdot n}[Y]$, and it has integral coefficients, hence it is a $\mathbb{Z}$–linear combination of Schur polynomials in y_1 and y_2. Thus $C(S_{\underline{k}}, \underline{k} \mid 1 + y) \odot C(S_{\underline{n}}, \underline{n}, [\alpha])$ is a sum of Schur polynomials $\{\alpha, Y\}$ taken at $y_1 := 1, y_2 := y$, and hence, by 5.4.10, we obtain

5.4.12 Corollary $C(S_{\underline{n}}, \underline{n}, [\alpha] \mid 1 + y + \dots + y^k)$ *is reciprocal and unimodal and it has natural coefficients.*

In order to complete the proof of the general theorem on unimodal and reciprocal polynomials we need to prove two further results on Schur polynomials:

5.4.13 Lemma (Cauchy) *If X and Y are two disjoint finite sets of indeterminates, then*

$$\prod_{x \in X, y \in Y} (1 - xy)^{-1} = \sum_{n \in \mathbb{N}} \sum_{\alpha \vdash n} h_{\alpha}(X) k_{\alpha}(Y) = \sum_{n, \alpha} \{\alpha, X\}\{\alpha, Y\},$$

and

$$\prod_{x \in X, y \in Y} (1 + xy) = \sum_{n \in \mathbb{N}} \sum_{\alpha \vdash n} e_{\alpha}(X) k_{\alpha}(Y) = \sum_{n, \alpha} \{\alpha', X\}\{\alpha, Y\}.$$

Proof: $\prod (1 - xy)^{-1}$ is a formal power series, defined by

$$\prod_{x, y} (1 - xy)^{-1} = \prod_{x, y} (1 + xy + x^2 y^2 + \dots) = \sum_{n \in \mathbb{N}} \sum_{\lambda, \mu \models n} m_{\lambda \mu} X^{\lambda} Y^{\mu}$$

$$= \sum_{n} \sum_{\alpha \vdash n} \sum_{\lambda \models n} st^{\alpha}(\lambda) X^{\lambda} \sum_{\mu \models n} st^{\alpha}(\mu) Y^{\mu} = \sum_{n, \alpha} \{\alpha, X\}\{\alpha, Y\}.$$

The second statement follows analogously.   □

The next equation we would like to derive uses the notion of *skew representation* $[\alpha\backslash\beta]$, which is defined as follows. For $\alpha \vdash n$ and $\beta \vdash m \leq n$ we put

5.4.14
$$[\alpha\backslash\beta] := \sum_{\gamma\vdash n-m} ([\beta][\gamma], [\alpha])[\gamma].$$

The corresponding *skew Schur polynomials* have the following property:

5.4.15 Lemma *If X and Y denote two disjoint finite sets of indeterminates, then*
$$\{\alpha, X \cup Y\} = \sum_{m<n} \sum_{\beta\vdash n} \{\alpha\backslash\beta, X\}\{\beta, Y\}.$$

Proof: For $m < n$ and a third finite set Z of indeterminates, disjoint with X and Y, we have, by definition of $\{\alpha\backslash\beta\}$:

$$\sum_{\alpha\vdash n} \sum_{m<n} \sum_{\beta\vdash m} \{\alpha\backslash\beta, X\}\{\alpha, Z\}\{\beta, Y\} =$$

$$= \sum_{\alpha,\beta} \left(\sum_{\gamma\vdash n-m} ([\beta][\gamma], [\alpha])\{\gamma, X\} \right) \{\alpha, Z\}\{\beta, Y\}$$

$$= \sum_{\beta,\gamma} \{\beta, Y\}\{\gamma, X\} \sum_{\alpha} ([\beta][\gamma], [\alpha])\{\alpha, Z\}$$

$$= \sum_{\beta,\gamma} \{\beta, Y\}\{\gamma, X\}\{\beta, Z\}\{\gamma, Z\}$$

$$= \prod_{y,z}(1 - yz)^{-1} \prod_{x,z}(1 - xz)^{-1} = \sum_{\alpha} \{\alpha, X \cup Y\}\{\alpha, Z\}.$$

This proves the lemma since the $\{\alpha, Z\}$ form a basis.

□

We are now in the position to prove the theorem that the Pólya insertion of any reciprocal and unimodal polynomial with natural coefficients into a cycle indicator of a finite action gives a reciprocal and unimodal polynomial. But instead of formally proving this, we demonstrate it by an example which shows that all this works in the general case, too.

Consider $u(y) := 1 + 2y + 2y^2 + y^3$, which is a unimodal and reciprocal polynomial with coefficients in $\mathbb{N}$. By Foulkes' Lemma $C(G, X \mid u(y))$

is reciprocal and unimodal if this is also true for $C(S_{\underline{n}}, \underline{n}, [\alpha] \mid u(y))$. In order to prove that the latter polynomials are in fact reciprocal and unimodal, we use 5.4.13 which implies the last of the following equations: $C(S_{\underline{n}}, \underline{n}, [\alpha] \mid 1 + 2y + 2y^2 + y^3)$ is equal to

$$C(S_{\underline{n}}, \underline{n}, [\alpha] \mid 1 + y + y^2 + y^3 + z + z^2)|_{z:=y}$$

$$= \{\alpha, \{y_1, y_2, y_3, y_4\} \cup \{z_1, z_2\}\}|_{y_i := y^{i-1}, z_i := y^i}$$

$$= \sum_{\beta} C(S_{\underline{n-m}}, \underline{n-m}, [\alpha \backslash \beta] \mid 1 + y + y^2 + y^3) C(S_{\underline{m}}, \underline{m}, [\beta] \mid z + z^2)|_{z:=y}.$$

We now remark that

$$C(S_{\underline{m}}, \underline{m}, [\beta] \mid z + z^2) = z^m C(S_{\underline{m}}, \underline{m}, [\beta] \mid 1 + z),$$

which is reciprocal and unimodal by 5.4.9/ 5.4.10. Moreover

$$C(S_{\underline{n-m}}, \underline{n-m}, [\alpha \backslash \beta] \mid 1 + y + y^2 + y^3)$$

$$= \sum_{\gamma} ([\beta][\gamma], [\alpha]) C(S_{\underline{n-m}}, \underline{n-m}, [\gamma] \mid 1 + y + y^2 + y^3)$$

is also reciprocal and unimodal since each of the summands has this property and all the summands have the same middle. Thus, by 5.4.13, each $C(S_{\underline{n}}, \underline{n}, [\alpha] \mid 1 + 2y + 2y^2 + y^3)$ and hence also each $C(G, X \mid 1 + 2y + 2y^2 + y^3)$ is reciprocal and unimodal. In the same way we can prove

5.4.16 Theorem *Pólya insertion of an unimodal and reciprocal polynomial $u(y)$ with natural coefficients into a cycle indicator of a finite action $_G X$ gives the polynomial $C(G, X \mid u(y))$ which is reciprocal and unimodal.*

Note that the above argument needs in fact that $u(y)$ has all its coefficients in $\mathbb{N}$. But more than that: 5.4.16 *does not hold* if we allow $u(y)$ to have rational coefficients:

$$C(S_{\underline{2}}, 2 \mid \frac{1}{2} + \frac{1}{2}y) = \frac{3}{8} + \frac{2}{8}y + \frac{3}{8}y^2.$$

We finally determine which numbers are generated by these unimodal and reciprocal polynomials $C(G, X \mid 1 + y + y^2 + y^3)$. From the preceeding sections it should in fact be clear that this polynomial generates the numbers of G–classes on $Y^X := (k+1)^X$ by weight, if we take for the weight the function

$$w: Y^X \to \mathbb{R}: f \mapsto y^{\Sigma f(x)},$$

so that, for example, $C(S_{\underline{v}}, \binom{v}{2}) \mid 1 + y + \ldots + y^k)$ generates the numbers of k–graphs on v vertices with respect to the number of edges, the coefficient of y^e in this polynomial is in fact equal to the number of k–graphs on v vertices which have a total of e edges.

Exercises

E 5.4.1 Prove lemma 5.4.9.

5.5 The Littlewood–Richardson Rule

If $_G X$ is an action then we call $x \in X$ a G–*invariant* or simply an *invariant* if and only if $gx = x$, for each $g \in G$. If X is not only a set but also a vector space and the action $_G X$ a representation of G on X, then we can generalize this definition of G–invariant to that of a *relative G–invariant* by which we now mean an $x \in X$ such that, for a suitable 1–dimensional character χ of G, we have

$$\forall\ g \in G:\ gx := D(g)x = \chi(g)x.$$

(Thus G–invariants which are sometimes called *absolute* G–invariants are the relative G–invariants corresponding to the identity character.) In other words, a relative G–invariant is an element of a vector space affording a 1–dimensional representation of G.
The symmetric polynomials over $\mathbb{Q}$ and in the set of indeterminates $Y = \{y_1, \ldots, y_m\}$ were defined to be the absolute invariants of the natural action of $S_{\underline{m}}$ on $\mathbb{Q}[Y]$. Since ι and ϵ are the only onedimensional characters of $S_{\underline{m}}$, the relative $S_{\underline{m}}$–invariants of $\mathbb{Q}[Y]$ which are not absolute invariants are the polynomials p which satisfy

$$\forall\ \pi \in S_{\underline{m}}:\ p(y_{\pi 1}, \ldots, y_{\pi m}) = \epsilon(\pi)p(y_1, \ldots, y_m),$$

we call them the *alternating polynomials* in the $y_i \in Y$ over $\mathbb{Q}$. Clearly the following is true (exercise 5.5.1):

5.5.1 Lemma *The polynomial* $p \in \mathbb{Q}[Y]$ *is alternating if and only if it is a* $\mathbb{Q}$*–linear combination of the polynomials*

$$\sum_{\pi \in S_m} \epsilon(\pi) y_{\pi 1}^{d_1} \ldots y_{\pi m}^{d_m} = \det(y_i^{d_k}),$$

where $d_1 > \ldots > d_m \geq 0$.

As each such d_i is greater than or equal to $m - i$, we can replace $d = (d_1, \ldots, d_m)$ by $\alpha := (\alpha_1, \ldots, \alpha_m)$, where $\alpha_i := d_i - m + i$, obtaining in this way a proper partition α of $\sum d_i - \binom{m}{2}$. Thus 5.5.1 can be rephrased as follows:

5.5.2 Corollary $p \in \mathbb{Q}[Y]$ *is alternating if and only if it is a* $\mathbb{Q}$*–linear combination of the polynomials*

$$\Delta_\alpha := \sum_{\pi \in S_m} \epsilon(\pi) y_{\pi 1}^{\alpha_1 + m - 1} \ldots y_{\pi m}^{\alpha_m + m - m} = \det\left(y_i^{\alpha_k + m - k}\right),$$

where $\alpha := (\alpha_1, \ldots, \alpha_m)$ *denotes a proper partition of some* $n \in \mathbb{N}$ *such that* $\alpha_1' \leq m$.

The Δ_α are obviously linearly independent, we therefore denote by

$$A_n[Y] = \ll \Delta_\alpha \mid \alpha \vdash n, \alpha_1' \leq m \gg_\mathbb{Q}$$

the subspace of $\mathbb{Q}[Y]$ consisting of the *homogeneous* alternating polynomials of degree $n + \binom{m}{2}$ which has the Δ_α as $\mathbb{Q}$–basis. The vector space $A[Y]$ containing *all* the alternating polynomials therefore satisfies

5.5.3 $$A[Y] = \bigoplus_{n \in \mathbb{N}} A_n[Y].$$

We now consider the particular alternating polynomial corresponding to the zero partition $\alpha := (0, \ldots)$:

$$\Delta_0 = \det(y_i^{m-k}) = \prod_{i<j}(y_i - y_j),$$

the well known *Vandermonde determinant*. It yields an interesting endomorphism of $\mathbb{Q}[Y]$ via left multiplication:

$$\Delta_0 : \mathbb{Q}[Y] \to \mathbb{Q}[Y] : p \mapsto \Delta_0 \cdot p.$$

This mapping is obviously linear, injective, and it maps $\Sigma_n[Y]$ into $A_n[Y]$. But even more is valid, it establishes a $\mathbb{Q}$– isomorphism between these two spaces:

5.5.4 $$\Delta_0 : \Sigma_n[Y] \simeq_{\mathbb{Q}} A_n[Y].$$

Proof: As Δ_0 is injective and the Δ_α are a basis of $A_n[Y]$, we need only show that they occur in the image which again means that they should be divisible by Δ_0. Now Δ_α can be considered as a polynomial in the single indeterminate y_j by taking $\mathbb{Q}[Y \backslash \{y_j\}]$ as a ring of coefficients, i.e. we consider Δ_α as an element of the polynomial ring $\mathbb{Q}[Y \backslash \{y_j\}][y_j]$. But as Δ_α is alternating, we get zero if we replace the indeterminate y_j by the element $y_i \in \mathbb{Q}[Y \backslash \{y_j\}]$, and so Δ_α must be divisible by $(y_i - y_j)$ (recall that $\mathbb{Q}[Y \backslash \{y_j\}][y_j]$ is also Gaussian, and $y_i - y_j$ is an irreducible element therein) and hence also by the Vandermonde determinant $\prod(y_i - y_j)$.

$\square$

We aim in fact to show that the inverse image Δ_α / Δ_0 of Δ_α is the Schur polynomial $\{\alpha\}$. The first step to prove this is to examine

$$\Delta_\alpha \cdot e_p = \det(y_i^{\alpha_k + m - k}) \sum_{M \in \binom{m}{p}} \prod_{i \in M} y_i$$

$$= \sum_{\pi \in S_{\underline{m}}} \epsilon(\pi) \prod_{k=1}^m y_{\pi k}^{\alpha_k + m - k} \sum_{M \in \binom{m}{p}} \prod_{k \in M} y_{\pi k}$$

$$= \sum_M \sum_\pi \epsilon(\pi) \prod_k y_{\pi k}^{\alpha_k + m - k + I_M(k)},$$

where I_M denotes the *characteristic function* of $M \subseteq \underline{m}$:

$$I_M(k) := \begin{cases} 1 & \text{if } k \in M, \\ 0 & \text{otherwise.} \end{cases}$$

Thus we have obtained that

5.5.5 $$\Delta_\alpha \cdot e_p = \sum_{M \in \binom{m}{p}} \det \left(y_i^{\alpha_k + m - k + I_M(k)} \right).$$

In order to simplify the right hand side of this equation we notice that such a determinantal summand is zero if and only if, for some $k < l$, we have $\alpha_k - k + I_M(k) = \alpha_l - l + I_M(l)$. Since $\alpha_k \geq \alpha_l$ and

$I_M(k), I_M(l) \in \{0,1\}$ this equation implies $l = k+1, \alpha_k = \alpha_k + 1$ and $I_M(k) = 0, I_M(k+1) = 1$. Thus the nonzero summands correspond to p–subsets M of $\underline{m}$, for which $\beta := (\ldots, \alpha_k + I_M(k), \ldots)$ is a *proper partition* of $m + p$. Hence we have proved

5.5.6 Corollary *For each* $\alpha \vdash n$ *and any* $p \in \mathbb{N}$ *we have*

$$\Delta_\alpha \cdot e_p = \sum \Delta_\beta,$$

if the sum is taken over all the $\beta \vdash n + p$ *the diagrams* $[\beta]$ *of which arise from* $[\alpha]$ *by adding* p *nodes in* p *different rows.*

Iteration of this yields, for $\alpha \vdash n$:

$$\Delta_0 \cdot e_\alpha = \sum_{(\beta_1, \ldots, \beta_m) \vdash n} st^{\beta'}(\alpha) \Delta_\beta,$$

or, equivalently:

$$e_\alpha = \sum_{(\beta_1, \ldots, \beta_m) \vdash n} st^{\beta'}(\alpha) \frac{\Delta_\beta}{\Delta_0}.$$

On the other hand, 5.2.1 gives

$$e_\alpha = \sum_\gamma m'_{\alpha\gamma} k_\gamma = \sum_{\gamma, \beta} m'_{\alpha\gamma} \epsilon_{\beta\gamma} \{\beta\}$$

$$= \sum_{\beta, \gamma} \epsilon_{\beta\gamma} m'_{\gamma\alpha} \{\beta\} = \sum_\beta st^{\beta'}(\alpha) \{\beta\}.$$

Comparing these two expressions of e_α we finally obtain

5.5.7 Corollary *For* $\alpha = (\alpha_1, \ldots, \alpha_m) \vdash n$ *and* $Y = \{y_1, \ldots, y_m\}$ *we have*

$$\frac{\Delta_\alpha(Y)}{\Delta_0(Y)} = \{\alpha, Y\}.$$

Besides the representation theoretical consequences which will be discussed later, this result yields, for combinatorial purposes, a useful method for decomposing a given symmetric polynomial into a linear combination of Schur polynomials.

5.5.8 Corollary *The coefficient of* $\{\alpha, Y\}$ *in* $p \in \Sigma_n[Y]$ *is equal to the coefficient of* $\prod y_i^{\alpha_i + m - i}$ *in* $\Delta_0(Y) \cdot p$.

Proof: The statement follows immediately from 5.5.4 since $\Delta_0(Y) \cdot p \in A_n[Y]$ and the $\Delta_\alpha(Y)$ form a basis of $A_n[Y]$ while $\prod y_i^{\alpha_i+m-i}$ is the leading term in $\Delta_\alpha(Y)$.

□

The identification 5.5.7 allows to rephrase 5.5.6 in terms of representations. For 5.5.6 says that $\{\alpha\} \cdot e_p = \sum \{\beta\}$, where the $[\beta]$ arise from $[\alpha]$ by adding p nodes in p different rows, and e_p is the symmetric polynomial corresponding to the alternating representation of S_p (cf. 5.2.4), which is $[1^p]$. This yields

5.5.9 Corollary *The diagrams $[\beta]$ of the constituents of $[\alpha][1^p]$ are obtained by adding p nodes to pairwise different rows of $[\alpha]$.*

As multiplication by the alternating character means taking instead of $\alpha, (1^p)$ or β its associate $\alpha', (p)$ or β', we also get

5.5.10 Young's Rule *The diagrams $[\beta]$ of the constituents of $[\alpha][p]$ are obtained by adding p nodes to pairwise different columns of $[\alpha]$.*

For example, if $\alpha := (3, 2^2)$ and $p := 2$ we obtain, indicating the added nodes by 1, the following diagrams according to 5.5.10:

$$
\begin{array}{ccccc}
\times & \times & \times & 1 & 1 \\
\times & \times & & & \\
\times & \times & & &
\end{array}
\quad
\begin{array}{cccc}
\times & \times & \times & 1 \\
\times & \times & 1 & \\
\times & \times & &
\end{array}
\quad
\begin{array}{cccc}
\times & \times & \times & 1 \\
\times & \times & & \\
\times & \times & & \\
1 & & &
\end{array}
\quad ,
$$

$$
\begin{array}{ccc}
\times & \times & \times \\
\times & \times & 1 \\
\times & \times & \\
1 & &
\end{array}
\quad
\begin{array}{ccc}
\times & \times & \times \\
\times & \times & \\
\times & \times & \\
1 & 1 &
\end{array} \quad .
$$

which yields the decomposition

$$[3, 2^2][2] = [5, 2^2] + [4, 3, 2] + [4, 2^2, 1] + [3^2, 2, 1] + [3, 2^3].$$

We can apply this process repeatedly in order to get the constituents of $IS_\alpha \uparrow S_n$. For example if we want to decompose $[3][2][1]$, we first evaluate $[3][2]$ obtaining

$$
\begin{array}{ccccc}
\times & \times & \times & 1 & 1
\end{array}
+
\begin{array}{cccc}
\times & \times & \times & 1 \\
1 & & &
\end{array}
+
\begin{array}{ccc}
\times & \times & \times \\
1 & 1 &
\end{array} \quad .
$$

Thus $[3][2] = [5] + [4, 1] + [3, 2]$, which yields the decomposition of $[3][2][1]$:

$$
\begin{array}{cccccc}
\times & \times & \times & 1 & 1 & 2
\end{array}
+
\begin{array}{ccccc}
\times & \times & \times & 1 & 1 \\
2 & & & &
\end{array}
+
\begin{array}{ccccc}
\times & \times & \times & 1 & 2 \\
1 & & & &
\end{array}
$$

$$+\ \begin{array}{cccc} \times & \times & \times & 1 \\ 1 & 2 & & \end{array} \quad + \begin{array}{ccc} \times & \times & \times \\ 1 & & \\ 2 & & \end{array}\ \ 1$$

$$+\ \begin{array}{cccc} \times & \times & \times & 2 \\ 1 & 1 & & \end{array} \quad + \begin{array}{cccc} \times & \times & \times & 2 \\ 1 & 1 & 2 & \end{array} \quad + \begin{array}{ccc} \times & \times & \times \\ 1 & 1 & \\ 2 & & \end{array}$$

so that we have received the following decomposition:

$$[3][2][1] = [6] + 2 \cdot [5,1] + 2 \cdot [4,2] + [4,1^2] + [3^2] + [3,2,1].$$

More generally the constituents $[\alpha], \alpha \vdash m + n$, of the representation

$$[\beta][\delta_1][\delta_2]\ldots = ([\beta] \# IS_\delta \uparrow S_{\underline{n}}) \uparrow S_{\underline{m+n}}, \ \beta \vdash m, \ \delta \models n,$$

are obtained by first adding to the diagram $[\beta]$ δ_1 nodes 1 in all the admissible ways (see 5.5.10), then to each one of the resulting diagrams add δ_2 further nodes 2 in all the admissible ways, and so on. This procedure motivates the introduction of *skew diagrams* $[\alpha \backslash \beta]$ arising from $[\alpha]$ by deleting the subdiagram $[\beta]$, e.g.

$$[8, 7^2, 5\backslash 4, 3^2] = \begin{array}{ccccc} & & \times & \times & \times & \times \\ & & \times & \times & \times & \times \\ & & \times & \times & \times & \times \\ \times & \times & \times & \times & \times & \end{array}.$$

The reader notices that the resulting diagram does *not* determine $[\alpha]$ or $[\beta]$, e.g. $[8, 7^2, 5\backslash 4, 3^2] = [9, 8^2, 6\backslash 5, 4^2, 1]$.

To each skew diagram there correspond *skew tableaux* and *standard skew tableaux* in the obvious way. Let

$$st^{\alpha \backslash \beta}(\lambda)$$

denote the number of standard tableaux of shape $\alpha \backslash \beta$ and content λ. If we are given a skew tableau, say

$$\begin{array}{cc} 1 & 1 \\ 2 & \\ 2 & 3 \end{array} \ \in \ ST^{(3,2^2)\backslash(1^2)}(2,2,1),$$

then we can read its entries from *right to left* in each row and one row after the other, *downwards*, obtaining a sequence of natural numbers. The given example yields 11232. Such a sequence is called a *lattice permutation* if the following holds: For each place j of the sequence the number of i's which occur among the first j elements is greater than or equal to the number of $(i+1)$'s, for each i and any j. Hence 11232 is a lattice permutation, while 11322 is not.

For the sake of simplicity we now allow the nodes of a diagram or a skew diagram to be replaced by elements of an arbitrary totally ordered set. We prove a combinatorial lemma which will turn out to be crucial:

5.5.11 Lemma *Assume that* $\alpha \vdash n_1 + n_2 + b$, *where* $n_i, b \in \mathbb{N}$ *and* $\beta \vdash n_2, \gamma \vdash n_1$. *Then the number of standard tableaux of shape* $\alpha \backslash \gamma$ *which contain* β_i *numbers* $i, i \in \mathbb{N}$, *together with* b *symbols* x *such that the elements* i *form a lattice partition, is the same if the order is defined by*

$$x < 1 < 2 < \ldots < \beta_1',$$

as if it is defined by

$$1 < 2 < \ldots < \beta_1' < x.$$

Proof: For $0 \leq k \leq \beta_1'$ and the corresponding order $1 < \ldots < k < x < k+1 < \ldots < \beta_1'$ we denote by

$$M_k$$

the set of standard tableaux of shape $\alpha \backslash \gamma$ which contain β_i numbers i, b symbols x. The subset of M_k, consisting of the tableaux the entries i of which yield lattice permutations, will be indicated by

$$L_k.$$

Our method of proof is to construct bijections

$$\varphi_k : M_k \to M_{k-1}, 1 \leq k \leq \beta_1',$$

which satisfy

$$\varphi_0 \varphi_1 \ldots \varphi_{\beta_1'}[L_{\beta_1'}] = L_0,$$

so that the statement immediately follows by definition of $L_{\beta_1'}$ and L_0 from the fact that the φ_k are bijections.

i)*The bijections*: We define φ_k on M_k. If $T \in M_k$, then $\varphi_k(T)$ arises from T in the following way:

a) In each column of T which contains both x and k, we interchange x and k (remember that T is standard, so that each
column of T contains both x and k at most once and next to
each other), and afterwards

b) in each row containing both x's and k's which were left fixed
under a), we shift the x's to the left of the k's.

Obviously $\varphi_k(T) \in M_{k-1}$, so that $\varphi_k : M_k \to M_{k-1}$. Furthermore φ_k
is a bijection, since it is inverted by $\psi_k : M_{k-1} \to M_k$, which is defined
by its operation on an element of M_k as follows.

a') interchange x and k when they occur in the same column, and
then

b') in each row which contains both x's and k's fixed under a'), shift
the x's to the right of the k's.

ii) $\varphi_1 \ldots \varphi_{\beta'_1}[L_{\beta'_1}] \subseteq L_0$: Take a $T_{\beta'_1} \in L_{\beta'_1}$. Suppose, inductively, that
the i's in each of the following tableaux form a lattice permutation:

$$T_{\beta'_1}, \varphi_{\beta'_1}(T_{\beta'_1}), \ldots, \varphi_{k+1} \ldots \varphi_{\beta'_1}(T_{\beta'_1}) =: T_k.$$

We have to show that this is also true for

$$T_{k-1} := \varphi_k(T_k) = \varphi_k \ldots \varphi_{\beta'_1}(T_{\beta'_1}).$$

(Note that we do *not* prove that $\varphi_k[L_k] \subseteq L_{k-1}$, which is in fact
false.) The definition of φ_k shows that the lattice property holds for
all the numbers in $\varphi_k(T_k)$, except, perhaps, between the numbers k
and $k+1$. In particular $\varphi_{\beta'_1}(T_{\beta'_1}) \in L_{\beta'_1 - 1}$. We may therefore assume
$k < \beta'_1$. Suppose now that there is a $k+1$ in the i-th row of T_k. Then
the required lattice property in $\varphi_k(T_k)$ is true for $k+1$ unless there is
an x to the left of it in the same row of T_k and this x lies below a k.
We must examine the latter case more closely:

$$\begin{array}{c|ccccc}
< k & k \ldots k & k \ldots k & x \ldots x & x \ldots \\
\hline
\ldots x & \underbrace{x \ldots x}_{>0} & \underbrace{k+1 \ldots k+1}_{a} & \underbrace{k+1 \ldots k+1}_{b} & \left| \overline{> k+1} \right. \leftarrow i
\end{array}$$

Every $k+1$ in the i-th row of T_k has a k or an x immediately above
it, since $k < x < k+1$, and there is an x in the i-th row with a k
above it. Let $a \ (\geq 0)$ be the number of $(k+1)$'s in this row which lie

below an x. Suppose that the last k in the $(i-1)$-th row of T_k lies in the j-th column. Since $T_k = \varphi_{k+1}(T_{k+1}) \in L_k$, we have

$$b \leq |\{(i',j') \mid k \text{ in } (i',j') \text{ of } T_k, i' < i-1, \text{ or } i' = i-1 \text{ and } j' > j\}|$$

$$-|\{(i',j') \mid k+1 \text{ in } (i',j') \text{ of } T_k, i' < i-1 \text{ or } i' = i-1 \text{ and } j' > j\}| \,.$$

Thus, in $\varphi_k(T_k)$, the number of k's in the first $i-1$ rows minus the number of $(k+1)$'s in the first $i-1$ rows is at least $a+b$. This shows that the lattice property holds for all the $(k+1)$'s in the i-th row of $\varphi_k(T_k)$, and completes the proof of ii).

iii) The inclusion $\psi_{\beta_1'} \dots \psi_1[L_0] \subseteq L_{\beta_1'}$ follows quite analogously.

$\square$

5.5.12 Corollary *The multiplicity* $([\beta][\delta_1][\delta_2] \dots, [\gamma]), \beta \vdash m, \delta \vdash n, \gamma \vdash m+n,$ *is equal to the number of standard tableaux of shape* γ *which contain* β_i *symbols* i, δ_j *symbols* $\bar{j}, 1 \leq i \leq \beta_1', 1 \leq j \leq \delta_1',$ *subject to the ordering* $\bar{1} < \dots < \bar{\delta_1'} < 1 < \dots < \beta_1'$ *and such that the* i's *yield a lattice permutation when we read the rows from the right to the left and downwards.*

Proof: The considerations above have shown that

$$([\beta][\delta_1][\delta_2] \dots, [\gamma]) = st^{\gamma \backslash \beta}(\delta),$$

which is the number of standard tableaux of shape $\gamma \backslash \beta$ and of content δ. Now the tableau

$$
\begin{array}{cccc}
1 & \dots & \dots & \dots & 1 \\
2 & \dots & \dots & 2 \\
\dots & \dots & \dots \\
\beta_1' & \dots & \beta_1'
\end{array}
$$

is the only standard tableau of shape and content β, its entries form a lattice permutation. Thus $st^{\gamma \backslash \beta}(\delta)$ is equal to the number of standard tableaux of shape γ which contain β_i i's and δ_j $\bar{j}$'s, subject to the order $1 < \dots < \beta_1' < \bar{1} < \dots < \bar{\delta_1'}$ and such that the i's form a lattice permutation. Successive applications of 5.5.11 to $x := \bar{1}, \bar{2}, \dots, \bar{\delta_1'}$ yield the statement.

$\square$

We are now in a position to prove the main theorem:

5.5.13 The Littlewood–Richardson Rule *The multiplicity*

$$([\alpha][\beta], [\gamma]), \alpha \vdash m, \beta \vdash n, \gamma \vdash m + n,$$

is equal to the number of standard tableaux of shape $\gamma \backslash \alpha$ and content β which yield lattice permutations when we read their entries from the right to the left and downwards.

Proof: Let $g_{\alpha\beta}^{\gamma}$ denote this number of standard tableaux. 5.5.12 yields

$$([\delta_1][\delta_2] \ldots [\beta], [\gamma]) = \sum_{\alpha \vdash m} st^{\alpha}(\delta) g_{\alpha\beta}^{\gamma},$$

so that, for each $\delta \vdash m$:

$$\sum_{\alpha} st^{\alpha}(\delta) g_{\alpha\beta}^{\gamma} = ([\delta_1][\delta_2] \ldots [\beta], [\gamma]) = \sum_{\alpha} \kappa_{\delta\alpha}([\alpha][\beta], [\gamma]).$$

The statement now follows from $st^{\alpha}(\delta) = \kappa_{\delta\alpha}$ and the regularity of the Kostka matrix.

□

In terms of Schur polynomials and in terms of ordinary irreducible representations this reads as follows:

5.5.14 Corollary *For each $\alpha \vdash m, \beta \vdash n$ we have:*

$$\{\alpha\}\{\beta\} = \sum_{\gamma \vdash m+n} g_{\alpha\beta}^{\gamma} \{\gamma\}, \ and \ [\alpha][\beta] = \sum_{\gamma \vdash m+n} g_{\alpha\beta}^{\gamma} [\gamma].$$

Moreover

$$\{\gamma \backslash \alpha\} = \sum g_{\alpha\beta}^{\gamma} \{\beta\}, \ and \ [\gamma \backslash \alpha] = \sum g_{\alpha\beta}^{\gamma} [\beta],$$

in accordance with the definition of skew representation, so that skew representations correspond to skew diagrams and skew tableaux.

An application of this result yields all the irreducible constituents of the restriction $[\alpha] \downarrow S_{n-1}$. In order to describe this *branching* of the irreducible representations of symmetric groups, we introduce the following notation. Let α denote a partition of n, and put

$$\alpha^{i\pm} := (\alpha_1, \ldots, \alpha_{i-1}, \alpha_i \pm 1, \alpha_{i+1}, \ldots).$$

In terms of this we get (already from 5.5.10):

5.5.15 The Branching Theorem *If $\alpha \vdash n$, then we have, for the corresponding irreducible representation $[\alpha]$ of S_n and its restriction to S_{n-1}, the stabilizer of the subset $\underline{n-1} \subseteq \underline{n}$:*

$$[\alpha] \downarrow S_{n-1} = \sum_{i: \alpha_i > \alpha_{i+1}} [\alpha^{i-}],$$

which means that the irreducible components of this restriction correspond to the diagrams $[\beta]$ that can be obtained from $[\alpha]$ by deleting one node, wherever this is possible. Conversely, if S_n denotes the stabilizer of $\underline{n} \subseteq \underline{n+1}$, then the representation of S_{n+1} induced by $[\alpha]$, has the following decomposition into irreducible constituents:

$$[\alpha] \uparrow S_{n+1} = \sum_{i: \alpha_i < \alpha_{i-1}} [\alpha^{i+}].$$

This means that the irreducible components of this representation correspond to the diagrams $[\beta]$ that can be obtained from $[\alpha]$ by adding just one node.

For example

$$[3,2,1^2] \downarrow S_{\underline{6}} = [2^2, 1^2] + [3, 1^3] + [3, 2, 1],$$

while

$$[3,2,1^2] \uparrow S_{\underline{8}} = [4,2,1^2] + [3^2, 1^2] + [3, 2^2, 1] + [3, 2, 1^3].$$

An iterative application of the Branching Theorem shows that, for $\alpha \vdash n, m \in \mathbb{N}$ and $\beta \vdash m + n$, we have the implication

5.5.16 $\qquad ([\alpha] \uparrow S_{m+n}, [\beta]) > 0 \iff \alpha \subseteq \beta,$

where $\alpha \subseteq \beta$ means that $\alpha_i \le \beta_i$, for each i. We therefore consider the set

$$P(\mathbb{N}) := \bigcup_{n \in \mathbb{N}} P(n) = \{\alpha \mid \exists n \in \mathbb{N} : \alpha \vdash n\}, \quad \text{where } P(0) := \{\emptyset\},$$

consisting of *all* the proper partitions and partially ordered by *inclusion*:

$$\alpha \subseteq \beta \iff \forall i : \alpha_i \le \beta_i.$$

This poset $(P(\mathbb{N}), \subseteq)$ has the following canonical lattice structure:

$$\alpha \wedge \beta = (\min\{\alpha_1, \beta_1\}, \min\{\alpha_2, \beta_2\}, \ldots),$$

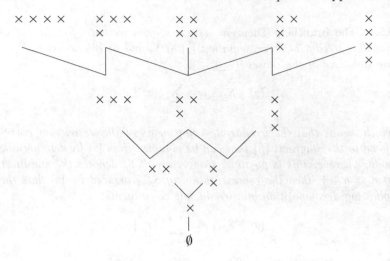

Figure 5.2: Young's Lattice, lower part

$$\alpha \vee \beta = (\max\{\alpha_1, \beta_1\}, \max\{\alpha_2, \beta_2\}, \ldots).$$

We call this lattice $(P(\mathbb{N}), \wedge, \vee)$ *Young's Lattice*. The first part of its order diagram is shown in figure 5.2. Figure 5.3 again shows this lower part of Young's lattice, but the diagrams are replaced by bullets, and furthermore in each of its levels the dominance order is indicated.

5.5.17 Corollary *Young's Lattice visualizes the branching of the ordinary irreducible representations of symmetric groups.*

Exercises

E 5.5.1   Prove 5.5.1.

E 5.5.2   Use 5.2.1 and 5.5.7 in order to give another proof of the Standard Inversion Theorem 4.5.3. (Hint: Multiply both sides of $k_\alpha = \Sigma_\beta \epsilon_{\beta\alpha}\{\beta\}$ by Δ_0, use 5.5.7 and compare coefficients.)

5.6   The Murnaghan–Nakayama Rule

Besides the direct methods using character polynomials there are recursion formulae for the evaluation of characters of symmetric groups. Suppose we want to know the value ζ_a^γ, where $\gamma \vdash n$, $a \vdash n$

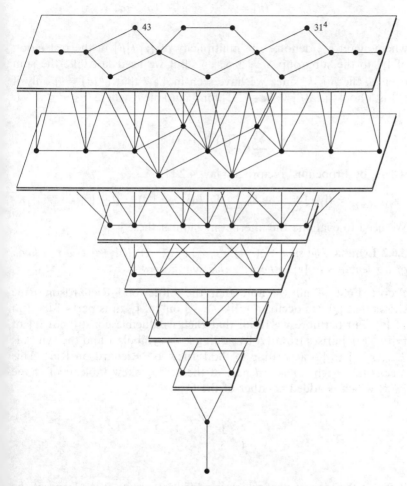

Figure 5.3: Young's Lattice, lower part, with dominance and branching

and $a_k > 0$. We can use the fact that $\zeta_a^\gamma = \zeta^\gamma(\pi)$, where $\pi = \rho \cdot \sigma$, $\rho \in S_{n-k}$ and σ is the k–cycle $(n - k + 1 \ldots n) \in S_{n\setminus n-k}$. Thus, by restriction to the subgroup $S_{n-k} \oplus S_{n\setminus n-k}$, we obtain

$$\zeta_a^\gamma = \zeta^\gamma(\pi) = \sum_{\alpha \vdash n-k, \beta \vdash k} g_{\alpha\beta}^\gamma \zeta^\alpha(\rho)\zeta^\beta(\sigma),$$

where again $g_{\alpha\beta}^\gamma$ denotes the multiplicity of $[\alpha]\#[\beta]$ in the restriction of $[\gamma]$ to the subgroup $S_{n-k} \oplus S_{n\setminus n-k}$. But we need not take the sum over *all* the $\beta \vdash k$, since we have seen in 4.5.7 that $\zeta^\beta(\sigma) \neq 0$ only if $[\beta]$ is a hook, i.e. $[\beta] = [k - r, 1^r]$, for a suitable r, where $0 \leq r \leq k-1$. Hence

5.6.1 $$\zeta_a^\gamma = \sum_{\alpha \vdash n-k} \zeta^\alpha(\rho) \sum_{r=0}^{k-1} (-1)^r g_{\alpha,(k-r,1^r)}^\gamma,$$

where, by Frobenius' reciprocity law 4.2.11,

$$g_{\alpha,(k-r,1^r)}^\gamma := ([\gamma] \downarrow S_{n-k} \oplus S_{n\setminus n-k}, [\alpha]\#[k - r, 1^r]) = ([\gamma], [\alpha][k - r, 1^r]).$$

We need to evaluate the alternating sum of these $g_{\alpha,(k-r,1^r)}^\gamma$.

5.6.2 Lemma *The sum* $\sum_r (-1)^r g_{\alpha,(k-r,1^r)}^\gamma$ *is* $(-1)^s$ *if* $[\gamma\setminus\alpha]$ *is a rim hook of leg length s in* $[\gamma]$, *otherwise this sum is zero.*

Proof: First of all we note that the Littlewood–Richardson Rule shows that $[\gamma]$ can occur in $[\alpha][k-r, 1^r]$ only if $[\gamma\setminus\alpha]$ is part of the rim of $[\gamma]$. Furthermore we recall that each irreducible constituent $[\gamma]$ of $[\alpha][k - r, 1^r]$ arises from $[\alpha]$ by adding $k - r$ symbols 1 and the symbols $2, \ldots, r + 1$ to $[\alpha]$ according to the Littlewood–Richardson Rule. This means that each *connected* part of the arising skew tableau of shape $[\gamma\setminus\alpha]$ which is added is either of the form

$$
\begin{array}{ccccccc}
 & & & & & 1 & \ldots 1 \\
 & & & 1 & \ldots & 1 & 2 \\
 & \ldots & 1 & 3 & & & \\
\ddots & & & & & &
\end{array}
$$

if this is the highest part which is added, otherwise it is of one of the following forms:

$$
\begin{array}{ccccccc}
 & & & & 1 & \ldots & 1 & i \\
 & & 1 & \ldots & 1 & i+1 & \\
 & \ldots & i+2 & & & & \\
\ddots & & & & & &
\end{array} \quad ,
$$

or

$$
\begin{array}{ccccc}
 & & & 1 & \ldots & 1 \\
 & 1 & \ldots & 1 & j \\
\ldots & j+1 & & & \\
\end{array}
$$

We now distinguish the cases if this rim part $[\gamma \backslash \alpha]$ is connected or not.

i) In the case when $[\gamma \backslash \alpha]$ is connected, there is a unique skew tableau that fits into $[\gamma \backslash \alpha]$ according to the Littlewood–Richardson Rule and hence also a unique r such that $g^{\gamma}_{\alpha,(k-r1^r)} \neq 0$, and for this r we have $g^{\gamma}_{\alpha,(k-r,1^r)} = 1$, which proves the statement for this particular case.

ii) If $[\gamma \backslash \alpha]$ is a disconnected part of the rim of $[\gamma]$ then everything cancels as we shall show next. Recall that the second highest connected component either starts with a row of the form $1 \ldots 1$ or with a row of the form $1 \ldots 1 j$, where the entry j is defined by the highest connected component. Hence each skew tableau, the second component of which starts with the row $1 \ldots 1$, corresponds to a *unique* skew tableau arising by replacing the last 1 of this row by the unique admissible j and corresponding renumbering of the other entries > 1, and conversely. If the first one of these tableaux, with first row $1 \ldots 1$ in its second highest connected component, arises by adding the hook $[k-r,1^r]$ according to the Littlewood–Richardson Rule, then the second one arises by adding the hook $[k-r-1,1^{r+1}]$, and hence the corresponding contributions to $(-1)^r g^{\gamma}_{\alpha,(k-r,1^r)}$ cancel.

□

This shows that the α occuring on the right hand side of 5.6.1 are the partitions of $n - k$ the diagrams of which can be obtained from $[\gamma]$ by erasing a (connected) part R^{γ}_{ij} of its rim, in short: replace γ by $\gamma \backslash R^{\gamma}_{ij}$. In terms of the corresponding hook H^{γ}_{ij} we can express k as follows: $k = b^{\gamma}_{ij} := \gamma'_j - i$, the so-called *leg length* of this hook. This yields the desired recursion formula for the irreducible characters of $S_{\underline{n}}$:

5.6.3 The Murnaghan–Nakayama Formula *If $a \vdash n$, $a_k > 0$, and $a' := (a_1, \ldots, a_{k-1}, a_k - 1, a_{k+1}, \ldots, a_n) \vdash n - k$, then we have, for the value ζ^{γ}_a of $\zeta^{\gamma}, \gamma \vdash n$, on the class of elements of cycle type a in S_n the following recursion:*

$$
\zeta^{\gamma}_a = \sum_{i,j:h^{\gamma}_{ij}=k} (-1)^{b^{\gamma}_{ij}} \zeta^{\gamma \backslash R^{\gamma}_{ij}}_{a'},
$$

if we put $\zeta^{\emptyset}_0 := 1$.

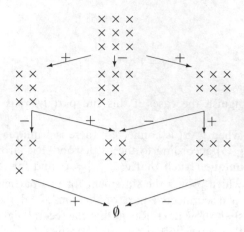

Figure 5.4: The destruction process

A particular example is $\zeta^{(3^3)}((1234)(56)(789))$, which satisfies

$$= \zeta^{(2^3)}((1234)(56)) - \zeta^{(3,2,1)}((1234)(56)) + \zeta^{(3^2)}((1234)(56))$$

$$= -\zeta^{(2,1^2)}((1234)) + \zeta^{(2^2)}((1234)) - \zeta^{(2^2)}((1234)) + \zeta^{(3,1)}((1234))$$

$$= -1 - 1 = -2.$$

The Murnaghan–Nakayama Formula means that the value ζ_a^γ can be obtained by summing all the values ± 1 which we obtain while completely erasing the diagram $[\gamma]$ by erasing hooks. The lengths of the hooks in question are the lengths of the cyclic factors of an element of type a in some fixed order, i.e. these hook lengths form an improper partition $\lambda \models n$, and $[\gamma]$ has to be erased in all possible ways by successively erasing hooks of lengths λ_1, λ_2, and so on. Such a complete erasement of nodes will be called an $(\gamma, \lambda, \emptyset)$–path. Notice that this is a *directed* path. For the above example we used $\lambda := (3, 2, 4)$, and a picture of the corresponding destruction process is shown in figure 5.4. The *weight of the edge*, defined to be $(-1)^{b_{ij}}$, where b_{ij} is the leg length of the hook erased, is indicated for each edge. Now we define the *weight of a directed path* to be the *product* of the edges which form this path. Using this notion we can reformulate the Murnaghan–Nakayama Formula as follows:

5.6.4 Corollary *For each* $\lambda \models n$ *such that* $\lambda^* = \beta$, *the character value* ζ_β^γ *is equal to the sum of weights of all the* $(\gamma, \lambda, \emptyset)$–*paths. In particular* $\zeta_\beta^\gamma = 0$, *if there exists no such path.*

An application of the Murnaghan–Nakayama Rule is (exercise 5.6.1):

5.6.5 Corollary *For* $\gamma \vdash n$ *and the partition* $\beta := (h_{11}^\gamma, h_{22}^\gamma, \ldots) \vdash n$, *consisting of the lengths of the hooks with corner in the main diagonal of* $[\gamma]$, *we have that*

$$\zeta_\beta^\gamma = (-1)^{\Sigma_i(\gamma_i' - i)}.$$

Furthermore, for any $\delta \vdash n$, *the following holds:*

$$\zeta_\delta^\gamma \neq 0 \implies \delta \trianglelefteq \beta.$$

The Murnaghan–Nakayama formula can be generalized considerably as we shall show next. In order to do this we recall the *skew representation* $[\gamma \backslash \alpha]$ which was introduced in 5.4.14: For $\gamma \vdash m + n$ and each $\alpha \vdash m$ such that every $\alpha_i \leq \gamma_i$ we have

5.6.6
$$[\gamma \backslash \alpha] = \sum_{\beta \vdash n} g_{\alpha\beta}^\gamma [\beta],$$

and it is our aim to show that this skew *representation* is in fact closely related to the skew *diagram* $[\gamma \backslash \alpha]$. A first indication of this close relationship shows

5.6.7 Lemma *The dimension of the skew representation* $[\gamma \backslash \alpha]$ *is the number of standard Young tableaux with skew diagram shape* $[\gamma \backslash \alpha]$:

$$f^{\gamma \backslash \alpha} = st^{\gamma \backslash \alpha}(1^n).$$

Proof: Young's Rule shows that

$$st^{\gamma \backslash \alpha}(1^n) = ([\alpha][1] \cdots [1], [\gamma]).$$

Since $[1] \cdots [1]$ is the regular representation $\sum_\beta f^\beta [\beta]$, an application of the Littlewood–Richardson Rule completes the proof as follows:

$$= \sum_{\beta \vdash n} f^\beta ([\alpha][\beta], [\gamma]) = \sum_{\beta \vdash n} f^\beta g_{\alpha\beta}^\gamma.$$

$\square$

But the relationship between skew representations and skew diagrams is much closer as we shall show by deriving the corresponding determinantal form and a Murnaghan–Nakayama formula. In order to do this we need a generalization of the notion of proper and improper partition of n. A *composition* λ of n is a sequence $(\lambda_1, \lambda_2, \ldots)$ with the following properties:

$$\lambda_i \in \mathbb{Z}, \text{ only finitely many } \lambda_i \neq 0, \text{ and } \sum \lambda_i = n.$$

We now slightly generalize the definition of ξ^λ to compositions λ of n by putting

$$\xi^\lambda := \begin{cases} \text{the character of } IS_\lambda \uparrow S_{\underline{n}} & \text{if } \lambda \models n, \\ \text{the zero mapping on } S_{\underline{n}} & \text{otherwise.} \end{cases}$$

Now we note that $S_{\underline{n}}$ can be considered as the subgroup of the *restricted symmetric group on* $\mathbb{N}^*$

$$\mathscr{S} := \{\pi : \mathbb{N}^* \to \mathbb{N}^* \mid \pi \text{ bijective, moves only finitely many points}\}$$

which consists of the $\pi \in \mathscr{S}$ that fix each $i \in \mathbb{N}^* \backslash \underline{n}$. Using pointwise addition on the set of mappings from $\mathbb{N}^*$ to $\mathbb{Z}$, so that e.g.

$$\lambda - \text{id} + \pi = (\lambda_1 - 1 + \pi 1, \lambda_2 - 2 + \pi 2, \ldots),$$

we can introduce the generalized character

$$\chi^\lambda := \sum_{\pi \in \mathscr{S}} \text{sign}(\pi) \xi^{\lambda - \text{id} + \pi},$$

(Note that $\text{sign}(\pi)$ is well defined, and that this sum is a finite sum.) Since there exists $h \in \mathbb{N}$ such that $\lambda_i = 0$ for each $i > h$ we have, for each $i \geq h$, that

5.6.8
$$\chi^\lambda = \sum_\pi \text{sign}(\pi) \xi^{\lambda - \text{id} + \pi},$$

where the sum is taken over the $\pi \in S_{\underline{i}}$. Moreover the determinantal form of ζ^α shows that, for each proper partition α, we have

5.6.9
$$\chi^\alpha = \zeta^\alpha.$$

It will turn out crucial for the following derivations to note that for each composition λ and the related sequence

$$\mu := (\lambda_1, \ldots, \lambda_{i-1}, \lambda_{i+1} - 1, \lambda_i + 1, \lambda_{i+2}, \ldots)$$

we have the identity

5.6.10
$$\chi^\mu = -\chi^\lambda.$$

Proof: Consider the transposition $\tau := (i, i+1) \in \mathscr{S}$. It Hence $\xi^{\mu-id+\pi\tau} = \xi^{\lambda-id+\pi}$, so that

$$\chi^\lambda = \sum_\pi \text{sign}(\pi)\xi^{\lambda-id+\pi} = \sum_\pi \text{sign}(-\pi\tau)\xi^{\mu-id+\pi\tau} = -\chi^\mu.$$

$\square$

Now we consider restrictions to certain Young subgroups:

5.6.11 Lemma *If λ is a composition of $m+k$, then*

$$\xi^\lambda \downarrow S_{(m,k)} = \sum_{\mu \models k} \xi^{\lambda-\mu} \# \xi^\mu,$$

and

$$\chi^\lambda \downarrow S_{(m,k)} = \sum_{\mu \models k} \chi^{\lambda-\mu} \# \xi^\mu.$$

Proof: In order to prove the first statement we note that both sides of the equation are zero if λ has negative parts λ_i. We can therefore assume that $\lambda \models m+k$. Since ξ^λ is zero or a permutation character, its restriction to the Young subgroup in question satifies

$$\xi^\lambda \downarrow S_{(m,k)} = \sum_{S_{(m,k)}\pi S_\lambda} I(S_{(m,k)} \cap \pi S_\lambda \pi^{-1}) \uparrow S_{(m,k)}.$$

But the double coset symbol associated with $S_{(m,k)}\pi S_\lambda$ is the matrix

$$\begin{pmatrix} \cdots & |\underline{m} \cap \pi[n_j^\lambda]| & \cdots \\ \cdots & |\underline{n}\backslash\underline{m} \cap \pi[n_j^\lambda]| & \cdots \end{pmatrix}, j \in \underline{n}.$$

This matrix is uniquely determined by its second row from which we obtain the improper partition

$$\mu := (\dots, |\underline{n}\backslash\underline{m} \cap \pi[n_j^\lambda]|, \dots) \models k.$$

Moreover the intersection $S_{(m,k)} \cap \pi S_\lambda \pi^{-1}$ is conjugate to the Young subgroup $S_{\lambda-\mu} \oplus S_\mu$, so that finally we obtain

$$I(S_{(m,k)} \cap \pi S_\lambda \pi^{-1}) \uparrow S_{(m,k)} = I(S_{\lambda-\mu} \oplus S_\mu) \uparrow S_{(m,k)}$$

$$= IS_{\lambda-\mu} \uparrow S_{\underline{m}} \# IS_\mu \uparrow S_{\underline{k}} = \xi^{\lambda-\mu} \# \xi^\mu,$$

which completes the proof of the first statement. In order to prove the second statement we consider the definition of χ^λ together with an application of the first statement which yield that

$$\chi^\lambda \downarrow S_{(m,k)} = \sum_\pi \text{sign}(\pi) \xi^{\lambda-id+\pi} \downarrow S_{(m,k)}$$

$$= \sum_{\mu\models k} \sum_\pi \text{sign}(\pi) \xi^{\lambda-id+\pi-\mu} \# \xi^\mu = \sum_{\mu\models k} \chi^{\lambda-\mu} \# \xi^\mu.$$

□

Now we introduce another generalized character by putting

$$\chi^{\lambda\backslash\mu} := \sum_{\pi\in\mathscr{S}} \text{sign}(\pi) \xi^{\lambda-id-(\mu-id)\circ\pi}.$$

It is the aim to show that this is in fact the character of the skew representation $[\gamma\backslash\alpha]$. In order to prove this we first state

5.6.12 Lemma *For each composition λ of $m+k$ we have that*

$$\chi^\lambda \downarrow S_{(m,k)} = \sum_{\pi\in\mathscr{S}} \sum_{\beta\vdash k} \chi^{\lambda\backslash\beta} \# \chi^\beta.$$

Proof: From the proof of lemma 5.6.11 we derive that

$$\chi^\lambda \downarrow S_{(m,k)} = \sum_{\pi\in\mathscr{S}} \text{sign}(\pi) \sum_{\mu\models k} \xi^{\lambda-id+\pi-\mu} \# \xi^\mu,$$

where we can replace μ by $\mu\circ\pi$ obtaining

$$\sum_\pi \text{sign}(\pi) \sum_\mu \xi^{\lambda-id-(\mu-id)\circ\pi} \# \xi^\mu.$$

Now, for each μ, μ_i is eventually zero. Moreover we can assume that $\mu - id$ does not contain equal parts, since otherwise $\chi^{\lambda\backslash\mu} = 0$. Thus there exists a unique sequence β and unique $\sigma \in \mathscr{S}$, for which

$$\mu - id = (\beta - id) \circ \sigma,$$

and

$$\beta_1 - 1 \geq \beta_2 - 2 \geq \ldots.$$

Thus way we can continue as follows:

$$= \sum_{\pi} \text{sign}(\pi) \sum_{\beta:} \sum_{\sigma \in S_N^r \bullet} \zeta^{\lambda - id - (\beta - id) \circ \sigma \circ \pi} \# \zeta^{(\beta - id) \circ \sigma + id}$$

$$= \sum_{\pi, \sigma} \text{sign}(\pi\sigma)\text{sign}(\sigma) \sum_{\beta} \zeta^{\lambda - id - (\beta - id) \circ \sigma \circ \pi} \# \sum_{\sigma} \text{sign}(\sigma)\zeta^{(\beta - id) + \sigma^{-1}}$$

$$= \sum_{\beta} \sum_{\rho} \text{sign}(\rho)\zeta^{\lambda - id - (\beta - id)\rho} \# \chi^{\beta} = \sum_{\beta} \chi^{\lambda \backslash \beta} \# \chi^{\beta} = \sum_{\beta \vdash k} \chi^{\lambda \backslash \beta} \# \chi^{\beta}.$$

The last equation holds since $\chi^{\beta} = 0$, if $\beta_i - i = \beta_{i+1} - (i+1)$, by 5.6.10.
$\square$

In the next step we show that $\chi^{\gamma \backslash \alpha}$ is in fact the character of the skew representation $[\gamma \backslash \alpha]$:

5.6.13 Theorem *If* $\gamma \vdash m + n, \alpha \vdash n, \alpha_i \leq \gamma_i$, *then*

$$\chi^{\gamma \backslash \alpha} = \sum_{\pi} \text{sign}(\pi)\zeta^{\gamma - id - (\alpha - id) \circ \pi}$$

is in fact the character of

$$[\gamma \backslash \alpha] = \sum_{\beta} g^{\gamma}_{\alpha\beta}[\beta].$$

Proof: The definition of $[\gamma \backslash \alpha]$ shows that we have to prove the following identity

$$[\chi^{\gamma \backslash \alpha} \mid \zeta^{\beta}] = [\zeta^{\gamma} \downarrow S_{(m,n)} \mid \zeta^{\alpha}\zeta^{\beta}],$$

or, in more detail, that

$$\frac{1}{n!} \sum_{\pi \in S_n} \chi^{\gamma \backslash \alpha}(\pi)\zeta^{\beta}(\pi) = \frac{1}{m!n!} \sum_{(\rho,\sigma) \in S_m \times S_n} \zeta^{\gamma}(\rho,\sigma)\zeta^{\alpha}(\rho)\zeta^{\beta}(\sigma).$$

The right hand side of this equation is, by 5.6.12, equal to

$$\frac{1}{m!n!} \sum_{(\rho,\sigma)} \sum_{\epsilon \vdash n} \chi^{\gamma \backslash \epsilon}(\sigma)\zeta^{\epsilon}(\rho)\zeta^{\alpha}(\rho)\zeta^{\beta}(\sigma)$$

$$= \frac{1}{n!} \sum_{\sigma} \chi^{\gamma \backslash \epsilon}(\sigma)\zeta^{\beta}(\sigma) \underbrace{\frac{1}{m!} \sum_{\rho} \zeta^{\epsilon}(\rho)\zeta^{\alpha}(\rho)}_{\delta_{\epsilon,\alpha}} = \frac{1}{n!} \sum_{\sigma \in S_n} \chi^{\gamma \backslash \alpha}(\sigma)\zeta^{\beta}(\sigma),$$

as we have to show.

□

This yields the desired determinantal form:

5.6.14 Corollary *The skew representation* $[\gamma \backslash \alpha]$ *(to be exact: its character) can be expressed as follows in determinantal form:*

$$[\gamma \backslash \alpha] = \det([\gamma_i - \alpha_j + j - i]),$$

if we agree upon putting $[0] := 1$ *and* $[r] := 0,$ *if* $r < 0.$

In order to derive also a Murnaghan–Nakayama formula, we prove

5.6.15 Lemma *If* λ *is a composition of* $n + r,$ *and* v *a composition of* r *and* $m + k = n,$ *then we have that*

$$\chi^{\lambda \backslash v} \downarrow S_{(m,k)} = \sum_{\mu \models k} \chi^{(\lambda - \mu) \backslash v} \# \zeta^{\mu}.$$

Moreover, if $\pi \in S_{\underline{n}}$ *contains a* k*–cycle, and if*

$$a' := (a_1(\pi), \ldots, a_{k-1}(\pi), a_k(\pi) - 1, a_{k+1}(\pi), \ldots),$$

while $\rho \subset S_{\underline{m}}$ *is of type* $a',$ *then*

$$\chi^{\lambda \backslash v}(\pi) = \sum_{i=1}^{\infty} \chi^{(\lambda_1, \ldots, \lambda_i - k, \ldots) \backslash v}(\rho).$$

Proof: The definition of $\chi^{\lambda \backslash v}$ shows that

$$\chi^{\lambda \backslash v} \downarrow S_{(m,k)} = \sum_{\pi} \operatorname{sign}(\pi) \zeta^{\lambda - id - (v - id) \circ \pi} \downarrow S_{(m,k)},$$

which, by 5.6.11, is equal to

$$\sum_{\pi} \operatorname{sign}(\pi) \sum_{\mu \models k} \zeta^{\lambda - \mu - id - (v - id) \circ \pi} \# \zeta^{\mu}$$

$$= \sum_{\mu \models k} \underbrace{\left(\sum_{\pi} \operatorname{sign}(\pi) \zeta^{\lambda - \mu - id - (v - id) \circ \pi} \right)}_{= \chi^{(\lambda - \mu) \backslash v}} \# \zeta^{\mu},$$

as it is claimed. An element $\pi \in S_{\underline{n}}$ containing a k–cycle can be considered as being an element of the Young subgroup $S_{(m,k)},$ for charcter theoretic purposes. Hence, by an application of the statement just proved, we obtain

$$\chi^{\lambda \backslash \nu}(\pi) = \chi^{\lambda \backslash \nu} \downarrow S_{(m,k)}(\pi) = \sum_{\mu \vdash k} \chi^{(\lambda - \mu) \backslash \nu}(\rho) \xi^{\mu}_{(k)}.$$

but $\xi^{\mu}_{(k)}$ is nonzero only if $\mu = (0, \ldots, 0, k, 0, \ldots)$, in which case ξ^{μ} is the identity character. This completes the proof.

$\square$

As we can delete from $[\gamma \backslash \alpha]$ in an obvious way all the parts of its rim which correspond to hooks that contain no node of the subdiagram $[\alpha]$, we finally get

5.6.16 The Murnaghan–Nakayama Formula for skew representations

$$\chi^{\gamma \backslash \alpha}(\pi) = \sum_{i,j : h^{\gamma}_{ij} = k} (-1)^{b^{\gamma}_{ij}} \chi^{(\gamma \backslash \alpha) \backslash R^{\gamma}_{ij}}(\rho).$$

Exercises

E 5.6.1 Prove 5.6.5.

5.7 Symmetrization and permutrization

Having all these concepts and results on ordinary representations and their characters at hand we are now in a position to refine the permutation theoretical considerations of actions on Y^X to representation theoretical ones. In order to do this we simply take Y^X as a basis by forming the free vector space over $\mathbb{C}$ with Y^X as basic set, i.e. we consider

$$\mathbb{C}^{(Y^X)} = \ll f \in Y^X \gg_{\mathbb{C}}.$$

Assume now a representation D of H on $\mathbb{C}^Y$ (which replaces the action $_HY$) and an action $_GX$. Denoting by $\mathbf{D}$ the corresponding matrix representation with respect to the basis Y of $\mathbb{C}^Y$, we obtain a matrix representation $\widetilde{\mathbf{D}}$ of $H \wr_x G$ on $\mathbb{C}^{(Y^X)}$ in a canonic way by defining the (linear) action of $(\psi, g) \in H \wr_x G$ on an element f of the basis as follows:

5.7.1
$$(\psi, g)f := \sum_{f' \in Y^X} d_{f', f \circ g^{-1}}(\psi) f',$$

where

$$d_{f',f\circ g^{-1}}(\psi) := \prod_x d_{f'(x),f(g^{-1}x)}(\psi(x)).$$

It is not difficult to check that this is in fact a representation, and it is obvious that it generalizes the permutation representation of $H \wr_x G$ on Y^X which we introduced in 1.2.11 for enumerative purposes. The permutation character with its values (cf. 1.5.2)

$$\chi((\psi,g)) = \prod_{v \in c(\overline{g})} a_1(h_v(\psi,g))$$

is now replaced by

5.7.2 $$\qquad \chi^{\widetilde{D}}((\psi,g)) = \prod_v \chi^D(h_v(\psi,g)),$$

as can be shown in an analogous way. We now restrict this representation to the subgroup $H^* \cdot G' \simeq H \times G$, i.e. to the elements $(\psi,g) \in H \wr_x G$, where ψ is constant. We can identify such a (ψ,g) with $(h,g) \in H \times G$, h being the value of ψ, and get

5.7.3 $$\qquad \chi^{\widetilde{D}}((h,g)) = \prod_{i=1}^{|X|} \chi^D(h^i)^{a_i(\overline{g})},$$

a character of $H \times G$ arising from D of H and the action $_G X$ in a natural way. A further restriction to the subgroup $G' \simeq G$ gives

5.7.4 $$\qquad \chi^{\widetilde{D}}(g) = |Y|^{c(\overline{g})} = (\dim D)^{c(\overline{g})}.$$

The restriction to the diagonal subgroup of H^* which is isomorphic to H gives

5.7.5 $$\qquad \chi^{\widetilde{D}}(h) = (\chi^D(h))^{|X|}.$$

The representation $\widetilde{D} \downarrow H^* \cdot G'$ of $H \times G$, the character of which is given in 5.7.3, gives rise to a few more general remarks concerning representations of direct products of groups. They will turn out to be useful since they show that there is a close connection between the decomposition of $\widetilde{D} \downarrow H^*$ and the decomposition of $\widetilde{D} \downarrow G'$.

Assume that we are given a vector space V affording a representation $\widetilde{D}$ of $H \times G$ and define D^1 and D^2 by $D^1(h) := \widetilde{D}(h,1)$ and $D^2(g) := \widetilde{D}(1,g)$. Then we first note that

5.7.6 $$\qquad \forall\, (h,g) \in H \times G: \; D^1(h)D^2(g) = D^2(g)D^1(h).$$

Assuming that G is finite, since D^2 of G is completely reducible, we may consider a basis of V whith respect to which D^2 decomposes as follows

$$\mathbf{D}^2(g) = \begin{pmatrix} \mathbf{D}_1^2(g) & & & & & & \\ & \ddots & & & & 0 & \\ & & \mathbf{D}_1^2(g) & & & & \\ & & & \ddots & & & \\ & & & & \mathbf{D}_r^2(g) & & \\ & 0 & & & & \ddots & \\ & & & & & & \mathbf{D}_r^2(g) \end{pmatrix}$$

$$= \sum_{i=1}^{r} n_i \mathbf{D}_i^2(g).$$

The direct summand of V which affords n_i times the irreducible constituent $\mathbf{D}_i^2$ is called the *homogeneous component of type* $\mathbf{D}_i^2$ of V (as representation space for G).

With respect to the same basis the matrix representation $\mathbf{D}^1$ of H takes the following form:

$$\mathbf{D}^1(h) - \begin{pmatrix} \mathbf{D}_{11}^{11}(h) & \cdots & \mathbf{D}_{1n_1}^{11}(h) & \mathbf{D}_{11}^{12}(h) & \cdots & \mathbf{D}_{1n_2}^{12}(h) & \cdots \\ \vdots & & \vdots & \vdots & & \vdots & \\ \mathbf{D}_{n_11}^{11}(h) & \cdots & \mathbf{D}_{n_1n_1}^{11}(h) & \mathbf{D}_{11}^{12}(h) & \cdots & \mathbf{D}_{1n_1}^{12}(h) & \cdots \\ \vdots & & \vdots & \vdots & & \vdots & \end{pmatrix}$$

The submatrices satisfy (cf. 5.7.6), for each h, g, i, j, k and l:

$$\mathbf{D}_{kl}^{ij}(h)\mathbf{D}_j^2(g) = \mathbf{D}_i^2(g)\mathbf{D}_{kl}^{ij}(h),$$

and so we obtain, by an application of Schur's Lemma:

$$\mathbf{D}_{kl}^{ij}(h) = \begin{cases} 0\text{–matrix} & \text{if } i \neq j, \\ d_{kl}^i(h) \cdot \mathbf{I} & \text{otherwise,} \end{cases}$$

where $\mathbf{I}$ denotes the identity matrix and $d_{kl}^i(h) \in \mathbb{C}$ is a numerical factor. Using these numbers, we define

$$\mathbf{D}_i^1(h) := (d_{kl}^i(h)), k, l \in \underline{n_i}, 1 \leq i \leq r.$$

Hence there exists a permutation matrix P such that, for each $h \in H$, $P\mathbf{D}^1(h)P^{-1}$ is equal to

$$
\begin{pmatrix}
\mathbf{D}_1^1(h) & & & & & \\
& \ddots & & & & 0 \\
& & \mathbf{D}_1^1(h) & & & \\
& & & \ddots & & \\
& & & & \mathbf{D}_r^1(h) & \\
& 0 & & & & \ddots \\
& & & & & \mathbf{D}_r^1(h)
\end{pmatrix}
= \sum_{i=1}^r f_i \mathbf{D}_i^1(h).
$$

We notice in particular that the multiplicity n_i of $\mathbf{D}_i^2$ is equal to the dimension of $\mathbf{D}_i^1$, while the dimension f_i of $\mathbf{D}_i^2$ is equal to the multiplicity of $\mathbf{D}_i^1$ in $\mathbf{D}^1$. An application of this general argument to the particular case $D^1(h) := \widetilde{D}(h, 1)$ and $D^2(g) := \widetilde{D}(1, g)$ gives (since, by 5.7.5, D^1 is equivalent to $\otimes^{|X|}D$, the $|X|$–fold inner tensor power):

5.7.7 Theorem *Let H denote a group, D an ordinary representation of H on the vector space $\mathbb{C}^Y$, ${}_GX$ a finite action, D_i an ordinary irreducible representation of G, f_i its dimension. Then the homogeneous component of type D_i of $\mathbb{C}^{(Y^X)}$ affords, if it is nonzero, f_i–times a representation of H (which need not be irreducible). We denote this representation by*

$$
D \,\square\, D_i
$$

and call it the $|X|$–fold symmetrization of D by D_i corresponding to the action ${}_GX$. Its dimension is equal to the multiplicity $n_i := (P_Y^X, D_i)$ of D_i in P_Y^X, the permutation representation of G afforded by $\mathbb{C}^{(Y^X)}$. $D \,\square\, D_i$ satisfies, for each $h \in H, g \in G$, and with respect to a suitable basis of $\mathbb{C}^{(Y^X)}$ the equation

$$
\widetilde{\mathbf{D}}((h, g)) = \otimes^{|X|}\mathbf{D}(h) \cdot \mathbf{P}_Y^X(g) = \sum_i (\mathbf{D} \,\square\, \mathbf{D}_i)(h) \otimes \mathbf{D}_i(g).
$$

(We allow $D \,\square\, D_i$ to denote the zero "representation" of H if D_i is not an irreducible constituent of P_Y^X, and so the corresponding homogeneous component of type D_i is the zero subspace. In this sense $D \,\square\, D_i$ is defined for each irreducible D_i of G, but the corresponding summand in the equation above may have to be neglected.)

An important particular case is that when ${}_GX$ is the natural action of S_X on X, in which we meet the symmetrization $D \,\square\, [\alpha], \alpha \vdash |X|$, obtaining the following decomposition of the n–fold tensor power of D:

5.7.8 $$\otimes^{|X|} D = \sum_{\alpha \vdash |X|} f^{\alpha}(D \; \square \; [\alpha]),$$

for example

$$D \otimes D \otimes D = D \; \square \; [3] + 2(D \; \square \; [2,1]) + D \; \square \; [1^3].$$

Returning to the general case we note that the character of $D \; \square \; D_i$ satisfies (cf. 5.7.7 and use 5.7.3):

$$\forall \; h \in H, g \in G: \prod_{k=1}^{|X|} \chi^{D}(h^k)^{a_k(\bar{g})} = \sum_i \chi^{D \, \square \, D_i}(h) \zeta^i(g).$$

An application of the orthogonality relations now gives

5.7.9 $$\chi^{D \, \square \, D_i}(h) = \frac{1}{|G|} \sum_g \zeta^i(g^{-1}) \prod_{k=1}^{|X|} \chi^{D}(h^k)^{a_k(\bar{g})}.$$

For the particular case where $_G X$ is the natural action of S_X on X, this right hand side takes the form

$$\frac{1}{|X|!} \sum_{\pi \subset S_X} \zeta^{\alpha}(\pi^{-1}) \prod_{k=1}^{|X|} \chi^{D}(h^k)^{a_k(\pi)},$$

and so we have proved

5.7.10 $$\chi^{D \, \square \, [\alpha]}(h) = \{\alpha, Y\}(\epsilon_1, \ldots, \epsilon_m),$$

which means that we obtain the character value of $D \; \square \; [\alpha]$ at h by taking the *Schur function* $\{\alpha, Y\}$, i.e. the polynomial *function* corresponding to the *polynomial* $\{\alpha, Y\}$ and applying it to the eigenvalues $\epsilon_1, \ldots, \epsilon_m$ of $D(h)$. In particular we obtain for the dimension of this representation:

5.7.11 $$f^{D \, \square \, [\alpha]} = \sum_{(\lambda_1, \ldots, \lambda_m) \models |X|} \kappa_{\lambda^*, \alpha},$$

which implies

5.7.12 Corollary $D \; \square \; [\alpha]$ *is nonzero if and only if the number* α'_1 *of parts of* α *is less than or equal to the dimension of* D.

The same argument used in proving theorem 5.7.7 on symmetrization gives another construction which is, in a certain sense, its dual:

5.7.13 Theorem *Let H denote a finite group, D an ordinary representation of H on the vector space $\mathbb{C}^Y$ and assume $_GX$ to be a finite action. If D_i denotes an ordinary irreducible representation of H and f_i its dimension, then the homogeneous component of $\mathbb{C}^{(Y^X)}$ (as representation space for H, affording $\otimes^{|X|}D$) gives, if it is nonzero, f_i–times a representation of G (which may be reducible). We denote it by $D \bigtriangleup_{|X|} D_i$ and call it the $|X|$–fold permutrization of D by D_i corresponding to the action $_GX$. Its dimension is equal to the multiplicity $(\otimes^{|X|}D, D_i)$, and it satisfies, for each $h \in H, g \in G$, and with respect to a suitable basis of $\mathbb{C}^{(Y^X)}$ the equation*

$$\widetilde{\mathbf{D}}(h,g) = \otimes^{|X|}\mathbf{D}(h) \cdot \mathbf{P}_Y^X(g) = \sum_i \mathbf{D}_i(h) \otimes (\mathbf{D} \bigtriangleup \mathbf{D}_i)(g).$$

(We allow $D \bigtriangleup_{|X|} D_i$ to denote the zero "representation" of G if D_i is not an irreducible constituent of $\otimes^{|X|}D$, and so the corresponding homogeneous component of type D_i is the zero subspace. In this sense $D \bigtriangleup_{|X|} D_i$ is defined for each irreducible D_i of H, but the corresponding summand in the equation above may have to be neglected.)

To 5.7.8 there corresponds the following equation:

$$5.7.14 \qquad\qquad P_Y^X = \sum_i f^i(D \bigtriangleup_{|X|} D_i),$$

while we have for the character

$$5.7.15 \qquad \chi^{D \bigtriangleup_{|X|} D_i}(g) = \frac{1}{|H|} \sum_{h \in H} \zeta^i(h^{-1}) \prod_{k=1}^{|X|} \chi^D(h^k)^{a_k(\overline{g})}.$$

These equations, in particular the last, have important consequences. First of all there is a close relationship between symmetrization and permutrization expressed in the following equality of multiplicities which is immediate from 5.7.15 and 5.7.9:

5.7.16 The Duality Theorem *For each ordinary irreducible representation D_i of H and D_k of G we have*

$$(D \bigtriangleup_{|X|} D_i, D_k) = (D \,\square\, D_k, D_i).$$

Various other results follow from the consideration of particular cases of 5.7.15. Interpreting $D \triangle_{|X|} D_i$ as a representation of $\bar{G} \leq S_X$, we see that it can be extended to S_X since $_G X$ is a subaction of the natural action of S_X. Thus we obtain

5.7.17 Corollary *If H denotes a finite group with an ordinary character χ and an ordinary irreducible character ζ^i, then, for each $a_1, \ldots, a_n \in \mathbb{N}$, the expression*

$$\frac{1}{|H|} \sum_{h \in H} \zeta^i(h^{-1}) \prod_k \chi(h^k)^{a_k}.$$

is the value of a character of $S_{\underline{n}}$, where $n := \sum_i i \cdot a_i$, at an element π of cycle type $(a_1, \ldots, a_n)$:

$$\chi^{D \triangle_n D_i}(\pi) = \frac{1}{|H|} \sum_{h \in H} \zeta^i(h^{-1}) \prod_k \chi(h^k)^{a_k(\pi)}.$$

Hence the right hand side is an integer, and so in particular the mapping

$$\chi_{(k)} \colon H \to \mathbb{C} \colon h \mapsto \chi(h^k)$$

is a generalized character, for each χ and any $k \in \mathbb{N}$.

Exercises

E 5.7.1 Show that the dimensions $f^{D \square [|X|]}$ and $f^{D \square [1^{|X|}]}$ are binomial coefficients in terms of $|X|$ and $|Y|$.

5.8 Plethysm of representations

Recall the representation $\widetilde{D}$ of $H \wr_x G$ defined in 5.7.1: For (ψ, g) in $H \wr_x G$, $f \in Y^X$, and the matrix representation $\mathbf{D}$ of H on $\mathbb{C}^Y$, we have put

$$(\psi, g)f := \sum_{f' \in Y^X} d_{f', f \circ g^{-1}}(\psi)f', \quad d_{f', f \circ g^{-1}}(\psi) := \prod_x d_{f'(x), f(g^{-1}x)}(\psi(x)).$$

We shall multiply this representation with $\mathbf{E}'$, another matrix representation of $H \wr_x G$, arising from the matrix representation $\mathbf{E}$ of G on $\mathbb{C}^X$, and defined by

$$\mathbf{E}'(\psi, g) := \mathbf{E}(g).$$

The inner tensor product $\widetilde{\mathbf{D}} \otimes \mathbf{E}'$ of these two representations is a matrix representation of $H \wr_x G$ on the vector space $\mathbb{C}^{(Y^X)}$, and its character has the values (cf. 5.7.2)

$$5.8.1 \qquad \chi^{\widetilde{D} \otimes E'}(\psi, g) = \chi^E(g) \prod_v \chi^D(h_v(\psi, g)).$$

In the case when $H \wr_x G = S_{\underline{m}} \wr S_{\underline{n}}$, $D := [\alpha]$, $\alpha \vdash m$, and $E := [\beta]$, $\beta \vdash n$, we write

$$(\alpha; \beta) := \widetilde{[\alpha]} \otimes [\beta]',$$

and as $S_{\underline{m}} \wr S_{\underline{n}}$ embeds into $S_{\underline{mn}}$ in a natural way (cf. 1.4.1), this representation induces in a canonical way a representation of $S_{\underline{mn}}$ which we call the *plethysm* of $[\alpha]$ and $[\beta]$ and which we indicate as follows:

$$[\alpha] \odot [\beta] := (\alpha; \beta) \uparrow S_{\underline{mn}}.$$

An important particular case is the plethysm of identity representations

$$[m] \odot [n] = (m; n) \uparrow S_{\underline{mn}} = I S_{\underline{m}} \odot S_{\underline{n}} \uparrow S_{\underline{mn}},$$

which gives, according to Foulkes' Lemma, the following helpful expression for the *plethysm* of cycle indicator polynomials (cf. 2.2.8):

$$5.8.2 \qquad C(S_{\underline{m}} \odot S_{\underline{n}}, \underline{mn}) = \sum_{\alpha \vdash mn} ([m] \odot [n], [\alpha]) C(S_{\underline{mn}}, \underline{mn}, [\alpha]).$$

But there are only very few results known on the decomposition of plethysm. One of them is

5.8.3 Theorem *For each* $n \in \mathbb{N}^*$ *we have the following decomposition of plethysm of identity representations of symmetric groups:*

$$[2] \odot [n] = \sum_{\alpha \vdash n} [2\alpha],$$

if $2\alpha := (2\alpha_1, 2\alpha_2, \ldots)$.

Proof: By induction on n. The case $n = 1$ is obvious: $[2] \odot [1] = [2]$. If $n > 1$, the induction hypothesis together with (exercise 5.8.1)

$$5.8.4 \qquad [2] \odot [n] \downarrow S_{\underline{2n-1}} = [2] \odot [n-1] \uparrow S_{\underline{2n-1}}$$

and the branching theorem yields that $[2] \odot [n] \downarrow S_{\underline{2n-1}}$ is equal to $\sum [\beta]$, where β runs through the partitions of $2n - 1$ which contain exactly one odd part. Another application of the branching rule shows that for these β the following is true:

$$\sum_{\beta} [\beta] = \sum_{\alpha \vdash n} [2\alpha] \downarrow S_{2n-1}.$$

It therefore suffices to prove that $[2] \odot [n]$ cannot contain any constituent $[\gamma]$ with odd parts γ_i. Since for each such γ every constituent of $[\gamma] \downarrow S_{2n-1}$ has exactly one odd part, γ must be of the form $\gamma = (\gamma_1, \gamma_2)$, γ_i odd. Hence it remains to show that no $\gamma = (\gamma_1, \gamma_2)$, γ_i odd, can be a constituent of $[2] \odot [n]$.

In order to prove this we notice that by 5.8.4 together with the induction hypothesis, $[2] \odot [n]$ must be multiplicity–free, i.e. it contains no constituent more than once. Now $[2n]$ is a constituent of $[2] \odot [n]$ since this is a permutation representation. We would like to check that $[2n-1, 1]$ cannot occur. As $[2n-1, 1] \downarrow S_{2n-1} = [2n-2, 1] + [2n-1]$, the occurrence of both $[2n]$ and $[2n-1, 1]$ in $[2] \odot [n]$ would imply that $[2n-1]$ occurs *twice* in $[2] \odot [n-1] \uparrow S_{2n-1}$, which is in fact multiplicity–free. Thus $[2n]$ is a constituent of $[2] \odot [n]$, while $[2n-1, 1]$ is not.

In order to prove that $[2n-2, 2]$ is a constituent of $[2] \odot [n]$, we consider $[2n-2, 1]$, a constituent of $[2] \odot [n-1] \uparrow S_{2n-1}$. It satisfies

$$[2n-2, 1] \uparrow S_{2n} = [2n-1, 1] + [2n-2, 2] + [2n-2, 1^2].$$

Hence $[2n-2, 1]$ arises from the restriction of $[2n-2, 2]$, for we have seen already that neither $[2n-1, 1]$ nor $[2n-2, 1^2]$ occur in $[2] \odot [n]$. This gives us an idea how to procede inductively. Let us assume that we have shown that $[2n-k, k]$, k even, is a constituent of $[2] \odot [n]$. We have to check that $[2n-k-1, k+1]$ does not occur, while $[2n-k-2, k+2]$ does. As

$$[2n-k-1, k+1] \downarrow S_{2n-1} = [2n-k-2, k+1] + [2n-k-1, k],$$

$$[2n-k, k] \downarrow S_{2n-1} = [2n-k-1, k] + [2n-k, k-1],$$

$[2n-k-1, k+1]$ cannot occur, for otherwise $[2] \odot [n-1] \uparrow S_{2n-1}$ would not be multiplicity–free. On the other hand

$$([2] \odot [n-1] \uparrow S_{2n-1}, [2n-k-2, k+1]) > 0$$

and $[2n-k-2, k+1] \uparrow S_{2n}$ is equal to

$$[2n-k-1, k+1] + [2n-k-2, k+2] + [2n-k-2, k+1, 1],$$

so that $[2n-k-2, k+1]$ stems from the restriction of $[2n-k-2, k+2]$, which therefore must occur in $[2] \odot [n]$. This completes the proof.

$\square$

Hence, for example,

$$[2] \odot [4] = [8] + [6, 2] + [4^2] + [4, 2^2] + [2^4].$$

These particular plethysms, arising from the hyperoctahedral group $S_2 \wr S_m$, can be used in order to construct a natural *model* for the symmetric group S_n, i.e. a representation that decomposes into $\sum_\alpha [\alpha]$, which means that it contains each irreducible representation of S_n *exactly once* as an irreducible constituent. How this can be done will be described next. Later on we shall see that the character of the model can be used in order to count square roots in symmetric groups.

The result 5.8.3 together with the special case 5.5.9 of the Littlewood–Richardson Rule shows that $([2] \odot [m])[1^r]$ decomposes into $\sum [\beta]$, where β runs through the partitions of $n := 2m + r$ which contain exactly r odd parts β_i. This implies

5.8.5 Theorem *For each $n > 2$ we have the decomposition*

$$\sum_{0 \leq m \leq n/2} ([2] \odot [m])[1^{n-2m}] = \sum_{\alpha \vdash n} [\alpha] = \sum_{0 \leq m \leq n/2} ([1^2] \odot [m])[n - 2m],$$

i.e. the left and the right hand side is a model for the symmetric group S_n.

Now we shall show that this model of S_n is contained in the *conjugation representation* κ of S_n, by which we mean the linear representation of S_n arising from the permutation representation of S_n on itself via conjugation:

$$S_n \times S_n \to S_n : (\pi, \rho) \mapsto \pi \rho \pi^{-1}.$$

It is obvious that the character χ^κ of κ at π is the order of the centralizer of π:

5.8.6 $$\chi^\kappa(\pi) = |C_S(\pi)|,$$

and it is easy to check that the multiplicity of $[\alpha]$ in κ is the sum of the corresponding row of the character table:

5.8.7 $$[\chi^\kappa \mid \zeta^\alpha] = \sum_{a \vdash n} \zeta_a^\alpha.$$

On the other hand the conjugation action of S_n on itself has the conjugacy classes of elements as orbits. Hence, if $\mathscr{C}$ denotes a transversal of the conjugacy classes of S_n, κ is the following sum of transitive permutation representations:

5.8.8 $$\kappa = \sum_{\pi \in \mathscr{C}} IC_S(\pi) \uparrow S_n.$$

Hence, in order to show that κ contains the model, it suffices to prove that the model is contained in a suitable partial sum of the right hand side of 5.8.8. We shall do this in three steps.

5.8.9 Lemma *If* $\pi \in S_n$, $n = 2m + r$, *r odd, consists of an r–cycle together with m 2–cycles, then* $IC_S(\pi) \uparrow S_n$ *contains* $([2] \odot [m])[1^r]$.

Proof: The centralizer of π is similar to $(S_2 \odot S_m) \oplus C_r$. Hence

$$IC_S(\pi) \uparrow S_n = (IS_2 \odot S_m \uparrow S_{2m} \# IC_r \uparrow S_r) \uparrow S_n.$$

But $(IC_r \uparrow S_r, [1^r]) = ([1^r] \downarrow C_r, IC_r) = 1$, as r is odd. This yields the statement.

$\square$

5.8.10 Lemma *If* $\pi \in S_n$, $n = 2m + r$, *r even and* $\neq 2$, *consists of a 1–cycle, an* $(r - 1)$*–cycle and m 2–cycles, then* $IC_S(\pi) \uparrow S_n$ *contains* $([2] \odot [m])[1^r]$.

Proof: The proof of 5.8.9 shows, since $r - 1$ is odd, that $IC_S(\pi) \uparrow S_n$ contains

$$([2] \odot [m])([1^{r-1}][1]) = ([2] \odot [m])([1^r] + [2, 1^{r-1}]),$$

which implies the statement.

$\square$

It remains to consider the case when $r = 2$.

5.8.11 Lemma *Assume that* $n = 2m + 2 > 2$ *and* $\alpha(\pi) = (1, 2^{m-1}, 3)$. *Then the induced representation* $IC_S(\pi) \uparrow S_n$ *contains each* $[\beta]$, *where* $\beta \vdash n$ *has exactly two odd parts.*

Proof: The induced representation $IC_S(\pi) \uparrow S_n$ is equal to

$$([2] \odot [m-1])(IC_3 \uparrow S_3)[1] = ([2] \odot [m-1])([4] + [3, 1] + [2, 1^2] + [1^4]).$$

Assume that $\alpha \vdash n$ contains exactly two odd parts, we have to show that $[\alpha]$ is contained in the right hand side.

There exists $\beta \vdash n - 4$ such that each β_i is even and $\leq \alpha_i$. The representation $[\beta]$ is a constituent of $[2] \odot [m - 1]$, and, for each i, we have that $\alpha_i - \beta_i \leq 3$. The sequence of nonzero differences $\alpha_i - \beta_i$, ordered according to i, is therefore one of the following five sequences:

$$(2,1,1), (1,2,1), (1,1,2), (3,1), (1,3).$$

The Littlewood–Richardson Rule now shows, that $[\alpha]$ is contained in $[\beta][2, 1^2]$ or in $[\beta][3, 1]$. This implies the statement.

$\square$

Summarizing we obtain

5.8.12 Corollary *For $n \neq 2$ the conjugation representation of S_n contains each $[\alpha]$, where $\alpha \vdash n$, at least once, or, equivalently, the sum of each row in the character table of S_n is strictly positive, if $n > 2$.*

An application of plethysm is provided by a proof of certain results on the so–called *Gaussian coefficient* $p(k; m, n)$ which, for $k, m, n \in \mathbb{N}$, is defined to be the number of partitions of k into $\leq m$ parts, each one being $\leq n$. The corresponding polynomial

$$G_{mn}(x) = \sum_{k=0}^{mn} p(k; m, n) x^k$$

was already introduced (cf. 5.4.7) and we called it a *Gaussian polynomial*. We have seen that the sequence of its coefficients is *unimodal*, i.e. that

$$p(0; m, n) \leq p(1; m, n) \leq \ldots \leq p(\lfloor mn/2 \rfloor; m, n)$$
$$= p(\lfloor mn/2 + 1 \rfloor; m, n) \geq \ldots \geq p(mn; m, n).$$

We are now in a position to express these Gaussian coefficients as multiplicities. An application of 5.1.10 gives

$$p(k; m, n) = ([mn - k][k], [m] \odot [n]) = \sum_{j=0}^{k} ([mn - j, j], [m] \odot [n]).$$

Conversely we can use this in order to derive a result on plethysms:

$$([mn - k, k], [n] \odot [m]) = p(k; m, n) - p(k - 1; m, n)$$
$$= p(k; n, m) - p(k - 1; n, m) = ([mn - k, k], [m] \odot [n]).$$

5.8.13 Corollary *For two–rowed diagrams* $[\alpha]$, $\alpha \vdash mn$, *we have the following equation for multiplicities*:

$$([n] \odot [m], [\alpha]) = ([m] \odot [n], [\alpha]).$$

Still open is the following generalization which is called *Foulkes' Conjecture*:

5.8.14 $\quad \forall m \leq n, \alpha \vdash mn : ([m] \odot [n], [\alpha]) \geq ([n] \odot [m], [\alpha]).$

There are various helpful rules for calculating with plethysms. First of all plethysm is distributive on the right hand side:

5.8.15 $\quad [\alpha] \odot ([\beta] + [\gamma]) = [\alpha] \odot [\beta] + [\alpha] \odot [\gamma].$

Since the embedding of $S_m \wr (S_r \oplus S_s)$ into $S_{m(r+s)}$ yields a subgroup which is conjugate to $(S_m \wr S_r) \oplus (S_m \wr S_s)$, we have

5.8.16 $\quad [\alpha] \odot ([\beta][\gamma]) = ([\alpha] \odot [\beta])([\alpha] \odot [\gamma]).$

Hence there is also a *determinantal form* for plethysm:

5.8.17 $\quad [\alpha] \odot [\beta] = \det([\alpha] \odot [\beta_i + j - i]).$

This reduces the problem of decomposing $[\alpha] \odot [\beta]$ to the problem of decomposing plethysms of the special form $[\alpha] \odot [m]$. But still there is no explicit formula for the decomposition of $[\alpha] \odot [\beta]$, this problem is one of the big open problems in representation theory of symmetric groups.

One of the most interesting rules known for plethysms is

$$([\lambda] + [\mu]) \odot [\nu] = \sum_{(r,s):\nu\vdash r+s} \sum_{\alpha\vdash r,\beta\vdash s} ([\nu], [\alpha][\beta])([\lambda \odot [\alpha])([\mu] \odot [\beta]).$$

The definition 5.4.14 allows to rephrase it as follows:

$$([\lambda] + [\mu]) \odot [\nu] = \sum_{r,s,\alpha,\beta} ([\nu \backslash \alpha], [\beta])([\lambda] \odot [\alpha])([\mu] \odot [\beta])$$

$$= \sum_{r,s,\alpha} ([\lambda] \odot [\alpha])([\mu] \odot [\nu \backslash \alpha]),$$

and so we obtain

5.8.18 $\quad ([\lambda] + [\mu]) \odot [\nu] = \sum_{0 \leq r \leq |\nu|} \sum_{\alpha \vdash r} ([\lambda] \odot [\alpha])([\mu] \odot [\nu \backslash \alpha]).$

Plethysm allows to generalize the plethysm of cycle indicator polynomials as follows:

5.8.19 Lemma *For $\alpha \vdash m$ and $\beta \vdash n$ the following is true:*

$$C(S_{\underline{mn}}, \underline{mn}, [\alpha] \odot [\beta]) = C(S_{\underline{m}}, \underline{m}, [\alpha]) \odot C(S_{\underline{n}}, \underline{n}, [\beta]),$$

i.e. in terms of $(\alpha; \beta)$ we have:

$$\frac{1}{m!^n n!} \sum_{(\varphi,\rho) \in S_m \wr S_n} \chi^{(\alpha;\beta)}((\varphi,\rho)^{-1}) \prod_{k=1}^{mn} x_k^{a_k(\overline{(\varphi,\rho)})}$$

$$= \frac{1}{n!} \sum_{\rho \in S_{\underline{n}}} \zeta^\beta(\rho^{-1}) \prod_{k=1}^{n} \left(\frac{1}{m!} \sum_{\pi \in S_{\underline{m}}} \zeta^\alpha(\pi^{-1}) \prod_{i=1}^{m} x_{ik}^{a_i(\pi)} \right)^{a_k(\rho)}.$$

Proof: First of all we rewrite the right hand side obtaining

$$\frac{1}{m!^n n!} \sum_{\rho} \zeta^\beta(\rho^{-1}) m!^{n-c(\rho)} \sum_{(\pi_1,\dots,\pi_{c(\rho)})} \zeta^\alpha(\pi_1^{-1}) \cdots \zeta^\alpha(\pi_{c(\rho)}^{-1}) \prod_k \prod_i x_{il_k(\rho)}^{a_i(\pi_k)},$$

where $l_k(\rho)$ denotes the length of the k-th cycle of $\rho \in S_{\underline{n}}$, with respect to the standard cycle notation

$$\prod_{k=1}^{c(\rho)} \left(j_k \dots \pi^{l_k(\rho)-1}(j_k) \right),$$

where j_k is the smallest entry in the corresponding cycle. Now, to $\psi : \underline{n} \to S_{\underline{m}}$ and $\widetilde{\varphi} : \underline{n} \setminus \{j_1, \dots, j_{c(\rho)}\} \to S_{\underline{m}}$ there exists exactly one $\varphi : \underline{n} \to S_{\underline{m}}$ that extends $\widetilde{\varphi}$ and for which

$$\psi(j_k) \cdots \psi(\rho^{l_k(\rho)-1}(j_k)) = \varphi(j_k) \cdots \varphi(\rho^{l_k(\rho)-1}(j_k)), \text{ for each } k \in \underline{c(\rho)}.$$

But these elements are just the cycle products $h_k(\psi, \rho)$ and $h_k(\varphi, \rho)$. Thus, to a fixed $c(\rho)$–tuple $(\pi_1, \dots, \pi_{c(\rho)})$ of elements of $S_{\underline{m}}$, there exist exactly $m!^{n-c(\rho)}$ mappings $\varphi : \underline{n} \to S_{\underline{m}}$ such that

$$\pi_k = h_k(\varphi, \rho), \text{ for each } k \in \underline{c(\rho)}.$$

This shows that the above expression is equal to

$$\frac{1}{m!^n n!} \sum_{(\varphi,\rho) \in S_m \wr S_n} \chi^{(\alpha;\beta)}((\varphi,\rho)^{-1}) \prod_k \prod_i x_{il_k(\rho)}^{a_i(h_k(\varphi,\rho))}.$$

$\square$

Exercises

E 5.8.1 Prove 5.8.4. (Hint: use exercise 1.2.5.)

Chapter 6

Permutations

The first section contains a consideration of multiply transitive actions. Numbers will be derived that allow directly to see from the cycle structure of the group elements if the action is multiply transitive. Afterwards we shall enumerate permutations with prescribed algebraic and combinatorial properties. At first we consider roots in finite groups, which means that we take a fixed natural number k and ask for the number of group elements, the k-th power of which is equal to a given element g of the group G. The case when $g = 1$ is of particular interest. Then we restrict attention to the symmetric group, in order to derive expressions for the number of roots in terms of characters and to show how permutrizations can be applied. It will be shown that the function that maps a permutation onto the number of its k-th roots is in fact a proper character.

Afterward we examine combinatorial properties, in particular rises and falls of permutations, and we introduce Foulkes characters for this purpose. It is in fact true that the enumeration theory of permutations by rises and falls is a very good link between combinatorics and representation theory. The character of the action of $S_{\underline{n}}$ on $\underline{m}^{\underline{n}}$ will be decomposed into Foulkes characters, and the dimensions of the Foulkes characters are the well–known Eulerian numbers.

The final section of this chapter contains an introduction of a class of polynomials that correspond to the permutations. These Schubert polynomials form a very important $\mathbb{Z}$–basis of the union of the polynomial rings $\mathbb{Z}[z_1, \ldots, x_n]$, they generalize the Schur polynomials, and they are the main tool used in the computer algebra system

$SYMCHAR$ for the examination and application of representation
theory, invariant theory and combinatorics of symmetric groups.

6.1   Multiply transitive groups

Let P denote a subgroup of S_n. We derive first a few characterizations
of multiple transitivity of P in terms of the cycle structure of its
elements. Recall that, for a natural $k \le n$, we denoted by $\binom{n}{k}$ the set
of all the k–subsets of $\underline{n}$. P acts canonically on this set as well as on
$\underline{n}^k$, the set of k–tuples, and on the set $\underline{n}^k_i$, which consists of all the
injective k–tuples over $\underline{n}$. The corresponding permutation groups on
$\binom{n}{k}, \underline{n}^k$, and $\underline{n}^k_i$ will be denoted by $P^{[k]}, P^{(k)}$, and $P^{\langle k \rangle}$, respectively, and
they will be called the k–subsets group, the k–tuples group, and the
injective k–tuples group. The permutations corresponding to $\pi \in P$
will be indicated by $\pi^{[k]}, \pi^{(k)}$ and $\pi^{\langle k \rangle}$, respectively. The following
result is very easy to check:

6.1.1 Lemma The number of fixed points of $\pi \in S_{\underline{n}}$ on $\binom{n}{k}$, $\underline{n}^k$ and $\underline{n}^k_i$,
respectively, is

$$a_1(\pi^{[k]}) = \sum_{b \vdash k} \prod_{i=1}^{k} \binom{a_i(\pi)}{b_i}, \ \ a_1(\pi^{(k)}) = a_1(\pi)^k, \ \ a_1(\pi^{\langle k \rangle}) = [a_1(\pi)]_k.$$

The permutation group P is by definition k–fold transitive if and only
if $P^{\langle k \rangle}$ is transitive, and so in particular k–fold transitivity implies
$(k-1)$–fold transitivity. The Cauchy-Frobenius Lemma yields the first
characterization of k–fold transitivity:

6.1.2 Corollary A subgroup $P \le S_n$ is k–fold transitive if and only if

$$|P| = \sum_{\pi \in P} [a_1(\pi)]_k.$$

This is a characterization in terms of the character of $P^{\langle k \rangle}$. The second
one will be in terms of the character of $P^{(k)}$, and it will be obtained by
comparing the actions of $P^{(k)}$ and of $S_{\underline{n}}^{(k)}$. $S_{\underline{n}}$ is k–fold transitive, i.e.
$S_{\underline{n}}^{\langle k \rangle}$ is transitive. $S_{\underline{n}}^{(k)}$ is intransitive if $k > 1$ and $n > 1$. Furthermore
the k-tuples $(i_1, \ldots, i_k), (j_1, \ldots, j_k) \in \underline{n}^{(k)}$ are in the same orbit of $S_{\underline{n}}^{(k)}$ if
and only if the following holds, for each μ and v:

6.1.3 $i_\mu = i_v \iff j_\mu = j_v.$

Therefore the following is true:

6.1.4 Corollary *The group $S_{\underline{n}}^{(k)}$ possesses as many orbits as there are partitions of the set $\underline{k}$.*

Hence, in terms of the Bell numbers (cf. 1.7.9), we obtain:

6.1.5 $$|S_{\underline{n}}^{(k)} \backslash\backslash \underline{n}^{\underline{k}}| = |S_{\underline{n}} \backslash\backslash \underline{n}^{\underline{k}}| = B_k.$$

Thus $B_k = |P \backslash\backslash \underline{n}^{\underline{k}}|$ is equivalent to the fact that P has the *same* orbits on $\underline{n}^{\underline{k}}$ as $S_{\underline{n}}$. But if P has the same orbits on $\underline{n}^{\underline{k}}$ it has the same orbits on the subset $\underline{n}_{i}^{\underline{k}}$ as well. The converse is also true, as it is not difficult to see.

6.1.6 Corollary *A subgroup $P \leq S_{\underline{n}}$ is k–fold transitive if and only if*

$$\frac{1}{|P|} \sum_{\pi \in P} a_1(\pi)^k = B_k.$$

The third characterization uses the character of $P^{[k]}$:

6.1.7 Lemma *A subgroup $P \subseteq S_{\underline{n}}$ is k–fold transitive if and only if, for every choice of $b_1, \ldots, b_k \in \mathbb{N}$, we have*

$$\sum_i i b_i \leq k \implies \frac{1}{|P|} \sum_{\pi \in P} \prod_i \binom{a_i(\pi)}{b_i} = \frac{1}{\prod_i i^{b_i} b_i!}.$$

Proof:
i) If each such equation holds, then in particular

$$\frac{1}{|P|} \sum_{\pi \in P} \binom{a_1(\pi)}{k} = \frac{1}{k!},$$

so that P is k–fold transitive by 6.1.2.
ii) Now let P be k–fold transitive, and $b_i \in \mathbb{N}$ such that $\sum i b_i = k$. The expression

$$\sum_{\pi \in P} \binom{a_1(\pi)}{b_1} \cdots \binom{a_k(\pi)}{b_k}$$

is equal to the number of ways of picking from the elements $\pi \in P$ just b_1 1–cycles, b_2 2–cycles, ..., b_k k–cycles. Each such choice

$$\{(i_1), \ldots, (i_{b_1})\}, \{(i_{b_1+1}, i_{b_1+2}), \ldots, (i_{b_1+2b_2-1}, i_{b_1+2b_2})\}, \ldots$$

yields a k–tuple $(i_1, \ldots, i_k)$, and the expression

6.1.8 $$\left(\prod_{i=1}^{k} i^{b_i} b_i! \right) \left(\sum_{\pi \in P} \binom{a_1(\pi)}{b_1} \cdots \binom{a_k(\pi)}{b_k} \right)$$

is equal to the number of k–tuples which arise in this way, if each k–tuple is counted with its multiplicity. (Notice that, in order to form $(i_1, \ldots, i_k)$, we take first the chosen 1–cycles, then the chosen 2–cycles, and so on, respecting the order of the choices of 1–cycles, 2–cycles, etc., while from each chosen i–cycle we obtain i different i–tuples by cyclically permuting the points.

For a given $(i_1, \ldots, i_k)$ there always exists a permutation $\pi \in P$ from which it arises by a suitable choice. If $(i_1, \ldots, i_k)$ arises from $\pi \in P$, then it arises exactly from the elements ρ in the left coset

$$\pi P_{\{i_1\} \ldots \{i_k\}}$$

of the stabilizer of the points $i_1, \ldots, i_k$. Hence $(i_1, \ldots, i_k)$ occurs $|P_{\{i_1\} \ldots \{i_k\}}|$ times. but all these stabilizers are conjugate subgroups, since P is k–fold transitive, so each k–tuple arises with the same multiplicity $|P_{\{i_1\} \ldots \{i_k\}}|$. Furthermore, by the k–fold transitivity of P, there are exactly $|P/P_{\{i_1\} \ldots \{i_k\}}|$ pairwise different k–tuples, and hence if each one of them is counted with its multiplicity, there are $|P|$ of them. Thus 6.1.8 is equal to $|P|$, and this completes the proof, for k–fold transitivity implies $(k-1)$–fold transitivity.

□

Here are a few examples

6.1.9 Corollary *If P is 2–fold transitive, then*

$$\frac{1}{|P|} \sum_{\pi \in P} a_2(\pi) = \frac{1}{2}.$$

If P is 3–fold transitive, then

$$\frac{1}{|P|} \sum_{\pi \in P} a_1(\pi) a_2(\pi) = \frac{1}{2}.$$

If P is 4–fold transitive, then both

$$\frac{1}{|P|} \sum_{\pi \in P} a_2(\pi)^2 = \frac{3}{4} \quad and \quad \frac{1}{|P|} \sum_{\pi \in P} a_1(\pi)^2 a_2(\pi) = 1.$$

These examples show how we can get results on expressions of the form

6.1.10
$$\frac{1}{|P|} \sum_{\pi \in P} a_1(\pi)^{b_1} \cdots a_k(\pi)^{b_k}$$

recursively from 6.1.7 once P is $(\Sigma_i i b_i)$–fold transitive. In order to provide a direct approach, we shall define a matrix of combinatorial numbers in terms of which we can formulate *all* the results of this form. In order to do this we introduce, for each $i, k \in \mathbf{N}^*$, the number t_{ik} defined by

$$t_{ik} := \frac{i^k}{(i \cdot k)!} \sum_{\pi \in S_{ik}} a_i(\pi)^k,$$

and form the matrix

$$T := (t_{ik}).$$

This is a matrix with infinitely many rows and columns. Later on we shall prove that P is k–fold transitive if and only if $\sum i b_i \leq k$ implies that 6.1.10 is equal to the following expression:

6.1.11
$$\prod_{i : b_i > 0} \frac{t_{ib_i}}{i^{b_i}}$$

But let us show first how T can be evaluated and that it is a matrix over $\mathbf{N}^*$. In order to do this we use exercise 1.7.4 which implies

6.1.12
$$\frac{1}{|P|} \sum_{\pi} a_i(\pi)^k = \sum_{j=0}^{k} S(k, j) \frac{1}{|P|} \sum_{\pi} [a_i(\pi)]_j.$$

6.1.13 Lemma *For each $i, k \in \mathbf{N}$ we have*

$$\frac{1}{(i \cdot k)!} \sum_{\pi \in S_{ik}} a_i(\pi)^k = \sum_{j=0}^{k} \frac{S(k, j)}{i^j},$$

so that in particular the following is true:

$$t_{ik} = \sum_{j=0}^{k} S(k, j) \cdot i^{k-j} \in \mathbf{N}^*.$$

Proof: For $j \leq k$ the symmetric group $S_{\underline{ik}}$ is $(i \cdot j)$–fold transitive, so that, by 6.1.7, we obtain

$$\frac{1}{(i \cdot k)!} \sum_{\pi \in S_{\underline{ik}}} \binom{a_i(\pi)}{j} = \frac{1}{i^j j!},$$

which is in fact the same as

6.1.14 $$\frac{1}{(i \cdot k)!} \sum_{\pi} [a_i(\pi)]_j = \frac{1}{i^j}.$$

The statement now follows from 6.1.12.

$\square$

This result shows how we can evaluate the coefficients of T. The upper left–hand corner of this matrix is

6.1.15 $$T = \begin{pmatrix} 1 & 2 & 5 & 15 & 52 & 203 & \cdots \\ 1 & 3 & 11 & 49 & 257 & 1539 & \cdots \\ 1 & 4 & 19 & 109 & 742 & 5815 & \cdots \\ 1 & 5 & 29 & 201 & 1657 & 15821 & \cdots \\ 1 & 6 & 41 & 331 & 3176 & 35451 & \cdots \\ 1 & 7 & 55 & 505 & 5497 & 69823 & \cdots \\ \vdots & \vdots & \vdots & \vdots & \vdots & \vdots & \end{pmatrix}$$

We notice that the first row of T contains the sequence of Bell numbers. Furthermore we are now in the position to prove the desired theorem which characterizes multiple transitivity in terms of the entries of T.

6.1.16 Theorem *A subgroup $P \leq S_{\underline{n}}$ is k–fold transitive if and only if, for every choice of natural numbers b_i, the following holds:*

$$\sum ib_i \leq k \implies \frac{1}{|P|} \sum_{\pi \in P} \prod_{i=1}^{k} a_i(\pi)^{b_i} = \prod_{i:b_i>0} \frac{t_{ib_i}}{i^{b_i}}.$$

Proof:
i) If P is k–fold transitive and $\sum ib_i \leq k$, then from 6.1.12 we get

$$\frac{1}{|P|} \sum_{\pi} \prod_{i=1}^{k} a_i(\pi)^{b_i} = \frac{1}{|P|} \sum_{\pi} \prod_{i=1}^{k} \sum_{j_i=0}^{b_i} S(b_i, j_i) [a_i(\pi)]_{j_i}$$

$$= \sum_{j_1,\ldots,j_k=0}^{b_1,\ldots,b_k} \left(\prod_{i=1}^{k} S(b_i, j_i) \right) \frac{1}{|P|} \sum_{\pi} \prod_{i} [a_i(\pi)]_{j_i},$$

which is (use 6.1.2) equal to

$$\sum_{j_1,\ldots,j_k} \left(\prod_i S(b_i, j) \right) \prod_i i^{-j_i} = \prod_i \sum_{j_i=0}^{b_i} \frac{S(b_i, j_i)}{i^{j_i}} = \prod_i \frac{t_{ib_i}}{i^{b_i}}.$$

ii) Conversely, suppose that $\sum ib_i \leq k$ implies that

$$\frac{1}{|P|} \sum_{\pi} \prod_i a_i(\pi)^{b_i} = \prod_i \frac{t_{ib_i}}{i^{b_i}}.$$

Then in particular

$$\frac{1}{|P|} \sum a_1(\pi)^k = t_{1k} = B_k,$$

and hence P is k–fold transitive by 6.1.6.

□

It is a reasonable guess that these results can be reformulated in terms of characters, in order to emphasize the representation theoretical aspect. The permutation group $S_{\underline{n}}^{\langle k \rangle}$ which is induced by $S_{\underline{n}}$ on the set $\underline{n}^{\langle k \rangle}$ of injective k–tuples over $\underline{n}$ is a transitive permutation representation of $S_{\underline{n}}$, and hence it is induced from the identity representation of the stabilizer of any such tuple. The stabilizer of the particular k–tuple $(n - k + 1, \ldots, n)$, for example, is the Young subgroup

$$S_{(n-k,1^k)} := S_{\underline{n-k}} \oplus S_{\underline{1}} \oplus \ldots \oplus S_{\underline{1}}$$

of $S_{\underline{n}}$. Hence $S_{\underline{n}}^{\langle k \rangle}$ has the same character as

$$IS_{(n-k,1^k)} \uparrow S_{\underline{n}} = [n - k][1] \cdots [1] =: [n - k][1]^k.$$

Thus $P^{\langle k \rangle}$ has the same character as has the following representation of P:

$$IS_{(n-k,1^k)} \uparrow S_{\underline{n}} \downarrow P = [n - k][1]^k \downarrow P.$$

Since the number of orbits of a permutation representation equals the multiplicity of the identity representation in that permutation representation, we have the following equivalences:

6.1.17 Lemma *The subgroup* $P \leq S_{\underline{n}}$ *is k–fold transitive if and only if*

$$1 = (IS_{(n-k,1^k)} \uparrow S_{\underline{n}} \downarrow P, IP),$$

i.e. if and only if

$$1 = (IS_{(n-k,1^k)} \uparrow S_{\underline{n}}, IP \uparrow S_{\underline{n}}),$$

or, equivalently, if and only if $IS_{\underline{n}} = [n]$ *is the only irreducible constituent which* $IS_{(n-k,1^k)} \uparrow S_{\underline{n}}$ *and* $IP \uparrow S_{\underline{n}}$ *have in common.*

The last of these characterizations leads us to the concept of *depth* of the partition $\alpha \vdash n$, defined by

$$d_\alpha := n - \alpha_1.$$

The following lemma gives an estimate for the depth of the constituents of $IP \uparrow S_{\underline{n}}$, P being multiply transitive.

6.1.18 Lemma *A subgroup* $P \leq S_{\underline{n}}$ *is k–fold transitive if and only if* $[n]$ *is the only constituent* $[\alpha]$ *of depth* $d_\alpha \leq k$ *which is contained in* $IP \uparrow S_{\underline{n}}$.

Proof: The Littlewood–Richardson Rule shows that the irreducible constituents of $[n-k][1^k]$ are just the $[\alpha]$ of depth $d_\alpha \leq k$.

□

Since the Kostka matrix K_n of $S_{\underline{n}}$ is upper triangular (cf. 4.3.22), the Young characters ξ^α of depth $d_\alpha \leq k$ form a basis of the space generated by the ζ^α with this same estimate (exercise 6.1.1):

6.1.19 $V_{n,k} := \ll \zeta^\alpha \mid d_\alpha \leq k \gg_{\mathbb{C}} = \ll \xi^\alpha \mid d_\alpha \leq k \gg_{\mathbb{C}}.$

Thus by linearity we get

6.1.20 Corollary *A subgroup* $P \leq S_{\underline{n}}$ *is k–fold transitive if and only if, for each* $\chi \in V_{n,k}$, *we have*

$$[\chi^{IP\uparrow S_{\underline{n}}} \mid \chi] = [\xi^{(n)} \mid \chi],$$

or, equivalently, if and only if, for each $\alpha \vdash n$ *such that* $d_\alpha \leq k$,

$$[\chi^{IP\uparrow S_{\underline{n}}} \mid \xi^\alpha] = [\xi^{(n)} \mid \xi^\alpha] = 1.$$

Exercises

E 6.1.1 Prove 6.1.19.

6.2   Root number functions

We want to enumerate roots in finite groups, later on we shall restrict attention to roots of permutations. In order to derive a few results concerning this problem we indicate the set and the number of k-th *roots* of $g \in G$ as follows:

$$R_k(g) = \{x \in G \mid x^k = g\}, \; r_k(g) := |R_k(g)|.$$

The corresponding power map

$$p_k: G \to G: g \mapsto g^k$$

induces the following set partition of G which consists of the inverse images:

$$G = \bigcup_{g \in G} R_k(g).$$

The mapping $r_k: G \to \mathbb{N}: g \mapsto r_k(g)$, let us call it the k-th *root number function*, is clearly a class function, moreover the following holds:

6.2.1 Lemma *The k-th root number function r_k is a $\mathbb{Z}$-linear combination of the irreducible characters of G, and hence a generalized character:*

$$r_k - \sum_i c_{i,k}\zeta^i, \; and \; c_{i,k} = \frac{1}{|G|} \sum_{g \in G} \zeta^i(g^k) = \chi^{D_i \triangle_k D_1}((1\ldots k)) \in \mathbb{Z}.$$

Proof: As

$$\sum_i c_{i,k}\zeta^i(g) = \frac{1}{|G|} \sum_{x \in G} \sum_i \zeta^i(x^k)\zeta^i(g),$$

an application of the second orthogonality relations yields that this is just $r_k(g)$, the rest of the statement follows from 5.7.17.

□

In order to examine the case $k = 2$ more closely we derive

6.2.2 Lemma *For each finite group G and any i we have that*

$$c_{i,2} \in \{0, 1, -1\},$$

and $c_{i,2} \neq 0$ if and only if the corresponding character ζ^i is real–valued.

Proof: $D_i \triangle_2 D_1$ is either zero, in which case $c_{i,2} = 0$, or it is a onedimensional representation of S_2 and $c_{i,2} \in \{1, -1\}$. Moreover $D_i \triangle_2 D_1$ is nonzero if and only if $\otimes^2 D_i$ contains the identity representation D_1, i.e. if and only if $1 = [\zeta^i \mid \overline{\zeta^i}]$, which completes the proof.   □

This yields, for numbers of square roots of elements in G:

6.2.3 $r_2(g) = \sum_{c_i=1} \zeta^i(g) - \sum_{c_j=-1} \zeta^j(g)$, and $r_2(1) = \sum_{c_i=1} f^i - \sum_{c_j=-1} f^j$.

In fact it can be shown that $c_{i,2} = 1$ if and only if D_i can be realized over $\mathbb{R}$. Hence, in the case when all the ordinary irreducible representations of G can be realized over $\mathbb{R}$, then $r_2(g) = \sum_i \zeta^i(g)$, the sum of the elements in the column of the character table of G corresponding to the conjugacy class of g. In other words, r_2 is the *model character* in this particular case. An example is the symmetric group. We have not shown yet that each of its irreducible representation is realizable over $\mathbb{R}$, but we can obtain that each $c_{\alpha,2} = 1$ also from the Robinson–Schensted construction in connection with 6.2.3. The Robinson–Schensted construction, which maps the permutation $\pi \in S_n$ onto the pair (T_1, T_2) of standard Young tableaux consisting of n entries, has the property that π^{-1} is mapped onto the pair (T_2, T_1). This implies that the number of elements of order ≤ 2 in S_n is equal to the total number of standard Young tableaux consisting of n entries, and hence, by 6.2.3, each coefficient $c_{\alpha,2}$ of an irreducible dimension f^α (which is the number of standard Young tableaux with diagram $[\alpha]$) must be positive. Putting, for $G := S_n$ and $\alpha \vdash n$,

$$r_k(\alpha) := \text{no. of } k\text{-th roots of an element with cycle partition } \alpha,$$

we have obtained:

6.2.4 Corollary *The number of square roots is the model character of the symmetric group S_n:*

$$r_2(\alpha) = \sum_{\beta \vdash n} \zeta_\alpha^\beta, \quad \text{in short: } r_2 = \sum_{\beta \vdash n} \zeta^\beta.$$

(Cf. 5.8.5 for the corresponding representation.)

This result shows in particular that r_2 is a *proper character* of the symmetric group S_n, which means that r_2 is an $\mathbb{N}$–linear combination of the irreducible characters $\zeta^\alpha, \alpha \vdash n$. But there are groups for which r_2 is *not* proper. Equation 6.2.3 shows that r_2 is not proper if and only if there exist irreducible characters ζ^i for which $c_{i,2} = -1$, and it was mentioned before that this holds if and only if ζ^i is real–valued, while D_i cannot be realized over $\mathbb{R}$. Here is another sufficient condition which has the advantage neither to use characters nor matrix representations:

6.2.5 Lemma *If the finite group G contains elements g for which $r_2(g) > r_2(1)$, then r_2 is not a proper character, or, equivalently, there exist ordinary irreducible characters ζ^i of G, for which $c_{i,2} = -1$.*

Proof: Indirectly. If $r_2 = \sum c_{i,2}\zeta^i$ is proper, then we obtain, using the first item of 4.2.1, that for each $g \in G$

$$|r_2(g)| \leq \sum_i c_{i,2}|\zeta^i(g)| \leq \sum_i c_{i,2}f^i = r_2(1).$$

□

The quaternion group $Q_8 = \{\pm 1, \pm j, \pm k, \pm l\}$ is an example since -1 has the six square roots $\pm j, \pm k$ and $\pm l$, while the identity element has the two square roots ± 1 only. Various calculations have shown that there exist many pairs (k, n) such that $k > 2$ and r_k is a proper character of S_n. It therefore was a reasonable guess that this holds for *each pair* (k, n) of natural numbers. This conjecture was recently proved by Th. Scharf, as it will be described next.

We introduce particular characters of centralizers. Recall from 1.4.3 that the centralizer of an element $\sigma \in S_n$ of type a is conjugate to a direct sum of plethysms. We abbreviate the centralizer of an element σ by $C(\sigma)$ and the conjugate direct sum of plethysms by $C(a)$, where a denotes the cycle type of σ, so that 1.4.3 gives

6.2.6 $$C(\sigma) \simeq C(a) := \oplus_i (C_{\underline{i}} \odot S_{a_i}) \simeq \times_i \left(C_i \wr S_{a_i} \right).$$

The permutation σ is a k-th root of the identity element if and only if each cycle length of σ divides k. We therefore abbreviate cycle types of this particular form by writing

$$a \vdash_k n :\Longleftrightarrow [a_i > 0 \Rightarrow i \mid k].$$

Now we pick a primitive k-th root of unity ϵ and map the cyclic factors σ_i of $\sigma = \sigma_1 \ldots \sigma_s$ onto powers of ϵ as follows:

6.2.7 $$\chi_\sigma : \sigma_i \mapsto \epsilon^{k/l_i},$$

where $l_i = |\langle\sigma_i\rangle|$, the length of the cyclic factor. This mapping trivially extends to a onedimensional character χ_σ of the centralizer of σ. Now we assume that we have chosen, for each cycle type $a \vdash_k n$, a representative $\sigma(a)$ of the conjugacy class C^a, and that $\chi_{\sigma(a)}$ is constructed according to 6.2.7. Consider the induced characters

$$\chi^{(a)} := \chi_{\sigma(a)} \uparrow S_{\underline{n}},$$

and take the sum of all of them:

$$\chi_n^k := \sum_{a\vdash_k n} \chi^{(a)}.$$

It is our aim to show that in fact $\chi_n^k = r_k$, the k-th root number function.

6.2.8 Lemma *If we denote by C_n^k the union of the conjugacy classes consisting of k-th roots of the identity element of $S_{\underline{n}}$:*

$$C_n^k := \bigcup_{a\vdash_k n} C^a,$$

then we have, for each $\pi \in S_{\underline{n}}$, that

$$\chi_n^k(\pi) = \sum \chi_\tau(\pi),$$

if the sum is taken over all the $\tau \in C_n^k$ which are contained in the centralizer of π.

Proof: Consider the chosen representative $\sigma(a) \in C^a, a \vdash_k n$, and the decomposition of $S_{\underline{n}}$ into the left cosets of its centralizer $C_{\underline{n}}(\sigma(a))$:

$$S_{\underline{n}} = \bigcup_i \tau_i C_{\underline{n}}(\sigma(a)).$$

By definition of $\chi^{(a)}$ we have (cf. 4.2.8)

$$\chi^{(a)}(\pi) = \sum_i \dot\chi_{\sigma(a)}(\tau_i^{-1}\pi\tau_i) = \sum \chi_{\sigma(a)}(\tau_i^{-1}\pi\tau_i),$$

if the last sum is taken over all the i such that $\tau_i^{-1}\pi\tau_i \in C_{\underline{n}}(\sigma(a))$ or, equivalently, $\pi \in \zeta_{\underline{n}}(\tau_i\sigma(a)\tau_i^{-1})$. Now we obtain from the definition of the τ_i that to each $\rho \in C^a \ni \sigma(a)$ there corresponds a unique index

$i = i(\rho)$ such that $\rho = \tau_{i(\rho)}\sigma(a)\tau_{i(\rho)}^{-1}$. Hence we can replace the above sum over certain i by the sum over the elements $\rho \in C^a$, for which $\pi \in C_{\underline{n}}(\rho)$, obtaining in this way that

$$\chi^{(a)}(\pi) = \sum_{\rho} \chi_{\sigma(a)}(\tau_{i(\rho)}^{-1}\pi\tau_{i(\rho)}) = \sum_{\rho} \chi_{\rho}(\pi).$$

The last equation follows from the fact that $\pi \mapsto \tau_{i(\rho)}^{-1}\pi\tau_{i(\rho)}$ is a bijection between the centralizer of $\tau_{i(\rho)}\sigma(a)\tau_{i(\rho)}^{-1}$ and the centralizer of π, that $\sigma(a)$ is mapped onto ρ by conjugation with $\tau_{i(\rho)}$, and from the definition of $\chi_{\sigma(a)}$. This completes the proof by taking the sum over all the conjugacy classes C^a contained in C_n^k.

$\square$

Our next aim is to show that we may restrict attention to conjugacy classes corresponding to rectangular partitions $\alpha = (d^r)$. In order to prove this we notice that the following holds:

6.2.9 Lemma *Assume that $\pi \in S_{\underline{n}}$ contains exactly r d–cycles which form the factor π_1 of $\pi = \pi_1\pi_2$. Then*

$$\chi_n^k(\pi) = \chi_{rd}^k(\pi_1)\chi_{n-rd}^k(\pi_2).$$

Proof: Without loss of generality we can assume that

$$\pi = (1\ldots d)(d+1\ldots 2d)\cdots((r-1)d+1\ldots rd).$$

From 6.2.6 we obtain for the centralizer of π that

$$C(\pi) = (C_{\underline{d}} \odot S_r) \oplus \ldots,$$

so that each $\tau \in C(\pi)$ is of the form $\tau = \tau_1\tau_2$, where the subset $\underline{n}\backslash \underline{rd}$ consists of fixed points of τ_1. Hence, as $\tau^k = 1$ if and only if each $\tau_i^k = 1$,

$$\chi_n^k(\pi) = \sum_{\tau} \chi_\tau(\pi) = \sum_{(\tau_1, \tau_2)} \chi_{\tau_1}(\pi_1)\chi_{\tau_2}(\pi_2)$$

$$= \sum_{\tau_1} \chi_{\tau_1}(\pi_1) \sum_{\tau_2} \chi_{\tau_2}(\pi_2) = \chi_{rd}^k(\pi_1)\chi_{n-rd}^k(\pi_2).$$

$\square$

This multiplicativity of χ_n^k allows us to restrict attention to elements π with rectangular cycle partition $\alpha(\pi) = (d^r)$, assuming now without loss of generality that

$$\pi = \underbrace{(1\ldots d)}_{=:\rho_1}\underbrace{(d+1\ldots 2d)}_{=:\rho_2}\cdots\underbrace{((r-1)d+1\ldots rd)}_{=:\rho_r}.$$

Consider the canonical epimorphism Φ from $C(\pi) = C_{\underline{d}} \odot S_{\underline{r}} \simeq C_{\underline{d}} \wr S_{\underline{r}}$ onto $S_{\underline{r}}$ which maps τ onto the permutation $\hat{\tau}$, defined by

6.2.10 $\qquad\qquad\qquad \tau \rho_i \tau^{-1} = \rho_{\hat{\tau}i}.$

Since $\tau \mapsto \hat{\tau}$ is homomorphic, $\tau \in C_n^k$ implies $\hat{\tau} \in C_r^k$. The surjectivity of this map yields that for each $\sigma \in C_r^k$ there exist $\tau \in C(\pi)$ such that $\hat{\tau} = \sigma$, moreover, by homomorphy, we can assume that τ lies in C_n^k. This gives the following decomposition into inverse images:

6.2.11 $\qquad\qquad C_n^k \cap C(\pi) = \bigcup_{bH_k r} \bigcup_{\sigma \in C^b} C_n^k \cap \Phi^{-1}(\sigma).$

Now we note that the inverse images of conjugate σ are bijective: For $\sigma, \sigma' \in C^b$ there exist $\rho \in S_{\underline{r}}$ such that $\rho \sigma' \rho^{-1} = \sigma = \hat{\tau}$, and each such ρ has an inverse image $\tilde{\rho}$ in $C(\pi)$, so that the following mapping is a bijection:

$$\phi: C_n^k \cap \Phi^{-1}(\sigma) \to C_n^k \cap \Phi^{-1}(\sigma'): \tau \mapsto \tilde{\rho}^{-1} \tau \tilde{\rho}.$$

Since ϕ means conjugation by an element in the centralizer $C(\pi)$, we have that $\chi_{\phi(\tau)}(\pi) = \chi_\tau(\pi)$, and hence we can derive from 6.2.11 that

6.2.12 Corollary *The character* χ_n^k *satisfies the equations*

$$\chi_n^k(\pi) = \sum_\tau \chi_\tau(\pi) = \sum_{bH_k r} |C^b| \sum_{\tau: \hat{\tau} = \hat{\tau}(b)} \chi_\tau(\pi)$$

$$= \sum_{bH_k r} \frac{r!}{\prod_i i^{b_i} b_i!} \sum_{\tau: \hat{\tau} = \hat{\tau}(b)} \chi_{\hat{\tau}(b)}(\pi),$$

where $\hat{\tau} = \hat{\tau}(b)$, *the representative of the conjugacy class* C^b *of* $S_{\underline{r}}$.

Let us simplify the last sum by considering the $\tau \in C_n^k \cap C(\pi)$. From the cycle decomposition $\prod_j \hat{\tau}(b)_j$ of $\hat{\tau}(b)$ we obtain the orbits of $\langle \tau, \pi \rangle$ on $\underline{n}$, since the elements of the cycle $\hat{\tau}(b)_j$ are the *numbers* i of the cyclic factors ρ_i of π that form an orbit under τ via conjugation (cf. 6.2.10). Let us denote by ω_j this orbit which is associated with $\hat{\tau}(b)_j$, and let us indicate the restrictions accordingly:

$$\tau_j := \tau \downarrow \omega_j, \ \pi_j := \pi \downarrow \omega_j.$$

As π consists of d–cycles only, also π_j is a product of cyles of this length. Moreover to the restrictions τ_j to subsets of $\underline{n}$ there correspond the restrictions $\hat{\tau}_j$ of $\hat{\tau}$ to the according subsets of $\underline{r}$. Hence we introduce

$$M_j := \{\tau_j \in C^k_{|\omega_j|} \cap C(\pi_j) \mid \hat{\tau}_j = \hat{\tau}(b)_j\}.$$

It is clear that

$$\{\tau \mid \hat{\tau} = \hat{\tau}(b)\} \rightarrow \times_j M_j : \tau \mapsto (\ldots, \tau_j, \ldots)$$

is a bijection and that $\chi_\tau(\pi) = \prod_j \chi_{\tau_j}(\pi_j)$. This implies

6.2.13
$$\sum_{\tau : \hat{\tau} = \hat{\tau}(b)} \chi_\tau(\pi) = \sum_{(\tau_j) \in \times_j M_j} \prod_j \chi_{\tau_j}(\pi_j) = \prod_j \sum_{\tau_j \in M_j} \chi_{\tau_j}(\pi_j).$$

We want to replace the last sum. Without loss of generality we can assume that π_j consists of the first t_j cyclic factors of π, i.e. $\pi_j = \rho_1 \cdots \rho_{t_j}$. Moreover we can assume that the representative $\hat{\tau}(b)$ of C^b was chosen in such a way that its factor $\hat{\tau}(b)_j$ is equal to the cyclic permutation $(1 \ldots t_j)$. Hence M_j can be rewritten in the following way:

$$M_j := \{\tau_j \in C^k_{t_j d} \cap C(\pi_j) \mid \forall i < t_j : \tau_j \rho_i \tau_j^{-1} = \rho_{i+1}\}.$$

This set can easily be decomposed by picking elements $z_1, \ldots, z_{t_j}$ from the cyclic factors $\rho_1, \ldots, \rho_{t_j}$ and putting

$$M_j(z_1, \ldots, z_{t_j}) := \{\tau_j \in M_j \mid \forall i < t_j : \tau_j z_i = z_{i+1}\}.$$

Since $\rho_1 = (1 \ldots d)$, we obtain a set partition of M_j for each $z \in \underline{d}$, arising from the choices of the elements $z_2, \ldots, z_{t_j}$:

$$M_j = \bigcup_{(z_2, \ldots, z_{t_j})} M_j(z, z_2, \ldots, z_{t_j}).$$

Moreover the blocks $M_j(z, z_2, \ldots, z_{t_j})$ are conjugates in $C_n(\pi_j)$, since, for each $(z_1, \ldots, z_{t_j})$, there exist $\sigma \in C(\pi_j)$ such that

$$M_j(1, d+1, \ldots, (t_j - 1)d + 1) = M_j(\sigma z_1, \ldots, \sigma z_{t_j}) = \sigma M_j(z_1, \ldots, z_{t_j})\sigma^{-1}.$$

We have therefore proved

6.2.14
$$\sum_{\tau_j \in M_j} \chi_{\tau_j}(\pi) = d^{t_j - 1} \sum_{\tau_j \in M_j(1, \ldots, (t_j - 1)d + 1)} \chi_{\tau_j}(\pi_j).$$

This, together with 6.2.12 and 6.2.13, yields

6.2.15 Corollary *The character χ_n^k has the following values:*

$$\chi_n^k(\pi) = \sum_{b \vdash_k r} \frac{r!}{\prod_i i^{b_i} b_i!} d^{r-c(b)} \prod_j \sum_{\tau_j \in M_j(1, d+1, \ldots, (t_j-1)d+1)} \chi_{\tau_j}(\pi_j),$$

where $c(b) := \sum b_i$.

Recall the definition of $M_j(1, d+1, \ldots, (t_j - 1)d + 1)$. Each of its elements is uniquely determined by the image of the point $(t_j-1)d+1$, say $\tau_j((t_j - 1)d + 1) = \pi^i 1$. We want to characterize these exponents. In terms of wreath product notation, this particular τ_j is of the form (ψ, σ), where σ is the t_j–cycle $(1, d + 1, \ldots, (t_j - 1)d + 1)$, and $\psi(1)$ is the i-th power of a d–cycle of π. Thus, by 1.3.11 and 1.4.7, we obtain that τ_j consists of $\gcd(i, d)$ cyclic factors, each of which is of length $t_j d / \gcd(i, d)$. Furthermore τ_j is a k–th root of unity, so that the lengths of its cyclic factors divide k or, equivalently (as t_j divides k since $|\omega_j| = t_j d$),

6.2.16 $d / \gcd(i, d)$ divides k/t_j.

If we put $d = d_1 d_2$, where $d_2 = \gcd(d, k/t_j)$, then 6.2.16 is equivalent to

$$i = i_0 d_1 \text{ and } d_2/ \gcd(d_2, i_0) \text{ divides } k/t_j,$$

which yields

6.2.17 $\tau_j \in M_j \iff i = i_0 d_1$, where $i_0 \in \underline{d_2}$.

In order to evaluate the desired sum $\sum_{\tau_j \in M_j} \chi_{\tau_j}(\pi_j)$, we fix $\tau_j \in M_j$, which in turn is characterized by a certain i_0 according to the equation

$$\tau_j((t_j - 1)d + 1) = \pi_j^{i_0 d_1} 1.$$

In order to apply the definition of χ_{τ_j} we have to find a decomposition $\pi_j = \rho_j \sigma_j$ such that ρ_j is a product of certain powers of the cyclic factors of τ_j and σ_j lies in the complement of this base group.

In order to visualize this decomposition of τ_j we consider the following array which contains in its rows the cyclic factors of π_j. Without loss of generality we can assume that it looks as follows:

1	$\pi_j 1 = 2$	$\ldots$	$\pi_j^{d-1} 1 = d$
$d + 1$	$d + 2$	$\ldots$	$2d$
$\vdots$			$\vdots$
$(t_j - 1)d + 1$	$(t_j - 1)d + 2$	$\ldots$	$t_j d$

Note that τ_j consists of cyclic factors of the same length and that each of them contains a union of columns in the above array: The order in which these columns have to be put together can be obtained from the wreath product notation which was already mentioned: $\tau_j = (\psi, \sigma)$ and $(\psi, \sigma) = (\psi(1), \ldots, \psi(t_j); \sigma)$ where the $\psi(k)$ and σ are as follows:

$$\underbrace{(\psi_j^i, 1, \ldots, 1}_{\psi}; \underbrace{(1, \ldots, t_j))}_{\sigma}.$$

If $\tau_{j,1}$, the first cyclic factor of τ_j is the one containing the first column, say, then it is therefore of the form

$$\tau_{j,1} = \underbrace{(1, d+1, \ldots, (t_j-1)d+1}_{\text{first column}}, \underbrace{\pi_j^i 1, d + \pi_j^i 1, \ldots, (t_j-1)d + \pi_j^i 1, \ldots)}_{\text{next column}}.$$

Thus the order in which the columns are put together is determined by the numbers $n_l := l \cdot i = l \cdot i_0 \cdot d_1$ (and their residue classes modulo d). If there exist further cyclic factors of τ_j, i.e. if $i' = \gcd(i, d) = d_1 \gcd(i_0, d_2) > 1$, then they are obtained from $\tau_{j,1}$ via conjugation by powers of π_j. The second cyclic factor $\tau_{j,2}$, for example, is

$$\tau_{j,2} = \underbrace{(2, d+2, \ldots, (t_j-1)d+2}_{\text{first column}}, \underbrace{\pi_j^i 2, d + \pi_j^i 2, \ldots, (t_j-1)d + \pi_j^i 2, \ldots)}_{\text{next column}}.$$

Moreover, the desired σ_j is the permutation which performs this conjugation operation. This shows that σ_j is the following product of cyclic factors:

$$(1, 2, \ldots, i')(i'+1, i'+2, \ldots, 2i') \ldots (\ldots, d)$$

$$\cdot (d+1, \ldots, d+i')(d+i'+1, d+i'+2, \ldots, d+2i') \ldots (\ldots, 2d).$$

This allows us to evaluate $\rho_j = \pi_j \sigma_j^{-1}$. For σ_j is defined as follows: (Note that, as d divides n and i' divides d, each element of $\underline{n}$ has a unique representation $fd + gi' + h$ with $1 \le h \le i', 0 \le g \le d/i' - 1, 0 \le f \le t_j - 1$.)

$$\sigma_j(fd + gi' + h) = \begin{cases} fd + gi' + h + 1 & \text{if } h < i', \\ fd + gi' + 1 & \text{else}, \end{cases}$$

from which it follows that $\sigma(fd + gi' + h) = \pi(fd + gi' + h)$, if $h < i'$. Thus the points $fd + gi' + h, h > 1$, are fixed points of ρ_j. For

$fd + gi' + 1$ we obtain

$$\rho_j(fd + gi' + 1) = \begin{cases} fd + gi' + i' + 1 & \text{if } gi' + i' < d, \\ fd + 1 & \text{else.} \end{cases}$$

This means that, for each f, the points $fd + gi' + 1$ belong to one d/i'-cycle

$$(fd + 1, fd + i' + 1, \ldots, (f + 1)d - i' + 1),$$

and, omitting fixed points, ρ_j is the product of these t_j cycles:

$$\rho_j := (1, i' + 1, \ldots, d - i' + 1)(d + 1, d + i' + 1, \ldots, 2d - i' + 1) \ldots$$

We have to rewrite ρ_j as a power of τ_j in order to evaluate $\chi_{\tau_j}(\pi_j) = \chi_{\tau_j}(\rho_j)$.

To make things clear it is useful to consider an example:

6.2.18 Example Let $\pi_j := (1, 2, 3, 4, 5, 6)(7, 8, 9, 10, 11, 12)$. The corresponding picture is

1	2	3	4	5	6
7	8	9	10	11	12

We choose $\tau_j = (1, 7, 5, 11, 3, 9)(2, 8, 6, 12, 4, 10)$. It is immediate that

$$\sigma_j = (1, 2)(3, 4)(5, 6)\,(7, 8)(9, 10)(11, 12), \quad \rho_j = (1, 3, 5)(7, 9, 11).$$

ρ_j contains only the entries of the cyclic factor $(1, 7, 5, 11, 3, 9)$ of τ_j. If we take the t_j-th power of this cycle, the resulting permutation acts only on the rows: $(1, 7, 5, 11, 3, 9)^2 = (1, 5, 3)(7, 11, 9)$. Note that this permutation and also ρ_j are elements of the same order in the cyclic group generated by π_j^2 and thus ρ_j is a certain power (in this case the square) of $(1, 5, 3)(7, 11, 9)$. ◇

Indeed, in the general case, ρ_j is a certain power of $\tau_{j,1}$ of order pt_j, where $p \in \underline{d_2/i_0'}$ is the unique solution of the equation

$$p \cdot (i_0/i_0') \equiv 1 \text{ modulo } (d_2/i_0').$$

Note that by definition of i_0' we have $\gcd(d_2/i_0', i_0/i_0') = 1$, thus a bijection from $\{j \in \underline{d_2} \mid \gcd(j, d_2) = i_0'\}$ to the set of units of the multiplicative group of $\mathbb{Z}/(d_2/i_0')\mathbb{Z}$. From this it follows that, if i_0/i_0'

runs through the the elements of the set of units, the corresponding solution p also does. And, applying the bijection in the other direction, the set of the elements $i_0' p$ is precisely $\{j \in \underline{d_2} \mid \gcd(j, d_2) = i_0'\}$. We can therefore deduce that

$$\chi_{\tau_j}(\pi_j) = \chi_{\tau_j}(\rho_j)\chi_{\tau_j}(\sigma_j) = \chi_{\tau_j}(\tau_{j,1})^{pt_j} = \epsilon^{(k/(t_j d/(i_0' d_1)))pt_j} = (\epsilon^{k/d_2})^{i_0' p},$$

thus obtaining

$$\sum_{\tau_j \in M_j} \chi_{\tau_j}(\pi_j) = \sum_{i_0=1}^{d_2} (\epsilon^{k/d_2})^{i_0}.$$

As ϵ^{k/d_2} is a primitive root of unity, this sum is nonzero if and only if $\epsilon^{k/d_2} = 1$, which means $d_2 = 1$, and in this case the sum is 1.

This allows us to give an explicit version of 6.2.15. Note that for a $b \vdash_k r$ the corresponding t_j give:

$$b_l = |\{j \mid t_j = l\}|$$

so that we conclude

For $\pi \in S_{\underline{n}}$ with cycle partition (d^r) we have

$$\chi_n^k(\pi) = \sum_{b \vdash_k r} \frac{r!}{\prod_i i^{b_i} b_i!} d^{r - c(b)}$$

where the sum is over all $b \vdash_k r$ with the property that each l with $b_l > 0$ obeys $\gcd(d, k/l) = d_2 = 1$. In the next section it will be shown that this number χ_n^k is the desired root number function!

6.3 Equations in groups

The k-th roots of $g \in G$ are the solutions of the equation $x^k = g$ in G. Hence the enumeration of roots is a particular case of the enumeration of solutions of *equations in finite groups*. A few remarks concerning this more general problem are therefore in order. A quite general result in this field of problems is

6.3.1 Theorem Let G denote a finite group and $C_1, \ldots, C_k$ some of its conjugacy classes (which need not be pairwise different) while m_j and n_j are given natural numbers, for $1 \le j \le k$. Then, for a fixed $g \in G$, the number of tupels $(g_1, \ldots, g_k) \in G^k$ such that

$$g_1^{n_1} \cdots g_k^{n_k} = g \text{ and } g_j^{m_j} \in C_j, \ j \in \underline{k},$$

is equal to

$$\sum_i \frac{f^i}{|G|} \zeta^i(g^{-1}) \prod_j (\frac{1}{f^i} \sum_{g_j : g_j^{m_j} \in C_j} \zeta^i(g_j^{n_j})),$$

where the ζ^i are the ordinary irreducible characters of G and the f^i their dimensions.

Proof: Let $\mathbf{D}_i$ denote a matrix representation corresponding to D_i. As $\{g_j^{n_j} \mid g_j^{m_j} \in C_j\}$ is a union of conjugacy classes of G, Schur's Lemma gives

$$\sum_{g_j : g_j^{m_j} \in C_j} \mathbf{D}_i(g_j^{n_j}) = \frac{1}{f^i} \sum_{g_j : g_j^{m_j} \in C_j} \zeta^i(g_j^{n_j}) \cdot \mathbf{I},$$

where $\mathbf{I}$ denotes the f^i–dimensional identity matrix. Multiplying k such equations we obtain

$$\sum \mathbf{D}_i(g_1^{n_1} \ldots g_k^{n_k} g^{-1}) = \left(\frac{1}{f^i}\right)^k \prod_j \sum_{g_j^{m_j} \in C_j} \zeta^i(g_j^{n_j}) \mathbf{D}_i(g^{-1}),$$

where the sum on the left hand side has to be taken over all the $(g_1, \ldots, g_k) \in G^k$ such that each $g_j^{m_j} \in C_j$. Taking trace on both sides and dividing by $|G|$, we get

$$\frac{1}{|G|} \sum f^i \zeta^i(g_1^{n_1} \ldots g_k^{n_k} g^{-1}) = \frac{1}{|G|} \left(\frac{1}{f^i}\right)^{k-1} \zeta^i(g^{-1}) \prod_j \sum \zeta^i(g_j^{n_j}).$$

The left hand side of this equation is equal to

$$\frac{1}{|G|} \sum \chi^R(g_1^{n_1} \ldots g_k^{n_k} g^{-1}),$$

(χ^R the character of the regular representation) which is just the desired number of solutions.

$\square$

A special case of 6.3.1 is the number of ways to express $\pi \in S_{\underline{n}}$ as a product $\sigma_1 \ldots \sigma_k$ of k n–cycles $\sigma_i \in C^{(n)} \subseteq S_{\underline{n}}$, the class of n–cycles. The theorem shows that this number is equal to

$$\sum_{\alpha \vdash n} \frac{f^\alpha}{n!} \zeta^\alpha(\pi^{-1}) \prod_j \left(\frac{1}{f^\alpha} \sum_{\sigma_j \in C^{(n)}} \zeta^\alpha(\sigma_j)\right).$$

We now remember that $\zeta^\alpha(\sigma_j), \sigma_j \in C^{(n)}$, is nonzero if and only if α is a hook, say $\alpha = (n - r, 1^r)$, in which case $\zeta^\alpha(\sigma_j) = (-1)^r$ and $f^\alpha = \binom{n-1}{r}$. This gives

6.3.2 Corollary *The number of ways to express* $\pi \in S_{\underline{n}}$ *as a product* $\sigma_1 \ldots \sigma_k$ *of n–cycles* σ_i *is equal to*

$$\frac{1}{n} \sum_{r=0}^{n-1} (r!(n - r - 1)!)^{k-1} (-1)^{rk} \zeta^{(n-r,1^r)}(\pi).$$

Particular cases are described in

6.3.3 Corollary

- *The number of ways to write* $1 \in S_{\underline{n}}$ *as a product of k n–cycles is equal to*

$$\frac{1}{n} \sum_{r=0}^{n-1} (r!(n - r - 1)!)^{k-2} (-1)^{rk} (n - 1)!.$$

- *The number of ways to express an n–cycle as a product of k n–cycles is equal to*

$$\frac{1}{n} \sum_{r=0}^{n-1} (r!(n - r - 1)!)^{k-1} (-1)^{r(k+1)}.$$

The proof of theorem 6.3.1 allows a generalization. Instead of conjugacy classes $C_1, \ldots, C_k$ we can consider subsets $V_1, \ldots, V_k$ which are unions of conjugacy classes, for example $V_1 = \ldots = V_k = G$:

6.3.4 Corollary *Let G denote a finite group, and consider, for* $1 \leq j \leq k$, *the natural numbers* n_j. *Then, for a given element* $h \in G$ *the number of solutions* $(g_1, \ldots, g_k) \in G^{\underline{k}}$ *such that* $g_1^{n_1} \ldots g_k^{n_k} = h$ *is equal to*

$$\sum_i \left(\frac{|G|}{f^i} \right)^{k-1} \left(\prod_j c_{i,n_j} \right) \zeta^i(h^{-1}).$$

Since, according to 5.7.17, the c_{i,n_j} are integers, we also obtain

6.3.5 Corollary *The number*

$$|\{(g_1, \ldots, g_k) \mid g_1^{n_1} \ldots g_k^{n_k} = g\}|$$

is, for each element g ∈ G, divisible by the greatest common divisor

$$\gcd\left\{\left(\frac{|G|}{f^i}\right)^{k-1} \mid \zeta^i \text{ irreducible}\right\}.$$

Now we woulk like to take a closer look at numbers of roots in symmetric groups. Recall that

$$r_m(\pi) := |\{\rho \in S_{\underline{n}} \mid \rho^m = \pi\}| =: r_m(\alpha), \text{ if } \alpha = \alpha(\pi).$$

Aiming at a recursion we use the following multiplicativity property. If $\pi = \rho^m$ and $\rho = \rho_1 \dots \rho_r$ is the cycle decomposition of ρ, then $\rho^m = \rho_1^m \dots \rho_r^m = \pi$. Hence $r_m(\alpha)$, the number of m-th roots of any element with cycle partition α, is multiplicative in the following sense:

6.3.6 $$r_m(n^{a_n}, \dots, 1^{a_1}) = \prod_i r_m(i^{a_i}).$$

It therefore remains to evaluate the numbers $r_m(i^{a_i})$.

6.3.7 Lemma *If $\pi \in S_{\underline{n}}$ consists of k–cycles only, i.e. if $a_k(\pi) \cdot k = n$, then*

$$r_m(\pi) = r_m(k^{a_k}) = \sum_{j \in \underline{a_k} : \gcd(k, m/j) = 1} [a_k - 1]_{j-1} k^{j-1} r_m(k^{a_k - j}).$$

In particular the following holds:

$$r_m(1^n) = \sum_{j \in \underline{n} : j \mid m} [n-1]_{j-1} r_m(1^{n-j}),$$

and,

$$\forall n \geq 2: \ r_2(1^n) = r_2(1^{n-1}) + (n-1) r_2(1^{n-2}).$$

In terms of dimensions of the irreducibles, i.e. in terms of numbers of standard Young tableaux, this reads as follows:

$$\forall n \geq 2: \sum_{\alpha \vdash n} f^\alpha = \sum_{\beta \vdash n-1} f^\beta + (n-1) \sum_{\gamma \vdash n-2} f^\gamma.$$

Proof: We consider $\rho \in R_m(\pi)$, where $\alpha(\pi) = (k^{a_k})$, and $a_k(\pi) > 0$. Assume that $(j_1 \dots j_k)$, a cyclic factor of π, arises from the cyclic factor $(i_1 \dots i_r)$ of ρ. Then, by 1.3.11, it is not only $(j_1 \dots j_k)$ which comes from $(i_1 \ldots i_r)$, but altogether $j := \gcd(r, m)$ k–cycles of π, and furthermore we have $k = r/j$. Canceling this cycle $(i_1 \ldots i_r)$ from ρ, we obtain ρ^*, a permutation of degree $n - r = n - jk$, the m-th power of which has the cycle partition $(k^{a_k - j})$. It remains to count the number of different $(i_1, \ldots, i_r)$ which contribute $(j_1, \ldots, j_k)$, together with $j - 1$ further k–cycles of π. As we can cyclically permute the points without changing the cyclic permutation, we may assume that $j_k = i_r$, which fixes the places of the j_ν in this cycle:

$$(i_1, \ldots, i_r) = (\ldots j_1 \ldots j_2 \ldots j_k).$$

Now the k points contained in one of the remaining $j - 1$ k–cycles $(j'_1 \ldots j'_k)$ of π which also arise from $(i_1 \ldots i_r)$ have also to be shuffled into this cycle. $(j'_1 \ldots j'_k)$ Fixing the place of j'_k also fixes the places of the other j'_ν:

$$(\ldots j_1 \ldots j_2 \ldots j'_k \ldots j_k),$$

and hence there are exactly so many admissible ways:

$$[a_k(\pi) - 1]_{j-1} = (a_k(\pi) - 1)(a_k(\pi) - 2) \ldots (a_k(\pi) - j + 1).$$

This completes the proof, since $[a_k(\pi) - 1]_{j-1} = 0$, if $j > a_k(\pi)$. $\qquad\square$

Besides the multiplicativity of r_m, we can use the following closed form for root numbers: If G denotes a finite group, $g \in G$, and $m \in \mathbb{N}$, then (exercise 6.3.1)

6.3.8 $$r_m(g) = |C_G(g)| \sum_x{}' |C_G(x)|^{-1},$$

if the sum $\sum'$ is taken over a system of representatives x of such conjugacy classes of G that contain m-th roots of g. In order to apply this to the symmetric group case, we have to characterize the conjugacy classes which contain m-th roots of an element of cycle partition (k^{a_k}). Each such conjugacy class corresponds to a cycle type $c \vdash k \cdot a_k$, where $c_i > 0$ implies that k divides i, say $i = jk$. We can therefore replace $c_i = c_{j \cdot k}$ by b_j, obtaining in this way a cycle type $b \vdash a_k$. Notice that $b_j > 0$ means that there is a $j \cdot k$–cycle, in the root, the m-th power of which consists of k–cycles. Thus, by 1.3.11, $j = \gcd(m, j \cdot k)$, so that the cycle types $b \vdash a_k$ in question are just the cycle types, the nonzero elements b_j of which satisfy the conditions

$$j \mid m \wedge \gcd(m/j, k) = 1.$$

This leads us to the following result:

6.3.9 Theorem *The number of m-th roots of an element consisting of a_k cycles of length k satisfies the equation*

$$r_m(k^{a_k}) = \sum_{b \vdash a_k, b_i \neq 0 \Rightarrow [i \mid m \wedge gcd(m/i,k)=1]} k^{a_k - \Sigma b_i} \frac{a_k!}{\prod_i i^{b_i} b_i!}.$$

The number of m-th roots of an element $\pi \in S_{\underline{n}}$ of cycle type a is

$$r_m(\pi) = \prod_{k:a_k>0} k^{a_k} a_k! \sum_{b \vdash a_k, b_i \neq 0 \Rightarrow [i \mid m \wedge gcd(m/i,k)=1]} k^{a_k - \Sigma b_i} \frac{a_k!}{\prod_i i^{b_i} b_i!}.$$

Hence, in particular, $r_m = \chi_n^m$, and so, r_m, the root number function, is a proper character.

Exercises

E 6.3.1 Prove that

$$r_2((2i)^{a_{2i}}) = \begin{cases} 0 & \text{if } a_{2i} \text{ is odd,} \\ (2i)^m (2m)! (2^m m!)^{-1} & \text{if } a_{2i} = 2m. \end{cases}$$

E 6.3.2 Derive the following in two ways, first using the multiplicativity of the root number function, and then by using character theory only:

$$r_2(\alpha) = 0, \text{ if an } a_{2i} \text{ is odd.}$$

6.4   Up–down sequences

Recall the method of displaying a permutation $\pi \in S_{\underline{n}}$ by putting down the *list* of its values:

$$\pi = [\pi 1 \ldots \pi n].$$

The *i*-th position, $i \leq n - 1$, of this list is called an *up* if $\pi i < \pi(i + 1)$, otherwise it is called a *down*. Replacing an up by "+", a down by "−", we obtain the *up–down sequence* $U\pi$ of π, for example

$$U[13248765] = (+ - + + - - -).$$

Before we enumerate permutations with given up–down sequence, we take a look at permutations with prescribed *number* of ups. The

Eulerian number $E(n,k)$ is defined to be the number of $\pi \in S_n$ such that π contains exactly k ups. Hence in particular the following holds:

6.4.1
$$\sum_{k=0}^{n-1} E(n,k) = n!.$$

H.O Foulkes was the first to notice that in order to examine Eulerian numbers we can associate with the up–down sequences *rims of Young diagrams*. In order to describe this we take a node "×" and we successively add further nodes to the left or downwards according to $U\pi$ and the following rule:

6.4.2
$$\begin{array}{cc} + \leftarrow & \times \\ \downarrow\, - & \end{array}$$

This means that to an entry $+$ of U there corresponds a node $\times$ that has to be added at the left of the last node added, and in the same row. Correspondingly to an entry $-$ of U there corresponds a node that has to be added just below the last node. For example the sequence $(+-++---)$ mentioned above gives

$$
\begin{array}{ccc}
 & \times & \times \\
\times & \times & \times \\
\times & & \\
\times & & \\
\times & &
\end{array}
\qquad \text{according to} \qquad
\begin{array}{ccc}
 & + & \times \\
+ & + & - \\
- & & \\
- & & \\
- & &
\end{array}
\;.
$$

We consider the resulting skew diagram as the rim R_{11}^{α} of a Young diagram $[\alpha]$ the shape α of which we denote by $\alpha(U)$, while we indicate the rim hook of $[\alpha(U)]$ as follows:

$$R(U) := R_{11}^{\alpha(U)}.$$

The partition $\alpha := \alpha(U)$ is uniquely determined, and $\alpha_1 = k + 1$, k the number of ups, while $\alpha_1' = n - k$, one more than the number of downs. For our example we obtain

$$
[\alpha(+-++---)] =
\begin{array}{cccc}
\times & \times & \times & \times \\
\times & \times & \times & \\
\times & & & \\
\times & & & \\
\times & & &
\end{array}
= [4,3,1^3].
$$

If we want to erase the rim R_{11}^{α} from $[\alpha(U)]$ by successively removing nodes in such a way that each step leaves a Young diagram, then we usually have many possibilities to do this. Each of these possibilities can be described by replacing the nodes of the rim by numbers $1, \ldots, n$, according to the sequence of removals. The above example offers, among others, the following two ways of removing the rim of $[4, 3, 1^3]$:

$$
\begin{array}{cccc}
& 8 & 7 & \\
6 & 5 & 4 & \\
3 & & & \\
2 & & & \\
1 & & & \\
\end{array}
\quad , \quad
\begin{array}{cccc}
& 8 & 7 & \\
6 & 2 & 1 & \\
5 & & & \\
4 & & & \\
3 & & & \\
\end{array}
\quad .
$$

Reading these numbers row by row from top to bottom and in the rows from right to left, we obtain lists of permutations, for example

$$[78456321], \quad [78126543].$$

The rule 6.4.2 implies that they all have the same up–down sequence, namely the up–down sequence which lead to $[\alpha]$. Hence the number of permutations with prescribed up–down sequence U is equal to the number of ways to remove the rim $R(U)$ from $[\alpha(U)]$ subject to the condition that in each step we remove just one node and the remaining rest is still a Young diagram. Replacing the entry i by $n - i$, for each $i \in \underline{n}$, we clearly obtain the standard Young tableaux of shape $[R(U)]$, and hence, according to 5.6.7 or the Murnaghan Nakayama formula for skew representations, this is just the dimension $f^{R(U)}$ of the corresponding skew representation $[R(U)]$. This yields the following result on Eulerian numbers, since the leg length of $R(U)$ is equal to $\alpha_1' - 1 = n - k - 1$:

6.4.3 Corollary *The Eulerian numbers satisfy the following identities:*

$$
E(n, k) = \sum_{\alpha} f^{R_{11}^{\alpha}} = \sum_{U} f^{R(U)},
$$

if the first sum is taken over all the proper partitions α such that $\alpha_1 = k + 1$ and $\alpha_1' = n - k$, while the second sum is taken over all the up–down sequences U containing exactly k entries $+$.

This looks circumstantial at first glance, but it allows to express $E(n, k)$ as a sum of dimensions of irreducible representations of S_n, i.e. $E(n, k)$ is a sum of numbers of standard Young tableaux. Moreover it opens a natural way of generalizing the Eulerian numbers by replacing the dimensions by the characters, this will be described later.

The summand $f(U)$ of $E(n, k)$ in 6.4.3, i.e. the dimension of the skew representation $[R(U)]$, is the sum of the dimensions of its irreducible components. The Murnaghan–Nakayama formula shows that it is the number of $(\alpha, (1^n), \alpha \backslash R_{11}^{\alpha})$-paths in Young's lattice, i.e. it is the number of ways to erase R_{11}^{α} from $[\alpha]$, as it was described above. The crucial point is now to construct, according to R_{11}^{α} or to the up–down sequence U which lead to α, the Young diagrams $[\beta]$ (together with the corresponding multiplicities) which form the irreducible constituents. In order to do this we start with a node "$\times$" together with an up–down sequence U and add further nodes according to U and the following rule:

6.4.4
$$
\begin{array}{l}
\times \quad \nearrow + \\
\swarrow -
\end{array}
$$

By this pictorial description I mean that to an entry $+$ of U there corresponds a node $\times$ which has to be added to the right of the last node, maybe in a higher row, while to an entry $-$ there corresponds a node added to the left of the last node or in a lower row. Consider once more the example $U = (+ - + + - - -)$. We start with a node $\times$, and the first entry of U is a $+$, so the corresponding node has to be added, according to 6.4.4, to the right of the starting node, i.e. we obtain the diagram $\times\otimes$, where the last node added is encircled. Now the second entry of U is a minus sign, hence the corresponding addition of a node is again uniquely determined, and we get the diagram

$$
\begin{array}{cc}
\times & \times \\
\otimes &
\end{array} .
$$

The next entry of U is a plus sign, so that there are two places open for an additional node which are to the right of the node which was added last time:

$$
\begin{array}{ccc}
\times & \times & \otimes \\
\times & &
\end{array}
\quad \text{and} \quad
\begin{array}{ccc}
\times & \times & \\
\times & \otimes &
\end{array} .
$$

The next steps yield the following cascade of diagrams:

$$
\begin{array}{cccc}
\times & \times & \times & \otimes \\
\times & & & \\
& \swarrow & \searrow &
\end{array}
\qquad
\begin{array}{ccc}
\times & \times & \otimes \\
\times & \times & \\
\swarrow & \searrow &
\end{array}
$$

```
× × × ×    × × × ×    × × ×    × × ×
×          × ⊗        × ×      × × ⊗
⊗                     ⊗
   ↓          ↓          ↓         ↓

× × × ×    × × × ×    × × ×    × × × ×
×          × ×        × ×      × × ×
×          ×          ×        ×
×          ×          ×        ×
×          ×          ×
```

Hence from $U = (+ - + + - - -)$ we obtain the diagrams

$$[4, 1^4], [4, 2, 1^2], [3, 2, 1^3], [3^2, 1^2],$$

and each one of them exactly once. It is the aim to show that this is in fact the decomposition of $[R(U)]$ into its irreducible constituents. We therefore denote by

$$[\widetilde{R}(U)]$$

the sum of the representations $[\beta]$ obtained from U by 6.4.2, where each of them occurs with the multiplicity by which the diagram $[\beta]$ shows up. We have to prove the equation $[R(U)] = [\widetilde{R}(U)]$, and the following lemma will turn out to be the crucial step towards this:

6.4.5 Lemma *For each k and any up–down sequence U we have:*

$$[k + 1][\widetilde{R}(U)] = [\widetilde{R}(U + + \ldots +)] + [\widetilde{R}(U - + \ldots +)].$$

Proof: Young's rule shows that the irreducible constituents of $[k + 1][\widetilde{R}(U)]$ arise from the $[\mu]$ of $[\widetilde{R}(U)]$ by adding nodes in $k+1$ *different columns*. Now we consider, how these $[\nu]$ can be reached from $[\emptyset]$ in Young's lattice. $[\mu]$ comes from 6.4.2 by working through U, so that $[\nu]$ is obtained by working through $U + \ldots +$ or through $U - + \ldots +$, depending on the lowest node of $[\nu \backslash \mu]$. This proves the statement.

$\qquad\qquad\qquad\qquad\qquad\qquad\qquad\qquad\qquad\qquad\qquad\qquad\qquad$ □

We are now in a position to prove the desired equality $[R(U)] = [\widetilde{R}(U)]$, but let us first work out an example. Since

$$R(+ - - + + - - + + +) = [7, 6^2, 4^2 \backslash 5^2, 3^2],$$

the determinantal form for skew representations yields that

$$[R(+ - - + + - - + ++)] = \det \begin{pmatrix} [2] & [3] & [6] & [7] & [1] \\ 1 & [1] & [4] & [5] & [9] \\ 0 & 1 & [3] & [4] & [8] \\ 0 & 0 & 1 & [1] & [5] \\ 0 & 0 & 0 & 1 & [4] \end{pmatrix},$$

which, according to its last row, is equal to

$$[4] \det \begin{pmatrix} [2] & [3] & [6] & [7] \\ 1 & [1] & [4] & [5] \\ 0 & 1 & [3] & [4] \\ 0 & 0 & 1 & [1] \end{pmatrix} - \det \begin{pmatrix} [2] & [3] & [6] & [11] \\ 1 & [1] & [4] & [9] \\ 0 & 1 & [3] & [8] \\ 0 & 0 & 1 & [5] \end{pmatrix}$$

$$= [4][7, 6^2, 4 \backslash 5^2, 3^2] - [8, 7^2, 5 \backslash 6^2, 4]$$

$$= [4][R(+ - - + + -)] - [R((+ - - + + - + + ++)].$$

We note that $(+ - - + + -)$ is shorter than the original sequence $(+ - - + + - - + ++)$, while the other sequence $(+ - - + + - + + ++)$ is of the same length, but it has *one down less*. This allows to prove the statement via induction on the length $n - 1$ of U together with an induction on the number of downs (using that clearly $[\tilde{R}(+ \ldots +)] = [R(+ \ldots +)] = [n]$) inside the induction on the length of U. But this same double induction procedure applies in the general case, too, as we can assume without loss of generality that U ends with a $+$. For otherwise we can use that for the *complementary* up–down sequence U', which arises from U by changing each $+$ into a $-$ and each $-$ into $+$, we have both

6.4.6 $[\tilde{R}(U)] = [\tilde{R}(U')] \otimes [1^n]$, and $[R(U)] = [R(U')] \otimes [1^n]$.

In fact, if $U = (u_1, \ldots, u_{n-1})$ closes with a down and then k ups, the determinantal form gives that $[R(U)]$ is equal to

$$[k + 1][R(u_1, \ldots, u_{n-k-2})] - [R(u_1, \ldots, u_{n-k-2}, +, u_{n-k}, \ldots, u_{n-1})].$$

This shows that the same argumentation goes through in the general case as well, and we have therefore proved

6.4.7 Theorem *For each up down sequence U the rule 6.4.4 yields the decomposition of $[R(U)]$ into its irreducible constituents, or, more formally:*

$$[R(U)] = [\tilde{R}(U)].$$

Therefore the number of permutations with sequence $(+-++---)$ is equal to

$$f^{(4,1^4)} + f^{(4,2,1^2)} + f^{(3,2,1^3)} + f^{(3^2,1^2)} = 35 + 90 + 64 + 56 = 245.$$

Summarizing we obtain the following result about Eulerian numbers:

6.4.8 Theorem *The Eulerian number $E(n,k)$, i.e. the number of elements $\pi \in S_{\underline{n}}$ containing exactly k ups, satisfies the equation*

$$E(n,k) = \sum_U f^{R(U)},$$

if the sum is taken over the $\binom{n-1}{k}$ up–down sequences U of length $n-1$ which contain exactly k entries $+$, and where $f^{R(U)}$ denotes the dimension of the skew representation $[R(U)]$. The summand $f^{R(U)}$ therefore satisfies the equation

$$f^{R(U)} = \sum_\beta ([R(U)], [\beta]) f^\beta,$$

where f^β denotes the dimension of $[\beta]$. The multiplicity $([R(U)], [\beta])$ of the irreducible constituent $[\beta]$ can be obtained by carrying out the procedure indicated by 6.4.4 which yields the decomposition of $[R(U)]$. Hence the Eulerian number $E(n,k)$ is the following linear combination of numbers of standard Young tableaux, the coefficients of which can be obtained via 6.4.4:

$$E(n,k) = \sum_{U:\, k \text{ ups}} \sum_\beta ([R(U)], [\beta]) f^\beta.$$

Moreover we have obtained a recursion for $f^{R(U)}$ by the number of downs in U:

6.4.9 Corollary *Let U denote an up–down sequence containing at least one entry $-$, say*

$$U = (u_1 \dots u_{n-1}) = (\underbrace{u_1 \dots u_{n-k-2}}_{=:\widetilde{U}} - \underbrace{+ \dots +}_{k}),$$

then we have the following recursion (on the number of entries $-$ of U):

$$f(U) = \binom{n}{k+1} f(\widetilde{U}) - f(\widetilde{U} + u_{n-k} \dots u_{n-1}),$$

where $f(+ \dots +) = 1$, and $f(\emptyset) = 1$.

For example $f(+) = 1$ yields that

$$f(-) = \binom{2}{1} f(\emptyset) - f(+) = 2 \cdot 1 - 1 = 1,$$

so that, using $f(++) = 1$, we obtain

$$f(+-) = \binom{3}{1} f(+) - f(++) = 3 \cdot 1 - 1 = 2,$$

$$f(-+) = \binom{3}{2} f(\emptyset) - f(++) = 3 \cdot 1 - 1 = 2,$$

$$f(--) = \binom{3}{1} f(-) - f(-+) = 3 \cdot 1 - 2 = 1,$$

and so on. Up–down sequences of particular interest are the *alternating* sequences, i.e. the sequences of the form $(- + - + \ldots)$, or $(+ - + - \ldots)$. Again we may assume that they end with an entry $+$, and we put

$$t_n := |\{\pi \in S_n \mid U\pi = (\ldots +) \text{ is alternating}\}|.$$

These numbers satisfy the following recursions (exercise 6.4.1):

6.4.10 Corollary *For odd numbers* $n = 2k + 1$ *we have*

$$t_n = (-1)^k + \sum_{i=1}^{k} (-1)^{i-1} t_{n-2i},$$

while, for even $n = 2k$, *the following is true:*

$$t_n = (-1)^{k-1} + \sum_{i=1}^{k-1} (-1)^{i-1} \binom{n}{2i} t_{n-2i}.$$

The starting values for these recursions are $t_1 = t_2 = 1$.

These numbers are often called the *Euler numbers* . They are in fact the coefficients in the tangens (for even n) and in the secans series (for odd n). The smallest of these numbers are shown in the following table:

$t_1 = 1$	$t_{10} = 50521$
$t_2 = 1$	$t_{11} = 353792$
$t_3 = 2$	$t_{12} = 2702765$
$t_4 = 5$	$t_{13} = 22368256$
$t_5 = 16$	$t_{14} = 199360981$
$t_6 = 61$	$t_{15} = 1903757312$
$t_7 = 272$	$t_{16} = 19391512145$
$t_8 = 1385$	$t_{17} = 209865342976$
$t_9 = 7936$	$t_{18} = 2404879675441$

Exercises

E 6.4.1 Check the recursions of 6.4.9.

6.5   Foulkes characters

The above considerations and results have shown that a natural generalization of the Eulerian numbers arises when we replace the *number $E(n,k)$* by the *character*

$$\chi^{n,k} := \sum_{U:k \ ups} \chi^{R(U)},$$

where the sum is taken over all the up–down sequences U of length $n - 1$ which contain exactly k entries $+$. Thus, first of all, the dimensions of these characters are the Eulerian numbers:

6.5.1 $\chi^{n,k}(1) = E(n,k).$

I call these characters the *Foulkes characters* since they were apparently discovered by H. O. Foulkes. According to 6.4.4 we have, for example, that

6.5.2 $\chi^{n,0} = \zeta^{(1^n)}, \ \chi^{n,n-1} = \zeta^{(n)}, \ \chi^{n,k} = \chi^{n,n-k-1} \otimes \zeta^{(1^n)}.$

The most important property of these characters is the fact that their value on $\pi \in S_n$ *does only depend on the number of cyclic factors of π*:

6.5.3 Theorem *If the elements $\pi, \rho \in S_n$ consist of the same number of cyclic factors, i.e. if $c(\pi) = c(\rho)$, then, for each k, we have*

$$\chi^{n,k}(\pi) = \chi^{n,k}(\rho).$$

Proof: By induction on n. We use that

$$\chi^{R(U)}(\pi) = \text{sum of the weights of all } (\alpha(U), \mu, \alpha(U)\backslash R(U))\text{--chains,}$$

where μ is a fixed improper partition, the summands μ_i of which are the lengths of the cyclic factors of π.

We have to take the sum over all these expressions, where U runs through all the $\binom{n-1}{k}$ up–down sequences containing k ups. From the corresponding rims $R(U)$ we obtain, by canceling the starting node, $\binom{n-1}{k}$ skew diagrams consisting of $n - 1$ nodes. Each of those either belongs to the $\binom{n-2}{k}$ up–down sequences of length $n - 2$ which still contain k ups or to the $\binom{n-2}{k-1}$ up–down sequences of length $n - 2$ with $k - 1$ ups, depending on the form of the rim which is either of the form

$$R_- = \begin{matrix} & \times \\ & \times \\ \cdot\cdot & \end{matrix} \quad \text{or of the form} \quad R_+ = \begin{matrix} & \times & \times \\ \cdot\cdot & \end{matrix}.$$

Denoting this shorter sequence of length $n - 2$ by U^*, we see that the proof amounts to show that there is a close connection between the

$$(\alpha(U), \mu, \alpha(U)\backslash R(U))\text{--chains}$$

and the

$$(\alpha(U^*), \mu^*, \alpha(U^*)\backslash R(U^*))\text{--chains.}$$

We therefore consider a fixed $(\alpha(U), \mu, \alpha(U)\backslash R(U))$– chain, assuming that the starting node is canceled together with a skew hook of length μ_i. This determines a $(\alpha(U^*), \mu^*, \alpha(U^*)\backslash R(U^*))$–chain, where

$$\mu^* := (\mu_1, \ldots, \mu_{i-1}, \mu_i - 1, \mu_{i+1}, \ldots).$$

In the case when $R(U)$ is of the form R_+, then the resulting shorter chain has the *same weight*, in case R_- the new weight is the opposite of the old one. This proves the helpful recursion

6.5.4
$$\chi_\mu^{n,k} = \underbrace{\chi_{\mu^*}^{n-1,k-1}}_{R_+} - \underbrace{\chi_{\mu^*}^{n-1,k}}_{R_-}.$$

Now the induction hypothesis yields, that the summands on the right hand side of this equation only depend on the number of cyclic factors, and this completes the proof. $\square$

This theorem allows us to introduce the following notation:

$$\chi_j^{n,k} := \chi^{n,k}(\pi), \text{ if } c(\pi) = j, j \in \underline{n},$$

and to define the *Foulkes table* F_n of $S_{\underline{n}}$ by

$$F_n := \quad
\begin{array}{c|cccc}
k \backslash j & n & n-1 & \cdots & 1 \\
\hline
0 & \chi_n^{n,0} & \chi_{n-1}^{n,0} & \cdots & \chi_1^{n,0} \\
\vdots & \vdots & \vdots & \vdots & \vdots \\
n-1 & \chi_n^{n,n-1} & \chi_{n-1}^{n,n-1} & \cdots & \chi_1^{n,n-1}
\end{array}.$$

This table is a square table consisting of n rows and columns, and we shall show in a minute that it is invertible. Let us evaluate, for example, the fourth row of F_5, which contains the character $\chi^{5,3}$. The up–down sequences of length $5 - 1 = 4$ containing 3 ups are the sequences

$$(+ + + -), (+ + - +), (+ - + +), (- + + +).$$

The corresponding Young diagrams (use 6.4.4) show that

6.5.5 $\chi^{5,3} = 4\zeta^{(4,1)} + 2\zeta^{(3,2)}.$

We therefore obtain from the character table of S_5 that

$$\chi_5^{5,3} = 26, \ \chi_4^{5,3} = 10, \ \chi_3^{5,3} = 2, \ \chi_2^{5,3} = -2, \ \chi_1^{5,3} = -4.$$

The complete Foulkes table of $S_{\underline{5}}$ is:

$$F_5 = \quad
\begin{array}{c|ccccc}
k \backslash j & 5 & 4 & 3 & 2 & 1 \\
\hline
0 & 1 & -1 & 1 & -1 & 1 \\
1 & 26 & -10 & 2 & 2 & -4 \\
2 & 66 & 0 & -6 & 0 & 6 \\
3 & 26 & 10 & 2 & -2 & -4 \\
4 & 1 & 1 & 1 & 1 & 1
\end{array}.$$

Further Foulkes tables can be found in the appendix. We note that 6.5.4 allows a recursive evaluation of the entries of F_n, except for the entries in the first column, for which we can use any recursion for the Eulerian numbers, see exercise 6.5.1:

6.5.6 Corollary *The Foulkes character values satisfy the recursion*

$$\chi_j^{n,k} = \chi_j^{n-1,k-1} - \chi_j^{n-1,k}, \text{ if } j < n, k > 0.$$

For $j = n$ we have

$$\chi_n^{n,k} = E(n,k),$$

while, for $k = 0$, we have

$$\chi_j^{n,0} = (-1)^{n-j}.$$

The starting value for the recursion is, of course,

$$\chi_1^{1,0} = 1.$$

Moreover we remark that from 6.4.4 it follows that

6.5.7 $$[\chi^{n,k} \mid \zeta^\alpha] > 0 \implies \alpha_1 \leq k+1, \alpha_1' \leq n - k.$$

Hence the particular hook constituent $[k+1, 1^{n-k-1}]$ is the only hook that occurs in $\chi^{n,k}$, and it occurs with multiplicity $\binom{n-1}{k}$. This implies

6.5.8 Theorem *The Foulkes characters $\chi^{n,k}$ are linearly independent over $\mathbb{Q}$, and each character $\chi: S_n \to \mathbb{Q}$, the value of which on π does only depend on $c(\pi)$, is a unique $\mathbb{Q}$–linear combination*

$$\chi = \sum_{k=0}^{n-1} m_k \cdot \chi^{n,k}$$

of the Foulkes characters. Moreover the coefficients m_k satisfy the condition

$$m_k = \left[\chi \mid \zeta^{(k+1,1^{n-k-1})}\right] \Big/ \binom{n-1}{k} \in \mathbb{N}.$$

An example is provided by 6.5.5. It is important to notice that this example shows that also

$$\frac{1}{2}\chi^{5,3}$$

is in fact a character the values of which do only depend on the numbers $c(\pi)$. Hence we *cannot* hope that such characters are $\mathbb{Z}$–linear combinations of Foulkes characters, and hence the preceding result cannot be sharpened in this way.

An important character to which the preceding theorem applies is the character $\chi^{(m)}$ of the natural action of $S_{\underline{n}}$ on $\underline{m}^{\underline{n}}$:

$$\chi^{(m)}(\pi) := m^{c(\pi)}.$$

If we assume the following theorem from representation theory of symmetric groups (cf. 5.2.20 in the book by James and Kerber):

6.5.9 $$[\chi^{(m)} \mid \zeta^\alpha] = \frac{f^\alpha}{n!} \prod_{(i,j)\in[\alpha]} (m - i + j),$$

then we obtain (since $\binom{n-1}{k}$ is the dimension of the hook representation $[k+1, 1^{n-k-1}]$):

6.5.10 Corollary *The character $\chi^{(m)}$ of the natural action of $S_{\underline{n}}$ on $\underline{m}^{\underline{n}}$ has the following decompositions into irreducibles and Foulkes characters:*

$$\chi^{(m)} = \sum_{\alpha \vdash n} \left(\prod_{(i,j)\in[\alpha]} \frac{m-i+j}{h_{ij}^\alpha} \right) \zeta^\alpha = \sum_{k=0}^{n-1} \binom{m+k}{n} \chi^{n,k}.$$

Hence in particular we have, for each $m, n \in \mathbb{N}^*$:

$$m^n = \sum_{k=0}^{n-1} \binom{m+k}{n} E(n,k).$$

Exercises

E 6.5.1 Derive the following recursion for the Eulerian numbers:

$$E(n,k) = (n-k)E(n-1,k-1) + (k+1)E(n-1,k), \text{ if } k > 0,$$

the starting value is $E(n,0) = 1$.

E 6.5.2 Prove 6.5.6.

6.6   Schubert polynomials

Now we are going to associate with each permutation π a so–called Schubert polynomial X_π. These polynomials have very interesting properties. For example they form a $\mathbb{Z}$–basis of the union of the polynomial rings $\mathbb{Z}[z_1, \ldots, x_n]$. Moreover, X_π is a monomial if $L(\pi)^+$ is a weakly decreasing sequence, and it is a Schur polynomial, if $L(\pi)$ is a weakly increasing sequence.

Consider the polynomial ring $\mathbb{Z}[z_1, \ldots, x_n]$ and the natural action

$$S_{\underline{n}} \times \mathbb{Z}[z_1, \ldots, x_n] \to \mathbb{Z}[z_1, \ldots, x_n] : (\pi, f) \mapsto f(x_{\pi 1}, \ldots, x_{\pi n}).$$

Hence, for each $f \in \mathbb{Z}[z_1, \ldots, x_n]$, and every elementary transposition σ_i in $\Sigma_{\underline{n}}$, we have a well defined $\sigma_i f \in \mathbb{Z}[z_1, \ldots, x_n]$, and so we can introduce, for each $i \leq n - 1$, the linear operator ∂_i on $\mathbb{Z}[z_1, \ldots, x_n]$ by putting

$$\partial_i f := \frac{f - \sigma_i f}{x_i - x_{i+1}}.$$

The resulting $\partial_i f$ is a polynomial which is symmetric in x_i and x_{i+1} (check this). Moreover, if f is already symmetric in x_i and x_{i+1}, then clearly $\partial_i f = 0$. In the case when f is homogeneous, then $\partial_i f$ is homogeneous, too, if it is nonzero, then its degree is the degree of f minus 1. The polynomial $\partial_i f$ is called a *divided difference*. For example

$$\partial_1 x_1^3 x_2^2 x_3^1 = \frac{x_1^3 x_2^2 x_3^1 - x_1^2 x_2^3 x_3^1}{x_1 - x_2} = x_1^2 x_2^2 x_3.$$

A straightforward check shows that these operators ∂_i satisfy the relations

6.6.1 $$\partial_i \partial_j = \begin{cases} 0 & \text{if } i = j \\ \partial_j \partial_i & \text{if } |i - j| > 1 \end{cases},$$

and

6.6.2 $$\partial_i \partial_{i+1} \partial_i = \partial_{i+1} \partial_i \partial_{i+1}.$$

They are crucial for

6.6.3 Theorem *For any finite sequence* $(i) := (i_1, \ldots, i_l), i_v \in \underline{n-1}$*, the following holds:*

- *If* $(i_1, \ldots, i_l) \in R(\pi^{-1}) \ni (j_1, \ldots, j_l)$*, for some* $\pi \in S_{\underline{n}}$*, then*

$$\partial_{i_1} \ldots \partial_{i_l} = \partial_{j_1} \ldots \partial_{j_l},$$

and hence to each $\pi \in S_{\underline{n}}$ *there corresponds a unique operator*

$$\partial_\pi := \partial_{(i)} := \partial_{i_1} \ldots \partial_{i_l}.$$

- *If $(i_1,\ldots,i_l)$ is* not *a reduced sequence, then*

$$\partial_{i_1}\ldots\partial_{i_l}=0,$$

the zero mapping on $\mathbb{Z}[z_1,\ldots,x_n]$.

Proof: The first item will be proved by induction on the reduced length $l=l(\pi)$. If $l=0$, then $\pi=id$, the identity element. The corresponding operator is $\partial_\emptyset$, the identity mapping, and therefore the statement holds in this case.

Let us consider the case when $l>0$. The induction hypothesis says that, if $i_1=j_1$ or $i_l=j_l$, the corresponding operators $\partial_{(i)}$ and $\partial_{(j)}$ are equal. In the other cases we shall apply the Exchange Lemma 1.3.29. Consider the sequence

$$(\hat{i}):=(j_1,i_1,\ldots,\hat{i}_k,\ldots,i_l)\in R(\pi^{-1}),$$

and the corresponding operator $\partial_{(\hat{i})}$.

If $k\neq l$, then $\partial_{(j)}=\partial_{(\hat{i})}=\partial_{(i)}$, by induction hypothesis, and the statement holds in this case.

If $k=l$, we distinguish two cases:

- If $|j_1-i_1|>1$, then $\sigma_{i_1}\sigma_{j_1}=\sigma_{j_1}\sigma_{i_1}$, and so

$$(i'):=(i_1,j_1,i_2,\ldots,i_{l-1})\in R(\pi^{-1}),$$

moreover $\partial_{(i')}=\partial_{(\hat{i})}$, and hence we have

$$\partial_{(i)}=\partial_{(i')}=\partial_{(\hat{i})}=\partial_{(j)},$$

by the induction hypothesis.

- In the case when $|j_1-i_1|=1$, we consider $(\hat{i})$, which is

$$(j_1,i_1,\ldots,i_{l-1}),$$

so that, by the Exchange Lemma, one of the following three sequences is contained in $R(\pi^{-1})$, too:

$$(a):=(i_1,i_1,\ldots,i_{l-1}),$$

$$(b):=(i_1,j_1,i_2,\ldots,i_{l-2}),$$

$$(c):=(i_1,j_1,i_1,\ldots,\hat{i}_r,\ldots,i_{l-1}),$$

where $r \geq 2$ in the last case. Easy checks show that neither (a) nor (b) correspond to a reduced decomposition of π^{-1}, so that we obtain (c) $\in R(\pi^{-1})$. Now $|i - j| = 1$ implies that $\partial_{i_1} \partial_{j_1} \partial_{i_1} = \partial_{j_1} \partial_{i_1} \partial_{j_1}$, and hence also

$$(d) := (j_1, i_1, j_1, \ldots, \hat{i}_r, \ldots, i_{l-1}) \in R(\pi^{-1}).$$

This sequence serves very well for a completion of the proof:

$$\partial_{(j)} = \partial_{(d)} = \partial_{(c)} = \partial_{(i)}.$$

This completes the proof of the first item.

The second item will be proved by induction on the length l of the sequence $(i) := (i_1, \ldots, i_l)$, which is now assumed *not to be a reduced sequence*, so that in particular $l \geq 2$.

If $l = 2$, then $i_1 = i_2$, since otherwise $\sigma_{i_1} \sigma_{i_2}$ were a reduced decomposition. Hence $l = 2$ implies $\partial_{(i)} = 0$, by 6.6.1. For the inductive step we can therefore assume that $l \geq 3$ and that $(i_2, \ldots, i_l)$ is a reduced sequence, since in all the other cases $\partial_{(i)} = 0$, as it is stated. We put

$$\rho^{-1} := \sigma_{i_2} \cdots \sigma_{i_l}, \text{ and } \pi^{-1} := \sigma_{i_1} \cdots \sigma i_l = \sigma_{i_1} \rho^{-1}.$$

Since (i) is not reduced, $l(\pi) = l(\pi^{-1}) \leq l - 1$, and so, by 1.3.26, $l(\pi) = l(\rho \sigma_{i_1}) = l - 2$, or, equivalently, $l(\rho) = \overset{\cdot}{l}(\pi \sigma_{i_1}) = l(\pi) + 1$, and

$$\partial_{(i)} = \partial_{i_1} \partial_\rho = (\partial_{i_1})^2 \partial_\pi = 0,$$

which completes the proof.

□

Now we recall that

$$\omega_n := [n \ldots 1] = (1, n)(2, n - 1) \ldots = \omega_n^{-1}$$

is the permutation of maximal reduced length in S_n: $l(\omega_n) = \binom{n}{2}$. Using this permutation we can associate with an arbitrary permutation $\pi \in S_n$ the operator $\partial_{\omega_n \pi}$. We apply this operator to the monomial

$$X^E := X^{E_n} := x_1^{n-1} x_2^{n-2} \ldots x_{n-1}^1,$$

obtaining the *Schubert polynomial*

$$X_\pi := \partial_{\omega_n \pi} X^E.$$

For example, if $n := 4$ and $\pi := (132)$, so that $\omega_n\pi = [2431]$, $L(\omega_n\pi) = \overline{1210}$, $l(\omega_n\pi) = 4$, and

$$\omega_n\pi = (34)(12)(23)(34) = \sigma_3\sigma_1\sigma_2\sigma_3$$

is a reduced decomposition. We obtain

$$X_{(132)} = \partial_3\partial_1\partial_2\partial_3 x_1^3 x_2^2 x_3 = \partial_3\partial_1\partial_2 \frac{x_1^3 x_2^2 x_3 - x_1^3 x_2^2 x_4}{x_3 - x_4}$$

$$= \partial_3\partial_1\partial_2 x_1^3 x_2^2 = \partial_3\partial_1 \frac{x_1^3 x_2^2 - x_1^3 x_3^2}{x_1 - x_2}$$

$$= \partial_3\partial_1(x_1^3 x_2 + x_1^3 x_3) = \partial_3 x_1^3 x_2 + x_1^3 x_3 - x_2^3 x_1 - x_2^3 x_3$$

$$= \partial_3(x_1^2 x_2 + x_1 x_2^2 + x_1^2 x_3 + x_1 x_2 x_3 + x_2^2 x_3) = x_1^2 + x_1 x_2 + x_2^2.$$

6.6.4 Lemma *The Schubert polynomials $X_\pi \in \mathbb{Z}[z_1,\ldots,x_n]$ have the following properties:*

- *The polynomial X_π is homogeneous with rational integral coefficients.*

- *The degree of X_π is equal to the reduced length of π.*

- *In the case when $\pi(i) < \pi(i+1)$, the polynomial X_π is symmetric in x_i and x_{i+1}.*

- *The application of ∂_i has the following effect:*

$$\partial_i X_\pi = \begin{cases} X_{\pi\sigma_i} & \text{if } \pi(i) > \pi(i+1) \\ 0 & \text{otherwise.} \end{cases}$$

- *In particular we have:* ·

$$X_{\omega_n} = X^E, \quad X_1 = 1.$$

The checks are easy and left as exercise 6.6.2. The main property of Schubert polynomials is that they generalize Schur polynomials and that they form a $\mathbb{Z}$–basis of $\mathbb{Z}[X] := \cup_n \mathbb{Z}[z_1,\ldots,x_n]$. The last statement will follow from the next two lemmas.

6.6.5 Lemma *For each monomial $X^D := x_1^{d_1} \cdots x_n^{d_n}$ that occurs in $\partial_\pi X^E$ with a nonzero coefficient, we have that $D \le E$, which means that for all v we have $d_v \le n - v$.*

Proof: By induction on the reduced length $k := l(\pi)$. The case $k = 0$ is trivial since $\pi = 1$.

For the inductive step we assume that there exists a reduced decomposition of the form $\pi^{-1} = \sigma_i \cdots$ and we put $\pi' := \sigma_i \pi$. Since $l(\pi') = l(\pi) - 1$, the induction hypothesis applies to π'. The monomial summand X^D of $\partial_\pi X^E = \partial_i \partial_{\pi'} X^E$ is a summand of some

$$\partial_i X^B = \frac{X^B - \sigma_i X^B}{x_i - x_{i+1}},$$

X^B being a monomial summand of $\partial_{\pi'} X^E$. Hence the induction hypothesis applies to X^B: $B \leq E$. We distinguish three cases:

i) If $b_i = b_{i+1}$, then $\partial_i X^B = 0$, as X^B is symmetric in x_i and x_{i+1}. This cannot happen since X^D was supposed to occur.

ii) If $b_i > b_{i+1}$, then, by long division,

$$\partial_i X^B = \cdots x_i^{b_i-1} x_{i+1}^{b_{i+1}} \cdots$$

$$+ \cdots x_i^{b_i-2} x_{i+1}^{b_{i+1}+1} \cdots + \ldots + \cdots x_i^{b_{i+1}} x_{i+1}^{b_i-1} \cdots.$$

This gives the following inequalities for the exponents of X^D:

$$d_i \leq b_{i+1}, \text{ and } d_{i+1} \leq b_{i+1},$$

and hence the induction hypothesis, applied to the elements of B, gives

$$d_i \leq n - i, \text{ and } d_{i+1} \leq n - (i + 1),$$

as it is stated.

iii) If $b_i < b_{i+1}$, then

$$\partial_i X^B = - \cdots x_i^{b_{i+1}-1} x_{i+1}^{b_i} \cdots$$

$$- \cdots x_i^{b_{i+1}-2} x_{i+1}^{b_i+1} \cdots - \ldots - x_i^{b_i} x_{i+1}^{b_{i+1}-1} \cdots.$$

This shows that

$$d_i \leq b_i \leq n - i, d_{i+1} \leq b_i < b_{i+1} \leq n - (i + 1),$$

which completes the proof.

$\square$

6.6.6 Lemma *Assume that the monomial* $X^D = x_1^{d_1} \cdots x_n^{d_n}$ *occurs in* $\partial_\pi X^E$ *with nonzero coefficient, and suppose that D is the lexicographically smallest sequence of exponents with this property. Then*

- *The sequence D satisfies the equation*

$$D = E - L(\pi) := (n - 1 - l_1(\pi), \ldots, 1 - l_{n-1}(\pi), l_n(\pi)),$$

and

- *the coefficient of X^D in $\partial_\pi X_\pi$ is equal to 1.*

Proof: By induction on the reduced length $l(\pi)$ of π. The case $l(\pi) = 0$, which means $\pi = 1$, is trivial, since $X_1 = 1$, as we mentioned already, and $L(1) = \overline{0\ldots0}$, so that $E - L(\pi) = E$ in this case, and the statement holds in this case.

Consider now a permutation with reduced length $l(\pi) = k > 0$. There exists an m such that

$$L(\pi) = \overline{l_1 \ldots l_m 0 \ldots 0}, \text{ and } l_m \neq 0.$$

According to the position of m we distinguish the following two cases:
i) In the case when $m = n - 1$, we have that $L(\pi) = \overline{\ldots 10}$ and $\pi(n-1) > \pi(n)$. We put

$$\rho := L^{-1}(\overline{\ldots l_{n-2}00}), \text{ i. e. } \rho = \pi\sigma_{n-1}, \text{ by } 1.3.22.$$

Thus $\partial_\pi X^E = \partial_{n-1}\partial_\rho X^E$. The induction hypothesis yields that the monomial X^C in $\partial_\rho X^E$ with lexicographically smallest C satisfies

$$C = E - L(\rho) = (\ldots, 2 - l_{n-2}, 1, 0).$$

Since ∂_{n-1} only affects x_{n-1} and x_n, we have

$$X^D = \partial_{n-1}X^C = \frac{X^C - \sigma_{n-1}X^C}{x_{n-1} - x_n}$$

$$= X^{(\ldots, 2 - l_{n-2}, 0, 0)} = X^{E - L(\pi)}.$$

ii) In the case when $m < n - 1$ we put

$$\rho := L^{-1}(\overline{\ldots l_{m-1}, 0, l_m - 1, 0 \ldots 0}),$$

so that, by 1.3.22, $\rho = \pi\sigma_m$, and therefore $\partial_\pi X^E = \partial_m \partial_\rho X^E$. The monomial X^C in $\partial_\rho X^E$ with lexicographically smallest C has $C = E - L(\rho)$, which is the sequence

$$(\ldots, n - m + 1 - l_{m-1}, n - m, n - m - l_m, n - m - 2, \ldots, 1, 0).$$

The other monomials X^B occurring in $\partial_\rho X^E$ have lexicographically bigger sequences B of exponents and we distinguish two cases according to the relationship between $(b_1, \ldots, b_{m-1})$ and $(c_1, \ldots, c_{m-1})$.

1. Assume first that $(b_1, \ldots, b_{m-1}) > (c_1, \ldots, c_{m-1})$. As ∂_m only affects x_m and x_{m+1}, all these B are lexicographically bigger than the sequences of the monomials in $\partial_m X^C$, which, by long division, is equal to

$$\cdots x_m^{n-m-1} x_{m+1}^{n-m-l_m} \cdots + \cdots x_m^{n-m-2} x_{m+1}^{n-m-l_m+1} \cdots$$
$$+ \ldots + \cdots x_m^{n-m-l_m} x_{m+1}^{n-m-1} \cdots .$$

The last one of these summands is clearly the lexicographically smallest sequence D of exponents, and $D = E - L(\pi)$, moreover, the coefficient is 1, so that the statements hold in this particular case.

2. Finally we consider the case $(b_1, \ldots, b_{m-1}) = (c_1, \ldots, c_{m-1})$: As $c_m = n - m$, b_m cannot be bigger, by 6.6.5, and therefore it suffices to consider sequences B such that

$$(b_1, \ldots, b_m) = (c_1, \ldots, c_m), \text{ and } b_{m+1} > c_{m+1} = n - m - l_m.$$

Consider such a monomial summand X^B of $\partial_\rho X^E$. It contributes $\partial_m X^B$ to $\partial_\pi X^E$. Long division shows that the lexicographically smallest sequence of exponents which thereby occurs is

$$A := (b_1, \ldots, b_{m+1}, n - m - 1, b_{m+2}, \ldots) > C,$$

which completes the proof.

□

Since $L(\omega_n \pi) = E - L(\pi)$, this has the following consequence:

6.6.7 Corollary *The monomial X^D occurring in the Schubert polynomial X_π with lexicographically smallest sequence D of exponents is $X^D = X^{L(\pi)}$, and its coefficient is 1.*

This has very important implications. To begin with we note that, by 6.6.7, the Schubert polynomials $X_\pi, \pi \in S_n$, form a $\mathbb{Z}$-basis of the abelian subgroup generated by the monomials $X^B, B \leq E_n$, in formal terms:

6.6.8 $\quad \mathbb{Z}_E[x_1, \ldots, x_n] := \langle X^B \mid B \leq E_n \rangle_{\mathbb{Z}} = \ll X_\pi \mid \pi \in S_n \gg_{\mathbb{Z}} .$

Now we consider the ring of polynomials

$$\mathbb{Z}[X] := \bigcup_{n>0} \mathbb{Z}[z_1, \ldots, x_n],$$

together with the group

$$\mathscr{S} := \bigcup_{n>0} S_{\underline{n}},$$

using the natural embeddings of $\mathbb{Z}[z_1,\ldots,x_n]$ into $\mathbb{Z}[x_1,\ldots,x_m]$ and of $S_{\underline{n}}$ into $\mathscr{S}$, for each $n < m$. Let us see what happens with X_π, if we use this natural embedding of $S_{\underline{n}}$ into $S_{\underline{n+1}}$:

$$S_{\underline{n}} \hookrightarrow S_{\underline{n+1}} : \pi \mapsto \pi',$$

where $S_{\underline{n}}$ is mapped onto the set of elements π' that keep the point $n+1$ fixed. Since

$$X_{\pi'} = \partial_{\omega'_n \pi'} X^{E'} = \partial_{\omega_n \pi} \partial'_n \cdots \partial'_1 X^{E'} = \partial_{\omega_n \pi} X^E,$$

we obtain the following helpful result:

6.6.9 $X_\pi = X_{\pi'},$

which shows that the Schubert polynomials are invariant under embedding. We can therefore introduce the Schubert polynomial X_π for any $\pi \in \mathscr{S}$. As any monomial X^B satisfies $B \leq E_n$, for n large enough, the following is now obtained from 6.6.8:

6.6.10 Theorem *The Schubert polynomials* $X_\pi, \pi \in S_{\underline{n}}, n > 0$, *form a* $\mathbb{Z}$*–basis of* $\mathbb{Z}[X]$:

$$\mathbb{Z}[X] = \ll X_\pi \mid \pi \in \mathscr{S} \gg_{\mathbb{Z}}.$$

The coefficients of the $\mathbb{Z}$*–linear combination of Schubert polynomials which is equal to* $p \in \mathbb{Z}[X]$ *can be obtained by successive applications of 6.6.7.*

For example,

$$p := x_1 + x_1 x_2 + x_1 x_2 x_3 + x_1 x_2 x_3 x_4$$

has lexicographically smallest monomial summand $x_1 = X_{(12)}$, while the lexicographically smallest monomial which occurs in $p - X_{(12)}$ is $x_1 x_2 = X_{(123)}$, and so on. We finally obtain in this way that

$$p = X_{(12)} + X_{(123)} + X_{(1234)} + X_{(12345)}.$$

Certain Schubert polynomials are easily seen to be monomials. In fact, if $D \leq E$ is weakly decreasing, then there exists an i such that $d_i > d_{i+1}$, and so

$$X^D = \partial_i x_1^{d_1} \cdots x_i^{d_i+1} x_{i+1}^{d_i} \cdots,$$

and therefore, by decreasing induction we obtain

6.6.11 Corollary *For weakly decreasing sequences D of exponents we have that, for $\pi := L^{-1}(d_1 \ldots d_n)$, the following is true:*

$$X_\pi = X^D,$$

or, in formal terms,

$$X^D = X_{L^{-1}(D)}.$$

Thus weakly *decreasing* sequences D lead to monomials, and it is surprising to see that weakly *increasing* sequences lead to Schur polynomials. The proof is cumbersome but elementary. Let us consider its main steps.

The determinantal formula for Schur polynomials $\{\alpha, X\}$ over the set of indeterminates X reads as follows (recall 4.5.6):

$$\{\alpha, X\} = \det \left(\{\alpha_i + j - i, X\} \right).$$

(Recall that, by definition, $\{0, X\} := 1$, and $\{m, X\} := 0$, if $m < 0$.)

If we replace the set X of indeterminates of the Schur polynomials in the i-th row by the *subset* $\{x_1, \ldots, x_i\}$, then we obtain the *multi Schur polynomial*. For $\alpha := (\alpha_1, \ldots, \alpha_h) \vdash n$, where $\alpha_h > 0$, it is defined to be

$$\{\alpha, \{x_1\}, \ldots, \{x_1, \ldots, x_h\}\} := \det \left(\{\alpha_i + j - i, \{x_1, \ldots, x_i\}\} \right).$$

These polynomials have very interesting properties. The application of ∂_j amounts to the application of ∂_j to the j-th row of the determinant, since the other rows are symmetric in x_j and x_{j+1}. Moreover, it is not difficult to derive from the definitions of ∂_i and of $\{m\}$, that

$$\partial_j \{m, \{x_1, \ldots, x_j\}\} = \{m - 1, \{x_1, \ldots, x_{j+1}\}\}.$$

For example $\{(3, 2, 1), \{x_1\}, \ldots, \{x_1, x_2, x_3\}\}$ is equal to

$$\det \begin{pmatrix} x_1^3 & x_1^4 & x_1^5 \\ x_1 + x_2 & x_1^2 + x_1 x_2 + x_2^2 & x_1^3 + x_1^2 x_2 + x_1 x_2^2 + x_2^3 \\ 0 & 1 & x_1 + x_2 + x_3 \end{pmatrix}$$

$$= x_1^3 x_2^2 x_3^1,$$

and

$$\partial_3\{(3,2,1),\{x_1\},\dots,\{x_1,x_2,x_3\}\} = \partial_3 x_1^3 x_2^2 x_3^1 = x_1^3 x_2^2$$

$$= \det \begin{pmatrix} x_1^3 & x_1^4 & x_1^5 \\ x_1 + x_2 & x_1^2 + x_1 x_2 + x_2^2 & x_1^3 + x_1^2 x_2 + x_1 x_2^2 + x_2^3 \\ 0 & 0 & 1 \end{pmatrix}.$$

More generally, the following holds (exercise 6.6.3):

$$6.6.12 \qquad \{\alpha, \{x_1\}, \dots, \{x_1, \dots, x_h\}\} = X^\alpha := x_1^{\alpha_1} \cdots x_h^{\alpha_h}.$$

From this equation we obtain by induction, since the longest element $\omega_h \in S_{\underline{h}}$ and the longest element ω_{h-1} in the subgroup $S_{\underline{h-1}}$ (the stabilizer of 1) satisfy

$$\omega_h = \sigma_{h-1} \cdots \sigma_1 \omega_{h-1},$$

the identity

$$\partial_{\omega_h}\{\alpha, \{x_1\}, \dots, \{x_1, \dots, x_h\}\} = \{\alpha_1 - (h-1), \dots, \alpha_{h-1} - 1, \alpha_h, X\},$$

and from this we finally can derive

$$6.6.13 \qquad \partial_{\omega_h} X^{E+\alpha} = \{\alpha, X\}.$$

For example,

$$\partial_{\omega_2} X^{E+(3,2)} = \partial_1 x_1^4 x_2^2 = x_1^3 x_2^2 + x_1^2 x_2^3 = \{(3,2),\{x_1,x_2\}\}.$$

We are now in a position to prove that increasing sequences lead to Schur polynomials:

6.6.14 Theorem (Lascoux/Schützenberger) *Let* $D = (d_1, \dots, d_n)$ *denote a weakly increasing sequence of natural numbers and* α *the proper partition obtained by reordering the* d_i. *If* $\pi^{-1} \in \mathscr{S}$ *has reduced Lehmer code* D:

$$L(\pi^{-1})^+ = \overline{d_1 \dots d_n},$$

then

$$X_\pi = \{\alpha, \{x_1, \dots, x_n\}\}.$$

Proof: We put $m := \alpha_1 + n = d_n + n$, and we define the natural numbers k_i by

$$L((\omega_m \pi)^{-1})^+ = E_m - D = \overline{k_1, \ldots, k_n, m-n-1, \ldots, 1}.$$

Thus $k_j = m - j - d_j > m - (j+1) - d_{j+1} = k_{j+1}$, which means that the k_i form a strictly decreasing sequence of natural numbers. We can therefore apply 1.3.22, obtaining

$$(\omega_m \pi)^{-1} = L^{-1}(\overline{k_n, \ldots, k_1 - (n-1), m-n-1, \ldots, 1})\omega_n.$$

We now define a permutation ρ by

$$(\omega_m \rho)^{-1} := L^{-1}(\overline{k_n, \ldots, k_1 - (n-1), m-n-1, \ldots, 1}).$$

The above equation shows in particular, that a reduced decomposition of $(\omega_m \pi)^{-1}$ can be obtained by multiplying a reduced decomposition of $(\omega_m \rho)^{-1}$ by a reduced decomposition of ω_n, and therefore $\partial_{\omega_m \pi} = \partial_{\omega_n} \partial_{\omega_m \rho}$. This gives

$$X_\pi = \partial_{\omega_n} \partial_{\omega_m \rho} X^{E_m} = \partial_{\omega_n} X_\rho.$$

Hence, by 6.6.11, it suffices to prove that

$$X_\rho = X^{E_n + \alpha}.$$

This identity follows, by an application of 6.6.13, from

$$L(\rho)^+ = \overline{m - 1 - k_n, \ldots, m - n - (k_1 - (n-1)), 0, \ldots, 0}$$

$$= \overline{n - 1 + d_{n+1-1}, \ldots, n - n + d_{n+1-n}},$$

which is a decreasing sequence.

$\square$

Hence the Schubert polynomials generalize the Schur polynomials. Since they form a basis of the union of the $\mathbb{Z}[z_1, \ldots, x_n]$, they can also serve for a different approach to the Littelwood–Richardson Rule. This will not be described in detail here since lack of space, but it should be mentioned that this approach (introduced by Lascoux and Schützenberger) is very well suited for computer calculations, and therefore it was chosen for the corresponding procedure in the program system SYMCHAR. For this reason I add a section with the 120 first Schubert polynomials to the appendix of tables.

Exercises

E 6.6.1 Show that, for each $f, g \in \mathbb{Z}[X]$ and $1 \leq i \leq n - 1$

$$\partial_i(fg) = (\partial_i f)\sigma_i g + f(\partial_i g).$$

E 6.6.2 Prove 6.6.4.

E 6.6.3 Show that 6.6.12 is true.

Chapter 7

Constructions

We have counted the orbits of finite groups on finite sets and successively refined our methods by introducing enumeration by weight as well as enumeration by weight and stabilizer class. Moreover we discussed actions on structured sets like posets and semigroups. Later on the permutation group representations were refined by introducing linear representations, which led to applications in both directions. It remains to discuss the most difficult problem, the construction of a transversal of the orbits.

We shall briefly discuss the general case of this problem, in order to introduce the concept of Sims chains, for cases when the acting group is given by generators and relations. We shall then use it in a detailed description of a direct evaluation of a transversal of the orbits of G on Y^X with prescribed content λ. After that we describe a recursive method, using recursion on $|Y|$, and combining this recursion with the orderly generation method that was introduced by R. C. Read.

These methods can be used for the evaluation of catalogues of discrete structures that can be defined as orbits of finite groups on finite sets, and in particular of discrete structures which can be considered as symmetry classes of mappings. For example, a catalogue of all the graphs on $v \leq 10$ points was obtained in this way, as well as a catalogue of 0-1-matrices under the action of the direct product of the symmetric groups on the rows and columns (the *contexts* that are of interest for the concept analysis).

It is clear that for higher v it is nearly impossible to get such a catalogue of graphs, its cardinality is much too big. But nevertheless there are cases where one wants to try a hypothesis on graphs on 15 or 20 vertices, say. In these cases we can apply a recent and very important method of generating orbit representatives uniformly at random, which will also be described. It can be used, for example, in order to test graph invariants, and to do all kinds of examinations of structures that can be defined as orbits of finite actions by inspection of big sets of examples. It helps, say, easily to get nonisomorphic labelled graphs with same edge degree sequence and same characteristic polynomial, if we want to demonstrate that these two invariants are not complete, even if we put them together.

Finally we shall describe the corresponding problem in linear representation theory which is the evaluation of symmetry adapted bases. Such bases serve very well whenever there are symmetries.

7.1 Orbit evaluation

We consider a finite action $_G X$ in order to evaluate particular orbits, the whole set of orbits, a transversal of the orbits, stabilizers, and so on. It is clear that for all these calculations the orbit evaluation is basic, hence let us discuss this first.

In the case when both $|X|$ and $|G|$ or $|\bar{G}|$ are very small and G or $\bar{G}$ is given as a *set* together with the operation of each of its elements, then we may just apply this set to x in order to get the desired orbit $G(x)$. But quite often it is so that G is given by a set of generators: $G = \langle g_1, \ldots, g_r \rangle$, together with the actions of the g_i on X. Then, for $x \in X$, we can put

$$\Omega_0 := \{x\}, \text{ and } \Omega_i := \bigcup_{j=1}^{r} g_j \Omega_{i-1}, i \in \mathbb{N}^*.$$

It is obvious that the smallest i such that $\Omega_i = \Omega_{i-1}$ satisfies

7.1.1 $G(x) = \Omega_{i-1}.$

The concrete implementation of this way of evaluating $G(x)$ of course may heavily depend on our knowledge of X, G and $_G X$. For example, if $|X| = 1$, then $G(x) = \Omega_0$, while $G(x) = X$, if $|G\backslash\backslash X| = 1$, so that the Cauchy-Frobenius lemma can serve as a *stopping rule*. The knowledge of $|G\backslash\backslash X|$ is helpful in particular if we are after the whole set of orbits $G\backslash\backslash X$, in which case we proceed with the remaining subset $X\backslash G(x)$ correspondingly. The implementation of this method is obvious.

It is clear that a careful implementation of this procedure also yields products of the generators which lead from x to any other element of its orbit, and which therefore form a transversal of G/G_x. Thus we can also obtain generators of the stabilizer G_x by an application of the following fact:

7.1.2 Lemma (Schreier) *If U is a subgroup of $G = \langle g_1, \ldots, g_r \rangle$ which is finite and which decomposes as follows into left cosets of U:*

$$G = \bigcup_{i=1}^{s} h_i U, \quad where \ h_1 = 1,$$

and if the mapping ϕ is defined by

$$\phi : G \to \{h_1, \ldots, h_s\} : g \mapsto h_i, \ if \ g \in h_i U,$$

then U is generated by the elements $\phi(g_i h_k)^{-1} g_i h_k$:

$$U = \langle \phi(g_i h_k)^{-1} g_i h_k \mid i \in \underline{r}, k \in \underline{s} \rangle.$$

Proof: Assume that $u = a_1 \ldots a_t \in U$, where the a_i are elements of the generating set $\{g_1, \ldots, g_r\}$. We put

$$u_i := a_i \ldots a_t, \quad and \quad x_i := \phi(u_i),$$

so that in particular $x_1 = \phi(u) = 1$. Putting $x_{t+1} := 1$, we can rewrite u in the form

$$u = (x_1^{-1} a_1 x_2)(x_2^{-1} a_2 x_3) \ldots (x_t^{-1} a_t x_{t+1}).$$

Now $x_i = \phi(u_i) = \phi(a_i u_{i+1}) = \phi(a_i x_{i+1})$, for $x_{i+1} = \phi(u_{i+1})$ means that $u_{i+1} = x_{i+1} u'$, for a suitable $u' \in U$, and hence $a_i u_{i+1} = a_i x_{i+1} u$. Thus

$$u = \phi(a_1 x_2)^{-1} a_1 x_2 \phi(a_2 x_3)^{-1} a_2 x_3 \ldots,$$

which completes the proof.

□

A direct evaluation of the stabilizer G_x will be discussed later. In the case when X is too big to be stored, we can do the following in order to evaluate the set of orbits. We number the elements of X, being now faced with an operation of G on $\underline{n}$, say, so that there is a *canonic* transversal of $G \backslash\backslash \underline{n}$, consisting of the smallest orbit elements. So we take $1 \in \underline{n}$ as the first element of the desired transversal. Then we evaluate the minimal $i \in \underline{n}$ which is not contained in $G(1)$, take this point i as the second element of the transversal and evaluate the minimal $j \in \underline{n}$ that is not in $G(i)$ and bigger than i. There are now two cases. Either there is a $g \in G$ such that $gj < j$, in which case $j \in G(1)$, or there is no such g, so $j \notin G(1) \cup G(i)$, and therefore j has to be taken as the third element of the transversal, and so on.

In order to evaluate this canonic transversal of $G\backslash\backslash\underline{n}$ in an economic way we can use a problem oriented description of the elements of $\bar{G}$ so that not too many checks are necessary. We therefore introduce the *pointwise* stabilizer of the subset $\underline{k} \subseteq \underline{n}$ which we denote as follows:

$$C_{\bar{G}}(\underline{k}) := \{\pi \in \bar{G} \mid \forall i \in \underline{k} : \pi i = i\}.$$

We call this group the *centralizer* of $\underline{k}$ in order to distinguish it from the *setwise* stabilizer

$$N_{\bar{G}}(\underline{k}) := \{\pi \in \bar{G} \mid \pi\underline{k} = \underline{k}\},$$

which we call the *normalizer* of $\underline{k}$. (Correspondingly in the general case $_GX$ we have $C_{\bar{G}}(M)$ and $N_{\bar{G}}(M)$ for subsets $M \subseteq X$.) These centralizers form the chain of subgroups

$$\{1\} = C_{\bar{G}}(\underline{n}) \leq C_{\bar{G}}(\underline{n-1}) \leq \ldots \leq C_{\bar{G}}(\underline{0}) = \bar{G}.$$

Hence there exists a smallest $b \in \underline{n}$ such that

7.1.3 $$\{1\} = C_{\bar{G}}(\underline{b}) \leq \ldots \leq C_{\bar{G}}(\underline{0}) = \bar{G}.$$

We call $\underline{b}$ the *base* of the action of G on $\underline{n}$, b its *length*, and 7.1.3 the *Sims chain* of this action. Now we consider the left coset decompositions

$$C_{\bar{G}}(\underline{i-1}) = \bigcup_{j=1}^{r(i)} \pi_j^{(i)} C_{\bar{G}}(\underline{i}),$$

and note that each $\pi \in \bar{G}$ can uniquely be written in terms of these coset representatives as follows:

7.1.4 $$\pi = \pi_{j_1}^{(1)} \ldots \pi_{j_b}^{(b)}.$$

Hence in particular the following holds:

7.1.5 $$|\bar{G}| = \prod_{i=1}^{b} r(i).$$

This shows that storing the $\pi_j^{(i)}, i \in \underline{b}, j \in \underline{r(i)}$, allows an economic way to deal with the elements of $\bar{G}$. Moreover, as $\pi_j^{(i)} k = k$, if $i > k$, the following is true for the orbit of $k \in \underline{n}$ under G:

7.1.6 $$G(k) = \{\pi_{j_1}^{(1)} \ldots \pi_{j_k}^{(k)} i \mid j_1 \in \underline{r(1)}, \ldots, j_b \in \underline{r(k)}\}.$$

Thus the knowledge of the Sims chain considerably reduces the number of necessary checks for an orbit evaluation. The calculation of the base is therefore very important.

7.1.7 Example Let us consider for example the action of S_p on the set of 2–element subsets of $\underline{p}$. In order to evaluate the base of $\bar{G} = S_p^{[2]}$ we first of all embed the set of 2–element subsets into $\underline{n}$, where $n := \binom{p}{2}$, by ordering the pairs lexicographically:

$$\{1, 2\} < \{1, 3\} < \ldots < \{1, p\} < \{2, p\} < \ldots < \{p - 1, p\},$$

and by replacing the pairs correspondingly by the natural numbers $1, \ldots, \binom{p}{2}$. An easy check shows that, according to this numbering, the following chain of canonic Young subgroups

$$S_p \geq S_{(2,p-2)} \geq S_{(1,1,p-3)} \geq \ldots \geq S_{(1,\ldots,1,2)} \geq \{1\}$$

yields via embedding the Sims chain

$$\bar{G} = S_p^{[2]} \geq S_{(2,p-2)}^{[2]} \geq S_{(1,1,p-3)}^{[2]} \geq \ldots \geq S_{(1,\ldots,1,2)}^{[2]} \geq \{1\}.$$

Thus $p - 2$ is the base for the canonic action of $S_p^{[2]}$ on the set of 2–element subsets and its lexicographic ordering. Hence in particular for $p := 5$ we obtain the Sims chain (with respect to the above numbering of the pairs of points)

$$S_5^{[2]} \geq S_{(2,3)}^{[2]} \geq S_{(1,1,1,2)}^{[2]} \geq \{1\}.$$

$\diamond$

Another helpful property of the base is described in

7.1.8 Lemma *The elements* $\pi \in \bar{G}$ *are uniquely determined by their action on the base* $\underline{b}$.

Proof: If $\pi i = \rho i$, for each $i \in \underline{b}$, then $\pi^{-1}\rho \in C_{\bar{G}}(\underline{b}) = 1$, so that $\pi = \rho$.

$\square$

Once the base $\underline{b}$ is at hand we can evaluate the orbits $G(k), k \in \underline{b}$, as it is described above by 7.1.6. These orbits can serve very well for a check if $\pi \in S_{\underline{n}}$ is contained in $\bar{G}$ or not: Consider $\pi 1$ first. If $\pi 1 \notin G(1)$, then obviously $\pi \notin \bar{G}$, and we can stop. If otherwise $\pi 1 \in G(1)$, then there exists a left coset representative $\pi_j^{(1)}$ such that $\pi_j^{(1)} 1 = \pi 1 \in G(1)$, and therefore $(\pi_j^{(1)})^{-1}\pi \in C_G(\underline{1})$. Hence, by induction, we obtain

7.1.9 Corollary *Either there exist* $\pi_v^{(i)} \in C_{\bar{G}}(\underline{i})$, *for which*

$$(\pi_{j_b}^{(b)})^{-1} \dots (\pi_{j_1}^{(1)})^{-1}\pi \in C_{\bar{G}}(\underline{b}) = \{1_G\}, \text{ so that } \pi = \pi_{j_1}^{(1)} \dots \pi_{j_b}^{(b)} \in \bar{G},$$

or π *is* not *an element of* $\bar{G}$.

7.2   Transversals of symmetry classes

In this section we shall restrict attention to a redundancy free construction of a transversal of the G–classes on $Y^X := \underline{m}^{\underline{n}}$. Moreover, in order to decrease the complexity we restrict attention to G–classes of fixed content $\lambda = (\lambda_1, \dots) \models n$, starting off from the *canonic mapping* f with this content:

$$f_\lambda := (f_\lambda(1), \dots, f_\lambda(n)) := (\underbrace{1, \dots, 1}_{\lambda_1}, \underbrace{2, \dots, 2}_{\lambda_2}, \dots).$$

The set of all the mappings of this content will be indicated as follows:

$$\underline{m}_\lambda^{\underline{n}} := \{\pi f_\lambda = f_\lambda \circ \pi^{-1} \mid \pi \in S_{\underline{n}}\}.$$

Since a permutation of the arguments does not change the content, this set $\underline{m}_\lambda^{\underline{n}}$ is a union of orbits of G on $\underline{mn}$:

$$G\backslash\backslash\underline{m}_\lambda^{\underline{n}} \subseteq G\backslash\backslash\underline{m}^{\underline{n}}.$$

We would like to construct a transversal of $\underline{m}_\lambda^{\underline{n}}$. This reduces the complexity since the desired transversal of $G\backslash\backslash\underline{m}^{\underline{n}}$ is the union of the transversals of the sets $G\backslash\backslash\underline{m}_\lambda^{\underline{n}}$, taken over all the $\lambda \models n$. The crucial point is now that in each orbit of G on $\underline{m}_\lambda^{\underline{n}}$ there is a unique representative which is the *lexicographically smallest* element of its orbit. Therefore we may call these lexicographically smallest elements a *canonic transversal* of $G \backslash\backslash \underline{m}_\lambda^n$. A mapping $f \in \underline{m}_\lambda^n$ can be displayed by its λ–tabloid

$$\begin{array}{c} \overline{i_1 \dots i_{\lambda_1}} \\ \overline{j_1 \dots j_{\lambda_2}} \\ \dots \end{array},$$

where we put the elements of the inverse image $f^{-1}[\{k\}]$ of $k \in \underline{m}$ into the k-th row, in increasing order, so that e.g.

$$f(i_1) = \dots = f(i_{\lambda_1}) = 1, \text{ and } i_1 < \dots < i_{\lambda_1}.$$

Let us consider as an example the graphs on 4 vertices which contain exactly 2 edges, so that $n = \binom{4}{2} = 6$, $m = 2$, and $\lambda = (4, 2)$. Before we write down all the 15 $(4, 2)$-tabloids in full detail, it is practical to note that in each tabloid the first (or any other) row is uniquely determined by the remaining rows which form the *truncated* tabloid. Hence in the present case we need only to display the second rows, here they are:

$$\overline{12}, \ \overline{13}, \ \overline{14}, \ \overline{15}, \ \overline{16}, \ \overline{23}, \ \overline{24}, \ \overline{25}, \ \overline{26}, \ \overline{34}, \ \overline{35}, \ \overline{36}, \ \overline{45}, \ \overline{46}, \ \overline{56}.$$

According to the above arguments we have to find the orbits of $\bar{S}_4$ on this set. Recall that the elements $1, \dots, 6 \in \underline{6}$ on which S_6 acts, stand for the pairs $\{1, 2\}, \dots, \{5, 6\}$ of vertices. The subgroup

$$\bar{S}_4 := S_4^{[2]} \hookrightarrow S_6$$

is the permutation group induced by $S_4 = \langle (12), (1234) \rangle$ on this set of pairs of vertices. Thus

$$\bar{S}_4 = \langle (24)(35), (1463)(25) \rangle,$$

and therefore one of the two orbits of $\bar{S}_4$ on the set of $(4, 2)$-tabloids is

$$\omega_2 := \{\overline{16}, \overline{25}, \overline{34}\},$$

the other orbit ω_1 consists of the remaining 12 truncated tabloids. (Note that in a preprocessing calculation we can obtain, by an application of the enumeration theory described above, that the number of graphs with 4 vertices and 2 edges is *two*, a result which is very helpful as *stopping rule*, as the present example already shows!)

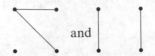

Figure 7.1: The graphs with 4 vertices and 2 edges

The lexicographically smallest elements of these orbits ω_1, ω_2 are the tabloids corresponding to $\overline{56} \in \omega_1$ and $\overline{34} \in \omega_2$. These tabloids are

$$\frac{1234}{56} \quad \text{and} \quad \frac{1256}{34} .$$

The corresponding mappings $f, f' \in \underline{2}^{\underline{6}}$ are

$$f = (1,1,1,1,2,2), \text{ and } f' = (1,1,2,2,1,1).$$

Hence the graphs shown in figure 7.1 form a complete set of graphs on 4 vertices containing 2 edges! This method is cumbersome, it can be used for cataloging the graphs on ≤ 7 vertices, say. We want therefore to describe further refinements which allow to catalog the graphs with $v = 10$ vertices (this is in fact the biggest v for which a complete such list is available, there are approximately $12 \cdot 10^6$ such graphs).

Having displayed an example in full, let us go into detail in order to make the procedure of finding the minimal representatives more efficient. Recall that we have to check if a given f is the lexicographically smallest element in its orbit, i.e. if the following is true:

7.2.1 $\forall \sigma \in \bar{G} : f \leq f \circ \sigma, \text{ for short: } f \leq \bar{G}(f).$

The verification of this condition is one of the crucial parts of the whole procedure. Let us call this check the *minimality test* for f. In order to carry it out in a reasonable way we recall what has been said about Sims chains. Assume that $\underline{b}$ is the base for the action of $\bar{G}$ on $\underline{n}$ (still $f \in \underline{m}^{\underline{n}}$), so that

$$\{1\} = C_{\bar{G}}(\underline{b}) \leq C_{\bar{G}}(\underline{b-1}) \leq \ldots \leq C_{\bar{G}}(\underline{0}) = \bar{G},$$

and we assume that left coset representatives $\pi_j^{(i)}$ ar at hand such that

$$C_{\bar{G}}(\underline{i-1}) = \bigcup_{j=1}^{r(i)} \pi_j^{(i)} C_{\bar{G}}(\underline{i}), \text{ where } \pi_1^{(i)} \in C_{\bar{G}}(\underline{i}).$$

Thus, in order to apply the minimality test 7.2.1, we have to run through the elements of $\bar{G}$, each of which can uniquely be written in the form

$$\sigma = \pi_{j_1}^{(1)} \cdots \pi_{j_b}^{(b)}.$$

This means that in order to apply *each* element of $\bar{G}$ to f, say, we have to run through the following tree:

7.2.2

$$
\begin{array}{ccccccc}
& \pi_1^{(1)} & \cdots & \cdots & \cdots & \pi_{r(1)}^{(1)} & \\
& \swarrow \quad \cdots \quad \searrow & \cdots & \swarrow & \cdots & \searrow & \\
\pi_1^{(1)}\pi_1^{(2)} & \cdots & \pi_1^{(1)}\pi_{r(2)}^{(2)} & \cdots & \pi_{r(1)}^{(1)}\pi_1^{(2)} & \cdots & \pi_{r(1)}^{(1)}\pi_{r(2)}^{(2)} \\
\swarrow \cdots \searrow & \cdots & \swarrow \cdots \searrow & \cdots & \swarrow \cdots \searrow & \cdots & \swarrow \cdots \searrow
\end{array}
$$

It is very important to cut this tree down as much as possible. This can be done, for example, by an application of

7.2.3 Lemma *If $f < f \circ \pi_j^{(i)}$ and $f(i) < f \circ \pi_j^{(i)}(i)$, then we have, for the orbit of f under the action of $C_{\bar{G}}(\underline{i}) \leq \bar{G}$:*

$$f < C_{\bar{G}}(\underline{i})(f \circ \pi_j^{(i)}).$$

Proof: For $\tau \in C_{\bar{G}}(\underline{i})$ and $k \in \underline{i-1}$ we have

$$f \circ \pi_j^{(i)} \circ \tau^{-1}(k) = f(k),$$

while

$$f \circ \pi_j^{(i)} \circ \tau^{-1}(i) = f \circ \pi_j^{(i)}(i) > f(i).$$

$\square$

This result allows us to *cut off the branch starting with the element* $\ldots \pi_j^{(i)}$ from the tree 7.2.2 formed by the elements of $\bar{G}$.

Besides this we can choose a suitable *way in which we work through the tree* 7.2.2 in order to find the smallest element in the orbit $G(f)$. A remark that will lead us to a good such choice makes use of the fact that $f \in \underline{m}^{\underline{n}}$ will not in general be injective. But in this case there exist $\tau, \sigma \in S_{\underline{n}} \setminus \{1\}$ such that $f \circ \sigma = f \circ \tau$, and so we have for each $i \in \underline{n}$ the equation

7.2.4
$$\sigma^{-1} C_{\bar{G}}(\underline{i})(f) = \tau^{-1} C_{\bar{G}}(\underline{i})(f).$$

We can therefore subdivide $\bar{G}$ according to the Sims chain and the base $\underline{b}$:

7.2.5
$$\bar{G} = \bigcup_{i=1}^{b} (C_{\bar{G}}(\underline{b-i}) \setminus C_{\bar{G}}(\underline{b-i+1})) \bigcup \{1\}.$$

Correspondingly we shall run through $\bar{G}$ (in any case, whether f is injective or not) by working through the following subsets, one row after the other, from top to bottom:

1. $C_{\bar{G}}(\underline{b-1})\backslash C_{\bar{G}}(\underline{b})$,
2. $C_{\bar{G}}(\underline{b-2})\backslash C_{\bar{G}}(\underline{b-1})$,

$\vdots$

b. $C_{\bar{G}}(\emptyset)\backslash C_{\bar{G}}(\underline{1})$.

The identity element can be left out since $f \circ 1 = f$. We note that in step number $b - i + 1$ we are running through the set

$$C_{\bar{G}}(\underline{i-1})\backslash C_{\bar{G}}(\underline{i}) = \bigcup_{j=2}^{r(i)} \pi_j^{(i)} C_{\bar{G}}(\underline{i}),$$

if we had $f \le C_{\bar{G}}(\underline{i})(f)$ before, assuming that $\pi_1^{(i)} = 1$, for each i, so that we can always start with $j = 2$. This way to procede allows to use the following remark: In the case when there exists *any* $\sigma \in C_{\bar{G}}(\underline{i})$ *for which* $f \circ \pi_j^{(i)} \circ \sigma = f$, then $\pi_j^{(i)} C_{\bar{G}}(\underline{i})(f) \ge f$, and so we can jump over the whole coset $\pi_j^{(i)} C_{\bar{G}}(\underline{i})$, by 7.2.4. This idea can also be used in order to derive *the Sims chain of the stabilizer of* f. Let us indicate this stabilizer as follows:

$$A := \{\rho \in \bar{G} \mid f \circ \rho = f\} \le \bar{G},$$

and note that, for each $i \in \underline{b}$:

7.2.6 $\qquad\qquad C_A(\underline{i}) \le C_{\bar{G}}(\underline{i}).$

A transversal of the set of left cosets $C_A(\underline{i-1})/C_A(\underline{i})$ can be obtained from the transversal $\{\pi_j^{(i)} \mid j \in r(i)\}$ of $C_{\bar{G}}(\underline{i-1})/C_{\bar{G}}(\underline{i})$ in the following way:

7.2.7 Lemma *If we denote by* $J(i)$ *the set*

$$J(i) := \{j \in \underline{r(i)} \mid \exists \sigma_j \in C_{\bar{G}}(\underline{i}): \pi_j^{(i)} \sigma_j \in A\},$$

and if we fix, for each $j \in J(i)$, *such an element* σ_j, *then*

$$\{\tau_j := \pi_j^{(i)} \sigma_j \mid j \in J(i)\}$$

is a transversal of $C_A(\underline{i-1})/C_A(\underline{i})$.

Proof: If $\sigma \in C_A(i)$, then, by 7.2.6, there exists a $j \in \underline{r(i)}$ such that $\sigma \in \pi_j^{(i)} C_{\bar{G}}(\underline{i})$, so that this j must lie in $J(i)$. Moreover the left cosets $\tau_j C_A(\underline{i})$ are pairwise different, since 7.2.6 holds.

□

7.2.8 Corollary *The set*

$$\{\tau_j = \pi_j^{(i)} \sigma_j \mid j \in J(i)\}$$

yields the Sims chain of the stabilizer A of f.

Another byproduct is the following test:

7.2.9 Corollary *If, for each i, j, $f'(i) \neq f \circ \pi_j^{(i)}(i)$, then*

$$f' \notin G(f).$$

Let us now summarize what has been said so far about the minimality test which we have to carry out in order to find the lexicographically smallest element of the orbit $G(f)$. We discussed the Sims chain for the action of G on $\underline{n}$, it leads to the tree 7.2.2, and we saw in 7.2.3 that certain cuts and jumps can be made while running through this tree. But still this does *not suffice* to carry out this test in an efficient way, say if we want to catalog the graphs on 10 vertices. We shall therefore continue by considering the evaluation of the orbits of the centralizers $C_{\bar{G}}(\underline{i})$.

7.3 Orbits of centralizers

We say that $\bar{G} \leq S_n$ is *compatible* (with the natural order on $\underline{n}$), if and only if the following holds:

7.3.1 $\forall i \in \underline{n} : C_{\bar{G}}(\underline{i}) \backslash\backslash \underline{n}$ consists of intervals of $\underline{n}$.

So in particular Young subgroups are compatible.

7.3.2 Lemma *For each subgroup $P \leq S_n$ there exist $\pi \in S_n$ such that $\pi P \pi^{-1}$ is compatible. For short: each subgroup P of S_n is compatible up to conjugation.*

Proof: We shall inductively construct a suitable π that does the appropriate conjugation. Before we start doing so we note that the following is true:

7.3.3 $$\pi C_P(\underline{i})\pi^{-1} = C_{\pi P \pi^{-1}}(\pi \underline{i}).$$

The basis of the induction is trivial since $C_P(\underline{0}) = P$ and hence there is a $\pi_0 \in S_{\underline{n}}$ such that $\pi_0 P \pi_0^{-1}$ has intervals as orbits. Moreover, by 7.3.3,

$$\pi_0 C_P(\underline{0})\pi_0^{-1} = C_{\pi_0 P \pi_0^{-1}}(\pi_0 \underline{0}) = C_{\pi_0 P \pi_0^{-1}}(\underline{0}).$$

In order to carry out the inductive step we assume that we have managed to construct π_i such that, for

$$Q := \pi_i \dots \pi_1 P \pi_1^{-1} \dots \pi_i^{-1},$$

each $C_Q(\underline{j}) \backslash\backslash \underline{n}$ consists of intervals, for each $j \in \underline{i}$. Consider now the subgroup $C_Q(\underline{i+1})$ of $C_Q(\underline{i})$, each orbit ω_{i+1} of which is contained in an orbit ω_i of $C_Q(\underline{i})$, and ω_i is an interval. Therefore we can find

$$\pi_{i+1} \in \oplus_i S_{\omega_i}$$

such that $\pi_{i+1} C_Q(\underline{i+1})\pi_{i+1}^{-1} = C_{\pi_{i+1} Q \pi_{i+1}^{-1}}(\pi_{i+1}\underline{i+1})$ has intervals as orbits. Since the orbit $\{i+1\}$ already is an interval, we can moreover assume that $\pi_{i+1}(i+1) = i+1$, so that in fact π_{i+1} is in the centralizer of $\underline{i}$, and hence

$$\pi_{i+1} C_Q(\underline{i+1})\pi_{i+1}^{-1} = C_{\pi_{i+1} Q \pi_{i+1}^{-1}}(\underline{i+1})$$

as well as

$$C_{\pi_{i+1} Q \pi_{i+1}^{-1}}(\underline{j}) \backslash\backslash \underline{n} \text{ consists of intervals,}$$

for each $j \in \underline{i}$, too, and this completes the proof.

□

We can therefore *assume without restriction that $\bar{G}$ is compatible*, and hence there is also a natural way of numbering the orbits $C_{\bar{G}}(\underline{i})$ as follows:

$$\omega_1^{(i)} = \{1\}, \dots, \omega_i^{(i)} = \{i\}, \dots, \omega_{t(i)}^{(i)}.$$

Let us consider *contents of restrictions* of mappings $f, g \in \underline{m}_\lambda^n$ to these orbits. We call $\omega_k^{(i)}, k < t(i)$, *content critical* for f and g, if and only if

$$\forall s < k : c(f \downarrow \omega_s^{(i)}) = c(g \downarrow \omega_s^{(i)}),$$

while

$$c(f \downarrow \omega_k^{(i)}) \neq c(g \downarrow \omega_k^{(i)}).$$

7.3.4 Lemma *If $\omega_k^{(i)}$ is content critical for f and f', then we have, for each $\sigma \in C_{\bar{G}}(\underline{i})$, that*

$$f \downarrow \omega_1^{(i)} \cup \ldots \cup \omega_k^{(i)} \neq f' \circ \sigma \downarrow \omega_1^{(i)} \cup \ldots \cup \omega_k^{(i)}.$$

Proof: σ fixes each $\omega_s^{(i)}$ setwise, and hence the contents of $f \downarrow \omega_s^{(i)}$ and of $f' \circ \sigma \downarrow \omega_s^{(i)}$ are the same, this also holds for $\omega_k^{(i)}$. Thus, by assumption, $\omega_k^{(i)}$ is content critical also for f and f'. This proves the statement.

□

Note that $\omega_1^{(i)}, \ldots, \omega_i^{(i)}$ are one element orbits, so $f = f \circ \pi$ and $f \circ \sigma = f \circ \pi \circ \sigma$ are *identical* there, so the preceding lemma means first of all that in order to carry out the minimality test, if $f < f \circ \sigma, \sigma \in C_{\bar{G}}(\underline{i})$, say, we can start from checking $f(i)$ instead of starting from the very beginning $f(1)$. Moreover the decision if $f \leq f \circ \sigma$ will be made at last by checking if $f(m) < f(\sigma m)$, where $\underline{m} = \omega_1^{(i)} \cup \ldots \cup \omega_k^{(i)}$. The next step will therefore be a discussion of content critical orbits. Let us say that $f \in \underline{m}^{\underline{n}}$ *lies below* $g \in \underline{m}^{\underline{n}}$ in $X \subseteq \underline{n}$ if and only if

$$\forall x \in X : f(x) \leq g(x), \text{ for short: } f \leq_X g,$$

and we say that f lies *strictly* below g in X if $f \leq_X g$ and

$$\exists x_0 \in X : f(x_0) < g(x_0).$$

This will be abbreviated by

$$f <_X g.$$

7.3.5 Lemma *Let $\pi, \rho \in \bar{G}$ and $\omega_k^{(i)}$ be content critical for $f := f_\lambda \circ \pi$ and $f' := f_\lambda \circ \rho$, while we put $\underline{m} := \omega_1^{(i)} \cup \ldots \cup \omega_{k-1}^{(i)}$. Now, if*

$$f \downarrow \underline{m} = f' \downarrow \underline{m}, \text{ and } f <_{\omega_k^{(i)}} f',$$

then the following is true:

$$f \leq C_{\bar{G}}(\underline{i})(f) \Rightarrow f' \leq C_{\bar{G}}(\underline{i})(f').$$

Proof: Take $\sigma \in C_{\bar{G}}(\underline{i})$. The assumed equality of the restrictions to $\underline{m}$ yields, first of all, that also

$$f \circ \sigma \downarrow \underline{m} = f' \circ \sigma \downarrow \underline{m}.$$

Moreover we assume that $f \downarrow \omega_k^{(i)} < f' \downarrow \omega_k^{(i)}$ so that there exists an $x_0 \in \omega_k^{(i)}$ for which $f(x_0) < f'(x_0)$. Since $y := \sigma^{-1}(x_0) \in \omega_k^{(i)}$ we have $f(\sigma(y)) < f'(\sigma(y))$, and hence

$$f \circ \sigma \downarrow \omega_k^{(i)} < f' \circ \sigma \downarrow \omega_k^{(i)},$$

which proves the statement.

$\square$

Note that 7.3.5 turns out to be a generalization of 7.2.3 if we identify the point i with the orbit $\{i\}$. Finally it should be mentioned that we can also *learn from a negative result in a minimality test*, which is absolutely necessary, since otherwise we would not have the slightest chance to overcome the complexity:

7.3.6 Lemma *If $f \circ \sigma < f$, so that there exists a $j < n$ such that*

$$\forall x < j : f(\sigma x) = f(x), \quad \text{while } f(\sigma j) > f(j),$$

we put

$$y := \max\{\sigma x \mid x < j \wedge f(\sigma x) < m\}, \text{ and } z := \max\{j, \sigma j, y\}.$$

Then, for each $f' \in \underline{m}_\lambda^n$ with $f' \downarrow \underline{z} = f \downarrow \underline{z}$ the following is true:

$$f' \circ \sigma < f'.$$

Proof: Since j and σj are contained in $\underline{z}$, we have

$$f' \circ \sigma(j) = f'(\sigma j) = f(\sigma j) < f(j) = f'(j).$$

Hence $f' \circ \sigma \geq f'$ would imply the existence of an $x < j$ such that $f' \circ \sigma(x) > f'(x)$. This leads to a contradiction:

- If, for this $x < j$, we had $f \circ \sigma(x) < m$, then, as x and $\sigma x \in \underline{z}$:

$$f' \circ \sigma(x) = f \circ \sigma(x) = f \circ \sigma(x) = f(x) = f'(x),$$

  a contradiction.

- On the other hand, if $f \circ \sigma(x) = m$, then $x \in \underline{z}$ gives

$$m = f'(x) = f(x) = f \circ \sigma(x),$$

  which is a contradiction, too.

$\square$

7.3.7 Corollary *Assume π, σ and z as in 7.3.6, and suppose that the restrictions of f and f' satisfy $f' \downarrow \underline{z} = f \downarrow \underline{z}$. Then also f' is not a canonical representative of its orbit. The lexicographically next candidate f' satisfies $f'(z) > f(z)$.*

7.4 Recursion and orderly generation

Besides this direct method of evaluating a transversal of the symmetry classes with prescribed content, there exists also a recursive method, where the recursion is on the cardinality of the range. We are going to describe this next and then we shall combine it with the so–called orderly generation. It is based on the following observation:

7.4.1 Lemma *Assume an action $_GX$, and that $B \subseteq X$ is a block or, as it is sometimes called a* system of imprimitivity *(which means that B is mapped under $g \in G$ either onto B or onto a subset gB which is disjoint with B). Then the following is true:*

- *For each orbit $\omega \in G\backslash\backslash X$ we have*

$$\omega \cap B \neq \emptyset \iff \omega \cap gB \neq \emptyset,$$

  which means that B and gB intersect with the same orbits.
- *For each $b \in B, g \in G$, $gb \in B$ is true if and only if*

$$g \in N_G(B) := \{g \in G \mid gB = B\}.$$

Therefore, if

$$X = \bigcup_{i \in I} B_i,$$

a disjoint union of blocks, and $J \subseteq I$ such that

$$\mathcal{T}(G\backslash\backslash\{B_i \mid i \in I\}) = \{B_j \mid j \in J\}$$

is a transversal of G on the set of these blocks, then a transversal $\mathcal{T}(G\backslash\backslash X)$ is the following union of transversals:

$$\mathcal{T}(G\backslash\backslash X) = \bigcup_{j \in J} \mathcal{T}(N_G(B_i)\backslash\backslash B_i),$$

where $\mathcal{T}(N_G(B_i)\backslash\backslash B_i)$ is an arbitrary transversal of $N_G(B_i)\backslash\backslash B_i$.

The checks are easy and left as exercise 7.4.1. This result shows that the direct evaluation of a transversal can be replaced by successive evaluations of blocks, their normalizers and transversals of the orbits of the normalizers on the blocks. An interesting method systematically to obtain blocks can be derived from

7.4.2 The Homomorphism Principle *Assume that G acts on the sets X_i, $i = 1, 2$, and that $\varphi: X_2 \to X_1$ commutes with the action:*

$$\varphi(gx_2) = g\varphi(x_2), \text{ for each } g \in G, x_2 \in X_2,$$

then each inverse image $\varphi^{-1}(x_1), x_1 \in X_1$, is a block. Moreover, the normalizer of this block is the stabilizer of x_1:

$$N_G(\varphi^{-1}(x_1)) = G_{x_1}.$$

This is easy to check but very important to remark since it is essential for

7.4.3 Surjective Resolution *Assume that G acts on the sets $X_i, i \in \underline{m}$, and that we are given surjective mappings*

$$\varphi_{i+1} : X_{i+1} \to X_i, \text{ for each } i \in \underline{m-1},$$

that commute with the action:

$$\varphi_{i+1}(gx_{i+1}) = g\varphi_{i+1}(x_{i+1}), \text{ for each } i \in \underline{m-1}, g \in G, x_{i+1} \in X_{i+1}.$$

Then we can obtain a transversal $\mathcal{T}$ of $G \backslash\!\backslash X_m$ by successively working backwards, starting by evaluating a transversal of $G \backslash\!\backslash X_1$ and the stabilizers of its elements, and then evaluating the inverse images $\varphi_2(x)$ of the elements x in this transversal, as well as the transversals $G_x \backslash\!\backslash \varphi_2^{-1}(x)$, and so on, in accordance with 7.4.1.

We would like now to apply this to symmetry classes in order to obtain a recursive evaluation of a transversal, using recursion on $|Y|$.

7.4.4 Example For sake of simplicity we assume that

$$Y^X = \underline{m}^{\underline{n}},$$

and that G acts on $\underline{n}$ and so on $Y^X = \underline{m}^{\underline{n}}$ in the canonic way.
The Surjective Resolution method 7.4.3 can be applied since the following mapping commutes with the action of G on the G–sets $\underline{k}^{\underline{n}}$:

$$\varphi_k : \underline{k}^{\underline{n}} \to (\underline{k-1})^{\underline{n}} : f \mapsto f',$$

where f' is defined by

$$f'(i) := \begin{cases} f(i) & \text{if } f(i) \in \underline{k-1} \\ k-1 & \text{otherwise.} \end{cases}$$

We can therefore start from $X_1 := \underline{1}^{\underline{n}}$, which consists of the single and constant mapping $i \mapsto 1, i \in \underline{n}$. The stabilizer is G, and the inverse image is the whole set $X_2 := \underline{2}^{\underline{n}}$. We therefore have to evaluate in this second step a transversal $\mathscr{T}_2$ of $G \backslash\backslash \underline{2}^{\underline{n}}$. Assume that this is done, and let f_2 denote an element of $\mathscr{T}_2$, G_{f_2} its stabilizer. It remains to evaluate in the third step, for each such f_2 and its stabilizer a transversal $\mathscr{T}_3$ of

$$G_{f_2} \backslash\backslash \varphi_3^{-1}(f_2).$$

This inductive step can be carried out as follows. Two elements f_3 and f_3' of $\varphi_3^{-1}(f_2)$ can differ only on the inverse image $f_2^{-1}(2)$ of the point 2, and the values there can only be 2 or 3. We therefore need only to evaluate a transversal T of

$$G_{f_2} \backslash\backslash \{2, 3\}^{f_2^{-1}(2)}.$$

The desired transversal $\mathscr{T}_3$ then consists of the mappings $f_3'' \in \underline{3}^{\underline{n}}$ such that

$$f_3''|_{f_2^{-1}(2)} \in T, \text{ and } f_3''|_{\underline{n} \backslash f_2^{-1}(2)} = f_2|_{\underline{n} \backslash f_2^{-1}(2)}.$$

$\diamond$

The method of Surjective Resolution can be combined with the method of *orderly generation* as described by R. C. Read. This way of generation is based on the fact that total orders on X and Y induce a canonic total order on Y^X, so that a *canonic transversal*

$$\mathscr{T}_>(G \backslash\backslash Y^X),$$

consisting of the biggest elements of the orbits does exist. Moreover, we can break this problem into pieces, if weights are at hand.

7.4.5 Example Recall that the graphs on v vertices correspond to the set of orbits

$$S_{\underline{v}} \backslash\backslash \underline{2}^{\binom{v}{2}}.$$

As $\underline{v}$ is totally ordered, so is the set of pairs $\binom{v}{2}$, and hence also the set of labelled graphs. This is in fact the lexicographic order $\leq$ on the set of 0-1-sequences obtained from the adjacency matrices by reading the upper triangular part row by row from left to right and from top

to bottom. For example

is mapped onto the sequence $(1, 1, 0, 0, 1, 0)$, and hence this labelled graph is a member of the canonic transversal, but $(0, 0, 1, 1, 1, 0)$, which corresponds to the isomorphic labelled graph

is *not* a canonic representative.

The problem of orderly generation now means the following. We would like to find an economic way of generating 0-1-sequences of length 6 in such a way that not too many sequences are generated, which do not correspond to the desired canonic representatives. Moreover, we should like to do this by increasing the number of ones successively by 1, which means by successively increasing the number of edges.

One way of doing this is to start off from the sequence $(0, 0, 0, 0, 0, 0)$, which forms the canonic transversal of the labelled graphs of total weight 0:

$$\mathscr{T}_>^{(0)} = \{(0, 0, 0, 0, 0, 0)\}.$$

Now we will evaluate $\mathscr{T}_>^{(1)}$, then $\mathscr{T}_>^{(2)}$, and so on, in the following way. Assume that $\mathscr{T}_>^{(i)}$ is at hand. Then, in order to obtain $\mathscr{T}_>^{(i+1)}$, we shall apply to each member of $\mathscr{T}_>^{(i)}$ the following *augmentation*. We change in each element of $\mathscr{T}_>^{(i)}$ in all the possible ways just one entry zero that is *to the right of the rightmost entry 1*. The resulting set of labelled graphs is either empty, if no such entry exists, or consists of labelled graphs with one more edge. These sets have to be checked carefully, the canonic sequences have to be kept, the others have be thrown away before going to the next step. The remaining set of labelled graphs is in fact the desired transversal $\mathscr{T}_>^{(i+1)}$. In our example this process runs as follows:

1. In the first step we get the six sequences containing exactly one entry 1. The canonic respresentative is, of course, $(1, 0, 0, 0, 0, 0)$, and so, clearly

$$\mathcal{T}_>^{(1)} = \{(1, 0, 0, 0, 0, 0)\}.$$

2. In the second step we start with $(1, 0, 0, 0, 0, 0)$ and obtain, after canceling the sequences which are not canonic, that

$$\mathcal{T}_>^{(2)} = \{(1, 1, 0, 0, 0, 0), (1, 0, 0, 0, 0, 1)\}.$$

3. The third step gives, from the first canonic representative of the second step, the sequences $(1, 1, 1, 0, 0, 0)$, $(1, 1, 0, 1, 0, 0)$ and $(1, 1, 0, 0, 0, 1)$, while the other representative of $\mathcal{T}_>^{(2)}$ needs not to be considered, as there is no zero entry to the right of the rightmost entry 1. Thus

$$\mathcal{T}_>^{(3)} = \{(1, 1, 1, 0, 0, 0), (1, 1, 0, 1, 0, 0), (1, 1, 0, 0, 0, 1)\}.$$

4. In the fourth step we get $(1, 1, 1, 1, 0, 0)$, from the first element of $\mathcal{T}_>^{(3)}$, nothing new from the second one, but $(1, 1, 0, 0, 1, 1)$ from the third element, and hence

$$\mathcal{T}_>^{(4)} = \{(1, 1, 1, 1, 0, 0), (1, 1, 0, 0, 1, 1)\}.$$

5. The next step gives

$$\mathcal{T}_>^{(5)} = \{(1, 1, 1, 1, 1, 0)\},$$

from which we obtain in

6. the final step that

$$\mathcal{T}_>^{(6)} = \{(1, 1, 1, 1, 1, 1)\}.$$

And so, summing up, we have obtained the desired canonic transversal of the isomorphism classes of labelled graphs on 4 vertices:

$$\mathcal{T}_> = \{(0, 0, 0, 0, 0, 0), (1, 0, 0, 0, 0, 0), (1, 1, 0, 0, 0, 0),$$

$$(1, 0, 0, 0, 0, 1), (1, 1, 1, 0, 0, 0), (1, 1, 0, 1, 0, 0), (1, 1, 0, 0, 0, 1),$$

$$(1, 1, 1, 1, 0, 0), (1, 1, 0, 0, 1, 1), (1, 1, 1, 1, 1, 0), (1, 1, 1, 1, 1, 1)\}.$$

$\diamond$

It is important to note that we had to check 24 sequences for canonicity, out of $2^6 = 64$ labelled graphs on 4 vertices, which is not bad. Moreover, we note that each of the canonic representatives arises *just once* from an element of smaller total weight. The corresponding generalization reads as follows:

7.4.6 Theorem (Read) *Assume a finite action $_GX$ where X is totally ordered by $\leq$ and a disjoint union*

$$X = \bigcup_{i=1}^{n} X_i,$$

of invariant and nonempty subsets X_i. Let A denote an algorithm that produces for each $x \in X$ either the empty set or a set $A(x) \subseteq X$ in descending order, such that the following conditions hold for the canonic transversals $\mathcal{T}_>^{(i)}$ of the orbit sets $G \backslash\backslash X_i$, for each $i \in \underline{n-1}$:

- $\mathcal{T}_>^{(i+1)} \subseteq \bigcup A(x)$, *union over the $x \in \mathcal{T}_>^{(i)}\}$,*
- *for each $x \in \mathcal{T}_>^{(i+1)}$ there exists a unique element $x' \in \mathcal{T}_>^{(i)}$ such that $x \in A(x')$, and finally,*
- *for any $x_1, x_2 \in \mathcal{T}_>^{(i+1)}$, $x_1 < x_2$, we have the implication*

$$x_1 \in A(x_1'), x_2 \in A(x_2') \text{ imply } x_1' < x_2'.$$

Then, computing $\mathcal{T}_>^{(1)}$ and recursively running through $\mathcal{T}_>^{(i)}$ with x, producing the augmentation $A(x)$, and eliminating representatives which are not canonic from $A(x)$, for $i \in \underline{n-1}$, gives the desired canonic transversal $\mathcal{T}_>$ of $G \backslash\backslash X$ as the following union:

$$\mathcal{T}_> = \bigcup_{i=1}^{n} \mathcal{T}_>^{(i)}.$$

$\square$

This orderly generation obviously will work as soon as we have found an augmentation procedure A that has the properties listed in the items of the above theorem of Read. We already saw such an augmentation that can be used for the graphs and which amounts to adding an edge in a certain set of places. The necessary canonicity test can be done quite efficiently using any suitable invariant that allows to put the canonic representatives in what is called an AVL–tree in computer science. For example, in the molecular graphs case, we can use a so-called *Morgan table*, which is a numbering well known to chemists, and used in the coding procedure for chemical substances in the *Chemical Abstracts*. It reduces the set of checks to a reasonable small number.

Summing up we should like to mention that an efficient way of evaluating a transversal of the symmetry of G on Y^X can be implemented by using the following methods:

- A recursion procedure, using recursion on $|Y|$.

- Read's orderly generation, by applying lexicographic or any other ordering of Y^X.

- A canonic form of the elements $f \in Y^X$ which allows to put the canonic representatives (canonic with respect to the ordering mentioned in the second item) together into an AVL-tree and which reduces the necessary number of checks to a reasonably small one.

Exercises

E 7.4.1 Check 7.4.1.

7.5 Generating orbit representatives

The evaluation of an orbit transversal is of limited use since these sets are usually very (for example there are approximately 10^9 graphs on $v = 11$ vertices). Thus we are looking for a method which allows to examine further cases, e.g. graphs of more than ten vertices, say. In order to cover such cases with some success, we have to accept redundancy and hence we shall ran into the isomorphism disease. Invariants, isomorphism tests and all that will have to be discussed. To begin with we need to check that we can generate orbit representatives *uniformly at random*.

7.5.1 The Dixon/Wilf Algorithm *If $_GX$ denotes a finite action, then we can generate orbit representatives uniformly at random in the following way:*

- *Choose a conjugacy class C of G with probability*

$$p(C) := \frac{|C||X_g|}{|G||G\backslash\!\backslash X|}, \ where \ g \in C.$$

- *Pick any $g \in C$ and generate a fixed point of g, uniformly at random.*

Then the probability that x is an element of the orbit $\omega \in G\backslash\backslash X$ is $1/|G\backslash\backslash X|$, i.e. x is uniformly distributed over the orbits of G on X.

Proof: Let $C_1, \ldots, C_r$ denote the conjugacy classes of G, with representatives $g_i \in C_i$. Then, by the Cauchy-Frobenius lemma, we have

$$\sum_{i=1}^{r} p(C_i) = \frac{\sum_i |C_i||X_{g_i}|}{\sum_g |X_g|} = 1,$$

so that $p(-)$ defines in fact a probability distribution. If $\omega \in G\backslash\backslash X$, then

$$p(x \in \omega) = \sum_i p(C_i)p(x \in C_i \cap \omega)$$

$$= \sum_i p(C_i)\frac{|X_{g_i} \cap \omega|}{|X_{g_i}|} = \sum_i \frac{|C_i||X_{g_i}|}{|G||G\backslash\backslash X|}\frac{|X_{g_i} \cap \omega|}{|X_{g_i}|}$$

$$= \frac{1}{|G||G\backslash\backslash X|}\sum_i |C_i||X_{g_i} \cap \omega| = \frac{1}{\sum_g |X_g|}\sum_g |X_g \cap \omega|,$$

where the last identity follows from exercise 7.5.1. Now

$$\sum_g |X_g \cap \omega| = \sum_{g \in G}\sum_{x \in X_g \cap \omega} 1 = \sum_{x \in \omega}\sum_{g \in X_g} 1 = \sum_{x \in \omega} |G_x|,$$

which is equal to $|G_y||\omega| = |G|$, for any $y \in \omega$, and we are done. □

The application of this method to the generation of representatives of G–classes, H–classes, $H \times G$–classes and $H \wr_x G$–classes on Y^X is easy, since we know the fixed points very well. Let us consider the G–classes, for example.

7.5.2 Corollary *For finite $_G X$ and Y the following procedure yields elements $f \in Y^X$ that are distributed over the G–classes on Y^X uniformly at random:*

- *Choose a conjugacy class C of G with the probability*

$$p(C) := \frac{|C||Y|^{c(\bar{g}')}}{\sum_g |Y|^{c(\bar{g})}}, g' \in C.$$

- Pick any $g \in C$, evaluate its cycle decomposition and construct an $f \in Y^X$ that takes values $y \in Y$ on these cycles which are distributed uniformly at random over Y.

Consider our standard example for this situation:

7.5.3 Example We would like to generate graphs on 4 vertices uniformly at random. The conjugacy classes are parametrized by the proper partitions $(4), (3, 1), (2^2), (2, 1^2)$ and (1^4) of 4. Their orders are 6,8,3,6 and 1. The corresponding numbers of cyclic factors of the permutations induced on the set $\binom{4}{2}$ of pairs of vertices are 2,2,4,4 and 6, so that the numbers of fixed points on the set $2^{\binom{4}{2}}$ of labeled graphs amount to 4,4,16,16 and 64. This yields for the probabilities $p(C)$ the values

$$3/33, 4/33, 6/33, 12/33, 8/33.$$

These numbers may be multiplied by the common denominator 33 in order to get the natural numbers 3,4,6,12,8, which we accumulate obtaining

$$3, 7, 13, 25, 33.$$

A generator that yields natural numbers between 1 and 33 uniformly at random is now used in order to choose C. As soon as it generates one of the numbers 1,2 or 3 this means that the first one of the conjugacy classes is chosen. If it generates 4,5,6 or 7, the second class is chosen, and so on. Assume that it generates 12, then the third conjugacy class is picked, an element of which is the permutation $(12)(34)$. It induces on the set of pairs of vertices

$$\{a = \{1,2\}, b = \{1,3\}, c = \{1,4\}, d = \{2,3\}, e = \{2,4\}, f = \{3,4\}\}$$

the permutation

$$\overline{(12)(34)} = (a)(be)(cd)(f).$$

A random generator of zeros and ones is now used in order to associate values 0 or 1 with the cyclic factors of $(a)(be)(cd)(f)$. If it generates the sequence 1,0,0,1,say, we obtain the labelled graph that has edges joining the elements of the pairs a and f, while all the other pairs of vertices remain disjoint. Its orbit is represented by the graph shown in figure 7.2.

$\diamond$

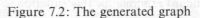

Figure 7.2: The generated graph

This method can easily be refined in order to generate graphs with prescribed number of edges or, more generally, representatives of orbits with a given weight, uniformly at random. If $_GX$ is a finite action, $w: X \to R$ a weight function, then G acts on the union of orbits with a prescribed weight $r \in R$, i.e. on the inverse image $w^{-1}[\{r\}]$ of r, and we need only to replace in 7.5.1 the corresponding factors in the numerator and in the denominator obtaining

7.5.4 Corollary *If we choose the conjugacy class $C \subseteq G$ with the probability*

$$p(C) := \frac{|C||w^{-1}[\{r\}]_g|}{|G||G\backslash\backslash w^{-1}[\{r\}]|},$$

pick any element $g \in C$ and generate a fixed point of weight r of g uniformly at random, then we obtain an element of X that is uniformly distributed over the orbits of weight r.

In the case when the acting group is a symmetric group, the choice of a conjugacy class amounts to the choice of a proper partition. We therefore should not forget that the number of proper partitions of $n \in \mathbb{N}$ is rapidly increasing with n. Here are a few of these numbers:

n	no. of proper partitions
10	42
20	627
40	37338
60	$\approx 10^6$
100	$\approx 2 \cdot 10^8$

This shows that it is worthwhile to try to avoid that this amount of probabilities is stored throughout the whole generating process. For practical purposes one can start the generation and evaluate probabilities only if required. This means that we need to evaluate $p(C_i)$ only if the generated random number exceeds $\sum_{j=1}^{i-1} p(C_j)$. The efficiency of this revised method heavily depends on the numbering of the conjugacy classes. The numbering should clearly be chosen in such a way that $p(C_i) \geq p(C_{i+1})$. Asymptotic considerations show (cf. Oberschelp, Dixon/Wilf) that in case of graph generation it is not bad to number the conjugacy classes of the symmetric group according to the lexicographic order of partitions.

In order to generate representatives of the orbits of G on X with prescribed type $\tilde{U}$, we can do the following. As each such orbit $\omega \in G\backslash\backslash X$ does contain elements x which have U as stabilizer, we can cut off from X_U each element that has a bigger stabilizer. It clearly suffices to remove from X_U the elements belonging to the X_V, where U is maximal in V. The remaining subset of X_U will be indicated as follows:

$$\hat{X}_U := X_U \backslash \bigcup_{U max. V} X_V.$$

The intersection of $\omega \in X\backslash\backslash\backslash\tilde{U}$ with $\hat{X}_U$ is the orbit of an $x \in \omega$, where $G_x = U$, under the normalizer subgroup $N_G(U)$, this is easy to check. As $G_x = U$ we can even consider the action of the factor group $N_G(U)/U$ on this intersection $\omega \cap \hat{X}_U$. This proves

7.5.5 Lemma *Each transversal of* $(N_G(U)/U)\backslash\backslash\hat{X}_U$ *is a transversal of the orbits of type* $\tilde{U}$ *of* G *on* X.

Moreover, if we want to apply probabilistic methods, we can use that the orbits of $N_G(U)/U$ on $\hat{X}_U$ are all of the same order $|N_G(U)/U|$. Hence we obtain

7.5.6 Theorem (Laue) *By picking elements from the orbits of* $N_G(U)/U$ *on* $\hat{X}_U$ *uniformly at random, we obtain elements that are uniformly distributed over the orbits of type* $\tilde{U}$ *of* G *on* X.

For example, if $U := \{1\}$, we have that $\hat{X}_U = \hat{X}_1$ is equal to X minus the union of the fixed point sets X_V, taken over all the minimal subgroups $V \leq G$. If in particular $G := C_n$, then the minimal subgroups V are just the cyclic subgroups $C_p \leq C_n$, where p is prime. the same holds for $G := S_n$, but in this case there may be, of course, several such C_p. As $N_G(1) = G$, we can, according to 7.5.6, easily generate representatives of the orbits of maximal length $|\bar{G}|$, uniformly at random. In order to display a concrete example, we recall the enumeration of primitive polynomials of degree n over $GF(q)$ (recall example 3.1.10). They correspond to the orbits of maximal length n of the Galois group C_n of $GF(q)^n$ over $GF(q)$. The above reasoning

shows that an orbit of $G = N_G(1)$ on $\hat{X}_1$ is also a transversal of these
orbits of maximal length n of G on X. But $\hat{X}_1$ is equal to $GF(q)^{\underline{n}}$
minus the set of fixed points $GF(q)_{C_p}$, where p runs through the prime
divisors of n. These subsets which have to be subtracted, can easily
be spotted. For example, if $n := 6, q := 2, C_{\underline{6}} := \langle (1 \dots 6) \rangle$, we obtain

$$GF(2)^{\underline{6}}_{C_2} = \{000000, 100100, 010010,$$

$$001001, 110110, 101101, 011011, 111111\},$$

$$GF(2)^{\underline{6}}_{C_3} = \{000000, 101010, 010101, 111111\}.$$

Subtracting the union of these sets from $GF(2)^{\underline{6}}$, we get $\hat{X}_1$, consisting
of the remaining $2^6 - 10$ binary sequences over $GF(2)$. A transversal
of the orbits of $C_{\underline{6}}$ on $\hat{X}_1$ is, for example. the set

100000, 110000, 101000, 10010, 111000, 110100, 110010, 111100, 111110.

Assuming a normal basis given, we can translate these sequences into
the 9 corresponding polynomials that are listed in many books.

Exercises

E 7.5.1 Prove that, for conjugate $g, g' \in G$, a finite action $_GX$ and an
orbit $\omega \in G\backslash\!\backslash X$, we have

$$|X_g \cap \omega| = |X_{g'} \cap \omega|.$$

7.6   Symmetry adapted bases

We discussed finite actions $_GX$ and their decomposition into orbits.
The corresponding problem in linear representation theory is the
decomposition of a representation space V, of $D: G \to GL(V)$ say,
into its irreducible constituents V_i:

$$V = V_1 \oplus \dots \oplus V_r.$$

This means that we have to find an *adapted basis*

$$\{v_1, \dots, v_{f^1}, v_{f^1+1}, \dots, v_{f^1+f^2}, \dots\},$$

where *adapted* means that $\{v_1, \dots, v_{f^1}\}$ is a basis of V_1, while the
following set $\{v_{f^1+1}, \dots, v_{f^1+f^2}\}$ is a basis of V_2, and so on. In the case

when we are given a complete set $\mathbf{D}^1, \ldots, \mathbf{D}^s$ of pairwise inequivalent and irreducible *matrix representations* of G, we can do much better. If the irreducible subspace V_1 affords an irreducible representation *equivalent* to $\mathbf{D}^i$, then we can find a basis $\{b_1, \ldots, b_{f^1}\}$ that affords $\mathbf{D}^i$ itself, which means, in formal terms, that the following holds, for each $g \in G$ and $1 \le f^1$:

$$gb_k := D(g)b_k = \sum_{j=1}^{f^1} d^i_{jk}(g)b_j, \text{ if } \mathbf{D}^i(g) = (d^i_{jk}(g)).$$

A basis of V which has this property, is called a *symmetry adapted basis* of V with respect to the given system $\mathbf{D}^1, \ldots, \mathbf{D}^s$ of irreducible matrix representations. Such a symmetry adapted basis has great advantages, since we know in advance, how each of the vectors $v \in V$ transforms under the action of $g \in G$ with respect to this particular basis. But the problem is that a complete system of ordinary irreducible matrix representations is available only in very few cases. Such a rare case is the symmetric group, as we have seen in the preceding section. Hence we would like to describe next, how a symmetry adapted basis can be evaluated for each representation space of the symmetric group S_n. (We restrict attention to the symmetric group, but the derivation of the symmetry adapted bases works in an analogous way for any other finite group G as well, as soon as we have the complete system of ordinary irreducible matrix representations at hand.)

Suppose we are given a complete system of ordinary irreducible matrix representations $\mathbf{D}^\alpha$ of S_n, and that V affords the representation $D: S_n \to GL(V)$, a representation that is assumed to be reducible. We denote by $m(\alpha)$ the multiplicity of the irreducible representation $[\alpha]$ in D, and f^α indicates the dimension of $[\alpha]$. It is our aim to construct a basis

$$B := \{b^\alpha_{ij} \mid \alpha \vdash n, 1 \le i \le m(\alpha), 1 \le j \le f^\alpha\},$$

such that

$$D(\pi)b^\alpha_{ij} = \sum_{k=1}^{f^\alpha} d^\alpha_{kj}(\pi)b^\alpha_{ik}.$$

Ordering this basis in a proper way:

$$B = \{\ldots, b^\alpha_{11}, \ldots, b^\alpha_{1,f^\alpha}, b^\alpha_{21}, \ldots, b^\alpha_{2,f^\alpha}, \ldots, b^\alpha_{m(\alpha),1}, \ldots, b^\alpha_{m(\alpha),f^\alpha}, \ldots\},$$

the matrix corresponding to the (linear) action of $\pi \in S_n$ takes the following form:

$$
7.6.1 \qquad \mathbf{D}(\pi) = \begin{pmatrix} \ddots & & & & & 0 \\ & \mathbf{D}^\alpha(\pi) & & & & \\ & & \mathbf{D}^\alpha(\pi) & & & \\ & & & \ddots & & \\ & & & & \mathbf{D}^\alpha(\pi) & \\ 0 & & & & & \ddots \end{pmatrix}.
$$

The square box containing the matrices $\mathbf{D}^\alpha(\pi)$ along its main diagonal is called the *homogeneous component of type* α.

First of all we note that such bases do in fact exist, this is obvious from linear algebra. In order to construct such a basis from given tabulated matrix representations $\mathbf{D}^\alpha$, i.e. from given numbers $d_{ik}^\alpha(\pi)$, for each $\pi \in S_n$, $1 \le i, k \le f^\alpha$, we introduce the following linear operators on V:

$$
P_{ji}^\alpha := \frac{f^\alpha}{n!} \sum_{\pi \in S_n} d_{ij}^\alpha(\pi^{-1}) D(\pi).
$$

Assume that the vectors e_{kl}^β, $1 \le k \le m(\beta)$, $1 \le l \le f^\beta$ form asymmetry adapted basis. Then

$$
P_{ji}^\alpha e_{kl}^\beta = \frac{f^\alpha}{n!} \sum_\pi d_{ij}^\alpha(\pi^{-1}) D(\pi) e_{kl}^\beta
$$

$$
= f^\alpha \sum_{m=1}^{f^\alpha} \left(\frac{1}{n!} \sum_\pi d_{ij}^\alpha(\pi^{-1}) d_{ml}^\beta(\pi) \right) e_{km}^\beta = \delta_{\alpha\beta} \delta_{il} b_{kj}^\alpha,
$$

where the last equation is obtained from 4.1.5. This shows that the following is true, for *any symmetry adapted basis* of V:

$$
7.6.2 \qquad P_{ji}^\alpha e_{kl}^\beta = \begin{cases} e_{kj}^\alpha & \text{if } \alpha = \beta, i = l, \\ 0 & \text{otherwise.} \end{cases}
$$

This yields, for the product of two such operators:

$$
7.6.3 \qquad P_{rs}^\gamma P_{ji}^\alpha = \delta_{\gamma\alpha} \delta_{sj} P_{ri}^\alpha.
$$

Another important consequence is

7.6.4 Corollary *The linear operator P_{ji}^{α} introduced above is a projection operator that maps V onto the subspace*

$$P_{ji}^{\alpha}(V) = W_j^{\alpha} := \ll e_{kj}^{\alpha} \mid 1 \le k \le m(\alpha) \gg .$$

We are now in a position to construct a symmetry adapted basis. For this purpose we pick, for each $\alpha \vdash n$ which is contained in D, *any vector $v \in V$* such that

$$b_1^{\alpha} := P_{11}^{\alpha}(v) \ne 0.$$

(Recall from 7.6.4 that the rank of P_{11}^{α} is nonzero if and only if $[\alpha]$ is contained in D.) Using this vector we put

$$b_{ij}^{\alpha} := P_{ji}^{\alpha}(b_1^{\alpha}),$$

and we claim that these vectors form a symmetry adapted basis of V. In order to check this we use 7.6.4 which says that, for a fixed symmetry adapted bases $\{e_{rs}^{\beta}\}$, the vector b_{ij}^{α}, being an element of the image of P_{ji}^{α}, is a linear combination of the following form:

$$b_{ij}^{\alpha} = \sum_{k=1}^{m(\alpha)} z_k e_{kj}^{\alpha}.$$

Using this linear combination we obtain:

$$D(\pi)b_{ij}^{\alpha} = \sum_k D(\pi)e_{kj}^{\alpha} = \sum_k z_k \sum_{l=1}^{f^{\alpha}} d_{lj}^{\alpha}(\pi)e_{kl}^{\alpha} = \sum_l d_{lj}^{\alpha}(\pi) \sum_k z_k e_{kl}^{\alpha}$$

$$= \sum_l d_{lj}^{\alpha}(\pi)P_{lj}^{\alpha} \sum_k z_k e_{kj}^{\alpha} = \sum_l d_{lj}^{\alpha}(\pi)P_{lj}^{\alpha}b_{ij}^{\alpha} = \sum_l d_{lj}^{\alpha}(\pi)P_{lj}^{\alpha}P_{ji}^{\alpha}(b_1^{\alpha}),$$

which is, by 7.6.3,

$$= \sum_l d_{lj}^{\alpha}(\pi)P_{li}^{\alpha}(b_1) = \sum_l d_{lj}^{\alpha}(\pi)b_{ij}^{\alpha},$$

as it is stated.

Some of the many interesting applications combine symmetry adapted bases with eigenvalue considerations. For example, the natural representation of the cyclic group $C_{\underline{n}} = \langle (1 \dots n) \rangle$ is generated by the matrix

$$\mathbf{D}((1\ldots n)) := \begin{pmatrix} 0 & 0 & \ldots & 0 & 1 \\ 1 & 0 & \ldots & 0 & 0 \\ \vdots & \vdots & \ddots & \vdots & \vdots \\ 0 & 0 & \ldots & 1 & 0 \end{pmatrix}.$$

Its characteristic polynomial

$$\det(x\mathbf{I} - \mathbf{D}((1\ldots n))) = x^n - 1$$

shows that the *eigenvalues* are exactly the powers of a primitive n-th root of unity $\omega := e^{2\pi i/n}$:

$$\omega_j := \omega^j = e^{2\pi i j/n}.$$

This implies that the homogeneous components are onedimensional (which means that the irreducible constituents of the natural representation of the cyclic group are pairwise different, this representation is in fact a *model* for the cyclic group). A symmetry adapted basis therefore consists of eigenvectors corresponding to pairwise different eigenvalues, and so the arguments used in the proof of 5.7.7 imply the following:

7.6.5 Corollary *Each matrix that commutes with* $\mathbf{D}((1\ldots n))$ *becomes diagonal if we change the basis into a symmetry adapted one. Hence in particular the eigenvectors of* $\mathbf{D}((1\ldots n))$ *are eigenvectors of the commuting matrix, too.*

A nice application is the following derivation of Cardano's formula for the solutions of cubic equations:

7.6.6 Example The following matrix clearly commutes with $\mathbf{D}((123))$:

$$M := \begin{pmatrix} 0 & a & b \\ b & 0 & a \\ a & b & 0 \end{pmatrix}.$$

The characteristic polynomial of this matrix is

$$x^3 - 3abx - a^3 - b^3.$$

In order to derive its roots we can use 7.6.5. Putting $\omega := e^{2\pi i/3}$, we obtain from 7.6.5 the following eigenvectors of M:

$$v_1 := \begin{pmatrix} 1 \\ 1 \\ 1 \end{pmatrix}, \quad v_2 := \begin{pmatrix} 1 \\ \omega^2 \\ \omega \end{pmatrix}, \quad v_3 := \begin{pmatrix} 1 \\ \omega \\ \omega^2 \end{pmatrix}.$$

Hence the eigenvalues of the matrix M turn out to be

$$\lambda_1 = a + b, \lambda_2 = a\omega^2 + b\omega, \lambda_3 = a\omega + b\omega^2.$$

We can apply this now to a cubic equation of the form

$$x^3 + px + q = 0,$$

obtaining $p = -3ab, q = -(a^3 + b^3)$, from which we derive *Cardano's formulae*

$$a = \sqrt[3]{-\frac{q}{2} + \sqrt{\left(\frac{q}{2}\right)^2 + \left(\frac{p}{3}\right)^3}}, \quad b = \sqrt[3]{-\frac{q}{2} - \sqrt{\left(\frac{q}{2}\right)^2 + \left(\frac{p}{3}\right)^3}}.$$

$\diamond$

A more important application of symmetry adapted bases is the evaluation of the irreducible polynomial representations $\langle \alpha \rangle$ of the general linear group $GL_m(\mathbb{Q})$, which arise by symmetrizing the identity map:

$$\langle \alpha \rangle := id \; \square \; [\alpha],$$

but the details of this form quite a long story, and so I refer to the corresponding literature (see the chapter with comments and references).

Chapter 8

Tables

This chapter contains tables of marks and Burnside matrices of the smallest cyclic, dihedral, symmetric and alternating groups. Moreover, the interested reader will find characters (reducible and irreducible) of symmetric groups, in order to support further applications by providing some numerical information. The irreducible characters are given, together with the Young characters and their decompositions. Also the scalar products of Young characters and products of Young characters and the alternating character are tabulated, since these numbers are numbers of 0-1–matrices with prescribed row and column sums. In addition the smallest Foulkes tables are shown since the characters occuring in enumeration theory of symmetry classes of mappings are linear combinations of Foulkes characters. Then the first 44 character polynomials are listed, each of them allows to evaluate an infinite series of ordinary irreducible characters of symmetric groups. The final section contains the 120 first Schubert polynomials.

The tables were obtained using different program systems like CAY-LEY for the tables of marks and MAPLE for inverting the tables of marks in order to obtain the Burnside matrices. SYMCHAR (which is due in particular to A. Kohnert) was used for the irreducible characters of the symmetric groups, the Young characters and their decompositions, the Foulkes tables and the Schubert polynomials. The character polynomials were taken from the thesis of P. Zeiss.

The reader who would like to do more can obtain SYMCHAR (which is still in progress, and which can do many other things, too, like handling Schur polynomials) on a 3.5 discette from the author for free (just send such a discette), including a LaTeX–file of the manual.

8.1   Tables of marks and Burnside matrices

This part of the appendix contains tables of marks and Burnside matrices of cyclic, dihedral, symmetric and alternating groups.

8.1.1   Cyclic groups

This section contains the system of subgroups, the table of marks and the Burnside matrix of the cyclic groups C_3, up to C_{20}. The groups C_p, where p is a prime number are trivial since they contain the trivial subgroups only, and so we have for the table of marks and its inverse, the Burnside matrix of this particular groups:

$$M(C_{\underline{p}}) = \begin{pmatrix} p & 1 \\ & 1 \end{pmatrix}, \quad B(C_{\underline{p}}) = \begin{pmatrix} 1/p & -1/p \\ & 1 \end{pmatrix}.$$

There is also an explicit expression for the table of marks in the general case since the subgroup lattice of $C_{\underline{n}}$ is the lattice of divisors of n, but in order to make life easier for the interested reader we show these matrices and their inverses, which are less trivial.

The group C_4: The subgroups are

$$U_1 = <1>, U_2 = <(1,3)(2,4)>, U_3 = <(1,2,3,4)> = C_{\underline{4}}.$$

The table of marks and the Burnside matrix:

$$\begin{pmatrix} 4 & 2 & 1 \\ & 2 & 1 \\ & & 1 \end{pmatrix}, \begin{pmatrix} 1/4 & -1/4 & \cdot \\ & 1/2 & -1/2 \\ & & 1 \end{pmatrix}$$

The group $C_{\underline{6}}$: The subgroups are

$$U_1 = <1>, U_2 = <(1,4)(2,5)(3,6)>, U_3 = <(1,3,5)(2,4,6)>,$$
$$U_4 = <(1,3,5)(2,4,6),(1,4)(2,5)(3,6)> = C_{\underline{6}}.$$

The table of marks and the Burnside matrix:

$$\begin{pmatrix} 6 & 3 & 2 & 1 \\ & 3 & \cdot & 1 \\ & & 2 & 1 \\ & & & 1 \end{pmatrix}, \begin{pmatrix} 1/6 & -1/6 & -1/6 & 1/6 \\ & 1/3 & \cdot & -1/3 \\ & & 1/2 & -1/2 \\ & & & 1 \end{pmatrix}.$$

The group C_8: The subgroups are

$$U_1 =< 1 >, U_2 =< (1,5)(2,6)(3,7)(4,8) >,$$

$$U_3 =< (1,3,5,7)(2,4,6,8) >, U_4 =< (1,2,3,4,5,6,7,8) >= C_8.$$

The table of marks and the Burnside matrix:

$$\begin{pmatrix} 8 & 4 & 2 & 1 \\ & 4 & 2 & 1 \\ & & 2 & 1 \\ & & & 1 \end{pmatrix}, \begin{pmatrix} 1/8 & -1/8 & . & . \\ & 1/4 & -1/4 & . \\ & & 1/2 & -1/2 \\ & & & 1 \end{pmatrix}.$$

The group C_9: The subgroups are

$$U_1 =< 1 >, U_2 =< (1,4,7)(2,5,8)(3,6,9) >,$$

$$U_3 =< (1,2,3,4,5,6,7,8,9) >= C.$$

The table of marks and the Burnside matrix:

$$\begin{pmatrix} 9 & 3 & 1 \\ & 3 & 1 \\ & & 1 \end{pmatrix}, \begin{pmatrix} 1/9 & -1/9 & . \\ & 1/3 & -1/3 \\ & & 1 \end{pmatrix}.$$

The group C_{10}: The subgroups are

$$U_1 =< 1 >, U_2 =< (1,6)(2,7)(3,8)(4,9)(5,10) >,$$

$$U_3 =< (1,3,5,7,9)(2,4,6,8,10) >, U_4 = C_{10}.$$

The table of marks and the Burnside matrix:

$$\begin{pmatrix} 10 & 5 & 2 & 1 \\ & 5 & . & 1 \\ & & 2 & 1 \\ & & & 1 \end{pmatrix}, \begin{pmatrix} 1/10 & -1/10 & -1/10 & 1/10 \\ & 1/5 & . & -1/5 \\ & & 1/2 & -1/2 \\ & & & 1 \end{pmatrix}.$$

The group C_{12}: The subgroups are

$$U_1 =< 1 >, U_2 =< (1,7)(2,8)(3,9)(4,10)(5,11)(6,12) >,$$

$$U_3 =< (1,5,9)(2,6,10)(3,7,11)(4,8,12) >,$$

$$U_4 =< (1,4,7,10)(2,5,8,11)(3,6,9,12) >,$$

$$U_5 =< (1,5,9)(2,6,10)(3,7,11)(4,8,12),$$

$$(1,7)(2,8)(3,9)(4,10)(5,11)(6,12) >,$$

$$U_6 = C_{\underline{12}}.$$

The table of marks is

$$\begin{pmatrix} 12 & 6 & 4 & 3 & 2 & 1 \\ & 6 & . & 3 & 2 & 1 \\ & & 4 & . & 2 & 1 \\ & & & 3 & . & 1 \\ & & & & 2 & 1 \\ & & & & & 1 \end{pmatrix}.$$

The Burnsidematrix looks as follows

$$\begin{pmatrix} 1/12 & -1/12 & -1/12 & . & 1/12 & . \\ & 1/6 & . & -1/6 & -1/6 & 1/6 \\ & & 1/4 & . & -1/4 & . \\ & & & 1/3 & . & -1/3 \\ & & & & 1/2 & -1/2 \\ & & & & & 1 \end{pmatrix}.$$

The group $C_{\underline{14}}$: The subgroups are

$$U_1 =< 1 >, U_2 =< (1,8)(2,9)(3,10)(4,11)(5,12)(6,13)(7,14) >,$$

$$U_3 =< (1,3,5,7,9,11,13)(2,4,6,8,10,12,14) >, U_4 = C_{\underline{14}}.$$

The table of marks and the Burnside matrix:

$$\begin{pmatrix} 14 & 7 & 2 & 1 \\ & 7 & . & 1 \\ & & 2 & 1 \\ & & & 1 \end{pmatrix}, \begin{pmatrix} 1/14 & -1/14 & -1/14 & 1/14 \\ & 1/7 & . & -1/7 \\ & & 1/2 & -1/2 \\ & & & 1 \end{pmatrix}.$$

The group $C_{\underline{15}}$: The subgroups are

$$U_1 =< 1 >, U_2 =< (1,6,11)(2,7,12)(3,8,13)(4,9,14)(5,10,15) >,$$

$$U_3 =< (1,4,7,10,13)(2,5,8,11,14)(3,6,9,12,15) >, U_4 = C_{\underline{15}}.$$

The table of marks and the Burnside matrix:

$$\begin{pmatrix} 15 & 5 & 3 & 1 \\ & 5 & . & 1 \\ & & 3 & 1 \\ & & & 1 \end{pmatrix}, \begin{pmatrix} 1/15 & -1/15 & -1/15 & 1/15 \\ & 1/5 & . & -1/5 \\ & & 1/3 & -1/3 \\ & & & 1 \end{pmatrix}.$$

The group C_{16}: The subgroups are

$$U_1 = <1>,$$

$$U_2 = <(1,9)(2,10)(3,11)(4,12)(5,13)(6,14)(7,15)(8,16)>,$$

$$U_3 = <(1,5,9,13)(2,6,10,14)(3,7,11,15)(4,8,12,16)>,$$

$$U_4 = <(1,3,5,7,9,11,13,15)(2,4,6,8,10,12,14,16)>, U_5 = C_{16}.$$

The table of marks is

$$\begin{pmatrix} 16 & 8 & 4 & 2 & 1 \\ & 8 & 4 & 2 & 1 \\ & & 4 & 2 & 1 \\ & & & 2 & 1 \\ & & & & 1 \end{pmatrix}.$$

The Burnsidematrix looks as follows

$$\begin{pmatrix} 1/16 & -1/16 & . & . & . \\ & 1/8 & -1/8 & . & . \\ & & 1/4 & -1/4 & . \\ & & & 1/2 & -1/2 \\ & & & & 1 \end{pmatrix}.$$

The group C_{18}: The subgroups are

$$U_1 = <1>,$$

$$U_2 = <(1,10)(2,11)(3,12)(4,13)(5,14)(6,15)(7,16)(8,17)(9,18)>,$$

$$U_3 = <(1,7,13)(2,8,14)(3,9,15)(4,10,16)(5,11,17)(6,12,18)>,$$

$$U_4 = <(1,7,13)(2,8,14)(3,9,15)(4,10,16)(5,11,17)(6,12,18),$$

$$(1,10)(2,11)(3,12)(4,13)(5,14)(6,15)(7,16)(8,17)(9,18)>,$$

$$U_5 = <(1,3,5,7,9,11,13,15,17)(2,4,6,8,10,12,14,16,18)>,$$

$$U_6 = C_{\underline{18}}.$$

The table of marks is

$$\begin{pmatrix} 18 & 9 & 6 & 3 & 2 & 1 \\ & 9 & . & 3 & . & 1 \\ & & 6 & 3 & 2 & 1 \\ & & & 3 & . & 1 \\ & & & & 2 & 1 \\ & & & & & 1 \end{pmatrix}.$$

The Burnsidematrix looks as follows

$$\begin{pmatrix} 1/18 & -1/18 & -1/18 & 1/18 & . & . \\ & 1/9 & . & -1/9 & . & . \\ & & 1/6 & -1/6 & -1/6 & 1/6 \\ & & & 1/3 & . & -1/3 \\ & & & & 1/2 & -1/2 \\ & & & & & 1 \end{pmatrix}.$$

The group $C_{\underline{20}}$: The subgroups are

$$U_1 = <1>,$$

$$U_2 = <(1,11)(2,12)(3,13)\cdots(10,20)>,$$

$$U_3 = <(1,5,9,13,17)(2,6,10,14,18)(3,7,11,15,19)(4,8,12,16,20)>,$$

$$U_4 = <(1,6,11,16)(2,7,12,17)(3,8,13,18)(4,9,14,19)(5,10,15,20)>,$$

$$U_5 = <(1,5,9,13,17)(2,6,10,14,18)(3,7,11,15,19)(4,8,12,16,20),$$

$$(1,11)(2,12)(3,13)(4,14)(5,15)(6,16)(7,17)(8,18)(9,19)(10,20)>,$$

$$U_6 = C_{\underline{20}}.$$

The table of marks is

$$\begin{pmatrix} 20 & 10 & 4 & 5 & 2 & 1 \\ & 10 & . & 5 & 2 & 1 \\ & & 4 & . & 2 & 1 \\ & & & 5 & . & 1 \\ & & & & 2 & 1 \\ & & & & & 1 \end{pmatrix}.$$

The Burnsidematrix looks as follows

$$\begin{pmatrix} 1/20 & -1/20 & -1/20 & . & 1/20 & . \\ & 1/10 & . & -1/10 & -1/10 & 1/10 \\ & & 1/4 & . & -1/4 & . \\ & & & 1/5 & . & -1/5 \\ & & & & 1/2 & -1/2 \\ & & & & & 1 \end{pmatrix}.$$

8.1.2 Dihedral groups

This section contains a system of representatives of the conjugacy classes of subgroups, the table of marks and the Burnside matrix of the dihedral groups $D_{\underline{3}}$ up to $D_{\underline{11}}$.

The group D_3: A transversal of the conjugacy classes of subgroups is

$$U_1 =< 1 >, U_2 =< (1, 2) >, U_3 =< (1, 2, 3) >,$$

$$U_4 =< (1, 2, 3), (1, 2) >= D_{\underline{3}}.$$

The table of marks is

$$\begin{pmatrix} 6 & 3 & 2 & 1 \\ & 1 & . & 1 \\ & & 2 & 1 \\ & & & 1 \end{pmatrix}.$$

The Burnside matrix looks as follows

$$\begin{pmatrix} 1/6 & -1/2 & -1/6 & 1/2 \\ & 1 & . & -1 \\ & & 1/2 & -1/2 \\ & & & 1 \end{pmatrix}.$$

The group D_4: A transversal of the conjugacy classes of subgroups is

$$U_1 =< 1 >, U_2 =< (1, 3)(2, 4) >, U_3 =< (1, 4)(2, 3) >, U_4 =< (1, 3) >,$$

$$U_5 =< (1, 4)(2, 3), (1, 2)(3, 4) >, U_6 =< (1, 3), (2, 4) >,$$

$$U_7 =< (1, 2, 3, 4) >, U_8 =< (1, 2, 3, 4), (1, 4)(2, 3) >= D_{\underline{4}}.$$

The table of marks is

$$\begin{pmatrix} 8 & 4 & 4 & 4 & 2 & 2 & 2 & 1 \\ & 4 & . & . & 2 & 2 & 2 & 1 \\ & & 2 & . & 2 & . & . & 1 \\ & & & 2 & . & 2 & . & 1 \\ & & & & 2 & . & . & 1 \\ & & & & & 2 & . & 1 \\ & & & & & & 2 & 1 \\ & & & & & & & 1 \end{pmatrix}.$$

The Burnside matrix looks as follows

$$\begin{pmatrix} 1/8 & -1/8 & -1/4 & -1/4 & 1/4 & 1/4 & . & . \\ & 1/4 & . & . & . & -1/4 & -1/4 & -1/4 & 1/2 \\ & & 1/2 & . & -1/2 & . & . & . \\ & & & 1/2 & . & -1/2 & . & . \\ & & & & 1/2 & . & . & -1/2 \\ & & & & & 1/2 & . & -1/2 \\ & & & & & & 1/2 & -1/2 \\ & & & & & & & 1 \end{pmatrix}.$$

The group D_5: A transversal of the conjugacy classes of subgroups is

$$U_1 = <1>, U_2 = <(1,2)(3,5)>, U_3 = <(1,2,3,4,5)>,$$

$$U_4 = <(1,2,3,4,5),(1,2)(3,5)> = D_5.$$

The table of marks is

$$\begin{pmatrix} 10 & 5 & 2 & 1 \\ & 1 & . & 1 \\ & & 2 & 1 \\ & & & 1 \end{pmatrix}.$$

The Burnside matrix looks as follows

$$\begin{pmatrix} 1/10 & -1/2 & -1/10 & 1/2 \\ & 1 & . & -1 \\ & & 1/2 & -1/2 \\ & & & 1 \end{pmatrix}.$$

The group D_6: A transversal of the conjugacy classes of subgroups is

$$U_1 =<1>, U_2 =<(1,4)(2,5)(3,6)>, U_3 =<(1,6)(2,5)(3,4)>,$$

$$U_4 =<(1,5)(2,4)>, U_5 =<(1,3,5)(2,4,6)>,$$

$$U_6 =<(1,6)(2,5)(3,4),(1,3)(4,6)>,$$

$$U_7 =<(1,3,5)(2,4,6),(1,4)(2,5)(3,6)>,$$

$$U_8 =<(1,3,5)(2,4,6),(1,6)(2,5)(3,4)>,$$

$$U_9 =<(1,3,5)(2,4,6),(1,5)(2,4)>,$$

$$U_{10} =<(1,3,5)(2,4,6),(1,6)(2,5)(3,4),(1,5)(2,4)>= D_6.$$

The table of marks is

$$\begin{pmatrix}
12 & 6 & 6 & 6 & 4 & 3 & 2 & 2 & 2 & 1 \\
 & 6 & . & . & . & 3 & 2 & . & . & 1 \\
 & & 2 & . & . & 1 & . & 2 & . & 1 \\
 & & & 2 & . & 1 & . & . & 2 & 1 \\
 & & & & 4 & . & 2 & 2 & 2 & 1 \\
 & & & & & 1 & . & . & . & 1 \\
 & & & & & & 2 & . & . & 1 \\
 & & & & & & & 2 & . & 1 \\
 & & & & & & & & 2 & 1 \\
 & & & & & & & & & 1
\end{pmatrix}.$$

The Burnside matrix is

$$\begin{pmatrix}
1/12 & -1/12 & -1/4 & -1/4 & -1/12 & 1/2 & 1/12 & 1/4 & 1/4 & -1/2 \\
 & 1/6 & . & . & . & -1/2 & -1/6 & . & . & 1/2 \\
 & & 1/2 & . & . & -1/2 & . & -1/2 & . & 1/2 \\
 & & & 1/2 & . & -1/2 & . & . & -1/2 & 1/2 \\
 & & & & 1/4 & . & -1/4 & -1/4 & -1/4 & 1/2 \\
 & & & & & 1 & . & . & . & -1 \\
 & & & & & & 1/2 & . & . & -1/2 \\
 & & & & & & & 1/2 & . & -1/2 \\
 & & & & & & & & 1/2 & -1/2 \\
 & & & & & & & & & 1
\end{pmatrix}$$

The group D_7: A transversal of the conjugacy classes of subgroups is

$$U_1 =<1>, U_2 =<(1,2)(3,7)(4,6)>, U_3 =<(1,2,3,4,5,6,7)>,$$

$$U_4 =<(1,2,3,4,5,6,7),(1,2)(3,7)(4,6)>= D_7.$$

The table of marks is

$$
\begin{pmatrix}
14 & 7 & 2 & 1\\
 & 1 & . & 1\\
 & & 2 & 1\\
 & & & 1
\end{pmatrix}.
$$

The Burnside matrix looks as follows

$$
\begin{pmatrix}
1/14 & -1/2 & -1/14 & 1/2\\
 & 1 & . & -1\\
 & & 1/2 & -1/2\\
 & & & 1
\end{pmatrix}.
$$

The group $D_{\underline{8}}$: A transversal of the conjugacy classes of subgroups is

$$U_1 =< 1 >, U_2 =< (1,5)(2,6)(3,7)(4,8) >,$$

$$U_3 =< (1,8)(2,7)(3,6)(4,5) >, U_4 =< (1,5)(2,4)(6,8) >,$$

$$U_5 =< (1,8)(2,7)(3,6)(4,5), (1,4)(2,3)(5,8)(6,7) >,$$

$$U_6 =< (1,5)(2,4)(6,8), (2,8)(3,7)(4,6) >,$$

$$U_7 =< (1,3,5,7)(2,4,6,8) >,$$

$$U_8 =< (1,3,5,7)(2,4,6,8), (1,8)(2,7)(3,6)(4,5) >,$$

$$U_9 =< (1,3,5,7)(2,4,6,8), (1,5)(2,4)(6,8) >,$$

$$U_{10} =< (1,2,3,4,5,6,7,8) >,$$

$$U_{11} =< (1,2,3,4,5,6,7,8), (1,8)(2,7)(3,6)(4,5) >= D_{\underline{8}}.$$

The table of marks is

$$
\begin{pmatrix}
16 & 8 & 8 & 8 & 4 & 4 & 4 & 2 & 2 & 2 & 1\\
 & 8 & . & . & 4 & 4 & 4 & 2 & 2 & 2 & 1\\
 & & 2 & . & 2 & . & . & 2 & . & . & 1\\
 & & & 2 & . & 2 & . & . & 2 & . & 1\\
 & & & & 2 & . & 2 & . & . & . & 1\\
 & & & & & 2 & . & . & 2 & . & 1\\
 & & & & & & 4 & 2 & 2 & 2 & 1\\
 & & & & & & & 2 & . & . & 1\\
 & & & & & & & & 2 & . & 1\\
 & & & & & & & & & 2 & 1\\
 & & & & & & & & & & 1
\end{pmatrix}.
$$

The Burnside matrix looks as follows

$$
\begin{pmatrix}
1/16 & -1/16 & -1/4 & -1/4 & 1/4 & 1/4 & . & . & . & . & . \\
 & 1/8 & . & . & -1/4 & -1/4 & -1/8 & 1/4 & 1/4 & . & . \\
 & & 1/2 & . & -1/2 & . & . & . & . & . & . \\
 & & & 1/2 & . & -1/2 & . & . & . & . & . \\
 & & & & 1/2 & . & . & -1/2 & . & . & . \\
 & & & & & 1/2 & . & . & -1/2 & . & . \\
 & & & & & & 1/4 & -1/4 & -1/4 & -1/4 & 1/2 \\
 & & & & & & & 1/2 & . & . & -1/2 \\
 & & & & & & & & 1/2 & . & -1/2 \\
 & & & & & & & & & 1/2 & -1/2 \\
 & & & & & & & & & & 1
\end{pmatrix}.
$$

The group D_9: A transversal of the conjugacy classes of subgroups is

$$U_1 = <1>, U_2 = <(1,2)(3,9)(4,8)(5,7)>,$$

$$U_3 = <(1,4,7)(2,5,8)(3,6,9)>,$$

$$U_4 = <(1,4,7)(2,5,8)(3,6,9),(1,2)(3,9)(4,8)(5,7)>,$$

$$U_5 = <(1,2,3,4,5,6,7,8,9)>,$$

$$U_6 = <(1,2,3,4,5,6,7,8,9),(1,2)(3,9)(4,8)(5,7)> = D_9.$$

The table of marks is

$$
\begin{pmatrix}
18 & 9 & 6 & 3 & 2 & 1 \\
 & 1 & . & 1 & . & 1 \\
 & & 6 & 3 & 2 & 1 \\
 & & & 1 & . & 1 \\
 & & & & 2 & 1 \\
 & & & & & 1
\end{pmatrix}.
$$

The Burnside matrix looks as follows

$$
\begin{pmatrix}
1/18 & -1/2 & -1/18 & 1/2 & . & . \\
 & 1 & . & -1 & . & . \\
 & & 1/6 & -1/2 & -1/6 & 1/2 \\
 & & & 1 & . & -1 \\
 & & & & 1/2 & -1/2 \\
 & & & & & 1
\end{pmatrix}.
$$

The group D_{10}: A transversal of the conjugacy classes of subgroups is

$$U_1 = <1>, U_2 = <(1,6)(2,7)(3,8)(4,9)(5,10)>,$$

$$\dot{U}_3 = <(1,10)(2,9)(3,8)(4,7)(5,6)>, U_4 = <(1,7)(2,6)(3,5)(8,10)>,$$

$$U_5 = <(1,3,5,7,9)(2,4,6,8,10)>,$$

$$U_6 = <(1,10)(2,9)(3,8)(4,7)(5,6),(1,5)(2,4)(6,10)(7,9)>,$$

$$U_7 = <(1,3,5,7,9)(2,4,6,8,10),(1,6)(2,7)(3,8)(4,9)(5,10)>,$$

$$U_8 = <(1,3,5,7,9)(2,4,6,8,10),(1,10)(2,9)(3,8)(4,7)(5,6)>,$$

$$U_9 = <(1,3,5,7,9)(2,4,6,8,10),(1,7)(2,6)(3,5)(8,10)>,$$

$$U_{10} = <(1,3,5,7,9)(2,4,6,8,10),(1,10)(2,9)(3,8)(4,7)(5,6),$$

$$(1,7)(2,6)(3,5)(8,10)> = D_{\underline{10}}.$$

The table of marks is

$$\begin{pmatrix}
20 & 10 & 10 & 10 & 4 & 5 & 2 & 2 & 2 & 1 \\
 & 10 & . & . & . & 5 & 2 & . & . & 1 \\
 & & 2 & . & . & 1 & . & 2 & . & 1 \\
 & & & 2 & . & 1 & . & . & 2 & 1 \\
 & & & & 4 & . & 2 & 2 & 2 & 1 \\
 & & & & & 1 & . & . & . & 1 \\
 & & & & & & 2 & . & . & 1 \\
 & & & & & & & 2 & . & 1 \\
 & & & & & & & & 2 & 1 \\
 & & & & & & & & & 1
\end{pmatrix}.$$

The Burnside matrix looks as follows

$$\begin{pmatrix}
1/20 & -1/20 & -1/4 & -1/4 & -1/20 & 1/2 & 1/20 & 1/4 & 1/4 & -1/2 \\
 & 1/10 & . & . & . & -1/2 & -1/10 & . & . & 1/2 \\
 & & 1/2 & . & . & -1/2 & . & -1/2 & . & 1/2 \\
 & & & 1/2 & . & -1/2 & . & . & -1/2 & 1/2 \\
 & & & & 1/4 & . & -1/4 & -1/4 & -1/4 & 1/2 \\
 & & & & & 1 & . & . & . & -1 \\
 & & & & & & 1/2 & . & . & -1/2 \\
 & & & & & & & 1/2 & . & -1/2 \\
 & & & & & & & & 1/2 & -1/2 \\
 & & & & & & & & & 1
\end{pmatrix}.$$

The group $D_{\underline{11}}$: A transversal of the conjugacy classes of subgroups is

$$U_1 = <1>, U_2 = <(1,2)(3,11)(4,10)(5,9)(6,8)>,$$

$$U_3 =< (1,2,3,4,5,6,7,8,9,10,11) >,$$

$$U_4 =< (1,2,3,4,5,6,7,8,9,10,11),(1,2)(3,11)(4,10)(5,9)(6,8) >= D_{11}.$$

The table of marks is

$$\begin{pmatrix} 22 & 11 & 2 & 1 \\ & 1 & . & 1 \\ & & 2 & 1 \\ & & & 1 \end{pmatrix}.$$

The Burnside matrix looks as follows

$$\begin{pmatrix} 1/22 & -1/2 & -1/22 & 1/2 \\ & 1 & . & -1 \\ & & 1/2 & -1/2 \\ & & & 1 \end{pmatrix}.$$

8.1.3 Alternating groups

This section contains a system of representatives of the conjugacy classes of subgroups, the table of marks and the Burnside matrix of A_3, A_4 and A_5. From A_6 only the table of marks can be shown in a reasonable way.

The group A_3: A transversal of the conjugacy classes of subgroups is

$$U_1 =< 1 >, U_2 =< (1,2,3) > .$$

The table of marks is

$$\begin{pmatrix} 3 & 1 \\ & 1 \end{pmatrix}.$$

The Burnside matrix looks as follows

$$\begin{pmatrix} 1/3 & -1/3 \\ & 1 \end{pmatrix}.$$

The group A_4: A transversal of the conjugacy classes of subgroups is

$$U_1 =< 1 >, U_2 =< (1,3)(2,4) >, U_3 =< (1,2,3) >,$$

$$U_4 =< (1,3)(2,4),(1,4)(2,3) >, U_5 =< (1,2,3),(1,4,2) >$$

The table of marks is

$$
\begin{pmatrix}
12 & 6 & 4 & 3 & 1 \\
   & 2 & . & 3 & 1 \\
   &   & 1 & . & 1 \\
   &   &   & 3 & 1 \\
   &   &   &   & 1
\end{pmatrix}.
$$

The Burnside matrix looks as follows

$$
\begin{pmatrix}
1/12 & -1/4 & -1/3 & 1/6 & 1/3 \\
     & 1/2 & .   & -1/2 & . \\
     &   & 1   & .   & -1 \\
     &   &   & 1/3 & -1/3 \\
     &   &   &   & 1
\end{pmatrix}.
$$

The group $A_{\underline{5}}$**:** A transversal of the conjugacy classes of subgroups is

$$U_1 = <1>, U_2 = <(1,5)(3,4)>, U_3 = <(2,3,4)>,$$

$$U_4 = <(1,3,4,2,5)>, U_5 = <(1,5)(3,4),(1,3)(4,5)>,$$

$$U_6 = <(2,3,4),(1,5)(3,4)>, U_7 = <(1,3,4,2,5),(1,3)(4,5)>,$$

$$U_8 = <(1,3,4),(1,5,3)>, U_9 = <(1,3,4,2,5),(1,5,3,2,4)> = A_{\underline{5}}.$$

The table of marks is

$$
\begin{pmatrix}
60 & 30 & 20 & 12 & 15 & 10 & 6 & 5 & 1 \\
   & 2 & . & . & 3 & 2 & 2 & 1 & 1 \\
   &   & 2 & . & . & 1 & . & 2 & 1 \\
   &   &   & 2 & . & . & 1 & . & 1 \\
   &   &   &   & 3 & . & . & 1 & 1 \\
   &   &   &   &   & 1 & . & . & 1 \\
   &   &   &   &   &   & 1 & . & 1 \\
   &   &   &   &   &   &   & 1 & 1 \\
   &   &   &   &   &   &   &   & 1
\end{pmatrix}.
$$

The Burnside matrix looks as follows

$$
\begin{pmatrix}
1/60 & -1/4 & -1/6 & -1/10 & 1/6 & 1/2 & 1/2 & 1/3 & -1 \\
     & 1/2 & .   & .   & -1/2 & -1 & -1 & .   & 2 \\
     &   & 1/2 & .   & .   & -1/2 & . & -1 & 1 \\
     &   &   & 1/2   & .   & .   & -1/2 & . & . \\
     &   &   &   & 1/3 & .   & .   & -1/3 & . \\
     &   &   &   &   & 1   & .   & .   & -1 \\
     &   &   &   &   &   & 1   & .   & -1 \\
     &   &   &   &   &   &   & 1   & -1 \\
     &   &   &   &   &   &   &   & 1
\end{pmatrix}.
$$

The group A_6: A transversal óf the conjugacy classes of subgroups is

$$U_1 =< 1 >, U_2 =< (2,3)(5,6) >,$$

$$U_3 =< (1,6,5)(2,4,3) >, U_4 =< (3,4,6) >,$$

$$U_5 =< (1,5,3,4,6) >, U_6 =< (1,4)(2,6,3,5) >,$$

$$U_7 =< (2,3)(5,6), (1,4)(5,6) >, U_8 =< (2,3)(5,6), (2,5)(3,6) >,$$

$$U_9 =< (1,6,5)(2,4,3), (2,3)(5,6) >, U_{10} =< (3,4,6), (1,2)(3,4) >,$$

$$U_{11} =< (1,6,5)(2,4,3), (1,6,5)(2,3,4) >,$$

$$U_{12} =< (1,5,3,4,6), (1,6)(4,5) >,$$

$$U_{13} =< (1,4)(2,6,3,5), (1,4)(5,6) >,$$

$$U_{14} =< (1,3,6)(2,5,4), (1,2,6)(3,5,4) >, U_{15} =< (3,6,5), (2,6,5) >,$$

$$U_{16} =< (1,6,5)(2,4,3), (1,6,5)(2,3,4), (2,3)(5,6) >,$$

$$U_{17} =< (1,4)(2,6,3,5), (1,6,4,5)(2,3) >,$$

$$U_{18} =< (1,4)(2,6,3,5), (1,4)(2,3,5,6) >,$$

$$U_{19} =< (1,4)(2,6,3,5), (1,2)(3,6,4,5) >,$$

$$U_{20} =< (1,5,3,4,6), (1,3,5,6,4) >,$$

$$U_{21} =< (1,4,6,2,5), (1,3,2,4,6) >, U_{22} = A_6.$$

The table of marks is

$$
\begin{pmatrix}
360 & 180 & 120 & 120 & 72 & 90 & 90 & 90 & 60 & 60 & 40 & 36 & 45 & 30 & 30 & 20 & 15 & 15 & 10 & 6 & 6 & 1 \\
 & 4 & . & . & . & 2 & 6 & 6 & 4 & 4 & . & 4 & 5 & 2 & 2 & 4 & 3 & 3 & 2 & 2 & 2 & 1 \\
 & & 6 & . & . & . & . & 3 & . & 4 & . & . & 6 & . & 2 & 3 & . & 1 & . & 3 & 1 \\
 & & & 6 & . & . & . & . & 3 & 4 & . & . & . & 6 & 2 & . & 3 & 1 & 3 & . & 1 \\
 & & & & 2 & . & . & . & . & . & 1 & . & . & . & . & . & . & . & 1 & 1 & 1 \\
 & & & & & 2 & . & . & . & . & . & 1 & . & . & 1 & 1 & 2 & . & . & 1 \\
 & & & & & & 6 & . & . & . & . & 3 & 2 & . & 1 & 3 & . & . & 2 & 1 \\
 & & & & & & & 6 & . & . & . & 3 & . & 2 & 3 & 1 & . & 2 & . & 1 \\
 & & & & & & & & 1 & . & . & . & . & 2 & 1 & . & 1 & . & 1 & 1 \\
 & & & & & & & & & 1 & . & . & . & . & 2 & . & 1 & 1 & 1 & . & 1 \\
 & & & & & & & & & & 4 & . & . & . & . & 2 & . & . & 1 & . & . & 1 \\
 & & & & & & & & & & & 1 & . & . & . & . & . & . & 1 & 1 & 1 \\
 & & & & & & & & & & & & 1 & . & . & 1 & 1 & . & . & . & 1 \\
 & & & & & & & & & & & & & 2 & . & . & 1 & . & . & 2 & 1 \\
 & & & & & & & & & & & & & & 2 & . & . & 1 & . & 2 & . & 1 \\
 & & & & & & & & & & & & & & & 2 & . & . & 1 & . & . & 1 \\
 & & & & & & & & & & & & & & & & 1 & . & . & . & . & 1 \\
 & & & & & & & & & & & & & & & & & 1 & . & . & . & 1 \\
 & & & & & & & & & & & & & & & & & & 1 & . & . & 1 \\
 & & & & & & & & & & & & & & & & & & & 1 & . & 1 \\
 & & & & & & & & & & & & & & & & & & & & 1 & 1 \\
 & & & & & & & & & & & & & & & & & & & & & 1
\end{pmatrix}
$$

The Burnsidematrix is 1/360 times the matrix

$$
\begin{pmatrix}
1 & -45 & -20 & -20 & -36 & . & 30 & 30 & 180 & 180 & 30 & 180 & . & 60 & 60 & -270 & -180 & -180 & . & -360 & -360 & 720 \\
 & 90 & . & . & . & -90 & -90 & -90 & -360 & -360 & . & -360 & 180 & . & . & 540 & 360 & 360 & 180 & 720 & 720 & -1800 \\
 & & 60 & . & . & . & -180 & . & -60 & . & . & . & -180 & . & . & 180 & 180 & . & . & . & 360 & -360 \\
 & & & 60 & . & . & . & . & . & -180 & -60 & . & . & . & -180 & 180 & . & 180 & . & 360 & . & -360 \\
 & & & & 180 & . & . & . & . & . & . & -180 & . & . & . & . & . & . & . & . & . & . \\
 & & & & & 180 & . & . & . & . & . & . & . & . & . & . & . & -360 & . & . & . & 360 \\
 & & & & & & 60 & . & . & . & . & -180 & -60 & . & . & 180 & . & . & . & . & . & . \\
 & & & & & & & 60 & . & . & . & -180 & . & -60 & . & . & 180 & . & . & . & . & . \\
 & & & & & & & & 360 & . & . & . & . & . & . & -360 & -360 & . & . & . & -360 & 720 \\
 & & & & & & & & & 360 & . & . & . & . & . & -360 & . & -360 & . & -360 & . & 720 \\
 & & & & & & & & & & 90 & . & . & . & . & -90 & . & . & . & . & . & . \\
 & & & & & & & & & & & 360 & . & . & . & . & . & . & . & -360 & -360 & 360 \\
 & & & & & & & & & & & & 360 & . & . & . & -360 & -360 & . & . & . & 360 \\
 & & & & & & & & & & & & & 180 & . & . & . & -180 & . & . & -360 & 360 \\
 & & & & & & & & & & & & & & 180 & . & . & . & -180 & . & . & . \\
 & & & & & & & & & & & & & & & 360 & . & . & . & . & . & -360 \\
 & & & & & & & & & & & & & & & & 360 & . & . & . & . & -360 \\
 & & & & & & & & & & & & & & & & & 360 & . & . & . & -360 \\
 & & & & & & & & & & & & & & & & & & 360 & . & . & -360 \\
 & & & & & & & & & & & & & & & & & & & 360 & -360 & . \\
 & & & & & & & & & & & & & & & & & & & & 360 &
\end{pmatrix}
$$

8.1.4 Symmetric groups

This section contains a system of representatives of the conjugacy classes of subgroups, the table of marks and the Burnside matrix of $S_{\underline{3}}$, $S_{\underline{4}}$ and $S_{\underline{5}}$, as well as a system of representatives of the conjugacy classes of their subgroups.

The group $S_{\underline{3}}$: A transversal of the conjugacy classes of subgroups is

$$U_1 = <1>, U_2 = <(1,2)>, U_3 = <(1,2,3)>,$$

$$U_4 = <(1,2,3),(1,2)> = S_{\underline{3}}.$$

The table of marks is

$$
\begin{pmatrix}
6 & 3 & 2 & 1 \\
 & 1 & . & 1 \\
 & & 2 & 1 \\
 & & & 1
\end{pmatrix}.
$$

The Burnside matrix looks as follows

$$
\begin{pmatrix}
1/6 & -1/2 & -1/6 & 1/2 \\
 & 1 & . & -1 \\
 & & 1/2 & -1/2 \\
 & & & 1
\end{pmatrix}.
$$

The group $S_{\underline{4}}$: A transversal of the conjugacy classes of subgroups is

$$U_1 =< 1 >, U_2 =< (2,4) >, U_3 =< (1,3)(2,4) >, U_4 =< (1,3,2) >,$$

$$U_5 =< (2,4),(1,3) >, U_6 =< (1,2,3,4) >,$$

$$U_7 =< (1,2)(3,4),(1,4)(2,3) >, U_8 =< (1,3,2),(1,3) >,$$

$$U_9 =< (1,2,3,4),(2,4) >, U_{10} =< (1,3,2),(1,4,2) >,$$

$$U_{11} =< (1,3,2,4),(1,3,4,2) >= S_{\underline{4}}.$$

The table of marks is

$$
\begin{pmatrix}
24 & 12 & 12 & 8 & 6 & 6 & 6 & 4 & 3 & 2 & 1 \\
   & 2 & . & . & 2 & . & . & 2 & 1 & . & 1 \\
   &   & 4 & . & 2 & 2 & 6 & . & 3 & 2 & 1 \\
   &   &   & 2 & . & . & . & 1 & . & 2 & 1 \\
   &   &   &   & 2 & . & . & . & 1 & . & 1 \\
   &   &   &   &   & 2 & . & . & 1 & . & 1 \\
   &   &   &   &   &   & 6 & . & 3 & 2 & 1 \\
   &   &   &   &   &   &   & 1 & . & . & 1 \\
   &   &   &   &   &   &   &   & 1 & . & 1 \\
   &   &   &   &   &   &   &   &   & 2 & 1 \\
   &   &   &   &   &   &   &   &   &   & 1
\end{pmatrix}.
$$

The Burnside matrix looks as follows

$$
\begin{pmatrix}
1/24 & -1/4 & -1/8 & -1/6 & 1/4 & . & 1/12 & 1/2 & . & 1/6 & -1/2 \\
     & 1/2 & .   & .   & -1/2 & . & . & -1 & . & . & 1 \\
     &   & 1/4 & .   & -1/4 & -1/4 & -1/4 & . & 1/2 & . & . \\
     &   &   & 1/2 & . & . & . & -1/2 & . & -1/2 & 1/2 \\
     &   &   &   & 1/2 & . & . & . & -1/2 & . & . \\
     &   &   &   & . & 1/2 & . & . & -1/2 & . & . \\
     &   &   &   &   &   & 1/6 & . & -1/2 & -1/6 & 1/2 \\
     &   &   &   &   &   &   & 1 & . & . & -1 \\
     &   &   &   &   &   &   &   & 1 & . & -1 \\
     &   &   &   &   &   &   &   &   & 1/2 & -1/2 \\
     &   &   &   &   &   &   &   &   &   & 1
\end{pmatrix}
$$

The group $S_{\underline{5}}$: A transversal of the conjugacy classes of subgroups is

$$U_1 =< 1 >, U_2 =< (4,5) >, U_3 =< (1,2)(4,5) >, U_4 =< (1,3,2) >,$$

$$U_5 =< (1,5,2,3,4) >, U_6 =< (4,5),(1,3) >, U_7 =< (1,5,2,4) >,$$

$$U_8 =< (1,2)(4,5),(1,5)(2,4) >, U_9 =< (1,3,2),(4,5) >,$$

$$U_{10} =, U_{11} =< (1,3,2),(1,2)(4,5) >,$$

$$U_{12} =< (1,5,2,3,4),(2,3)(4,5) >, U_{13} =< (1,5,2,4),(4,5) >,$$

$$U_{14} =< (1,3,2),(4,5),(1,3) >, U_{15} =< (1,5,2),(1,5,4) >,$$

$$U_{16} =< (2,5,3,4),(1,4,2,3) >, U_{17} =< (1,5,2,4),(1,2,5,4) >,$$

$$U_{18} =< (1,5,2,3,4),(1,2,3,5,4) >, U_{19} = S_{\underline{5}}.$$

The table of marks is

$$
\begin{pmatrix}
120 & 60 & 60 & 40 & 24 & 30 & 30 & 30 & 20 & 20 & 20 & 12 & 15 & 10 & 10 & 6 & 5 & 2 & 1 \\
 & 6 & . & . & . & 6 & . & . & 2 & 6 & . & . & 3 & 4 & . & . & 3 & . & 1 \\
 & & 4 & . & . & 2 & 2 & 6 & . & . & 4 & 4 & 3 & 2 & 2 & 2 & 1 & 2 & 1 \\
 & & & 4 & . & . & . & . & 2 & 2 & 2 & . & . & 1 & 4 & . & 2 & 2 & 1 \\
 & & & & 4 & . & . & . & . & . & . & 2 & . & . & . & 1 & . & 2 & 1 \\
 & & & & & 2 & . & . & . & . & . & . & 1 & 2 & . & . & 1 & . & 1 \\
 & & & & & & 2 & . & . & . & . & . & 1 & . & . & 2 & 1 & . & 1 \\
 & & & & & & & 6 & . & . & . & . & 3 & . & 2 & . & 1 & 2 & 1 \\
 & & & & & & & & 2 & . & . & . & . & 1 & . & . & . & . & 1 \\
 & & & & & & & & & 2 & . & . & . & 1 & . & . & 2 & . & 1 \\
 & & & & & & & & & & 2 & . & . & 1 & . & . & . & 2 & 1 \\
 & & & & & & & & & & & 2 & . & . & . & 1 & . & 2 & 1 \\
 & & & & & & & & & & & & 1 & . & . & . & 1 & . & 1 \\
 & & & & & & & & & & & & & 1 & . & . & . & . & 1 \\
 & & & & & & & & & & & & & & 2 & . & 1 & 2 & 1 \\
 & & & & & & & & & & & & & & & 1 & . & . & 1 \\
 & & & & & & & & & & & & & & & & 1 & . & 1 \\
 & & & & & & & & & & & & & & & & & 2 & 1 \\
 & & & & & & & & & & & & & & & & & & 1
\end{pmatrix}
$$

The Burnsidematrix is $1/120$ times the matrix

$$
\begin{pmatrix}
1 & -10 & -15 & -10 & -6 & 30 & . & 10 & 10 & 30 & 30 & 30 & . & -60 & 20 & . & -60 & -60 & 60 \\
 & 20 & . & . & . & -60 & . & . & -20 & -60 & . & . & . & 120 & . & . & 120 & . & -120 \\
 & & 30 & . & . & -30 & -30 & -30 & . & . & -60 & -60 & 60 & 60 & . & 60 & . & 120 & -120 \\
 & & & 30 & . & . & . & . & -30 & -30 & -30 & . & . & 60 & -60 & . & 60 & 60 & -60 \\
 & & & & 30 & . & . & . & . & . & . & . & -30 & . & . & . & . & . & . \\
 & & & & & 60 & . & . & . & . & . & -60 & -60 & -120 & . & . & . & . & 120 \\
 & & & & & & 60 & . & . & . & . & -60 & . & . & -120 & . & . & 120 \\
 & & & & & & & 20 & . & . & . & -60 & . & -20 & . & 60 & . & . & . \\
 & & & & & & & & 60 & . & . & . & -60 & . & . & . & . & . \\
 & & & & & & & & & 60 & . & . & -60 & . & . & -120 & . & 120 \\
 & & & & & & & & & & 60 & . & . & -60 & . & . & -60 & 60 \\
 & & & & & & & & & & & 60 & . & . & -60 & . & -60 & 60 \\
 & & & & & & & & & & & & 120 & . & . & . & -120 & . \\
 & & & & & & & & & & & & & 120 & . & . & . & -120 \\
 & & & & & & & & & & & & & & 60 & . & -60 & -60 & 60 \\
 & & & & & & & & & & & & & & & 120 & . & -120 \\
 & & & & & & & & & & & & & & & & 120 & . & -120 \\
 & & & & & & & & & & & & & & & & & 60 & -60 \\
 & & & & & & & & & & & & & & & & & & 120
\end{pmatrix}
$$

8.2 Characters of symmetric groups

8.2.1 Irreducible characters and Young characters

This section contains the irreducible characters ζ^α of the symmetric groups $S_{\underline{n}}, n \le 7$, together with the Young characters ξ^α and the scalar products or multiplicities

$$[\xi^\alpha \mid \zeta^\beta] = \kappa_{\alpha\beta} = st^\beta(\alpha).$$

Moreover the reader will find tables containing the scalar products

$$[\xi^\alpha \mid \xi^\beta] = m_{\alpha\beta}, \text{ and } [\epsilon \xi^\alpha \mid \xi^\beta] = m'_{\alpha\beta},$$

where ϵ denotes the alternating or sign character. Hence these tables contain the numbers of matrices over $\mathbb{N}$ and over $\{0,1\}$, resepectively, with prescribed row and column sum vectors α and β.

Each subsection starts with a table that shows the partition α corresponding to the irreducible character ζ_i, to the Young character ξ_i, and the conjugacy class C_i. The last but one column of this table contains the orders of the conjugacy class while the last column contains the order of the centralizer of an element in this class.

The second table is the character table, while the third one contains the multiplicities $[\xi_i \mid \zeta_j]$ of the irreducible characters ζ_j in the Young characters ξ_i. The values of the Young characters are shown in the fourth table.

The fifth and the sixth table of each subsection contain the scalar products $[\xi_i \mid \xi_j]$ and the scalar products $[\epsilon\xi_i \mid \xi_j]$, respectively, which can be interpreted as numbers of matrices with prescribed row and column sums, as it was mentioned above already.

The group S_2:

ζ_1	ξ_1	2	C_2	1	2
ζ_2	ξ_2	11	C_1	1	2

	C_1	C_2
ζ_1	1	1
ζ_2	1	−1

	ζ_1	ζ_2
ξ_1	1	0
ξ_2	1	1

	C_1	C_2
ξ_1	1	1
ξ_2	2	0

	ξ_1	ξ_2
ξ_1	1	1
ξ_2	1	2

	ξ_1	ξ_2
$\epsilon\xi_1$	0	1
$\epsilon\xi_2$	1	2

The group S_3:

ζ_1	ξ_1	3	C_3	2	3
ζ_2	ξ_2	21	C_2	3	2
ζ_3	ξ_3	111	C_1	1	6

	C_1	C_2	C_3
ζ_1	1	1	1
ζ_2	2	0	−1
ζ_3	1	−1	1

	ζ_1	ζ_2	ζ_3
ξ_1	1	0	0
ξ_2	1	1	0
ξ_3	1	2	1

	C_1	C_2	C_3
ξ_1	1	1	1
ξ_2	3	1	0
ξ_3	6	0	0

	ξ_1	ξ_2	ξ_3
ξ_1	1	1	1
ξ_2	1	2	3
ξ_3	1	3	6

	ξ_1	ξ_2	ξ_3
$\epsilon\xi_1$	0	0	1
$\epsilon\xi_2$	0	1	3
$\epsilon\xi_3$	1	3	6

The group S_4:

ζ_1	ξ_1	4	C_5	6	4
ζ_2	ξ_2	31	C_4	8	3
ζ_3	ξ_3	22	C_3	3	8
ζ_4	ξ_4	211	C_2	6	4
ζ_5	ξ_5	1111	C_1	1	24

	C_1	C_2	C_3	C_4	C_5
ζ_1	1	1	1	1	1
ζ_2	3	1	-1	0	-1
ζ_3	2	0	2	-1	0
ζ_4	3	-1	-1	0	1
ζ_5	1	-1	1	1	-1

	ζ_1	ζ_2	ζ_3	ζ_4	ζ_5
ξ_1	1	0	0	0	0
ξ_2	1	1	0	0	0
ξ_3	1	1	1	0	0
ξ_4	1	2	1	1	0
ξ_5	1	3	2	3	1

	C_1	C_2	C_3	C_4	C_5
ξ_1	1	1	1	1	1
ξ_2	4	2	0	1	0
ξ_3	6	2	2	0	0
ξ_4	12	2	0	0	0
ξ_5	24	0	0	0	0

	ξ_1	ξ_2	ξ_3	ξ_4	ξ_5
ξ_1	1	1	1	1	1
ξ_2	1	2	2	3	4
ξ_3	1	2	3	4	6
ξ_4	1	3	4	7	12
ξ_5	1	4	6	12	24

	ξ_1	ξ_2	ξ_3	ξ_4	ξ_5
$\epsilon\xi_1$	0	0	0	0	1
$\epsilon\xi_2$	0	0	0	1	4
$\epsilon\xi_3$	0	0	1	2	6
$\epsilon\xi_4$	0	1	2	5	12
$\epsilon\xi_5$	1	4	6	12	24

The group $S_{\underline{5}}$:

ζ_1	ξ_1	5	C_7	24	5
ζ_2	ξ_2	41	C_6	30	4
ζ_3	ξ_3	32	C_5	20	6
ζ_4	ξ_4	311	C_4	20	6
ζ_5	ξ_5	221	C_3	15	8
ζ_6	ξ_6	2111	C_2	10	12
ζ_7	ξ_7	11111	C_1	1	120

	C_1	C_2	C_3	C_4	C_5	C_6	C_7
ζ_1	1	1	1	1	1	1	1
ζ_2	4	2	0	1	-1	0	-1
ζ_3	5	1	1	-1	1	-1	0
ζ_4	6	0	-2	0	0	0	1
ζ_5	5	-1	1	-1	-1	1	0
ζ_6	4	-2	0	1	1	0	-1
ζ_7	1	-1	1	1	-1	-1	1

	ζ_1	ζ_2	ζ_3	ζ_4	ζ_5	ζ_6	ζ_7
ξ_1	1	0	0	0	0	0	0
ξ_2	1	1	0	0	0	0	0
ξ_3	1	1	1	0	0	0	0
ξ_4	1	2	1	1	0	0	0
ξ_5	1	2	2	1	1	0	0
ξ_6	1	3	3	3	2	1	0
ξ_7	1	4	5	6	5	4	1

	C_1	C_2	C_3	C_4	C_5	C_6	C_7
ξ_1	1	1	1	1	1	1	1
ξ_2	5	3	1	2	0	1	0
ξ_3	10	4	2	1	1	0	0
ξ_4	20	6	0	2	0	0	0
ξ_5	30	6	2	0	0	0	0
ξ_6	60	6	0	0	0	0	0
ξ_7	120	0	0	0	0	0	0

	ξ_1	ξ_2	ξ_3	ξ_4	ξ_5	ξ_6	ξ_7
ξ_1	1	1	1	1	1	1	1
ξ_2	1	2	2	3	3	4	5
ξ_3	1	2	3	4	5	7	10
ξ_4	1	3	4	7	8	13	20
ξ_5	1	3	5	8	11	18	30
ξ_6	1	4	7	13	18	33	60
ξ_7	1	5	10	20	30	60	120

	ξ_1	ξ_2	ξ_3	ξ_4	ξ_5	ξ_6	ξ_7
$\epsilon\xi_1$	0	0	0	0	0	0	1
$\epsilon\xi_2$	0	0	0	0	0	1	5
$\epsilon\xi_3$	0	0	0	0	1	3	10
$\epsilon\xi_4$	0	0	0	1	2	7	20
$\epsilon\xi_5$	0	0	1	2	5	12	30
$\epsilon\xi_6$	0	1	3	7	12	27	60
$\epsilon\xi_7$	1	5	10	20	30	60	120

The group S_6:

ζ_1	ξ_1	6	C_{11}	120	6
ζ_2	ξ_2	51	C_{10}	144	5
ζ_3	ξ_3	42	C_9	90	8
ζ_4	ξ_4	411	C_8	90	8
ζ_5	ξ_5	33	C_7	40	18
ζ_6	ξ_6	321	C_6	120	6
ζ_7	ξ_7	3111	C_5	40	18
ζ_8	ξ_8	222	C_4	15	48
ζ_9	ξ_9	2211	C_3	45	16
ζ_{10}	ξ_{10}	21111	C_2	15	48
ζ_{11}	ξ_{11}	111111	C_1	1	720

	C_1	C_2	C_3	C_4	C_5	C_6	C_7	C_8	C_9	C_{10}	C_{11}
ζ_1	1	1	1	1	1	1	1	1	1	1	1
ζ_2	5	3	1	-1	2	0	-1	1	-1	0	-1
ζ_3	9	3	1	3	0	0	0	-1	1	-1	0
ζ_4	10	2	-2	-2	1	-1	1	0	0	0	1
ζ_5	5	1	1	-3	-1	1	2	-1	-1	0	0
ζ_6	16	0	0	0	-2	0	-2	0	0	1	0
ζ_7	10	-2	-2	2	1	1	1	0	0	0	-1
ζ_8	5	-1	1	3	-1	-1	2	1	-1	0	0
ζ_9	9	-3	1	-3	0	0	0	1	1	-1	0
ζ_{10}	5	-3	1	1	2	0	-1	-1	-1	0	1
ζ_{11}	1	-1	1	-1	1	-1	1	-1	1	1	-1

	ζ_1	ζ_2	ζ_3	ζ_4	ζ_5	ζ_6	ζ_7	ζ_8	ζ_9	ζ_{10}	ζ_{11}
ξ_1	1	0	0	0	0	0	0	0	0	0	0
ξ_2	1	1	0	0	0	0	0	0	0	0	0
ξ_3	1	1	1	0	0	0	0	0	0	0	0
ξ_4	1	2	1	1	0	0	0	0	0	0	0
ξ_5	1	1	1	0	1	0	0	0	0	0	0
ξ_6	1	2	2	1	1	1	0	0	0	0	0
ξ_7	1	3	3	3	1	2	1	0	0	0	0
ξ_8	1	2	3	1	1	2	0	1	0	0	0
ξ_9	1	3	4	3	2	4	1	1	1	0	0
ξ_{10}	1	4	6	6	3	8	4	2	3	1	0
ξ_{11}	1	5	9	10	5	16	10	5	9	5	1

	C_1	C_2	C_3	C_4	C_5	C_6	C_7	C_8	C_9	C_{10}	C_{11}
ξ_1	1	1	1	1	1	1	1	1	1	1	1
ξ_2	6	4	2	0	3	1	0	2	0	1	0
ξ_3	15	7	3	3	3	1	0	1	1	0	0
ξ_4	30	12	2	0	6	0	0	2	0	0	0
ξ_5	20	8	4	0	2	2	2	0	0	0	0
ξ_6	60	16	4	0	3	1	0	0	0	0	0
ξ_7	120	24	0	0	6	0	0	0	0	0	0
ξ_8	90	18	6	6	0	0	0	0	0	0	0
ξ_9	180	24	4	0	0	0	0	0	0	0	0
ξ_{10}	360	24	0	0	0	0	0	0	0	0	0
ξ_{11}	720	0	0	0	0	0	0	0	0	0	0

	ξ_1	ξ_2	ξ_3	ξ_4	ξ_5	ξ_6	ξ_7	ξ_8	ξ_9	ξ_{10}	ξ_{11}
ξ_1	1	1	1	1	1	1	1	1	1	1	1
ξ_2	1	2	2	3	2	3	4	3	4	5	6
ξ_3	1	2	3	4	3	5	7	6	8	11	15
ξ_4	1	3	4	7	4	8	13	9	14	21	30
ξ_5	1	2	3	4	4	6	8	7	10	14	20
ξ_6	1	3	5	8	6	12	19	15	24	38	60
ξ_7	1	4	7	13	8	19	34	24	42	72	120
ξ_8	1	3	6	9	7	15	24	21	33	54	90
ξ_9	1	4	8	14	10	24	42	33	58	102	180
ξ_{10}	1	5	11	21	14	38	72	54	102	192	360
ξ_{11}	1	6	15	30	20	60	120	90	180	360	720

	ξ_1	ξ_2	ξ_3	ξ_4	ξ_5	ξ_6	ξ_7	ξ_8	ξ_9	ξ_{10}	ξ_{11}
$\epsilon\xi_1$	0	0	0	0	0	0	0	0	0	0	1
$\epsilon\xi_2$	0	0	0	0	0	0	0	0	0	1	6
$\epsilon\xi_3$	0	0	0	0	0	0	0	0	1	4	15
$\epsilon\xi_4$	0	0	0	0	0	0	1	0	2	9	30
$\epsilon\xi_5$	0	0	0	0	0	0	0	1	2	6	20
$\epsilon\xi_6$	0	0	0	0	0	1	3	3	8	22	60
$\epsilon\xi_7$	0	0	0	1	0	3	10	6	18	48	120
$\epsilon\xi_8$	0	0	0	0	1	3	6	6	15	36	90
$\epsilon\xi_9$	0	0	1	2	2	8	18	15	34	78	180
$\epsilon\xi_{10}$	0	1	4	9	6	22	48	36	78	168	360
$\epsilon\xi_{11}$	1	6	15	30	20	60	120	90	180	360	720

The group S_7:

ζ_i	ξ_i		C_j		
ζ_1	ξ_1	7	C_{15}	720	7
ζ_2	ξ_2	61	C_{14}	840	6
ζ_3	ξ_3	52	C_{13}	504	10
ζ_4	ξ_4	511	C_{12}	504	10
ζ_5	ξ_5	43	C_{11}	420	12
ζ_6	ξ_6	421	C_{10}	630	8
ζ_7	ξ_7	4111	C_9	210	24
ζ_8	ξ_8	331	C_8	280	18
ζ_9	ξ_9	322	C_7	210	24
ζ_{10}	ξ_{10}	3211	C_6	420	12
ζ_{11}	ξ_{11}	31111	C_5	70	72
ζ_{12}	ξ_{12}	2221	C_4	105	48
ζ_{13}	ξ_{13}	22111	C_3	105	48
ζ_{14}	ξ_{14}	211111	C_2	21	240
ζ_{15}	ξ_{15}	1111111	C_1	1	5040

	C_1	C_2	C_3	C_4	C_5	C_6	C_7	C_8	C_9	C_{10}	C_{11}	C_{12}	C_{13}	C_{14}	C_{15}
ζ_1	1	1	1	1	1	1	1	1	1	1	1	1	1	1	1
ζ_2	6	4	2	0	3	1	−1	0	2	0	−1	1	−1	0	−1
ζ_3	14	6	2	2	2	0	2	−1	0	0	0	−1	1	−1	0
ζ_4	15	5	−1	−3	3	−1	−1	0	1	−1	1	0	0	0	1
ζ_5	14	4	2	0	−1	1	−1	2	−2	0	1	−1	−1	0	0
ζ_6	35	5	−1	1	−1	−1	−1	−1	−1	1	−1	0	0	1	0
ζ_7	20	0	−4	0	2	0	2	2	0	0	0	0	0	0	−1
ζ_8	21	1	1	−3	−3	1	1	0	−1	−1	−1	1	1	0	0
ζ_9	21	−1	1	3	−3	−1	1	0	1	−1	1	1	−1	0	0
ζ_{10}	35	−5	−1	−1	−1	1	−1	−1	1	1	1	0	0	−1	0
ζ_{11}	15	−5	−1	3	3	1	−1	0	−1	−1	−1	0	0	0	1
ζ_{12}	14	−4	2	0	−1	−1	−1	2	2	0	−1	−1	1	0	0
ζ_{13}	14	−6	2	−2	2	0	2	−1	0	0	0	−1	−1	1	0
ζ_{14}	6	−4	2	0	3	−1	−1	0	−2	0	1	1	1	0	−1
ζ_{15}	1	−1	1	−1	1	−1	1	1	−1	1	−1	1	−1	−1	1

	ζ_1	ζ_2	ζ_3	ζ_4	ζ_5	ζ_6	ζ_7	ζ_8	ζ_9	ζ_{10}	ζ_{11}	ζ_{12}	ζ_{13}	ζ_{14}	ζ_{15}
ξ_1	1	0	0	0	0	0	0	0	0	0	0	0	0	0	0
ξ_2	1	1	0	0	0	0	0	0	0	0	0	0	0	0	0
ξ_3	1	1	1	0	0	0	0	0	0	0	0	0	0	0	0
ξ_4	1	2	1	1	0	0	0	0	0	0	0	0	0	0	0
ξ_5	1	1	1	0	1	0	0	0	0	0	0	0	0	0	0
ξ_6	1	2	2	1	1	1	0	0	0	0	0	0	0	0	0
ξ_7	1	3	3	3	1	2	1	0	0	0	0	0	0	0	0
ξ_8	1	2	2	1	2	1	0	1	0	0	0	0	0	0	0
ξ_9	1	2	3	1	2	2	0	1	1	0	0	0	0	0	0
ξ_{10}	1	3	4	3	3	4	1	2	1	1	0	0	0	0	0
ξ_{11}	1	4	6	6	4	8	4	3	2	3	1	0	0	0	0
ξ_{12}	1	3	5	3	4	6	1	3	3	2	0	1	0	0	0
ξ_{13}	1	4	7	6	6	11	4	6	5	6	1	2	1	0	0
ξ_{14}	1	5	10	10	9	20	10	11	10	15	5	5	4	1	0
ξ_{15}	1	6	14	15	14	35	20	21	21	35	15	14	14	6	1

	C_1	C_2	C_3	C_4	C_5	C_6	C_7	C_8	C_9	C_{10}	C_{11}	C_{12}	C_{13}	C_{14}	C_{15}
ξ_1	1	1	1	1	1	1	1	1	1	1	1	1	1	1	1
ξ_2	7	5	3	1	4	2	0	1	3	1	0	2	0	1	0
ξ_3	21	11	5	3	6	2	2	0	3	1	0	1	1	0	0
ξ_4	42	20	6	0	12	2	0	0	6	0	0	2	0	0	0
ξ_5	35	15	7	3	5	3	1	2	1	1	1	0	0	0	0
ξ_6	105	35	9	3	12	2	0	0	3	1	0	0	0	0	0
ξ_7	210	60	6	0	24	0	0	0	6	0	0	0	0	0	0
ξ_8	140	40	12	0	8	4	0	2	0	0	0	0	0	0	0
ξ_9	210	50	14	6	6	2	2	0	0	0	0	0	0	0	0
ξ_{10}	420	80	12	0	12	2	0	0	0	0	0	0	0	0	0
ξ_{11}	840	120	0	0	24	0	0	0	0	0	0	0	0	0	0
ξ_{12}	630	90	18	6	0	0	0	0	0	0	0	0	0	0	0
ξ_{13}	1260	120	12	0	0	0	0	0	0	0	0	0	0	0	0
ξ_{14}	2520	120	0	0	0	0	0	0	0	0	0	0	0	0	0
ξ_{15}	5040	0	0	0	0	0	0	0	0	0	0	0	0	0	0

	ξ_1	ξ_2	ξ_3	ξ_4	ξ_5	ξ_6	ξ_7	ξ_8	ξ_9	ξ_{10}	ξ_{11}	ξ_{12}	ξ_{13}	ξ_{14}	ξ_{15}
ξ_1	1	1	1	1	1	1	1	1	1	1	1	1	1	1	1
ξ_2	1	2	2	3	2	3	4	3	3	4	5	4	5	6	7
ξ_3	1	2	3	4	3	5	7	5	6	8	11	9	12	16	21
ξ_4	1	3	4	7	4	8	13	8	9	14	21	15	22	31	42
ξ_5	1	2	3	4	4	6	8	7	8	11	15	13	18	25	35
ξ_6	1	3	5	8	6	12	19	13	16	25	39	30	46	70	105
ξ_7	1	4	7	13	8	19	34	20	25	43	73	51	84	135	210
ξ_8	1	3	5	8	7	13	20	16	19	30	46	37	58	90	140
ξ_9	1	3	6	9	8	16	25	19	25	39	62	51	81	130	210
ξ_{10}	1	4	8	14	11	25	43	30	39	67	114	87	148	250	420
ξ_{11}	1	5	11	21	15	39	73	46	62	114	208	150	270	480	840
ξ_{12}	1	4	9	15	13	30	51	37	51	87	150	120	207	360	630
ξ_{13}	1	5	12	22	18	46	84	58	81	148	270	207	378	690	1260
ξ_{14}	1	6	16	31	25	70	135	90	130	250	480	360	690	1320	2520
ξ_{15}	1	7	21	42	35	105	210	140	210	420	840	630	1260	2520	5040

	ξ_1	ξ_2	ξ_3	ξ_4	ξ_5	ξ_6	ξ_7	ξ_8	ξ_9	ξ_{10}	ξ_{11}	ξ_{12}	ξ_{13}	ξ_{14}	ξ_{15}
$\epsilon\xi_1$	0	0	0	0	0	0	0	0	0	0	0	0	0	0	1
$\epsilon\xi_2$	0	0	0	0	0	0	0	0	0	0	0	0	0	1	7
$\epsilon\xi_3$	0	0	0	0	0	0	0	0	0	0	0	0	1	5	21
$\epsilon\xi_4$	0	0	0	0	0	0	0	0	0	0	1	0	2	11	42
$\epsilon\xi_5$	0	0	0	0	0	0	0	0	0	0	0	1	3	10	35
$\epsilon\xi_6$	0	0	0	0	0	0	0	0	0	1	4	3	11	35	105
$\epsilon\xi_7$	0	0	0	0	0	0	1	0	0	3	13	6	24	75	210
$\epsilon\xi_8$	0	0	0	0	0	0	0	0	1	2	6	7	18	50	140
$\epsilon\xi_9$	0	0	0	0	0	0	0	1	2	5	12	12	31	80	210
$\epsilon\xi_{10}$	0	0	0	0	0	1	3	2	5	13	34	27	68	170	420
$\epsilon\xi_{11}$	0	0	0	1	0	4	13	6	12	34	88	60	150	360	840
$\epsilon\xi_{12}$	0	0	0	0	1	3	6	7	12	27	60	51	117	270	630
$\epsilon\xi_{13}$	0	0	1	2	3	11	24	18	31	68	150	117	258	570	1260
$\epsilon\xi_{14}$	0	1	5	11	10	35	75	50	80	170	360	270	570	1200	2520
$\epsilon\xi_{15}$	1	7	21	42	35	105	210	140	210	420	840	630	1260	2520	5040

8.2.2 Foulkes tables

This section contains the Foulkes tables of the symmetric groups S_n, for $n \leq 12$. We recall that the j-th column of the Foulkes table contains in its i-th row the value of the Foulkes characters $\chi^{n,i}$ on the classes of elements which consist of j cyclic factors.

$$F_1 = \begin{array}{c|c} i\backslash j & 1 \\ \hline 0 & 1 \end{array}, \quad F_2 = \begin{array}{c|cc} i\backslash j & 2 & 1 \\ \hline 0 & 1 & -1 \\ 1 & 1 & 1 \end{array}, \quad F_3 = \begin{array}{c|ccc} i\backslash j & 3 & 2 & 1 \\ \hline 0 & 1 & -1 & 1 \\ 1 & 4 & 0 & -2 \\ 2 & 1 & 1 & 1 \end{array},$$

$$F_4 = \begin{array}{c|cccc} i\backslash j & 4 & 3 & 2 & 1 \\ \hline 0 & 1 & -1 & 1 & -1 \\ 1 & 11 & -3 & -1 & 3 \\ 2 & 11 & 3 & -1 & -3 \\ 3 & 1 & 1 & 1 & 1 \end{array}, \quad F_5 = \begin{array}{c|ccccc} i\backslash j & 5 & 4 & 3 & 2 & 1 \\ \hline 0 & 1 & -1 & 1 & -1 & 1 \\ 1 & 26 & -10 & 2 & 2 & -4 \\ 2 & 66 & 0 & -6 & 0 & 6 \\ 3 & 26 & 10 & 2 & -2 & -4 \\ 4 & 1 & 1 & 1 & 1 & 1 \end{array},$$

$$F_6 = \begin{array}{c|cccccc} i\backslash j & 6 & 5 & 4 & 3 & 2 & 1 \\ \hline 0 & 1 & -1 & 1 & -1 & 1 & -1 \\ 1 & 57 & -25 & 9 & -1 & -3 & 5 \\ 2 & 302 & -40 & -10 & 8 & 2 & -10 \\ 3 & 302 & 40 & -10 & -8 & 2 & 10 \\ 4 & 57 & 25 & 9 & 1 & -3 & -5 \\ 5 & 1 & 1 & 1 & 1 & 1 & 1 \end{array},$$

$$F_7 = \begin{array}{c|ccccccc} i\backslash j & 7 & 6 & 5 & 4 & 3 & 2 & 1 \\ \hline 0 & 1 & -1 & 1 & -1 & 1 & -1 & 1 \\ 1 & 120 & -56 & 24 & -8 & 0 & 4 & -6 \\ 2 & 1191 & -245 & 15 & 19 & -9 & -5 & 15 \\ 3 & 2416 & 0 & -80 & 0 & 16 & 0 & -20 \\ 4 & 1191 & 245 & 15 & -19 & -9 & 5 & 15 \\ 5 & 120 & 56 & 24 & 8 & 0 & -4 & -6 \\ 6 & 1 & 1 & 1 & 1 & 1 & 1 & 1 \end{array},$$

$$F_8 = \begin{array}{c|cccccccc} i\backslash j & 8 & 7 & 6 & 5 & 4 & 3 & 2 & 1 \\ \hline 0 & 1 & -1 & 1 & -1 & 1 & -1 & 1 & -1 \\ 1 & 247 & -119 & 55 & -23 & 7 & 1 & -5 & 7 \\ 2 & 4293 & -1071 & 189 & 9 & -27 & 9 & 9 & -21 \\ 3 & 15619 & -1225 & -245 & 95 & 19 & -25 & -5 & 35 \\ 4 & 15619 & 1225 & -245 & -95 & 19 & 25 & -5 & -35 \\ 5 & 4293 & 1071 & 189 & -9 & -27 & -9 & 9 & 21 \\ 6 & 247 & 119 & 55 & 23 & 7 & -1 & -5 & -7 \\ 7 & 1 & 1 & 1 & 1 & 1 & 1 & 1 & 1 \end{array},$$

$$F_9 = \begin{array}{c|rrrrrrrrr} i\backslash j & 9 & 8 & 7 & 6 & 5 & 4 & 3 & 2 & 1 \\ \hline 0 & 1 & -1 & 1 & -1 & 1 & -1 & 1 & -1 & 1 \\ 1 & 502 & -246 & 118 & -54 & 22 & -6 & -2 & 6 & -8 \\ 2 & 14608 & -4046 & 952 & -134 & -32 & 34 & -8 & -14 & 28 \\ 3 & 88234 & -11326 & 154 & 434 & -86 & -46 & 34 & 14 & -56 \\ 4 & 156190 & 0 & -2450 & 0 & 190 & 0 & -50 & 0 & 70 \\ 5 & 88234 & 11326 & 154 & -434 & -86 & 46 & 34 & -14 & -56 \\ 6 & 14608 & 4046 & 952 & 134 & -32 & -34 & -8 & 14 & 28 \\ 7 & 502 & 246 & 118 & 54 & 22 & 6 & -2 & -6 & -8 \\ 8 & 1 & 1 & 1 & 1 & 1 & 1 & 1 & 1 & 1 \end{array} ,$$

$$F_{10} = \begin{array}{c|rrrrrrrrrr} i\backslash j & 10 & 9 & 8 & 7 & 6 & 5 & 4 & 3 & 2 & 1 \\ \hline 0 & 1 & -1 & 1 & -1 & 1 & -1 & 1 & -1 & 1 & -1 \\ 1 & 1013 & -501 & 245 & -117 & 53 & -21 & 5 & 3 & -7 & 9 \\ 2 & 47840 & -14106 & 3800 & -834 & 80 & 54 & -40 & 6 & 20 & -36 \\ 3 & 455192 & -73626 & 7280 & 798 & -568 & 54 & 80 & -42 & -28 & 84 \\ 4 & 1310354 & -67956 & -11326 & 2604 & 434 & -276 & -46 & 84 & 14 & -126 \\ 5 & 1310354 & 67956 & -11326 & -2604 & 434 & 276 & -46 & -84 & 14 & 126 \\ 6 & 455192 & 73626 & 7280 & -798 & -568 & -54 & 80 & 42 & -28 & -84 \\ 7 & 47840 & 14106 & 3800 & 834 & 80 & -54 & -40 & -6 & 20 & 36 \\ 8 & 1013 & 501 & 245 & 117 & 53 & 21 & 5 & -3 & -7 & -9 \\ 9 & 1 & 1 & 1 & 1 & 1 & 1 & 1 & 1 & 1 & 1 \end{array} .$$

8.2.3 Character polynomials

This subsection contains character polynomials for the symmetric group. Recall that these are polynomial functions in variables a_i, corresponding to so-called *truncated partitions* $\hat{\alpha}$. This means the following: If you want to obtain the value of the ordinary irreducible character ζ^β on the conjugacy class C^γ, you can proceed as follows: put $\hat{\alpha} := (\beta_2, \beta_3, \ldots)$, and denote by $a = (a_1, \ldots)$ the cycle type corresponding to the cycle partition γ. Then ζ^β_γ is the the value of the character polynomial $\Xi^{\hat{\alpha}}$ at $a = (a_1, \ldots)$:

$$\zeta^\beta_\gamma = \Xi^{\hat{\alpha}}(a_1, \ldots).$$

On this and the following pages you will find the first character polynomials listed, they cover the character tables of S_n, for $n \leq 10$, and each of these polynomials allows to evaluate an *infinite series* of ordinary irreducible character of symmetric groups!

The character polynomial $\Xi^{\hat{\alpha}}$, for $\hat{\alpha} := (\alpha_2, \alpha_3, \ldots) := (0)$:

$$1$$

The character polynomial $\Xi^{\hat{\alpha}}$, for $\hat{\alpha} := (\alpha_2, \alpha_3, \ldots) := (1)$:

$$\binom{a_1}{1} - 1$$

The character polynomial $\Xi^{\hat{\alpha}}$, for $\hat{\alpha} := (\alpha_2, \alpha_3, \ldots) := (2)$:

$$\binom{a_2}{1} + \binom{a_1}{2} - \binom{a_1}{1}$$

The character polynomial $\Xi^{\hat{\alpha}}$, for $\hat{\alpha} := (\alpha_2, \alpha_3, \ldots) := (1^2)$:

$$\binom{a_1}{2} - \binom{a_2}{1} - \binom{a_1}{1} + 1$$

The character polynomial $\Xi^{\hat{\alpha}}$, for $\hat{\alpha} := (\alpha_2, \alpha_3, \ldots) := (3)$:

$$\binom{a_3}{1} + \binom{a_1}{1}\binom{a_2}{1} + \binom{a_1}{3} - \binom{a_2}{1} - \binom{a_1}{2}$$

The character polynomial $\Xi^{\hat{\alpha}}$, for $\hat{\alpha} := (\alpha_2, \alpha_3, \ldots) := (2; 1)$:

$$2\binom{a_1}{3} - \binom{a_3}{1} - 2\binom{a_1}{2} + \binom{a_1}{1}$$

The character polynomial $\Xi^{\hat{\alpha}}$, for $\hat{\alpha} := (\alpha_2, \alpha_3, \ldots) := (1^3)$:

$$\binom{a_1}{3} - \binom{a_1}{1}\binom{a_2}{1} + \binom{a_3}{1} - \binom{a_1}{2} + \binom{a_2}{1} + \binom{a_1}{1} - 1$$

The character polynomial $\Xi^{\hat{\alpha}}$, for $\hat{\alpha} := (\alpha_2, \alpha_3, \ldots) := (4)$:

$$\binom{a_4}{1} + \binom{a_1}{1}\binom{a_3}{1} + \binom{a_2}{2} + \binom{a_1}{2}\binom{a_2}{1} + \binom{a_1}{4}$$

$$- \binom{a_3}{1} - \binom{a_1}{1}\binom{a_2}{1} - \binom{a_1}{3}$$

The character polynomial $\Xi^{\hat{\alpha}}$, for $\hat{\alpha} := (\alpha_2, \alpha_3, \ldots) := (3, 1)$:

$$\binom{a_1}{2}\binom{a_2}{1} + 3\binom{a_1}{4} - \binom{a_4}{1} - \binom{a_2}{2} - \binom{a_1}{1}\binom{a_2}{1}$$

$$- 3\binom{a_1}{3} + \binom{a_2}{1} + \binom{a_1}{2}$$

The character polynomial $\Xi^{\hat{\alpha}}$, for $\hat{\alpha} := (\alpha_2, \alpha_3, \ldots) := (2^2)$:

$$2\binom{a_2}{2} + 2\binom{a_1}{4} - \binom{a_1}{1}\binom{a_3}{1} - 2\binom{a_1}{3} + \binom{a_1}{2} + \binom{a_3}{1} - \binom{a_2}{1}$$

The character polynomial $\Xi^{\hat{\alpha}}$, for $\hat{\alpha} := (\alpha_2, \alpha_3, \ldots) := (2, 1^2)$:

$$-\binom{a_1}{2}\binom{a_2}{1} + 3\binom{a_1}{4} - \binom{a_2}{2} + \binom{a_4}{1} - 3\binom{a_1}{3} + \binom{a_1}{1}\binom{a_2}{1}$$

$$+2\binom{a_1}{2} - \binom{a_1}{1}$$

The character polynomial $\Xi^{\hat{\alpha}}$, for $\hat{\alpha} := (\alpha_2, \alpha_3, \ldots) := (1^4)$:

$$\binom{a_1}{4} - \binom{a_1}{2}\binom{a_2}{1} + \binom{a_1}{1}\binom{a_3}{1} + \binom{a_2}{2} - \binom{a_4}{1}$$

$$-\binom{a_1}{3} + \binom{a_1}{1}\binom{a_2}{1} - \binom{a_3}{1} + \binom{a_1}{2} - \binom{a_2}{1} - \binom{a_1}{1} + 1$$

The character polynomial $\Xi^{\hat{\alpha}}$, for $\hat{\alpha} := (\alpha_2, \alpha_3, \ldots) := (5)$:

$$\binom{a_5}{1} + \binom{a_1}{1}\binom{a_4}{1} + \binom{a_2}{1}\binom{a_3}{1} + \binom{a_1}{2}\binom{a_3}{1} + \binom{a_1}{1}\binom{a_2}{2}$$

$$+\binom{a_1}{3}\binom{a_2}{1} + \binom{a_1}{5} - \binom{a_4}{1} - \binom{a_1}{1}\binom{a_3}{1} - \binom{a_2}{2} - \binom{a_1}{2}\binom{a_2}{1} - \binom{a_1}{4}$$

The character polynomial $\Xi^{\hat{\alpha}}$, for $\hat{\alpha} := (\alpha_2, \alpha_3, \ldots) := (4, 1)$:

$$\binom{a_1}{2}\binom{a_3}{1} + 2\binom{a_1}{3}\binom{a_2}{1} + 4\binom{a_1}{5} - \binom{a_5}{1} - \binom{a_2}{1}\binom{a_3}{1}$$

$$-\binom{a_1}{1}\binom{a_3}{1} - 2\binom{a_1}{2}\binom{a_2}{1} - 4\binom{a_1}{4} + \binom{a_3}{1} + \binom{a_1}{1}\binom{a_2}{1} + \binom{a_1}{3}$$

The character polynomial $\Xi^{\hat{\alpha}}$, for $\hat{\alpha} := (\alpha_2, \alpha_3, \ldots) := (3, 2)$:

$$\binom{a_2}{1}\binom{a_3}{1} - \binom{a_1}{2}\binom{a_3}{1} + \binom{a_1}{1}\binom{a_2}{2} + \binom{a_1}{3}\binom{a_2}{1} + 5\binom{a_1}{5}$$

$$-\binom{a_1}{1}\binom{a_4}{1} - \binom{a_2}{2} - \binom{a_1}{2}\binom{a_2}{1} - 5\binom{a_1}{4} + 2\binom{a_1}{3} + \binom{a_4}{1}$$

$$+ \binom{a_1}{1}\binom{a_3}{1} - \binom{a_3}{1}$$

The character polynomial $\Xi^{\hat{\alpha}}$, for $\hat{\alpha} := (\alpha_2, \alpha_3, \ldots) := (3, 1^2)$:

$$6\binom{a_1}{5} - 2\binom{a_1}{1}\binom{a_2}{2} + \binom{a_5}{1} - 6\binom{a_1}{4} + 2\binom{a_2}{2} + \binom{a_1}{1}\binom{a_2}{1}$$

$$+ 3\binom{a_1}{3} - \binom{a_2}{1} - \binom{a_1}{2}$$

The character polynomial $\Xi^{\hat{\alpha}}$, for $\hat{\alpha} := (\alpha_2, \alpha_3, \ldots) := (2^2, 1)$:

$$\binom{a_1}{1}\binom{a_2}{2} - \binom{a_1}{3}\binom{a_2}{1} + 5\binom{a_1}{5} - \binom{a_2}{1}\binom{a_3}{1}$$

$$- \binom{a_1}{2}\binom{a_3}{1} + \binom{a_1}{1}\binom{a_4}{1} + \binom{a_1}{2}\binom{a_2}{1} - 5\binom{a_1}{4} + \binom{a_1}{1}\binom{a_3}{1}$$

$$+ 3\binom{a_1}{3} - \binom{a_1}{2} - \binom{a_4}{1} - \binom{a_2}{2} - \binom{a_1}{1}\binom{a_2}{1} + \binom{a_2}{1}$$

The character polynomial $\Xi^{\hat{\alpha}}$, for $\hat{\alpha} := (\alpha_2, \alpha_3, \ldots) := (2, 1^3)$:

$$-2\binom{a_1}{3}\binom{a_2}{1} + 4\binom{a_1}{5} + \binom{a_2}{1}\binom{a_3}{1} + \binom{a_1}{2}\binom{a_3}{1} - \binom{a_5}{1} - 4\binom{a_1}{4}$$

$$+ 2\binom{a_1}{2}\binom{a_2}{1} - \binom{a_1}{1}\binom{a_3}{1} + 3\binom{a_1}{3} - \binom{a_1}{1}\binom{a_2}{1} - 2\binom{a_1}{2} + \binom{a_1}{1}$$

The character polynomial $\Xi^{\hat{\alpha}}$, for $\hat{\alpha} := (\alpha_2, \alpha_3, \ldots) := (1^5)$:

$$\binom{a_1}{5} - \binom{a_1}{3}\binom{a_2}{1} + \binom{a_1}{2}\binom{a_3}{1} + \binom{a_1}{1}\binom{a_2}{2} - \binom{a_1}{1}\binom{a_4}{1}$$

$$- \binom{a_2}{1}\binom{a_3}{1} + \binom{a_5}{1} - \binom{a_1}{4} + \binom{a_1}{2}\binom{a_2}{1} - \binom{a_1}{1}\binom{a_3}{1} - \binom{a_2}{2} + \binom{a_4}{1}$$

$$+ \binom{a_1}{3} - \binom{a_1}{1}\binom{a_2}{1} + \binom{a_3}{1} - \binom{a_1}{2} + \binom{a_2}{1} + \binom{a_1}{1} - 1$$

The character polynomial $\Xi^{\hat{\alpha}}$, for $\hat{\alpha} := (\alpha_2, \alpha_3, \ldots) := (6)$:

$$\binom{a_6}{1} + \binom{a_1}{1}\binom{a_5}{1} + \binom{a_2}{1}\binom{a_4}{1} + \binom{a_1}{2}\binom{a_4}{1} + \binom{a_3}{2}$$

$$+\binom{a_1}{1}\binom{a_2}{1}\binom{a_3}{1}+\binom{a_1}{1}\binom{a_3}{3}+\binom{a_2}{3}+\binom{a_1}{2}\binom{a_2}{2}+\binom{a_1}{4}\binom{a_2}{1}$$

$$+\binom{a_1}{6}-\binom{a_5}{1}-\binom{a_1}{1}\binom{a_4}{1}-\binom{a_2}{1}\binom{a_3}{1}-\binom{a_1}{2}\binom{a_3}{1}$$

$$-\binom{a_1}{1}\binom{a_2}{2}-\binom{a_1}{3}\binom{a_2}{1}-\binom{a_1}{5}$$

The character polynomial $\Xi^{\hat\alpha}$, for $\hat\alpha := (\alpha_2,\alpha_3,\ldots) := (5,1)$:

$$\binom{a_1}{2}\binom{a_4}{1}+2\binom{a_1}{3}\binom{a_3}{1}+\binom{a_1}{2}\binom{a_2}{2}+3\binom{a_1}{4}\binom{a_2}{1}+5\binom{a_1}{6}\quad\binom{a_6}{1}$$

$$-\binom{a_2}{1}\binom{a_4}{1}-\binom{a_3}{2}-\binom{a_2}{3}-\binom{a_1}{1}\binom{a_4}{1}-2\binom{a_1}{2}\binom{a_3}{1}-\binom{a_1}{1}\binom{a_2}{2}$$

$$-3\binom{a_1}{3}\binom{a_2}{1}-5\binom{a_1}{5}+\binom{a_4}{1}+\binom{a_1}{1}\binom{a_3}{1}$$

$$+\binom{a_2}{2}+\binom{a_1}{2}\binom{a_2}{1}+\binom{a_1}{4}$$

The character polynomial $\Xi^{\hat\alpha}$, for $\hat\alpha := (\alpha_2,\alpha_3,\ldots) := (4,2)$:

$$\binom{a_2}{1}\binom{a_4}{1}-\binom{a_1}{2}\binom{a_4}{1}+3\binom{a_2}{3}+\binom{a_1}{2}\binom{a_2}{2}+3\binom{a_1}{4}\binom{a_2}{1}+9\binom{a_1}{6}$$

$$-\binom{a_1}{1}\binom{a_5}{1}-\binom{a_1}{1}\binom{a_2}{2}-3\binom{a_1}{3}\binom{a_2}{1}-9\binom{a_1}{5}+\binom{a_1}{2}\binom{a_2}{1}$$

$$+3\binom{a_1}{4}+\binom{a_5}{1}+\binom{a_1}{1}\binom{a_4}{1}-\binom{a_4}{1}-\binom{a_2}{2}$$

The character polynomial $\Xi^{\hat\alpha}$, for $\hat\alpha := (\alpha_2,\alpha_3,\ldots) := (4,1^2)$:

$$\binom{a_1}{3}\binom{a_3}{1}-2\binom{a_1}{2}\binom{a_2}{2}+2\binom{a_1}{4}\binom{a_2}{1}+10\binom{a_1}{6}-\binom{a_1}{1}\binom{a_2}{1}\binom{a_3}{1}$$

$$-2\binom{a_2}{3}+\binom{a_6}{1}+\binom{a_3}{2}-\binom{a_1}{2}\binom{a_3}{1}-2\binom{a_1}{3}\binom{a_2}{1}-10\binom{a_1}{5}$$

$$+\binom{a_2}{1}\binom{a_3}{1}+2\binom{a_1}{1}\binom{a_2}{2}+\binom{a_1}{1}\binom{a_3}{1}+2\binom{a_1}{2}\binom{a_2}{1}$$

$$+4\binom{a_1}{4}-\binom{a_3}{1}-\binom{a_1}{1}\binom{a_2}{1}-\binom{a_1}{3}$$

The character polynomial $\Xi^{\hat{\alpha}}$, for $\hat{\alpha}:=(\alpha_2,\alpha_3,\ldots):=(3^2)$:

$$2\binom{a_3}{2}+\binom{a_1}{1}\binom{a_2}{1}\binom{a_3}{1}-\binom{a_1}{3}\binom{a_3}{1}+\binom{a_1}{2}\binom{a_2}{2}+\binom{a_1}{4}\binom{a_2}{1}$$

$$+5\binom{a_1}{6}-\binom{a_2}{1}\binom{a_4}{1}-\binom{a_1}{2}\binom{a_4}{1}-3\binom{a_2}{3}-\binom{a_2}{1}\binom{a_3}{1}+\binom{a_1}{2}\binom{a_3}{1}$$

$$-\binom{a_1}{1}\binom{a_2}{2}-\binom{a_1}{3}\binom{a_2}{1}-5\binom{a_1}{5}+2\binom{a_2}{2}+2\binom{a_1}{4}$$

$$+\binom{a_1}{1}\binom{a_4}{1}-\binom{a_1}{1}\binom{a_3}{1}$$

The character polynomial $\Xi^{\hat{\alpha}}$, for $\hat{\alpha}:=(\alpha_2,\alpha_3,\ldots):=(3,2,1)$:

$$-2\binom{a_1}{3}\binom{a_3}{1}+16\binom{a_1}{6}-2\binom{a_3}{2}+\binom{a_1}{1}\binom{a_5}{1}-16\binom{a_1}{5}+2\binom{a_1}{2}\binom{a_3}{1}$$

$$+8\binom{a_1}{4}-2\binom{a_1}{3}-\binom{a_5}{1}-\binom{a_1}{1}\binom{a_3}{1}+\binom{a_3}{1}$$

The character polynomial $\Xi^{\hat{\alpha}}$, for $\hat{\alpha}:=(\alpha_2,\alpha_3,\ldots):=(3,1^3)$:

$$\binom{a_1}{3}\binom{a_3}{1}-2\binom{a_1}{4}\binom{a_2}{1}+10\binom{a_1}{6}+\binom{a_1}{1}\binom{a_2}{1}\binom{a_3}{1}-2\binom{a_1}{2}\binom{a_2}{2}$$

$$+\binom{a_3}{2}+2\binom{a_2}{3}-\binom{a_6}{1}+2\binom{a_1}{3}\binom{a_2}{1}-10\binom{a_1}{5}+2\binom{a_1}{1}\binom{a_2}{2}$$

$$-\binom{a_2}{1}\binom{a_3}{1}-\binom{a_1}{2}\binom{a_3}{1}+6\binom{a_1}{4}-2\binom{a_2}{2}-\binom{a_1}{1}\binom{a_2}{1}$$

$$-3\binom{a_1}{3}+\binom{a_2}{1}+\binom{a_1}{2}$$

The character polynomial $\Xi^{\hat{\alpha}}$, for $\hat{\alpha}:=(\alpha_2,\alpha_3,\ldots):=(2^3)$:

$$3\binom{a_2}{3}+\binom{a_1}{2}\binom{a_2}{2}-\binom{a_1}{4}\binom{a_2}{1}+5\binom{a_1}{6}-\binom{a_1}{1}\binom{a_2}{1}\binom{a_3}{1}$$

$$-\binom{a_1}{3}\binom{a_3}{1}+\binom{a_1}{2}\binom{a_4}{1}+2\binom{a_3}{2}-\binom{a_2}{1}\binom{a_4}{1}-\binom{a_1}{1}\binom{a_2}{2}$$

$$+\binom{a_1}{3}\binom{a_2}{1}-5\binom{a_1}{5}+\binom{a_1}{2}\binom{a_3}{1}-\binom{a_1}{2}\binom{a_2}{1}+3\binom{a_1}{4}-\binom{a_1}{3}$$

$$+\binom{a_1}{1}\binom{a_2}{1}+\binom{a_2}{1}\binom{a_3}{1}-\binom{a_1}{1}\binom{a_4}{1}-\binom{a_2}{2}+\binom{a_4}{1}-\binom{a_3}{1}$$

The character polynomial $\Xi^{\hat{\alpha}}$, for $\hat{\alpha} := (\alpha_2, \alpha_3, \ldots) := (2^2, 1^2)$:

$$\binom{a_1}{2}\binom{a_2}{2}-3\binom{a_1}{4}\binom{a_2}{1}+9\binom{a_1}{6}-3\binom{a_2}{3}+\binom{a_2}{1}\binom{a_4}{1}$$

$$+\binom{a_1}{2}\binom{a_4}{1}-\binom{a_1}{1}\binom{a_5}{1}+3\binom{a_1}{3}\binom{a_2}{1}-9\binom{a_1}{5}-\binom{a_1}{1}\binom{a_2}{2}$$

$$-\binom{a_1}{1}\binom{a_4}{1}+6\binom{a_1}{4}-2\binom{a_1}{2}\binom{a_2}{1}-3\binom{a_1}{3}+\binom{a_1}{2}+\binom{a_5}{1}$$

$$+2\binom{a_2}{2}+\binom{a_1}{1}\binom{a_2}{1}-\binom{a_2}{1}$$

The character polynomial $\Xi^{\hat{\alpha}}$, for $\hat{\alpha} := (\alpha_2, \alpha_3, \ldots) := (2, 1^4)$:

$$-3\binom{a_1}{4}\binom{a_2}{1}+5\binom{a_1}{6}+\binom{a_1}{2}\binom{a_2}{2}+2\binom{a_1}{3}\binom{a_3}{1}+\binom{a_2}{3}$$

$$-\binom{a_2}{1}\binom{a_4}{1}-\binom{a_1}{2}\binom{a_4}{1}-\binom{a_3}{2}+\binom{a_6}{1}-5\binom{a_1}{5}+3\binom{a_1}{3}\binom{a_2}{1}$$

$$-2\binom{a_1}{2}\binom{a_3}{1}-\binom{a_1}{1}\binom{a_2}{2}+\binom{a_1}{1}\binom{a_4}{1}+4\binom{a_1}{4}-2\binom{a_1}{2}\binom{a_2}{1}$$

$$+\binom{a_1}{1}\binom{a_3}{1}-3\binom{a_1}{3}+\binom{a_1}{1}\binom{a_2}{1}+2\binom{a_1}{2}-\binom{a_1}{1}$$

The character polynomial $\Xi^{\hat{\alpha}}$, for $\hat{\alpha} := (\alpha_2, \alpha_3, \ldots) := (1^6)$:

$$\binom{a_1}{6}-\binom{a_1}{4}\binom{a_2}{1}+\binom{a_1}{3}\binom{a_3}{1}+\binom{a_1}{2}\binom{a_2}{2}-\binom{a_1}{2}\binom{a_4}{1}$$

$$-\binom{a_1}{1}\binom{a_2}{1}\binom{a_3}{1}+\binom{a_1}{1}\binom{a_5}{1}-\binom{a_2}{3}+\binom{a_2}{1}\binom{a_4}{1}+\binom{a_3}{2}-\binom{a_6}{1}$$

$$-\binom{a_1}{5}+\binom{a_1}{3}\binom{a_2}{1}-\binom{a_1}{2}\binom{a_3}{1}-\binom{a_1}{1}\binom{a_2}{2}+\binom{a_1}{1}\binom{a_4}{1}$$

$$+\binom{a_2}{1}\binom{a_3}{1}-\binom{a_5}{1}+\binom{a_1}{4}-\binom{a_1}{2}\binom{a_2}{1}+\binom{a_1}{1}\binom{a_3}{1}+\binom{a_2}{2}-\binom{a_4}{1}$$

$$-\binom{a_1}{3}+\binom{a_1}{1}\binom{a_2}{1}-\binom{a_3}{1}+\binom{a_1}{2}-\binom{a_2}{1}-\binom{a_1}{1}+1$$

The character polynomial $\Xi^{\hat{\alpha}}$, for $\hat{\alpha} := (\alpha_2, \alpha_3, \ldots) := (7)$:

$$\binom{a_7}{1}+\binom{a_1}{1}\binom{a_6}{1}+\binom{a_2}{1}\binom{a_5}{1}+\binom{a_1}{2}\binom{a_5}{1}+\binom{a_3}{1}\binom{a_4}{1}$$

$$+\binom{a_1}{1}\binom{a_2}{1}\binom{a_4}{1}+\binom{a_1}{3}\binom{a_4}{1}+\binom{a_1}{1}\binom{a_3}{2}+\binom{a_2}{2}\binom{a_3}{1}$$

$$+\binom{a_1}{2}\binom{a_2}{1}\binom{a_3}{1}+\binom{a_1}{4}\binom{a_3}{1}+\binom{a_1}{1}\binom{a_2}{3}+\binom{a_1}{3}\binom{a_2}{2}$$

$$+\binom{a_1}{5}\binom{a_2}{1}+\binom{a_1}{7}-\binom{a_6}{1}-\binom{a_1}{1}\binom{a_5}{1}-\binom{a_2}{1}\binom{a_4}{1}$$

$$-\binom{a_1}{2}\binom{a_4}{1}-\binom{a_3}{2}-\binom{a_1}{1}\binom{a_2}{1}\binom{a_3}{1}-\binom{a_1}{3}\binom{a_3}{1}$$

$$-\binom{a_2}{3}-\binom{a_1}{2}\binom{a_2}{2}-\binom{a_1}{4}\binom{a_2}{1}-\binom{a_1}{6}$$

The character polynomial $\Xi^{\hat{\alpha}}$, for $\hat{\alpha} := (\alpha_2, \alpha_3, \ldots) := (6, 1)$:

$$\binom{a_1}{2}\binom{a_5}{1}+2\binom{a_1}{3}\binom{a_4}{1}+\binom{a_1}{2}\binom{a_2}{1}\binom{a_3}{1}+3\binom{a_1}{4}\binom{a_3}{1}$$

$$+2\binom{a_1}{3}\binom{a_2}{2}+4\binom{a_1}{5}\binom{a_2}{1}+6\binom{a_1}{7}-\binom{a_7}{1}-\binom{a_2}{1}\binom{a_5}{1}$$

$$-\binom{a_3}{1}\binom{a_4}{1}-\binom{a_2}{2}\binom{a_3}{1}-\binom{a_1}{1}\binom{a_5}{1}-2\binom{a_1}{2}\binom{a_4}{1}$$

$$-\binom{a_1}{1}\binom{a_2}{1}\binom{a_3}{1}-3\binom{a_1}{3}\binom{a_3}{1}-2\binom{a_1}{2}\binom{a_2}{2}-4\binom{a_1}{4}\binom{a_2}{1}$$

$$-6\binom{a_1}{6}+\binom{a_5}{1}+\binom{a_1}{1}\binom{a_4}{1}+\binom{a_2}{1}\binom{a_3}{1}+\binom{a_1}{2}\binom{a_3}{1}$$

$$+\binom{a_1}{1}\binom{a_2}{2}+\binom{a_1}{3}\binom{a_2}{1}+\binom{a_1}{5}$$

The character polynomial $\Xi^{\hat{\alpha}}$, for $\hat{\alpha} := (\alpha_2, \alpha_3, \ldots) := (5, 2)$:

$$\binom{a_2}{1}\binom{a_5}{1} - \binom{a_1}{2}\binom{a_5}{1} + 2\binom{a_2}{2}\binom{a_3}{1} + 2\binom{a_1}{4}\binom{a_3}{1} + 2\binom{a_1}{1}\binom{a_2}{3}$$

$$+2\binom{a_1}{3}\binom{a_2}{2} + 6\binom{a_1}{5}\binom{a_2}{1} + 14\binom{a_1}{7} - \binom{a_1}{1}\binom{a_6}{1} - \binom{a_1}{1}\binom{a_3}{2}$$

$$-2\binom{a_1}{3}\binom{a_3}{1} - 2\binom{a_2}{3} - 2\binom{a_1}{2}\binom{a_2}{2} - 6\binom{a_1}{4}\binom{a_2}{1} - 14\binom{a_1}{6}$$

$$+\binom{a_1}{2}\binom{a_3}{1} + 2\binom{a_1}{3}\binom{a_2}{1} + 4\binom{a_1}{5} + \binom{a_6}{1}$$

$$+\binom{a_1}{1}\binom{a_5}{1} + \binom{a_3}{2} - \binom{a_5}{1} - \binom{a_2}{1}\binom{a_3}{1}$$

The character polynomial $\Xi^{\hat{\alpha}}$, for $\hat{\alpha} := (\alpha_2, \alpha_3, \ldots) := (5, 1^2)$:

$$\binom{a_1}{3}\binom{a_4}{1} - \binom{a_1}{2}\binom{a_2}{1}\binom{a_3}{1} + 3\binom{a_1}{4}\binom{a_3}{1} - \binom{a_1}{3}\binom{a_2}{2}$$

$$+5\binom{a_1}{5}\binom{a_2}{1} + 15\binom{a_1}{7} - \binom{a_1}{1}\binom{a_2}{1}\binom{a_4}{1} - \binom{a_2}{2}\binom{a_3}{1}$$

$$-3\binom{a_1}{1}\binom{a_2}{3} + \binom{a_7}{1} + \binom{a_3}{1}\binom{a_4}{1} - \binom{a_1}{2}\binom{a_4}{1} - 3\binom{a_1}{3}\binom{a_3}{1}$$

$$+\binom{a_1}{2}\binom{a_2}{2} - 5\binom{a_1}{4}\binom{a_2}{1} - 15\binom{a_1}{6} + \binom{a_2}{1}\binom{a_4}{1}$$

$$+\binom{a_1}{1}\binom{a_2}{1}\binom{a_3}{1} + 3\binom{a_2}{3} + \binom{a_1}{1}\binom{a_4}{1} + 2\binom{a_1}{2}\binom{a_3}{1}$$

$$+\binom{a_1}{1}\binom{a_2}{2} + 3\binom{a_1}{3}\binom{a_2}{1} + 5\binom{a_1}{5} - \binom{a_4}{1}$$

$$-\binom{a_1}{1}\binom{a_3}{1} - \binom{a_2}{2} - \binom{a_1}{2}\binom{a_2}{1} - \binom{a_1}{4}$$

The character polynomial $\Xi^{\hat{\alpha}}$, for $\hat{\alpha} := (\alpha_2, \alpha_3, \ldots) := (4, 3)$:

$$\binom{a_3}{1}\binom{a_4}{1} - 2\binom{a_1}{3}\binom{a_4}{1} + 2\binom{a_1}{1}\binom{a_3}{2} + \binom{a_1}{2}\binom{a_2}{1}\binom{a_3}{1}$$

$$-\binom{a_1}{4}\binom{a_3}{1} - \binom{a_2}{2}\binom{a_3}{1} + 2\binom{a_1}{3}\binom{a_2}{2} + 4\binom{a_1}{5}\binom{a_2}{1}$$

$$+14\binom{a_1}{7} - \binom{a_2}{1}\binom{a_5}{1} - \binom{a_1}{2}\binom{a_5}{1} - 2\binom{a_3}{2} - \binom{a_1}{1}\binom{a_2}{1}\binom{a_3}{1}$$

$$+\binom{a_1}{3}\binom{a_3}{1} - 2\binom{a_1}{2}\binom{a_2}{2} - 4\binom{a_1}{4}\binom{a_2}{1} - 14\binom{a_1}{6} + \binom{a_2}{1}\binom{a_3}{1}$$

$$-\binom{a_1}{2}\binom{a_3}{1} + \binom{a_1}{1}\binom{a_2}{2} + \binom{a_1}{3}\binom{a_2}{1} + 5\binom{a_1}{5} + \binom{a_1}{1}\binom{a_5}{1}$$

$$+2\binom{a_1}{2}\binom{a_4}{1} - \binom{a_1}{1}\binom{a_4}{1}$$

The character polynomial $\Xi^{\hat{\alpha}}$, for $\hat{\alpha} := (\alpha_2, \alpha_3, \ldots) := (4, 2, 1)$:

$$\binom{a_1}{1}\binom{a_2}{1}\binom{a_4}{1} - \binom{a_1}{3}\binom{a_4}{1} - \binom{a_1}{2}\binom{a_2}{1}\binom{a_3}{1} - \binom{a_1}{4}\binom{a_3}{1}$$

$$+\binom{a_1}{1}\binom{a_2}{3} - \binom{a_1}{3}\binom{a_2}{2} + 5\binom{a_1}{5}\binom{a_2}{1} + 35\binom{a_1}{7} - \binom{a_3}{1}\binom{a_4}{1}$$

$$-\binom{a_1}{1}\binom{a_3}{2} - \binom{a_2}{2}\binom{a_3}{1} + \binom{a_1}{1}\binom{a_6}{1} + \binom{a_1}{1}\binom{a_2}{1}\binom{a_3}{1}$$

$$+\binom{a_1}{3}\binom{a_3}{1} + \binom{a_1}{2}\binom{a_2}{2} - 5\binom{a_1}{4}\binom{a_2}{1} - 35\binom{a_1}{6} + \binom{a_3}{2}$$

$$+3\binom{a_1}{3}\binom{a_2}{1} + 15\binom{a_1}{5} - \binom{a_1}{2}\binom{a_2}{1}$$

$$-3\binom{a_1}{4} + \binom{a_1}{2}\binom{a_4}{1} - \binom{a_6}{1} - \binom{a_2}{1}\binom{a_4}{1} - \binom{a_2}{3} - \binom{a_1}{1}\binom{a_4}{1}$$

$$-\binom{a_1}{1}\binom{a_2}{2} + \binom{a_4}{1} + \binom{a_2}{2}$$

The character polynomial $\Xi^{\hat{\alpha}}$, for $\hat{\alpha} := (\alpha_2, \alpha_3, \ldots) := (4, 1^3)$:

$$2\binom{a_1}{4}\binom{a_3}{1} - 4\binom{a_1}{3}\binom{a_2}{2} + 20\binom{a_1}{7} + 2\binom{a_1}{1}\binom{a_3}{2} + 2\binom{a_2}{2}\binom{a_3}{1}$$

$$-\binom{a_7}{1} - 2\binom{a_1}{3}\binom{a_3}{1} - 20\binom{a_1}{6} + 4\binom{a_1}{2}\binom{a_2}{2} - 2\binom{a_3}{2} + \binom{a_1}{2}\binom{a_3}{1}$$

$$+2\binom{a_1}{3}\binom{a_2}{1} + 10\binom{a_1}{5} - \binom{a_2}{1}\binom{a_3}{1} - 2\binom{a_1}{1}\binom{a_2}{2} - \binom{a_1}{1}\binom{a_3}{1}$$

$$-2\binom{a_1}{2}\binom{a_2}{1} - 4\binom{a_1}{4} + \binom{a_3}{1} + \binom{a_1}{1}\binom{a_2}{1} + \binom{a_1}{3}$$

The character polynomial $\Xi^{\hat{\alpha}}$, for $\hat{\alpha} := (\alpha_2, \alpha_3, \ldots) := (3^2, 1)$:

$$\binom{a_1}{2}\binom{a_2}{1}\binom{a_3}{1} - 3\binom{a_1}{4}\binom{a_3}{1} + \binom{a_1}{3}\binom{a_2}{2} + \binom{a_1}{5}\binom{a_2}{1} + 21\binom{a_1}{7}$$

$$-\binom{a_3}{1}\binom{a_4}{1} - \binom{a_1}{1}\binom{a_2}{1}\binom{a_4}{1} - \binom{a_1}{3}\binom{a_4}{1} + \binom{a_2}{2}\binom{a_3}{1}$$

$$-3\binom{a_1}{1}\binom{a_2}{3} + \binom{a_2}{1}\binom{a_5}{1} + \binom{a_1}{2}\binom{a_5}{1} - \binom{a_1}{1}\binom{a_2}{1}\binom{a_3}{1}$$

$$+3\binom{a_1}{3}\binom{a_3}{1} - \binom{a_1}{2}\binom{a_2}{2} - \binom{a_1}{4}\binom{a_2}{1} - 21\binom{a_1}{6} + \binom{a_2}{1}\binom{a_4}{1}$$

$$+\binom{a_1}{2}\binom{a_4}{1} + 3\binom{a_2}{3} + 2\binom{a_1}{1}\binom{a_2}{2} + 10\binom{a_1}{5} - 2\binom{a_2}{2} - 2\binom{a_1}{4}$$

$$-\binom{a_1}{1}\binom{a_5}{1} - 2\binom{a_1}{2}\binom{a_3}{1} + \binom{a_1}{1}\binom{a_3}{1}$$

The character polynomial $\Xi^{\hat{\alpha}}$, for $\hat{\alpha} := (\alpha_2, \alpha_3, \ldots) := (3, 2^2)$:

$$\binom{a_2}{2}\binom{a_3}{1} - \binom{a_1}{2}\binom{a_2}{1}\binom{a_3}{1} - 3\binom{a_1}{4}\binom{a_3}{1} + 3\binom{a_1}{1}\binom{a_2}{3}$$

$$+\binom{a_1}{3}\binom{a_2}{2} - \binom{a_1}{5}\binom{a_2}{1} + 21\binom{a_1}{7} - \binom{a_1}{1}\binom{a_2}{1}\binom{a_4}{1} + \binom{a_1}{3}\binom{a_4}{1}$$

$$+\binom{a_1}{2}\binom{a_5}{1} + \binom{a_3}{1}\binom{a_4}{1} - \binom{a_2}{1}\binom{a_5}{1} - 3\binom{a_2}{3} - \binom{a_1}{2}\binom{a_2}{2}$$

$$+\binom{a_1}{4}\binom{a_2}{1} - 21\binom{a_1}{6} + \binom{a_1}{1}\binom{a_2}{1}\binom{a_3}{1} + 3\binom{a_1}{3}\binom{a_3}{1} - \binom{a_1}{1}\binom{a_2}{2}$$

$$-\binom{a_1}{3}\binom{a_2}{1} + 11\binom{a_1}{5} + \binom{a_1}{2}\binom{a_2}{1} - 3\binom{a_1}{4} - \binom{a_2}{1}\binom{a_3}{1}$$

$$-\binom{a_1}{2}\binom{a_3}{1} + \binom{a_2}{2} + \binom{a_2}{1}\binom{a_4}{1} - \binom{a_1}{2}\binom{a_4}{1} - \binom{a_1}{1}\binom{a_5}{1} + \binom{a_5}{1}$$

$$+\binom{a_1}{1}\binom{a_4}{1} - \binom{a_4}{1}$$

The character polynomial $\Xi^{\hat\alpha}$, for $\hat\alpha := (\alpha_2, \alpha_3, \ldots) := (3, 2, 1^2)$:

$$\binom{a_1}{2}\binom{a_2}{1}\binom{a_3}{1} - \binom{a_1}{4}\binom{a_3}{1} - \binom{a_1}{3}\binom{a_2}{2} - 5\binom{a_1}{5}\binom{a_2}{1} + 35\binom{a_1}{7}$$

$$- \binom{a_2}{2}\binom{a_3}{1} - \binom{a_1}{1}\binom{a_2}{3} - \binom{a_1}{1}\binom{a_3}{2} + \binom{a_3}{1}\binom{a_4}{1}$$

$$+ \binom{a_1}{1}\binom{a_2}{1}\binom{a_4}{1} + \binom{a_1}{3}\binom{a_4}{1} - \binom{a_1}{1}\binom{a_6}{1} + \binom{a_1}{2}\binom{a_2}{2}$$

$$+ 5\binom{a_1}{4}\binom{a_2}{1} - 35\binom{a_1}{6} + \binom{a_2}{3} - \binom{a_1}{1}\binom{a_2}{1}\binom{a_3}{1} + \binom{a_1}{3}\binom{a_3}{1}$$

$$- \binom{a_2}{1}\binom{a_4}{1} - \binom{a_1}{2}\binom{a_4}{1} - 2\binom{a_1}{3}\binom{a_2}{1} + 20\binom{a_1}{5} - 8\binom{a_1}{4} + 2\binom{a_1}{3}$$

$$+ \binom{a_6}{1} + \binom{a_3}{2} - \binom{a_1}{2}\binom{a_3}{1} + \binom{a_2}{1}\binom{a_3}{1} + \binom{a_1}{1}\binom{a_3}{1} - \binom{a_3}{1}$$

The character polynomial $\Xi^{\hat\alpha}$, for $\hat\alpha := (\alpha_2, \alpha_3, \ldots) := (3, 1^4)$:

$$3\binom{a_1}{4}\binom{a_3}{1} - 5\binom{a_1}{5}\binom{a_2}{1} + 15\binom{a_1}{7} + \binom{a_1}{2}\binom{a_2}{1}\binom{a_3}{1} - \binom{a_1}{3}\binom{a_2}{2}$$

$$- \binom{a_2}{2}\binom{a_3}{1} + 3\binom{a_1}{1}\binom{a_2}{3} - \binom{a_3}{1}\binom{a_4}{1} - \binom{a_1}{1}\binom{a_2}{1}\binom{a_4}{1}$$

$$- \binom{a_1}{3}\binom{a_4}{1} + \binom{a_7}{1} + 5\binom{a_1}{4}\binom{a_2}{1} - 15\binom{a_1}{6} + \binom{a_1}{2}\binom{a_2}{2}$$

$$- \binom{a_1}{1}\binom{a_2}{1}\binom{a_3}{1} - 3\binom{a_1}{3}\binom{a_3}{1} - 3\binom{a_2}{3} + \binom{a_2}{1}\binom{a_4}{1}$$

$$+ \binom{a_1}{2}\binom{a_4}{1} - 2\binom{a_1}{3}\binom{a_2}{1} + 10\binom{a_1}{5} - 2\binom{a_1}{1}\binom{a_2}{2} + \binom{a_2}{1}\binom{a_3}{1}$$

$$+ \binom{a_1}{2}\binom{a_3}{1} - 6\binom{a_1}{4} + 2\binom{a_2}{2} + \binom{a_1}{1}\binom{a_2}{1} + 3\binom{a_1}{3} - \binom{a_2}{1} - \binom{a_1}{2}$$

The character polynomial $\Xi^{\hat\alpha}$, for $\hat\alpha := (\alpha_2, \alpha_3, \ldots) := (2^3, 1)$:

$$2\binom{a_1}{3}\binom{a_2}{2} - 4\binom{a_1}{5}\binom{a_2}{1} + 14\binom{a_1}{7} - \binom{a_2}{2}\binom{a_3}{1} - \binom{a_1}{2}\binom{a_2}{1}\binom{a_3}{1}$$

$$- \binom{a_1}{4}\binom{a_3}{1} + 2\binom{a_1}{3}\binom{a_4}{1} + 2\binom{a_1}{1}\binom{a_3}{2} - \binom{a_1}{2}\binom{a_5}{1} - \binom{a_3}{1}\binom{a_4}{1}$$

$$+\binom{a_2}{1}\binom{a_5}{1}-2\binom{a_1}{2}\binom{a_2}{2}+4\binom{a_1}{4}\binom{a_2}{1}-14\binom{a_1}{6}$$

$$+\binom{a_1}{1}\binom{a_2}{1}\binom{a_3}{1}+\binom{a_1}{3}\binom{a_3}{1}-2\binom{a_1}{2}\binom{a_4}{1}-3\binom{a_1}{3}\binom{a_2}{1}$$

$$+9\binom{a_1}{5}-4\binom{a_1}{4}+\binom{a_1}{3}+\binom{a_1}{1}\binom{a_4}{1}+\binom{a_1}{1}\binom{a_2}{2}+2\binom{a_1}{2}\binom{a_2}{1}$$

$$-\binom{a_1}{1}\binom{a_2}{1}-2\binom{a_3}{2}+\binom{a_1}{1}\binom{a_5}{1}-\binom{a_5}{1}-\binom{a_1}{1}\binom{a_3}{1}+\binom{a_3}{1}$$

The character polynomial $\Xi^{\hat{\alpha}}$, for $\hat{\alpha} := (\alpha_2, \alpha_3, \ldots) := (2^7, 1^3)$:

$$2\binom{a_1}{3}\binom{a_2}{2}-6\binom{a_1}{5}\binom{a_2}{1}+14\binom{a_1}{7}-2\binom{a_1}{1}\binom{a_2}{3}+2\binom{a_2}{2}\binom{a_3}{1}$$

$$+2\binom{a_1}{4}\binom{a_3}{1}-\binom{a_2}{1}\binom{a_5}{1}-\binom{a_1}{2}\binom{a_5}{1}-\binom{a_1}{1}\binom{a_3}{2}+\binom{a_1}{1}\binom{a_6}{1}$$

$$+6\binom{a_1}{4}\binom{a_2}{1}-14\binom{a_1}{6}-2\binom{a_1}{2}\binom{a_2}{2}-2\binom{a_1}{3}\binom{a_3}{1}+\binom{a_1}{1}\binom{a_5}{1}$$

$$+10\binom{a_1}{5}-4\binom{a_1}{3}\binom{a_2}{1}+\binom{a_1}{2}\binom{a_3}{1}-6\binom{a_1}{4}+2\binom{a_1}{2}\binom{a_2}{1}+3\binom{a_1}{3}$$

$$-\binom{a_1}{2}+\binom{a_3}{2}+2\binom{a_2}{3}-\binom{a_6}{1}+2\binom{a_1}{1}\binom{a_2}{2}-\binom{a_2}{1}\binom{a_3}{1}$$

$$-2\binom{a_2}{2}-\binom{a_1}{1}\binom{a_2}{1}+\binom{a_2}{1}$$

The character polynomial $\Xi^{\hat{\alpha}}$, for $\hat{\alpha} := (\alpha_2, \alpha_3, \ldots) := (2, 1^5)$:

$$-4\binom{a_1}{5}\binom{a_2}{1}+6\binom{a_1}{7}+2\binom{a_1}{3}\binom{a_2}{2}-\binom{a_1}{2}\binom{a_2}{1}\binom{a_3}{1}$$

$$+3\binom{a_1}{4}\binom{a_3}{1}-2\binom{a_1}{3}\binom{a_4}{1}-\binom{a_2}{2}\binom{a_3}{1}+\binom{a_2}{1}\binom{a_5}{1}$$

$$+\binom{a_1}{2}\binom{a_5}{1}+\binom{a_3}{1}\binom{a_4}{1}-\binom{a_7}{1}-6\binom{a_1}{6}+4\binom{a_1}{4}\binom{a_2}{1}$$

$$-3\binom{a_1}{3}\binom{a_3}{1}-2\binom{a_1}{2}\binom{a_2}{2}+2\binom{a_1}{2}\binom{a_4}{1}+\binom{a_1}{1}\binom{a_2}{1}\binom{a_3}{1}$$

$$-\binom{a_1}{1}\binom{a_5}{1}+5\binom{a_1}{5}-3\binom{a_1}{3}\binom{a_2}{1}+2\binom{a_1}{2}\binom{a_3}{1}+\binom{a_1}{1}\binom{a_2}{2}$$

$$-\binom{a_1}{1}\binom{a_4}{1}-4\binom{a_1}{4}+2\binom{a_1}{2}\binom{a_2}{1}-\binom{a_1}{1}\binom{a_3}{1}+3\binom{a_1}{3}$$

$$-\binom{a_1}{1}\binom{a_2}{1}-2\binom{a_1}{2}+\binom{a_1}{1}$$

The character polynomial $\Xi^{\hat{\alpha}}$, for $\hat{\alpha}:=(\alpha_2,\alpha_3,\ldots):=(1^7)$:

$$\binom{a_1}{7}-\binom{a_1}{5}\binom{a_2}{1}+\binom{a_1}{4}\binom{a_3}{1}+\binom{a_1}{3}\binom{a_2}{2}-\binom{a_1}{3}\binom{a_4}{1}$$

$$-\binom{a_1}{2}\binom{a_2}{1}\binom{a_3}{1}+\binom{a_1}{2}\binom{a_5}{1}-\binom{a_1}{1}\binom{a_2}{3}+\binom{a_1}{1}\binom{a_2}{1}\binom{a_4}{1}$$

$$+\binom{a_1}{1}\binom{a_3}{2}-\binom{a_1}{1}\binom{a_6}{1}+\binom{a_2}{2}\binom{a_3}{1}-\binom{a_2}{1}\binom{a_5}{1}-\binom{a_3}{2}\binom{a_4}{1}$$

$$+\binom{a_7}{1}-\binom{a_1}{6}+\binom{a_1}{4}\binom{a_2}{1}-\binom{a_1}{3}\binom{a_3}{1}-\binom{a_1}{2}\binom{a_2}{2}+\binom{a_1}{2}\binom{a_4}{1}$$

$$+\binom{a_1}{1}\binom{a_2}{1}\binom{a_3}{1}-\binom{a_1}{1}\binom{a_5}{1}+\binom{a_2}{3}-\binom{a_2}{1}\binom{a_4}{1}-\binom{a_3}{2}+\binom{a_6}{1}$$

$$+\binom{a_1}{5}-\binom{a_1}{3}\binom{a_2}{1}+\binom{a_1}{2}\binom{a_3}{1}+\binom{a_1}{1}\binom{a_2}{2}-\binom{a_1}{1}\binom{a_4}{1}$$

$$-\binom{a_2}{1}\binom{a_3}{1}+\binom{a_5}{1}-\binom{a_1}{4}+\binom{a_1}{2}\binom{a_2}{1}-\binom{a_1}{1}\binom{a_3}{1}-\binom{a_2}{2}+\binom{a_4}{1}$$

$$+\binom{a_1}{3}-\binom{a_1}{1}\binom{a_2}{1}+\binom{a_3}{1}-\binom{a_1}{2}+\binom{a_2}{1}+\binom{a_1}{1}-1$$

8.3 Schubert polynomials

This section contains the 120 Schubert polynomials that correspond to the elements of the symmetric group S_5. The permutations are given first by the Lehmer code and by their list, then the Schubert polynomial follows.

$\overline{00000}\approx[12345]:1$

$\overline{00010} \approx [12354]: x_4 + x_3 + x_2 + x_1$

$\overline{00100} \approx [12435]: x_3 + x_2 + x_1$

$\overline{00110} \approx [12453]: x_3x_4 + x_2x_4 + x_2x_3 + x_1x_4 + x_1x_3 + x_1x_2$

$\overline{00200} \approx [12534]: x_3^2 + x_2x_3 + x_2^2 + x_1x_3 + x_1x_2 + x_1^2$

$\overline{00210} \approx [12543]: x_3^2x_4 + x_2x_3x_4 + x_2x_3^2 + x_2^2x_4 + x_2^2x_3 + x_1x_3x_4 + x_1x_3^2 + x_1x_2x_4 + 2\,x_1x_2x_3 + x_1x_2^2 + x_1^2x_4 + x_1^2x_3 + x_1^2x_2$

$\overline{01000} \approx [13245]: x_2 + x_1$

$\overline{01010} \approx [13254]: x_2x_4 + x_2x_3 + x_2^2 + x_1x_4 + x_1x_3 + 2\,x_1x_2 + x_1^2$

$\overline{01100} \approx [13425]: x_2x_3 + x_1x_3 + x_1x_2$

$\overline{01110} \approx [13452]: x_2x_3x_4 + x_1x_3x_4 + x_1x_2x_4 + x_1x_2x_3$

$\overline{01200} \approx [13524]: x_2x_3^2 + x_2^2x_3 + x_1x_3^2 + 2x_1x_2x_3 + x_1x_2^2 + x_1^2x_3 + x_1^2x_2$

$\overline{01210} \approx [13542]: x_2x_3^2x_4 + x_2^2x_3x_4 + x_1x_3^2x_4 + 2\,x_1x_2x_3x_4 + x_1x_2x_3^2 + x_1x_2^2x_4 + x_1x_2^2x_3 + x_1^2x_3x_4 + x_1^2x_2x_4 + x_1^2x_2x_3$

$\overline{02000} \approx [14235]: x_2^2 + x_1x_2 + x_1^2$

$\overline{02010} \approx [14253]: x_2^2x_4 + x_2^2x_3 + x_1x_2x_4 + x_1x_2x_3 + x_1x_2^2 + x_1^2x_4 + x_1^2x_3 + x_1^2x_2$

$\overline{02100} \approx [14325]: x_2^2x_3 + x_1x_2x_3 + x_1x_2^2 + x_1^2x_3 + x_1^2x_2$

$\overline{02110} \approx [14352]: x_2^2x_3x_4 + x_1x_2x_3x_4 + x_1x_2^2x_4 + x_1x_2^2x_3 + x_1^2x_3x_4 + x_1^2x_2x_4 + x_1^2x_2x_3$

$\overline{02200} \approx [14523]: x_2^2x_3^2 + x_1x_2x_3^2 + x_1x_2^2x_3 + x_1^2x_3^2 + x_1^2x_2x_3 + x_1^2x_2^2$

$\overline{02210} \approx [14532]: x_2^2x_3^2x_4 + x_1x_2x_3^2x_4 + x_1x_2^2x_3x_4 + x_1x_2^2x_3^2 + x_1^2x_3^2x_4 + x_1^2x_2x_3x_4 + x_1^2x_2x_3^2 + x_1^2x_2^2x_4 + x_1^2x_2^2x_3$

$\overline{03000} \approx [15234]: x_2^3 + x_1x_2^2 + x_1^2x_2 + x_1^3$

$\overline{03010} \approx [15243]: x_2^3x_4 + x_2^3x_3 + x_1x_2^2x_4 + x_1x_2^2x_3 + x_1x_2^3 + x_1^2x_2x_4 + x_1^2x_2x_3 + x_1^2x_2^2 + x_1^3x_4 + x_1^3x_3 + x_1^3x_2$

$\overline{03100} \approx [15324]: x_2^3x_3 + x_1x_2^2x_3 + x_1x_2^3 + x_1^2x_2x_3 + x_1^2x_2^2 + x_1^3x_3 + x_1^3x_2$

$\overline{03110} \approx [15342]: x_2^3x_3x_4 + x_1x_2^2x_3x_4 + x_1x_2^3x_4 + x_1x_2^3x_3 + x_1^2x_2x_3x_4 + x_1^2x_2^2x_4 + x_1^2x_2^2x_3 + x_1^3x_3x_4 + x_1^3x_2x_4 + x_1^3x_2x_3$

$\overline{03200} \approx [15423]: x_2^3x_3^2 + x_1x_2^2x_3^2 + x_1x_2^3x_3 + x_1^2x_2x_3^2 + x_1^2x_2^2x_3 + x_1^2x_2^3 + x_1^3x_3^2 + x_1^3x_2x_3 + x_1^3x_2^2$

$\overline{03210} \approx [15432]$: $x_2^3 x_3^2 x_4 + x_1 x_2^2 x_3^2 x_4 + x_1 x_2^3 x_3 x_4 + x_1 x_2^3 x_3^2 + x_1^2 x_2 x_3^2 x_4$
$+ x_1^2 x_2^2 x_3 x_4 + x_1^2 x_2^2 x_3^2 + x_1^2 x_2^3 x_4 + x_1^2 x_2^3 x_3 + x_1^3 x_3^2 x_4$
$+ x_1^3 x_2 x_3 x_4 + x_1^3 x_2 x_3^2 + x_1^3 x_2^2 x_4 + x_1^3 x_2^2 x_3$

$\overline{10000} \approx [21345]$: x_1

$\overline{10010} \approx [21354]$: $x_1 x_4 + x_1 x_3 + x_1 x_2 + x_1^2$

$\overline{10100} \approx [21435]$: $x_1 x_3 + x_1 x_2 + x_1^2$

$\overline{10110} \approx [21453]$: $x_1 x_3 x_4 + x_1 x_2 x_4 + x_1 x_2 x_3 + x_1^2 x_4 + x_1^2 x_3 + x_1^2 x_2$

$\overline{10200} \approx [21534]$: $x_1 x_3^2 + x_1 x_2 x_3 + x_1 x_2^2 + x_1^2 x_3 + x_1^2 x_2 + x_1^3$

$\overline{10210} \approx [21543]$: $x_1 x_3^2 x_4 + x_1 x_2 x_3 x_4 + x_1 x_2 x_3^2 + x_1 x_2^2 x_4 + x_1 x_2^2 x_3$
$+ x_1^2 x_3 x_4 + x_1^2 x_3^2 + x_1^2 x_2 x_4 + 2 x_1^2 x_2 x_3 + x_1^2 x_2^2 +$
$x_1^3 x_4 + x_1^3 x_3 + x_1^3 x_2$

$\overline{11000} \approx [23145]$: $x_1 x_2$

$\overline{11010} \approx [23154]$: $x_1 x_2 x_4 + x_1 x_2 x_3 + x_1 x_2^2 + x_1^2 x_2$

$\overline{11100} \approx [23415]$: $x_1 x_2 x_3$

$\overline{11110} \approx [23451]$: $x_1 x_2 x_3 x_4$

$\overline{11200} \approx [23514]$: $x_1 x_2 x_3^2 + x_1 x_2^2 x_3 + x_1^2 x_2 x_3$

$\overline{11210} \approx [23541]$: $x_1 x_2 x_3^2 x_4 + x_1 x_2^2 x_3 x_4 + x_1^2 x_2 x_3 x_4$

$\overline{12000} \approx [24135]$: $x_1 x_2^2 + x_1^2 x_2$

$\overline{12010} \approx [24153]$: $x_1 x_2^2 x_4 + x_1 x_2^2 x_3 + x_1^2 x_2 x_4 + x_1^2 x_2 x_3 + x_1^2 x_2^2$

$\overline{12100} \approx [24315]$: $x_1 x_2^2 x_3 + x_1^2 x_2 x_3$

$\overline{12110} \approx [24351]$: $x_1 x_2^2 x_3 x_4 + x_1^2 x_2 x_3 x_4$

$\overline{12200} \approx [24513]$: $x_1 x_2^2 x_3^2 + x_1^2 x_2 x_3^2 + x_1^2 x_2^2 x_3$

$\overline{12210} \approx [24531]$: $x_1 x_2^2 x_3^2 x_4 + x_1^2 x_2 x_3^2 x_4 + x_1^2 x_2^2 x_3 x_4$

$\overline{13000} \approx [25134]$: $x_1 x_2^3 + x_1^2 x_2^2 + x_1^3 x_2$

$\overline{13010} \approx [25143]$: $x_1 x_2^3 x_4 + x_1 x_2^3 x_3 + x_1^2 x_2^2 x_4 + x_1^2 x_2^2 x_3 + x_1^2 x_2^3 + x_1^3 x_2 x_4$
$+ x_1^3 x_2 x_3 + x_1^3 x_2^2$

$\overline{13100} \approx [25314]$: $x_1 x_2^3 x_3 + x_1^2 x_2^2 x_3 + x_1^3 x_2 x_3$

$\overline{13110} \approx [25341]$: $x_1 x_2^3 x_3 x_4 + x_1^2 x_2^2 x_3 x_4 + x_1^3 x_2 x_3 x_4$

$\overline{13200} \approx [25413]$: $x_1 x_2^3 x_3^2 + x_1^2 x_2^2 x_3^2 + x_1^2 x_2^3 x_3 + x_1^3 x_2 x_3^2 + x_1^3 x_2^2 x_3$

$\overline{13210} \approx [25431]$: $x_1 x_2^3 x_3^2 x_4 + x_1^2 x_2^2 x_3^2 x_4 + x_1^2 x_2^3 x_3 x_4 + x_1^3 x_2 x_3^2 x_4$
$+ x_1^3 x_2^2 x_3 x_4$

$\overline{20000} \approx [31245]$: x_1^2

$\overline{20010} \approx [31254]: x_1^2 x_4 + x_1^2 x_3 + x_1^2 x_2 + x_1^3$

$\overline{20100} \approx [31425]: x_1^2 x_3 + x_1^2 x_2$

$\overline{20110} \approx [31452]: x_1^2 x_3 x_4 + x_1^2 x_2 x_4 + x_1^2 x_2 x_3$

$\overline{20200} \approx [31524]: x_1^2 x_3^2 + x_1^2 x_2 x_3 + x_1^2 x_2^2 + x_1^3 x_3 + x_1^3 x_2$

$\overline{20210} \approx [31542]: x_1^2 x_3^2 x_4 + x_1^2 x_2 x_3 x_4 + x_1^2 x_2 x_3^2 + x_1^2 x_2^2 x_4 + x_1^2 x_2^2 x_3 +$
$\qquad\qquad\qquad\qquad x_1^3 x_3 x_4 + x_1^3 x_2 x_4 + x_1^3 x_2 x_3$

$\overline{21000} \approx [32145]: x_1^2 x_2$

$\overline{21010} \approx [32154]: x_1^2 x_2 x_4 + x_1^2 x_2 x_3 + x_1^2 x_2^2 + x_1^3 x_2$

$\overline{21100} \approx [32415]: x_1^2 x_2 x_3$

$\overline{21110} \approx [32451]: x_1^2 x_2 x_3 x_4$

$\overline{21200} \approx [32514]: x_1^2 x_2 x_3^2 + x_1^2 x_2^2 x_3 + x_1^3 x_2 x_3$

$\overline{21210} \approx [32541]: x_1^2 x_2 x_3^2 x_4 + x_1^2 x_2^2 x_3 x_4 + x_1^3 x_2 x_3 x_4$

$\overline{22000} \approx [34125]: x_1^2 x_2^2$

$\overline{22010} \approx [34152]: x_1^2 x_2^2 x_4 + x_1^2 x_2^2 x_3$

$\overline{22100} \approx [34215]: x_1^2 x_2^2 x_3$

$\overline{22110} \approx [34251]: x_1^2 x_2^2 x_3 x_4$

$\overline{22200} \approx [34512]: x_1^2 x_2^2 x_3^2$

$\overline{22210} \approx [34521]: x_1^2 x_2^2 x_3^2 x_4$

$\overline{23000} \approx [35124]: x_1^2 x_2^3 + x_1^3 x_2^2$

$\overline{23010} \approx [35142]: x_1^2 x_2^3 x_4 + x_1^2 x_2^3 x_3 + x_1^3 x_2^2 x_4 + x_1^3 x_2^2 x_3$

$\overline{23100} \approx [35214]: x_1^2 x_2^3 x_3 + x_1^3 x_2^2 x_3$

$\overline{23110} \approx [35241]: x_1^2 x_2^3 x_3 x_4 + x_1^3 x_2^2 x_3 x_4$

$\overline{23200} \approx [35412]: x_1^2 x_2^3 x_3^2 + x_1^3 x_2^2 x_3^2$

$\overline{23210} \approx [35421]: x_1^2 x_2^3 x_3^2 x_4 + x_1^3 x_2^2 x_3^2 x_4$

$\overline{30000} \approx [41235]: x_1^3$

$\overline{30010} \approx [41253]: x_1^3 x_4 + x_1^3 x_3 + x_1^3 x_2$

$\overline{30100} \approx [41325]: x_1^3 x_3 + x_1^3 x_2$

$\overline{30110} \approx [41352]: x_1^3 x_3 x_4 + x_1^3 x_2 x_4 + x_1^3 x_2 x_3$

$\overline{30200} \approx [41523]: x_1^3 x_3^2 + x_1^3 x_2 x_3 + x_1^3 x_2^2$

$\overline{30210} \approx [41532]: x_1^3 x_3^2 x_4 + x_1^3 x_2 x_3 x_4 + x_1^3 x_2 x_3^2 + x_1^3 x_2^2 x_4 + x_1^3 x_2^2 x_3$

$\overline{31000} \approx [42135]: x_1^3 x_2$

$\overline{31010} \approx [42153]: x_1^3 x_2 x_4 + x_1^3 x_2 x_3 + x_1^3 x_2^2$

$\overline{31100} \approx [42315]: x_1^3 x_2 x_3$

$\overline{31110} \approx [42351]: x_1^3 x_2 x_3 x_4$

$\overline{31200} \approx [42513]: x_1^3 x_2 x_3^2 + x_1^3 x_2^2 x_3$

$\overline{31210} \approx [42531]: x_1^3 x_2 x_3^2 x_4 + x_1^3 x_2^2 x_3 x_4$

$\overline{32000} \approx [43125]: x_1^3 x_2^2$

$\overline{32010} \approx [43152]: x_1^3 x_2^2 x_4 + x_1^3 x_2^2 x_3$

$\overline{32100} \approx [43215]: x_1^3 x_2^2 x_3$

$\overline{32110} \approx [43251]: x_1^3 x_2^2 x_3 x_4$

$\overline{32200} \approx [43512]: x_1^3 x_2^2 x_3^2$

$\overline{32210} \approx [43521]: x_1^3 x_2^2 x_3^2 x_4$

$\overline{33000} \approx [45123]: x_1^3 x_2^3$

$\overline{33010} \approx [45132]: x_1^3 x_2^3 x_4 + x_1^3 x_2^3 x_3$

$\overline{33100} \approx [45213]: x_1^3 x_2^3 x_3$

$\overline{33110} \approx [45231]: x_1^3 x_2^3 x_3 x_4$

$\overline{33200} \approx [45312]: x_1^3 x_2^3 x_3^2$

$\overline{33210} \approx [45321]: x_1^3 x_2^3 x_3^2 x_4$

$\overline{40000} \approx [51234]: x_1^4$

$\overline{40010} \approx [51243]: x_1^4 x_4 + x_1^4 x_3 + x_1^4 x_2$

$\overline{40100} \approx [51324]: x_1^4 x_3 + x_1^4 x_2$

$\overline{40110} \approx [51342]: x_1^4 x_3 x_4 + x_1^4 x_2 x_4 + x_1^4 x_2 x_3$

$\overline{40200} \approx [51423]: x_1^4 x_3^2 + x_1^4 x_2 x_3 + x_1^4 x_2^2$

$\overline{40210} \approx [51432]: x_1^4 x_3^2 x_4 + x_1^4 x_2 x_3 x_4 + x_1^4 x_2 x_3^2 + x_1^4 x_2^2 x_4 + x_1^4 x_2^2 x_3$

$\overline{41000} \approx [52134]: x_1^4 x_2$

$\overline{41010} \approx [52143]: x_1^4 x_2 x_4 + x_1^4 x_2 x_3 + x_1^4 x_2^2$

$\overline{41100} \approx [52314]: x_1^4 x_2 x_3$

$\overline{41110} \approx [52341]: x_1^4 x_2 x_3 x_4$

$\overline{41200} \approx [52413]: x_1^4 x_2 x_3^2 + x_1^4 x_2^2 x_3$

$\overline{41210} \approx [52431]: x_1^4 x_2 x_3^2 x_4 + x_1^4 x_2^2 x_3 x_4$

$\overline{42000} \approx [53124]: x_1^4 x_2^2$

$\overline{42010} \approx [53142]: x_1^4 x_2^2 x_4 + x_1^4 x_2^2 x_3$

$\overline{42100} \approx [53214]: x_1^4 x_2^2 x_3$

$\overline{42110} \approx [53241]: x_1^4 x_2^2 x_3 x_4$

$\overline{42200} \approx [53412]: x_1^4 x_2^2 x_3^2$

$\overline{42210} \approx [53421]: x_1^4 x_2^2 x_3^2 x_4$

$\overline{43000} \approx [54123]: x_1^4 x_2^3$

$\overline{43010} \approx [54132]: x_1^4 x_2^3 x_4 + x_1^4 x_2^3 x_3$

$\overline{43100} \approx [54213]: x_1^4 x_2^3 x_3$

$\overline{43110} \approx [54231]: x_1^4 x_2^3 x_3 x_4$

$\overline{43200} \approx [54312]: x_1^4 x_2^3 x_3^2$

$\overline{43210} \approx [54321]: x_1^4 x_2^3 x_3^2 x_4$

Chapter 9

Comments and References

This chapter begins with remarks on the history of finite group actions. The reader will then find comments that point to certain important articles and books, together with hints for further reading and additional references.

9.1 Historical remarks, books and reviews

The first chapter is mainly devoted to the Cauchy–Frobenius Lemma, the history of which is described in the following two articles:

> Neumann, P. M., "A lemma that is not Burnside's", *Math. Scientist* **4** (1979), 133-141.

> Wright, E. M., "Burnside's lemma: a historical note", *J. Comb. Theory (B)* **30** (1981), 89-90.

E. M. Wright mentions that Burnside himself correctly ascribes it to Frobenius in the *first edition* of his book

> *Burnside, W., "Theory of groups of finite order", *Cambridge University Press*, 1897.

But the lemma is contained in section 118, while the ascription is at the beginning of section 119. In the *second edition* of this book (1911) which is mostly quoted, these sections are completely rewritten, and Burnside omits the ascription, this might be the reason for usually attributing this lemma to Burnside. Burnside's reference is to

Frobenius, G., "Über die Congruenz nach einem aus zwei endlichen Gruppen gebildeten Doppelmodul", *Crelle's J.* **101** (1887), 273-299.

Frobenius gives credit to Cauchy who proved this lemma for the transitive case in

Cauchy, A. L., "Mémoire sur diverses propriétés remarquables des substitutions régulières ou irrégulières, et des systèmes de substitutions conjuguées (suite)", *C. R. Acad. Sci. Paris* **21** (1845), 972-987.

In fact Burnside proved a much stronger result which is described in the third chapter of the present book.

Besides this basic lemma the first chapter contains in particular the notion of symmetry classes of mappings and the corresponding enumerative results. The pioneering publication on this topic was the famous paper

Pólya, G., "Kombinatorische Anzahlbestimmungen für Gruppen, Graphen und chemische Verbindungen", *Acta Sci. Math.* **68** (1937), 145-254.

It had the following predecessor, which was overlooked for many years:

Redfield, J. H., "The theory of group–reduced distributions", *Amer. J. Math.* **49** (1927), 433-455.

In fact Redfield's paper contains stronger results than Pólya's, but it is very difficult to read since it expresses the results in terms of operations on polynomials that can be understood more or less only in terms of linear representation theory. There was at least one further paper written by Redfield, it was rejected but published recently:

Redfield, J. H., "Enumeration by frame group and range groups", *J. Graph Theory* **8** (1984), 205-223.

Another paper, entitled "Enumeration distinguishable arrangements for general frame groups", was found together with an untitled manuscript. They are not published yet.

A translation of Pólya's paper into English, together with an article on the fifty years' history of it, can be found in

*Pólya, G., and Read, R. C., "Combinatorial enumeration of groups, graphs, and chemical compounds", *Springer Verlag*, 1987.

The paper by Pólya was motivated by the problem of chemical isomerism, which amounts in a certain sense to the enumeration (or better: the construction) of all the connected multigraphs with a given degree sequence, i.e. which correspond to a given chemical formula. The history of this problem and its relationship with graph theory can be found in

*Biggs, N. L., Lloyd, K. E., and Wilson, R. J., "Graph theory 1736-1936", *Clarendon Press*, 1977.

This basic problem of constructing the molecular graphs that satisfy a given chemical formula, the so–called *connectivity isomers*, was attacked in a big and successful project called DENDRAL, which was started in 1965 by J. Lederberg. This project is described in the following book:

*Lindsay, R. K., Buchanan, B. G., Feigenbaum, E. A., and Lederberg, J., "Applications of Artificial Intelligence for Organic Chemistry: The Dendral Project", *McGraw–Hill*, 1980.

The present author, together with R. Laue and co–workers, also developed a big program system that allows to construct molecular graphs. This program system is called MOLGRAPH, its first version is due to D. Moser, a second one will be implemented by R. Grund, and the first publication concerning it is

Kerber, A., Laue, R., and Moser, D., "Ein Strukturgenerator für molekulare Graphen", *Analytica Chimica Acta* **235** (1990), 221-228.

The manual of the system will be published soon, and the C–version of the program system itself will be public domain. We hope that it will be ready by the end of this year.

The relevance of Redfield's work for chemistry is described in

Lloyd, K. E., "Redfield's papers and their relevance to counting isomers and isomerizations",*Discrete Appl. Math.* **19** (1988), 289-304.

One of the very first applications of Pólya's methods outside chemistry or graph theory is described in

> Slepian, D., "On the number of symmetry types of boolean functions of n variables", *Canad. J. Math.* **5** (1953), 185-193.

The nicest short introductions to the enumerative applications of finite group actions to graph theory can be found in the booklet

> *Harary, F., and Beineke, L. (ed.), "A seminar on graph theory", *Holt, Rinehart and Winston*, 1967,

and in the review articles

> de Bruijn, N. G., "Pólya's theory of counting", in: Beckenbach, E., (ed.) "Applied combinatorial mathematics", *Wiley and Sons*, 1964, 144-184,

which contains an enormous collection of interesting examples, while

> de Bruijn, N. G., "Pólya's Abzähl–Theorie: Muster für Graphen und chemische Verbindungen", in: Jakobs, K., (ed.) "Selecta Mathematica, III", *Springer-Verlag*, 1971,

emphasizes the applications in chemistry. The standard reference for graph theoretical applications is the book

> *Harary, F., and Palmer, E., "Graphical enumeration", *Academic Press* 1973.

An extensive description of this theory which emphasizes the fact that it is a particular case of finite group action theory was published in three parts by the present author and one of his collaborators:

> Kerber, A., and K.–J. Thürlings, "Symmetrieklassen von Funktionen und ihre Abzählungstheorie", *Bayreuther Math. Schriften* **12** (1983), iii+235 pp., **15** (1983), ii+338 pp., **21** (1986), 156-278.

These papers, books and review articles are also the standard references for the weighted enumeration. There are of course many other review articles on this subject, and it shows up more and more in books on general combinatorics, too.

The enumeration by stabilizer class is due to Burnside, it can be found in the second edition of the book that was already mentioned above:

*Burnside, G., "The theory of groups of finite order", 2nd ed. *Cambridge* 1911, reprinted by *Dover Publications*, 1955.

The weighted form of his lemma was proved first in the dissertation

Stockmeyer, P. K., "Enumeration of graphs with prescribed automorphism group", *Ann Arbor*, 1971.

See also

White, D. E., "Counting patterns with a given automorphism group", *Proc. Amer. Math. Soc.* **47** (1975), 41-44.

White, D. E., "Classifying patterns by automorphism group: an operator theoretic approach", *Discrete Math.* **13** (1975), 277-295.

The enumeration under finite group operations on posets and lattices is due to

Plesken, W., "Counting with groups and rings", *J. reine u. angew. Mathematik* **334** (1982), 40-68.

The introduction of species was done by

Joyal, A., "Une théorie combinatoire des séries formelles", *Advances in Math.* **42** (1981), 1-82.

The present introduction to the representation theory of symmetric groups along a chain of set theoretic bijections was used first in

Kerber, A., "La théorie combinatoire sous–tendant la théorie des représentations linéaires des groupes symétriques finis", in: M. Lothaire (ed.): "Mots", Paris 1990.

It is mixed with ideas coming from

Doubilet, P., Fox, J., and Rota, G.-C., "The elementary theory of the symmetric group", in: Young Day Proceedings, 31-65, *Marcel Dekker*, 1981,

and the following dissertation which was the first one to use standard bideterminants in representation theory of symmetric groups:

Clausen, M., "Letter–Place–Algebren und ein charakteri-
stik–freier Zugang zur Darstellungstheorie symmetrischer
und voller linearer Gruppen", *Bayreuther Math. Schriften*
4 (1980), xviii+133 pp.

The fifth chapter is devoted to some of the applications of representation theory to combinatorial enumeration and vice versa. The main
point is that Schur polynomials are very helpful here and, conversely,
enumeration theory can contribute elegant proofs of results on Schur
polynomials. These polynomials became important in particular in
connection with Schur's famous discovery of the close relationship
between the representation theories of symmetric and of general linear groups. But these polynomials were known before, as well as the
intertwining matrices between this basis of the space of symmetric
polynomials and the other bases mentioned. A reference which shows
this clearly is

Kostka, C., "Tafeln für symmetrische Funktionen bis zur
elften Dimension.   (Mit kurzen Erläuterungen)", *Wis-
senschaftliche Beilage zum Programm des königlichen Gym-
nasiums und Realgymnasiums zu Insterburg, Ostern* 1908,
10 pp.

A complete introduction to the representation theory of symmetric
groups along the line of considering Schur polynomials is

*Littlewood, D. E., "The theory of group characters and
matrix representations of groups", *Oxford University Press*,
1940.

A modern version of this theory and of important extensions of it is

*Macdonald, I. G., "Symmetric functions and Hall poly-
nomials", *Clarendon Press, Oxford*, 1979.

The relevance of representation theory and Schur polynomials for
combinatorial enumeration was elucidated in particular in the following papers:

Foulkes, H. O., "On Redfield's group reduction functions",
Can. J. Math **15** (1963), 272-284.

Foulkes, H. O., "On Redfield's range–correspondences",
Can. J. Math. **18** (1966), 1060-1071.

Read, R. C., "The use of *S*–functions in combinatorial analysis", *Can. J. Math.* **20** (1968), 808-841.

There are various other books where the representation theory of symmetric groups is described. An introduction which differs from the present one is given in

*Kerber, A., James, G. D., "The representation theory of the symmetric group", *Addison-Wesley* 1981.

The Schubert polynomials, which generalize the Schur polynomials, are due to

Lascoux, A., Schützenberger M.P., "Polynômes de Schubert", *Comptes Rendus de Acad. Sc. Paris* **294** (1982), 447-450.

Lascoux, A., Schützenberger, M.P., "Tableaux and non commutative Schubert polynomials", *Funk. Anal.* **23** (1989), 63-64.

They are the main tool in the computer algebra system SYMCHAR for the representation theory, invariant theory and combinatorics of the finite symmetric groups and related classes of groups (like wreath products of symmetric groups, alternating groups, general linear groups, and so on). The development and the implementation of SYMCHAR began with

Kohnert, A., "Die computerunterstützte Berechnung von Littlewood–Richardson Koeffizienten mit Hilfe von Schubertpolynomen", *Diplomarbeit, Bayreuth* 1987,

which contains a detailed description of an algorithm suggested by Lascoux and Schützenberger. Various extensions of the system are due to further diploma theses and research project results, in particular to

Golembiowski, A., "Zur Berechnung modular irreduzibler Matrixdarstellungen symmetrischer Gruppen mit Hilfe eines Verfahrens von M. Clausen", *Bayreuther Mathem. Schriften* **25** (1987), 135-222.

and the collaboration with A. Lascoux and his students, see e.g.

Carre, C., "Plethysm of elementary functions", *Bayreuther Mathem. Schriften* **31** (1990), 1-18.

as well as to the collaboration with T. McDonough and A. O. Morris.
The program system covers character decompositions, manipulations
with symmetric polynomials, base changes, Schubert polynomials,
irreducible matrix representations (ordinary and modular ones), evaluations of symmetry adapted bases, and so on. The program itself,
together with a LaTeX–file of the manual can be obtained by request
from the present author (send a 3.5″ diskette), it is free for non
commercial purposes.
Further results on the Schubert polynomials can be found in

> Kohnert, A., "Weintrauben, Polynome, Tableaux", *Doc-
> toral dissertation, Bayreuth* 1990.

9.2 Further comments

Having mentioned the history of the Cauchy–Frobenius Lemma and
of Burnside's Lemma as well as some basic sources, a few remarks on
the other contents may be in order.
A description of Coxeter groups, which are a natural generalization of
the symmetric groups (as generated by transpositions), can be found
in the following part of the Bourbaki series of books:

> *Bourbaki, N., "Groupes et algèbres de Lie, 4-6", *Herman,
> Paris* 1968.

The Lehmer code is ascribed in the following article by D. H. Lehmer
to another author with the same second name:

> Lehmer, D. H., "Teaching combinatorial tricks to a com-
> puter", *Proc. 10th Symp. Applied Math.* 1960, 179-193.

The Exchange Lemma is mentioned here since it is basic for the theory
of Schubert polynomials.
Concerning the Garsia–Milne bijection it should be mentioned that
P. Paule pointed to the fact that it is an easy corollary of a lemma
due to Ingleton and Piff, which gives a graph theoretic bijection (the
aim of Garsia and Milne were bijections between sets of partitions):

> Paule, P., "A remark on a lemma of Ingleton and Piff and
> the construction of bijections", *Bayreuther Math. Schriften*
> **25** (1987), 123-127.

Besides the papers on enumeration of symmetry classes of mappings which were already mentioned in the section on history, there are hundreds of further ones among which the papers by de Bruijn and Read should be mentioned in particular, as well as the papers of Harary and his school. The interested reader will easily find the precise references in the index volumes of the *Zentralblatt für Mathematik und ihre Grenzgebiete* or of the *Mathematical Reviews*, or in the book by Harary and Palmer, which was already mentioned, so that I do not need to list them all, otherwise the next hundred pages would have to be filled.

The weighted enumeration leads to the cycle indicator polynomials. Interesting papers on their enumeration and application are the papers by Oberschelp. It is important to note that weighted enumeration reduces complexity. It was mentioned that also weighted enumeration leads to congruences, see e.g.

> Rota, G.-C., and Sagan, B., "Congruences derived from group action", *European J. Combinatorics* **1** (1980), 67-76.

The enumeration by stabilizer class is due to Burnside. Its disadvantage is that it needs a detailed information on the lattice of subgroups of the acting group, which is usually difficult to obtain. Here the Aachen subgroup lattice program can be applied which is also incorporated in the program system CAYLEY (which was used for the evaluation of the tables of marks given in the appendix of tables). It is clear that there is much redundancy in this information, a paper that describes this is

> Rota, G.-C., and Smith, D. A., "Enumeration under group action", *Ann. Sc. Norm. Sup. di Pisa* **4** (1977), 637-646.

The theorem 3.3.7 is due to

> Rosenfeld, V. R., "The generalized Pólya's theorem, a novel method for enumerating equivalence classes of objects with a prescribed automorphism subgroup", (in preparation)

But it should be made clear that the philosophy of the present book is *not* to consider the induced *permutation* group $\bar{G}$ on X, but as long as possible the *abstract* group G instead. Correspondingly, it is important to use the notion of *Burnside ring*, here the names Dress, Morris/Wensley, Siebeneicher, Solomon and Kratzer/Thévenaz lead to important papers. The canonic mapping from the Burnside ring $\Omega(C(|G|))$ into $\Omega(G)$ was introduced by

Dress, A. W. M., Siebeneicher, Ch., and Yoshida, T., "An application of Burnside rings in elementary finite group theory", *preprint 90-033, SFB 343, Bielefeld*, 1990.

Here the interested reader can find further applications of Burnside ring methods, for which he or she should also consult

Wagner, B., "A permutation representation theoretical version of a theorem of Frobenius", *Bayreuther Math. Schriften* **6** (1980), 23-32.

The following papers discuss the evaluation of *complete catalogues* of graphs, so they are important under the general aspect of the exhaustive construction of discrete structures:

Read, R. C., "Every one a winner", *Ann. Discrete Math.* **2** (1978), 107-120.

Colbourn, C. J., Read, R. C., "Orderly algorithms for generating restricted classes of graphs", *J. Graph Theory* **3** (1979), 187-195.

Read, R. C., Wormald, N. C., "Catalogues of graphs and digraphs", *Discrete Math.* **31** (1980), 224.

Read, R. C., and Wormald, N. C., "Counting the 10-point graphs by partition ", *J. Graph Theory* **5** (1981), 183-196.

Cameron, P. J., Colbourn, C. J., Read, R. C., and Wormald, N. C., "Cataloguing the graphs on 10 vertices", *Journal of Graph Theory* **9** (1985), 551-562.

It should be mentioned that these catalogues can also be obtained using different methods, for example the Dixon–Wilf algorithm for generating orbit representatives uniformly at random. The original paper is

Dixon, J. D., and Wilf, H. S., "The random selection of unlabeled graphs", *J. Algorithms* **4** (1983), 205-213.

The application of this algorithm to the generation of unlabeled graphs is also described in

Kerber, A., Laue, R., and Moser, D., "Cataloging graphs by generating them uniformly at random", *J. Graph Theory* **14** (1990), 559-563.

The Dixon–Wilf algorithm can be applied to each mathematical structure that is defined as an orbit of a finite group on a finite set. We used it for so–called *contexts*, which are defined to be orbits of 0-1–matrices under the direct product of the symmetric groups on the sets of rows and columns. The problem is of course that one needs efficient isomorphism checks in order to build a catalogue, but catalogueing is in a sense an abuse of the Dixon–Wilf algorithm. This algorithm is in fact much better in just providing big sets of examples, and it solves this very important problem of constructing sets of examples without prejudice in an optimal way.

The most important references for the Robinson–Schensted correspondence, which was generalized by Knuth and made part of combinatorics by Schützenberger and Lascoux are

Knuth, D. E., "Permutations, matrices and generalized Young tableaux", *Pacific J. Math.* **34** (1970), 709-727.

Schensted, C., "Longest increasing and decreasing subsequences", *Can. J. Math.* **13** (1961), 179-191.

Schützenberger, M. P., "La correspondance de Robinson", *Combinatoire et Représentation du Groupe Symétrique*, Strasbourg, 1976 (D. Foata, Ed.), 59-113. Lecture Notes in Math. **579** *Springer–Verlag*, 1977.

The first complete proofs of the Littlewood–Richardson rule I was aware of can be found in the following diploma thesis:

Wagner, B., "Symmetrische Polynome und Darstellungen der symmetrischen Gruppen", *diploma thesis, Aachen* 1975.

and in the doctoral thesis

Thomas, G., "Baxter algebras and Schur–functions", *doctoral thesis, University of Wales* 1974.

The first published proof (which is based on an idea of Robinson) can be found in Macdonald's book, while the proof in the book of James/Kerber is based on Wagner's thesis which uses an idea of

Bender, E. A., and Knuth, D. E., "Enumeration of plane partitions", *J. Comb. Theory (A)* **13** (1972), 40-54.

The results on the root number functions on symmetric groups are due to

Scharf, Th., "Die Wurzelanzahlfunktion in symmetrischen Gruppen", *J. Algebra* (to appear).

9.3 Suggestions for further reading

Further reading is of course heavily a matter of personal taste. If you are primarily interested in foundations of combinatorics, I strongly recommend to read

*Aigner, M., "Combinatorial theory", *Springer–Verlag*, 1979.

If you prefer to concentrate on enumeration, then take

*Stanley, R., "Enumerative combinatorics, I", *Wadsworth and Brooks/Cole*, 1986.

Besides these books which are theory oriented, I think the reader should consider books on discrete structures, and in particular those that emphasize the constructive aspects of this theory. Here are several helpful books which emphasize these aspects:

*Jungnickel, D., "Graphen, Netzwerke und Algorithmen", 2nd ed., *BI–Wissenschaftsverlag*, 1990.

*Klin, M. Ch., Pöschel, R., and Rosenbaum, K., "Angewandte Algebra", *VEB Deutscher Verlag der Wissenschaften*, 1988.

(This book is of particular importance for people like me who do not speak Russian. It contains a long list of relevant and important references of Russian groups who are active in this field.)

*Knuth, D. E., "The art of computer programming I, II, III", *Addison–Wesley* 1973.

(In particular volume III contains a lot of interesting results on and applications of standard tableaux!)

*Lüneburg, H., "Tools and fundamental constructions of combinatorial mathematics", *BI–Wissenschaftsverlag*, 1989.

*Williamson, S. G., "Combinatorics for computer science", *Computer Science Press*, 1985.

The reader who is interested in group actions in their own right, should consult the following booklets, where the theory of permutation groups is described from the categorical point of view:

*Tamaschke, O., "Permutationsstrukturen", *Bibliographisches Institut*, 1969.

*Tamaschke, O., "Schur–Ringe", *Bibliographisches Institut*, 1970.

Applications to group theory are described in the following classical text, which is in fact a masterpiece:

*Wielandt, H., "Finite permutation groups", *Academic Press*, 1964.

An extended description of applications to groups and geometry is

*Tsuzuku, T., "Finite groups and finite geometries", *Cambridge University Press*, 1982.

Another booklet with a similar intention is

*Biggs, N. L, and White, A. T., "Permutation groups and combinatorial structures", *Cambridge University Press*, 1979.

The algebraic part of graph theory is nicely described in

*Bigg, N. L., "Algebraic graph theory", *Cambridge University Press*, 1974.

For the theory of actions on posets the interested reader is referred to Plesken's paper which was already mentioned above, and for the theory of species I recommend Joyal's original paper and the many publications of his school. Another important paper on species theory and it applications is

Strehl, V., "Zykel–Enumeration bei lokal–strukturierten Funktionen", *Habilitationsschrift, Erlangen*, 1989.

There are many other methods known that come from group theory, from linear representation theory, character theory, and so on. But there are also many results on the theory of generating functions that can be sharpened to constructions, e.g. the methods described in the books

*Goulden, I. P., and Jackson, D. M., "Combinatorial enumeration", *Wiley and Sons*, 1983.

Recently Schur polynomials and related structures like tableaux came up in books on combinatorics, too, e.g. in

*Krishnamurthy, V., "Combinatorics, theory and applications", *Wiley and Sons*, 1986.

*Stanton, D., and White, D., "Constructive Combinatorics", *Springer–Verlag*, 1986.

There is also the whole theory of enumeration of permutations with prescribed properties (like rises and falls). The corresponding theory of statistics on the symmetric group is a source of interesting problems and methods. The reader should consult the review article

Foata, D., "Distributions eulériennes et mahoniennes sur le groupe des permutations", in: Aigner, M. (ed.), "Higher combinatorics", *D. Reidel*, 1977.

This article refers (among other references) to the following important source for all kinds of combinatorial problems and results:

*MacMahon, P. A., "Combinatory analysis, I, II", *Cambridge University Press*, 1915/1916, reprint by *Chelsea Publishing Company*, 1960.

But there are many more recent publications by the Lotharingian seminar of combinatorics, the interested reader is strongly recommended to have a look at the corresponding series of proceedings:

*Séminaire Lotharingien de Combinatoire (Bayreuth, Erlangen, Strasbourg), *Publication de l'institut de recherche mathématique avancée, Strasbourg*.

More than twenty volumes have been published already. Another important source of results and questions is the book

*Comtet, L., "Advanced combinatorics", *D. Reidel*, 1974.

The related theory of words and of statistics on words is considered in

*Lothaire, M., "Combinatorics on words", *Addison-Wesley*, 1983.

The Robinson–Schensted construction and its generalization to matrices over $\mathbb{N}$, given by D. E. Knuth, is a source of interesting results and methods. Besides the review article by Schützenberger (who made this construction an important part of combinatorics) which was already mentioned, I should like to mention the names of W. H. Burge and E. R. Gansner. The standard reference for the theory of partitions is

*Andrews, G. E., "The theory of partitions", *Encyclopedia of Math. Appl.* **2**, *Addison-Wesley*, 1976.

An interesting thesis, where for each q a bijection on the set of proper partitions of n is derived such that these bijections generate the symmetric group on this set of partitions is

Stockhofe, D., "Bijektive Abbildungen auf der Menge der Partitionen einer natürlichen Zahl", *Bayreuther Math. Schriften* **10** (1982), 1-59.

More generally, replacing combinatorial identities by suitable bijections which give an insight into the relationship between various mathematical structures is of course a very important part of research. Here I strongly recommend to study the papers on the Robinson–Schensted construction which were mentioned already, and to consider the resulting theory on the enumeration of permutations. The book and the various papers by Andrews are full of interesting identities and bijections between various sets of partitions, the dissertation of Stockhofe invites to rewrite these bijections in terms of his bijections. A more general approach to identities and bijections is beautifully described in various papers of Zeilberger, for example in

Zeilberger, D., "Identities", *IMA Vol. Math. Appl.* **18**, 35-44, *Springer* 1989.

(Recall the above mentioned remarks by P. Paule on the lemma by Ingleton and Piff and the Garsia-Milne bijection!) The importance of the dominance order for representation theory of symmetric groups, combinatorics and sciences is described in

Ruch, E., Schönhofer, A., "Theorie der Chiralitätsfunktionen", *Theoretica Chimica Acta* **19** (1970), 225-287.

Ruch, E., "The diagram lattice as structural principle", *Theoretica Chimica Acta* **38** (1975), 167-183.

Ruch, E., Gutman, I., "The branching extent of graphs,"*J. Comb. Inf. Syst. Sci.* **4** (1980), 285-295.

Aigner, M., "Uses of the diagram lattice", *Mitt. Math. Sem. Univ. Gießen* **163** (1984), 61-77.

The theory of unimodality of finite sequences is also a very interesting field of research. A review of recent developments can be found in

Brenti, F., "Unimodal, log–concave and Pólya frequency sequences in combinatorics", *Am. Math. Soc. Memoirs* **81** (1989) 106 pp.

Anyone who wants to apply the concept of symmetry classes of mappings to a concrete situation, and who wants really to construct representatives, should take the following into account. The method of constructing representatives of the orbits of G on Y^X of content $\lambda, \lambda \models |X|$, can be interpreted as evaluating a transversal of the $(S_\lambda, \bar{G})$–double cosets in S_X. This is shown in

Ruch, E., Hässelbarth, W., Richter, B., "Doppelnebenklassen als Klassenbegriff und Nomenklaturprinzip für Isomere und ihre Abzählung", *Theoretica Chimica Acta* **19** (1970), 288-300.

A review article on further applications of double cosets in sciences is

Ruch, E., and Klein, D. J., "Double cosets in chemistry and physics", *Theoretica Chimica Acta* **63** (1983), 447-472.

Interesting applications to group theory (constructions of solvable groups) are given in

Laue, R., "Zur Konstruktion und Klassifikation endlicher auflösbarer Gruppen", *Bayreuther Math. Schriften* **9** (19), 309 pp.

Laue, R., "Computing double coset representatives for the generation of solvable groups", *Lecture Notes in Computer Science* **144**, *Springer Verlag*, 1982.

A careful implementation of the applications to symmetry classes of mappings can be found in:

Grund, R., "Symmetrieklassen von Abbildungen und die Konstruktion von diskreten Strukturen", *Bayreuther Math. Schriften* **31** (1990), 19-54.

Methods for the evaluation of a double cosets transversal in the general case are described in

Butler, G., "On computing double coset representatives in permutation groups", *Computational group theory, Durham* **1982**, 283-290, *Academic Press*, 1984.

Schmalz, B., "Verwendung von Untergruppenleitern zur Bestimmung von Doppelnebenklassen", *Bayreuther Math. Schriften* **31** (1990), 109-143.

The question of representatives with given stabilizer is considered in

Laue, R., "Eine konstruktive Version des Lemmas von Burnside", *Bayreuther Math. Schriften* **28** (1989), 111-125.

Helpful sources for computer methods using groups are

Felsch, V., "A bibliography on the use of computers in group theory and related topics: algorithms, implementations, and applications", *SIGSAM Bull.* **12**, 23-86.

Hoffman, C. M., "Group theoretic algorithms and graph isomorphism", *Lecture Notes in Computer Science*, **136**, Springer Verlag, 1982.

Sims, C., "Group–theoretic algorithms, a survey", *Proc. Internat. Congress of Math.*, **2** (1978), 979-985. O. Lehto (ed.), *Acad. Sci. Fennica, Helsinki*, 1978.

Stiefel, E., Fässler, A., "Gruppentheoretische Methoden und ihre Anwendung", *Teubner*, 1979.

The physical journals are full of applications, in particular the Journal of Mathematical Physics. There are many notions that deserve a better mathematical explanation. And there are many open questions the physicists would like to have answered. They want to really put their hands on the structures in question (like on the matrix representations), while the mathematicians quite often do not want to look at them as close as that. But nowadays, in the times of cheap and efficient computers, there is at least no excuse left for being unable to examine them in full detail. For the evaluation of the irreducible polynomial representations of the general linear groups I can refer the interested reader to

Grabmeier, J., Kerber, A., "The evaluation of irreducible polynomial representations of the general linear groups and of the unitary groups over fields of characteristic 0", *Acta Appl. Math.* **8** (1987), 271-291.

If you want to do sports, then you may take the following book that contains an enormous list of integer sequences:

*Sloane, N. J. A., "A handbook of integer sequences", *Academic Press* 1973.

Pick a sequence, and try to find a corresponding sequence of group actions that have the elements of the sequence as numbers of orbits. Hints, how this can be done, you may find in

Cameron, P. J., "Some sequences of integers", *Discrete Math.* **75** (1989), 89-102.

If you are interested in properties of actions and their applications to general group theory, then the papers of P. J. Cameron are a source of interesting results and problems, for example

Cameron, P. J., "A combinatorial tool kit for permutation groups", *Relations between combinatorics and other parts of mathematics (Proc. Sympos. Pure Math., Ohio State Univ., Columbus, Ohio, 1978)*, 77-96, Proc. Sympos. Pure Math., XXXIV, Amer. Math. Soc., Providence, R.I., 1979.

Cameron, P. J., "Orbits and enumeration", in: Jungnickel, D., Vedder, K. (ed.), "Combinatorial theory", *Proc. Conf. Schloß Rauischholzhausen, 1982*, 86-99, *Lecture Notes in Math.* **969**, Springer-Verlag, 1982.

Cameron, P. J., "Orbits, enumeration and colouring", *Combinatorial Mathematics, IX, Brisbane, 1981*, 34-66, *Lecture Notes in Math.* **952**, Springer-Verlag, 1982.

Cameron, P. J., "Colour schemes", *Algebraic and geometric combinatorics, North-Holland Math. Stud.* **65**, 81-95, North-Holland, 1982,

and his various papers on actions on *unordered sets*, for example the most recent one I saw:

Cameron, P. J., Thomas, S., "Groups acting on unordered sets", *Proc. London Math. Soc.* (3) **59** (1989), 541-557.

As far as equations and roots in groups are concerned, I recommend the review article

Finkelstein, H., "Solving equations in groups: a survey of Frobenius theorem", *Periodica Math. Hungarica* **9** (1978), 187-204.

Scharf, Th., "Wurzelanzahlfunktionen in vollständigen monomialen Gruppen"(in preparation).

In the near future the research on Schubert polynomials will be pushed forward since it pays by many applications to classical and modern algebra as well as to combinatorics and sciences, see the papers by Lascoux/Schützenberger and Kohnert which were already listed. A detailed manuscript by I. G. Macdonald apparently is in preparation.

Since powerful computers became very cheap, the research on the *construction* of discrete structures in mathematics and sciencies became more and more important. In particular, as these machines are in a sense algebraic machines, mixtures of algebraic and combinatorial approaches, as they are described in this book, seem to allow much more efficient attacks to many problems of enormous complexity. For example to the basic problem of enumeration theory of symmetry classes of mappings, which is the construction of the connectivity isomers corresponding to a given chemical formula. Here I recommend to have a glance at the above mentioned book by Lindsay et al. on the DENDRAL project, in order first of all to get an idea of what is wanted by chemists, and how difficult the problem is. Afterwards the interested reader should have a look at the papers by Read and others on the various methods of cataloguing graphs, and then to go on and consider his (or her) pet discrete structure under this aspect, if he or she can construct or even catalogue it. If not, then the Dixon/Wilf algorithm should be considered, maybe the structure in question can be defined as an orbit of a finite group on a finite set, and therefore generated uniformly at random. If this is true, then some sort of pattern recognition can be started in order to find interesting properties, hypotheses, invariants, and so on, and finally, if some hypotheses were formulated, he or she should start to prove them. This is part of the very interesting and brand new branch of *experimental mathematics*.

Index